The Finite Element Method in Engineering Science

Consulting Editor
Professor P. B. Morice
University of Southampton

The Finite Element Method in Engineering Science

(The second, expanded and revised, edition of
*The Finite Element Method in Structural and
Continuum Mechanics*)

O. C. Zienkiewicz
*Professor of Civil Engineering and
Dean of Applied Science,
University of Wales, Swansea*

McGRAW-HILL · LONDON

New York · St Louis · San Francisco · Düsseldorf · Johannesburg
Kuala Lumpur · Mexico · Montreal · New Delhi · Panama · Rio de
Janeiro · Singapore · Sydney · Toronto

Published by

McGRAW-HILL Publishing Company Limited
MAIDENHEAD · BERKSHIRE · ENGLAND

07 094138 6

PRINTED AND BOUND IN GREAT BRITAIN

To my wife and to my mother

Preface

When the author's first text on *The Finite Element Method in Structural and Continuum Mechanics* was published in 1967 much of the preface had to be devoted to explaining what was meant by the method described in the title. Today, such an explanation is almost unnecessary as an explosive expansion of activity in this field has taken place. What originally started as a process of structural analysis capable of dealing with a large variety of forms—has now become recognized as a general method of wide applicability to Engineering and Physical science problems. With such an expansion of activity in both application and research, it became apparent that a revision of the original text was due. Here, the difficulties of selecting new material and presentation soon became apparent if the conflicting needs of simplicity of presentation and comprehensiveness were to be met without a vast increase of volume. As a result of this exercise, the book was largely rewritten although its basic sequence and philosophy is unchanged.

The finite element method is essentially a process through which a continuum with infinite degrees of freedom can be approximated to by an assemblage of subregions (or elements) each with a specified but now finite number of unknowns. Further, each such element interconnects with others in a way familiar to engineers dealing with discrete structural or electrical assemblies. This essential simplicity in both physical interpretation and mathematical form has undoubtedly been as much behind its popularity as was the digital computer which permits today a realistic solution of most complex engineering situations. In many design offices, finite element processes are now used as an everyday engineering tool and this trend will doubtless expand.

The first chapter of the book has thus little to do with 'finite elements'. It summarizes the basic principles of structural and network assembly in a simple way so that reference to other texts is superfluous. For those whose interests may come from another field—such as electrical engineering—it is shown that the basic principles of assembly in these fields are essentially identical—and will be repeated throughout in the finite element process.

Chapter 2 describes the essentials of the finite element formulation of elasticity problems based on assumed displacements. A careful study of this chapter will be repayed as several subsequent ones dealing with various problems of elasticity are directly based on the theory here developed. The alternative 'virtual work' and 'energy minimization' processes outlined here lead to Chapter 3 where a generalization to *all variationally conceived problems* is made showing the essential similarity of the method with the Rayleigh–Ritz processes. However, in the same chapter alternative, non-variational formulation possibilities are examined.

While simplest element forms only are described in Chapters 4–6, a general discussion of element shape functions is presented in Chapters 7 and 8. Here, the reader will discover the common basis of much detailed calculation.

Chapters 16 and 17 deal with extension of the process to the time variable and in Chapters 18 and 19 a coverage of non-linear problems is discussed. Here, most rapid progress has been made in recent years and generality of formulation rather than details are stressed. Plasticity, large deformation, and allied problems are, however, discussed in some detail.

The real application of finite element methods requires not only the mastery of the theory but also a considerable computer programming effort. While many efficient computer systems have been developed, their complexity tends to defeat the newcomer—who would prefer to lose some efficiency to gain the possibility of solving medium-size problems simply. With this in mind, the concluding Chapter 20 has been written by two of my collaborators Dr I. P. King and Dr Y. K. Cheung who have contributed much to the developments in that aspect. Here, a simple collection of modular subroutines of medium size and efficiency is presented and it is hoped will allow the reader to implement his own program without the necessity of devising many new components.

The text is written for both graduate and undergraduate students as well as for professional engineers. To achieve directness and unity, mathematical elegance has sometimes been sacrificed (without—it is hoped—giving up rigour). Little mathematical knowledge beyond the usual calculus is required although for convenience matrix presentation is used throughout. For those not familiar with it, an Appendix presents essential details.

Matrix methods are however not an essential of the finite element process as is sometimes erroneously assumed. An indicial, tensor, notation could be used with equal convenience.

In the first text, a chapter dealing with some future developments was included. Most of these have now materialized—and here prophecy will not be indulged in although much detailed development will doubtless occur in the field. Indeed, some apology should probably be made for omission of such developments in the direct use of the Helinger–Reisner variational theorem and Hybrid approaches which have vigorously grown. Such omissions have been intentional—not only to save space but to preserve a unity of approach which it is felt presents the 'essential toolkit'.

Practical examples have been included from a variety of engineering fields—though the reader will probably recognize here the choice dictated by the author's chief interest of Civil Engineering. Extensions to other branches of engineering requires, one feels, little imagination.

O. C. ZIENKIEWICZ

Acknowledgements

To Professor Ray Clough whose early enthusiasm has drawn my attention to the method and whose lasting friendship has ensured collaboration with his active group at Berkeley, California.

To the research teams of Technical University of Norway (Trondheim), Cornell University, MIT, and many other groups and individuals who have exchanged information and contributed to the general development.

To my own students and collaborators at Swansea without whose efforts this volume would not be possible. Grateful thanks thus to Dr Y. K. Cheung, Dr I. P. King, Mrs M. Watson, Dr J. Ergatoudis, Dr S. Valliappan, Dr C. Parekh, Dr S. Ahmad, Mrs D. Phillips, Mr G. Nayak, Mr J. Campbell, Mr F. Scott, Mr C. Dullage, Mr G. Treharne, Mr R. Wood, Mr D. Phillips, Mr J. Too, Mr K. Hinton, and others whose names would make the list overlong.

To Mr B. M. Irons, my colleague, for his contribution to theory of isoparametric element (Ch. 7.8), and helpful discussions.

Finally, to the help of various sponsoring agencies whose financial assistance helped to keep up the pace of research. My thanks to the kind offices of Civil Engineering Research and Information Association, The Science Research Council, NATO, Ministry of Transport, United Kingdom Atomic Energy Authority, and others.

Contents

1. Some Preliminaries: Structural Stiffness and Network Analysis

1.1 Introduction

Conventional engineering structures can be visualized as an assemblage of structural elements interconnected at a discrete number of nodal points. If the force-displacement relationships for the individual elements are known it is possible, by using various well-known techniques of structural analysis,[1,2] to derive the properties and study the behaviour of the assembled structure.

In an elastic continuum the true number of interconnection points is infinite, and here lies the biggest difficulty of its numerical solution. The concept of finite elements, as originally introduced by Turner *et al.*,[3] attempts to overcome this difficulty by assuming the real continuum to be divided into elements interconnected only at a finite number of nodal points at which some fictitious forces, representative of the distributed stresses actually acting on the element boundaries, were supposed to be introduced. If such an idealization is permissible the problem reduces to that of a conventional structural type well amenable to numerical treatment.

At first glance the procedure, though intuitively appealing to a structural engineer, does not seem entirely convincing—in particular, leaving open the question of the load-displacement characteristics of the element. The problems of a consistent way of determination of these characteristics will be discussed in detail in Chapter 2, when a firm foundation for the method will be established. At this stage, however, it is important to recapitulate a general method of structural analysis which will be used throughout this book once the properties of the elements have been established.

The finite element method will be shown to apply to many problems of non-structural type. The essential properties of an element will even then be of the form encountered in structural analysis. Again, the general

1

procedures of assembly and solution will follow a pattern for which the structural analogy provides a convenient basis.

Indeed the 'structural' form of equations is not unique to this discipline. The same form of equations is typically present in problems of inter-connected electrical circuits or fluid-carrying pipes. Thus it is often referred to as network analysis.

1.2 The Structural Element

Let Fig. 1.1 represent a two-dimensional structure assembled from indi-vidual components and interconnected at the nodes numbered 1 to n. The joints at the nodes, in this case, are pinned so that moments cannot be transmitted.

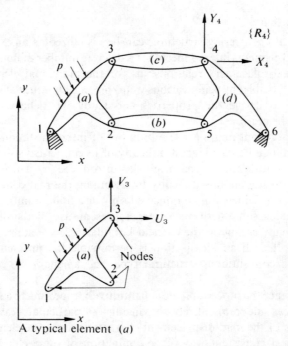

A typical element (a)

Fig. 1.1   A typical structure built up from interconnected elements

As a starting point it will be assumed that by separate calculation, or for that matter from the results of an experiment, the characteristics of each element are precisely known. Thus, if a typical element labelled (a) and associated with nodes 1, 2, 3 is examined, the forces acting at the nodes are uniquely defined by the displacements of these nodes, the distributed loading acting on the element (p), and its initial strain. The last may be due to temperature, shrinkage, or simply an initial 'lack of fit'. The forces and the corresponding displacements are defined by appropriate components (U, V and u, v) in a common co-ordinate system.

Listing the forces acting on all the nodes (three in the case illustrated) of the element (a) as a matrix† we have

$$\{F\}^a = \begin{Bmatrix} F_1 \\ F_2 \\ F_3 \end{Bmatrix} = \begin{Bmatrix} U_1 \\ V_1 \\ U_2 \\ V_2 \\ U_3 \\ V_3 \end{Bmatrix} \tag{1.1}$$

and for the corresponding nodal displacements as

$$\{\delta\}^a = \begin{Bmatrix} \delta_1 \\ \delta_2 \\ \delta_3 \end{Bmatrix} = \begin{Bmatrix} u_1 \\ v_1 \\ u_2 \\ v_2 \\ u_3 \\ v_3 \end{Bmatrix} \tag{1.2}$$

Assuming elastic behaviour of the element, the characteristic relationship will always be of the form

$$\{F\}^a = [k]^a\{\delta\}^a + \{F\}^a_p + \{F\}^a_{\varepsilon 0} \tag{1.3}$$

in which $\{F\}^a_p$, represents the nodal forces required to balance any distributed loads acting on the element, and $\{F\}^a_{\varepsilon 0}$ the nodal forces required to balance any initial strains such as may be caused by temperature change if the nodes are not subject to any displacement. The first of the terms represents the forces induced by displacement of the nodes.

Similarly, the preliminary analysis or experiment will permit a unique definition of stresses or internal reactions at any specified point or points of the element in terms of the nodal displacements. Defining such stresses by a matrix $\{\sigma\}^a$ a relationship of the form

$$\{\sigma\}^a = [S]^a\{\delta\}^a + \{\sigma\}^a_p + \{\sigma\}^a_{\varepsilon 0} \tag{1.4}$$

is obtained in which the last two terms are simply the stresses due to the distributed element loads or initial stresses respectively when no nodal displacement occurs.

† A limited knowledge of matrix algebra will be assumed throughout this book. This is necessary for reasonable conciseness and forms a convenient book-keeping form. For readers not familiar with the subject a brief appendix is included in which sufficient principles of matrix algebra are given to follow intelligently the development.

The matrix $[k]^a$ is known as the element stiffness matrix and the matrix $[S]^a$ as the element stress matrix.

Relationships Eqs. (1.3) and (1.4) have been illustrated on an example of an element with three nodes and with the interconnection points capable of transmitting only two components of force. Clearly, the same arguments and definitions will apply generally. An element (b) of the hypothetical structure will possess only two points of interconnection, others may have quite a large number of such points. Similarly, if the joints were considered as rigid, three components of generalized force and of generalized displacement would have to be considered, the last corresponding to a moment and a rotation respectively. For a rigidly jointed, three-dimensional structure the number of individual nodal components would be six. Quite generally therefore—

$$\{F\}^a = \begin{Bmatrix} F_i \\ \vdots \\ F_m \end{Bmatrix} \quad \text{and} \quad \{\delta\}^a = \begin{Bmatrix} \delta_i \\ \vdots \\ \delta_m \end{Bmatrix} \tag{1.5}$$

with each F_i and δ_i possessing the same number of components or degrees of freedom.

The stiffness matrices of the element will clearly always be square and of the form

$$[k]^e = \begin{bmatrix} k_{ii} & k_{ij} & k_{im} \\ \vdots & \vdots & \vdots \\ k_{mi} & k_{mj} & k_{mm} \end{bmatrix} \tag{1.6}$$

in which k_{ii}, etc., are submatrices which are again square and of the size $l \times l$, where l is the number of force components to be considered at the nodes.

As an example, the reader can consider a pin-ended bar of a uniform section A and modulus E in a two-dimensional problem shown in Fig. 1.2. The bar is subject to a uniform lateral load p and a uniform thermal expansion strain

$$\varepsilon_0 = \alpha T.$$

If the ends of the bar are defined by the co-ordinates x_i, y_i and x_n, y_n its length can be calculated as

$$L = \sqrt{\{(x_n - x_i)^2 + (y_n - y_i)^2\}}$$

and its inclination from the horizontal as

$$\alpha = \tan^{-1} \frac{y_n - y_i}{x_n - x_i}$$

Only two components of force and displacement have to be considered at the nodes.

The nodal forces due to the lateral load are clearly

$$\{F\}_p^a = \begin{pmatrix} F_i \\ F_n \end{pmatrix}_p = \begin{Bmatrix} U_i \\ V_i \\ U_n \\ V_n \end{Bmatrix}_p = \begin{Bmatrix} -\sin\alpha \\ \cos\alpha \\ -\sin\alpha \\ \cos\alpha \end{Bmatrix} \cdot \frac{pL}{2}$$

and represent the appropriate components of simple beam reactions, $pL/2$. Similarly, to restrain the thermal expansion ε_0 an axial force $(E\alpha T A)$ is needed, which gives the components

$$\{F\}_{\varepsilon 0}^a = \begin{Bmatrix} F_i \\ F_n \end{Bmatrix}_{\varepsilon 0} = \begin{Bmatrix} U_i \\ V_i \\ U_n \\ V_n \end{Bmatrix}_{\varepsilon 0} = -\begin{Bmatrix} -\cos\alpha \\ -\sin\alpha \\ \cos\alpha \\ \sin\alpha \end{Bmatrix} (E\alpha T A).$$

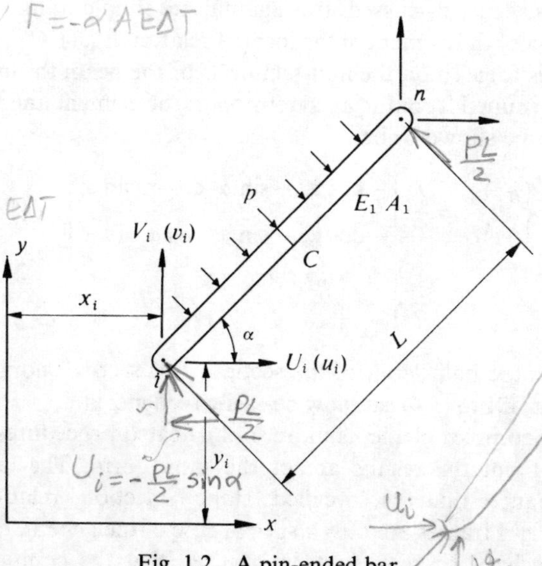

(handwritten annotations):

$\delta_T = \alpha L \Delta T$

$\delta_F = \dfrac{FL}{AE}$

$\delta_T = \delta_F$

$F = \alpha AE \Delta T$

$\Delta T > 0 \Rightarrow$ compres

$\Rightarrow$ negative (trying to) shorten it

$F = -\alpha A E \Delta T$

negative cause compression

$F = +\alpha A E \Delta T$

Fig. 1.2   A pin-ended bar

$U_i = -\frac{PL}{2}\sin\alpha$

Finally, the element displacements

$$\{\delta\}^a = \begin{Bmatrix} \delta_i \\ \delta_n \end{Bmatrix} = \begin{Bmatrix} u_i \\ v_i \\ u_n \\ v_n \end{Bmatrix}$$

will cause an elongation $(u_n - u_i)\cos\alpha + (v_n - v_i)\sin\alpha$. This when multiplied by EA/L, gives the axial force whose components can again be

(handwritten): $\delta = (u_n - u_i)\cos\alpha + (v_n - v_i)\sin\alpha$

found by substitution of this force in place of $-E\alpha TA$ in the previous equation. Rearranging these in the standard form gives

$$\{F\}_\delta^a = \begin{Bmatrix} F_i \\ F_n \end{Bmatrix}_\delta = \begin{Bmatrix} U_i \\ V_i \\ U_n \\ V_n \end{Bmatrix}_\delta =$$

$$= \frac{EA}{L} \left[\begin{array}{cc:cc} \cos^2\alpha & \sin\alpha\cos\alpha & -\cos^2\alpha & -\sin\alpha\cos\alpha \\ \sin\alpha\cos\alpha & \sin^2\alpha & -\sin\alpha\cos\alpha & -\sin^2\alpha \\ \hdashline -\cos^2\alpha & -\sin\alpha\cos\alpha & \cos^2\alpha & \sin\alpha\cos\alpha \\ -\sin\alpha\cos\alpha & -\sin^2\alpha & \sin\alpha\cos\alpha & \sin^2\alpha \end{array} \right] \begin{Bmatrix} u_i \\ v_i \\ u_n \\ v_n \end{Bmatrix}$$

$$= [k]^a\{\delta\}^a.$$

The components of the general Eq. (1.3) have thus been established for the elementary case discussed. It is again quite simple to find the stresses at any section of the element in the form of relation Eq. (1.4). For instance, if attention is focused on the mid-section C of the beam the extreme fibre stresses determined from the axial tension to the element and the bending moment can be shown to be

$$\begin{Bmatrix} \sigma_1 \\ \sigma_2 \end{Bmatrix}_C = \frac{E}{L} \begin{bmatrix} -\cos\alpha, & -\sin\alpha, & \cos\alpha, & \sin\alpha \\ -\cos\alpha, & -\sin\alpha, & \cos\alpha, & \sin\alpha \end{bmatrix} \{\delta\}^a$$

$$+ \begin{Bmatrix} 1 \\ -1 \end{Bmatrix} \frac{pL^2}{8} \frac{d}{I} - \begin{Bmatrix} 1 \\ 1 \end{Bmatrix} E\alpha T$$

in which d is the half depth of the section, I its second moment of area. All the terms of Eq. (1.4) can now be easily recognized.

For more complex elements more sophisticated procedures of analysis are required but the results are of the same form. The engineer will readily recognize that the so-called 'slope-deflection' relations used in analysis of rigid frames are only a special case of the general relations.

It may perhaps be remarked, in passing, that the complete stiffness matrix obtained for the simple element in tension turned out to be symmetric (as indeed was the case with some submatrices). This is by no means fortuitous but follows from the principle of energy conservation and from its corollary—the well-known Maxwell-Betti reciprocal theorem.

The element properties were assumed to follow a simple linear relationship. In principle, similar relationships could be established for nonlinear materials, but discussion of such problems will be held over at this stage.

1.3 Assembly and Analysis of a Structure

Consider again the hypothetical structure of Fig. 1.1. To obtain a complete solution the two conditions of

(*a*) displacement compatibility, and

(*b*) equilibrium

have to be satisfied throughout.

Any systems of nodal displacements $\{\delta\}$

$$\{\delta\} = \begin{Bmatrix} \delta_1 \\ \vdots \\ \delta_n \end{Bmatrix} \tag{1.7}$$

listed now for the whole structure in which all the elements participate, automatically satisfies the first condition.

As the conditions of overall equilibrium have already been satisfied *within* an element all that is necessary is to establish equilibrium conditions at the nodes of the structure. The resulting equations will contain the displacements as unknowns, and once these have been solved the structural problem is determined. The internal forces in elements, or the stresses, can easily be found by using the characteristics established *a priori* for each element by Eq. (1.4).

Consider the structure to be loaded by external forces $\{R\}$

$$\{R\} = \begin{Bmatrix} R_1 \\ \vdots \\ R_n \end{Bmatrix} \tag{1.8}$$

applied at the nodes in addition to the distributed loads applied to the individual elements. Again, any one of the forces R_i must have the same number of components as that of the element reactions considered. In the example in question

$$\{R_i\} = \begin{Bmatrix} X_i \\ Y_i \end{Bmatrix} \tag{1.9}$$

as the joints were assumed pinned, but at this stage a generality with an arbitrary number of components will be assumed.

If now the equilibrium conditions of a typical node, i, are to be established, each component of R_i has, in turn, to be equated to the sum of the component forces contributed by the elements meeting at the node. Thus, considering *all* the force components we have:

$$\{R_i\} = \sum \{F_i\}^a = \{F_i\}^1 + \{F_i\}^2 + \cdots \tag{1.10}$$

in which F_i^1 is the force contributed to node i by element 1, F_i^2 by element 2, etc. Clearly, only the elements which include point i will contribute (non-zero) forces but for tidiness all the elements are included in the summation.

Substituting from the definition (1.3) the forces contributed to node 'i' are

$$\{R_i\} = (\sum [k_{i1}]^a)\{\delta_1\} + (\sum [k_{i2}]^a)\{\delta_2\} + \cdots + \sum \{F_i\}_p^a + \sum \{F_i\}_{\varepsilon 0}^a. \quad (1.11)$$

The summation again only concerns the elements which contribute to node i. If all such equations are assembled we have simply

$$[K]\{\delta\} = \{R\} - \{F\}_p - \{F\}_{\varepsilon 0} \quad (1.12)$$

in which the submatrices are

$$
\begin{aligned}
[K_{im}] &= \sum [k_{im}]^a \\
\{F_i\}_p &= \sum \{F_i\}_p^a \\
\{F_i\}_{\varepsilon 0} &= \sum \{F_i\}_{\varepsilon 0}^a
\end{aligned}
\quad (1.13)
$$

with summations including all elements. This simple rule for assembly is very convenient because, as soon as a coefficient for a particular element is found it can be put in immediately into the appropriate 'location' specified in the computer. *This general assembly process can be found to be the common and fundamental feature of all finite element calculations and should be well understood by the reader.*

If different types of structural elements are used and are to be coupled it must be remembered that the rules of matrix summation permit this to be done only if these are of identical size. The individual submatrices to be added have therefore to be built up of the same number of individual components of force or displacement. Thus, for example, if a member capable of transmitting moments to a node is to be coupled at that node to one which in fact is hinged, it is necessary to complete the stiffness matrix of the latter by insertion of appropriate (zero) coefficients in the rotation or moment positions.

The system of equations resulting from Eq. (1.12) can be solved once the prescribed support displacements have been substituted. In the example of Fig. 1.1, where both components of displacement of nodes 1 and 6 are zero, this will mean the substitution of

$$\{\delta_1\} = \{\delta_6\} = \begin{Bmatrix} 0 \\ 0 \end{Bmatrix}$$

which is equivalent to reducing the number of equilibrium equations (in this instance twelve) by deleting the first and last pairs and thus reducing the total number of unknown displacement components to eight. It is, nevertheless, always convenient to assemble the equation according to relation Eq. (1.12) so as to include all the nodes.

Clearly, without substitution of a minimum number of prescribed displacements to prevent rigid body movements of the structure, it is impossible to solve this system, because the displacements cannot be uniquely determined by the forces in such a situation. This physically obvious fact will mathematically be interpreted in the matrix $[K]$ being singular, i.e., not possessing an inverse. The prescription of appropriate displacements after the assembly stage will permit a unique solution to be obtained by deleting appropriate rows and columns of the various matrices.

While the substitution of known displacements is relatively easy in manual computation and can be programmed for a digital computer, resulting in a reduction of the total number of equations to be solved, it is often convenient to proceed with a direct solution of the original number of equations to avoid reorganization of computer storage. This is very simply done by using an artifice due to Payne and Irons.[4]

Using this, instead of eliminating the equilibrium equation at which a particular displacement is specified (and the corresponding external force component is unknown) and proceeding with the substitution of that displacement component into the remaining equations, the diagonal coefficient of the matrix $[K]$ at the point concerned is multiplied by a very large number. At the same time the term on the right-hand side of the equation is replaced by the same large number multiplied by the prescribed displacement value. This has the effect of replacing the particular equation by one stating that the displacement in question is equal to the specified value, and retaining this equation in the system to be solved. Discussion of this point is elaborated in Ch. 20.

Once the solution of the unknown displacements has been obtained it is an easy matter to compute the stresses and internal forces by Eq. (1.4) applied to each element in turn.

1.4 Transformation of Co-ordinates

It is often convenient to establish the characteristics of an individual element in a co-ordinate system which is different from that in which the external forces and displacements of the assembled structure will be measured. A different co-ordinate system may, in fact, be used for every element, to ease the computation. It is a simple matter to transform the co-ordinates of the displacement and force components of Eq. (1.3) to any other co-ordinate system. Clearly, it is necessary to do so before an assembly of the structure can be attempted.

Let the local co-ordinate system in which the element properties have been evaluated be denoted by prime suffix, and the common co-ordinate system necessary for assembly be not annotated. The displacement components can be transformed by a suitable matrix of direction cosines $[L]$ as

$$\{\delta'\}^a = [L]\{\delta\}^a. \tag{1.14}$$

As the corresponding force components must perform the same amount of work in either system†

$$(\{F\}^a)^{\mathrm{T}}\{\delta\}^a = (\{F'\}^a)^{\mathrm{T}}\{\delta'\}^a$$

and inserting (1.14) we have

$$(\{F\}^a)^{\mathrm{T}}\{\delta\}^a = (\{F'\}^a)^{\mathrm{T}}[L]\{\delta\}^a$$

or

$$\{F\}^a = [L]^{\mathrm{T}}\{F'\}^a. \tag{1.15}$$

The set of transformations given by 1.14 and 1.15 is called *contra-gradient*.

To transform stiffnesses which may be available in local co-ordinates to global ones note that

$$\{F'\}^a = [k']^a\{\delta'\}^a \tag{1.16}$$

and by 1.14 and 1.15

$$\{F\} = [L]^{\mathrm{T}}[k']^a[L]\{\delta\}^a$$

or

$$[k]^a = [L]^{\mathrm{T}}[k'][L]. \tag{1.17}$$

The reader can verify the usefulness of the above transformations by re-working the sample example of the pin ended bar. In many complex problems an external constraint of some kind may be imagined enforcing the requirement (1.14) with the number of degrees of freedom of $\{\delta\}$ and $\{\delta'\}$ being quite different. Even in such instances the relations 1.15 and 1.16 continue to be valid.

1.5 Electrical or Fluid Network

Identical principles of deriving element characteristics and of assembly will be found in many non-structural fields. Consider for instance an assembly of electrical resistances shown in Fig. 1.3.

If a typical resistance-element, *ij*, is isolated from the system we can write by Ohm's law the relation between the currents *entering* the element at the ends and the end voltages as

$$I_i = \frac{1}{r^e}(V_i - V_j)$$

$$I_j = \frac{1}{r^e}(V_j - V_i)$$

† With $(\ )^{\mathrm{T}}$ standing for transpose of the matrix.

or in matrix form

$$\left\{ \begin{matrix} I_i \\ I_j \end{matrix} \right\} = \frac{1}{r^e} \begin{bmatrix} 1 & -1 \\ -1 & 1 \end{bmatrix} \left\{ \begin{matrix} V_i \\ V_j \end{matrix} \right\}$$

which in our standard form is simply

$$\{I\}^e = [k]^e \{V\}^e. \tag{1.18}$$

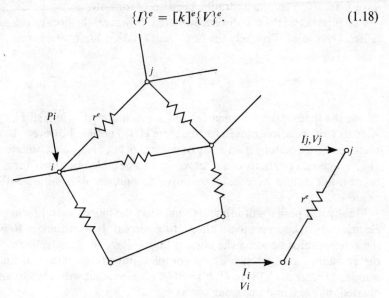

Fig. 1.3   A network of electrical resistances

This form clearly corresponds to the stiffness relationship (1.3), indeed if external current were supplied along the length of the element the element 'force' terms could also be found.

To assemble the whole network the continuity of potential at nodes is assumed and a current balance imposed there. If P_i now stands for an external imput of current at node i we must have with complete analogy to Eq. (1.11)

$$P_i = \sum_{m=1}^{m=h} \sum k_{im}^e V_m \tag{1.19}$$

where the second summation is over all 'elements' and once again for all the nodes

$$\{P\} = [K]\{V\} \tag{1.20}$$

in which

$$k_{ij} = \sum k_{ij}^e.$$

Brackets in the above have been dropped as the quantities such as voltage and current and hence also the coefficients of the 'stiffness' matrix are scalars.

If the resistances were replaced by fluid-carrying pipes in which a laminar regime pertained, identical formulation would once again result with V standing for the hydraulic head and I for flow.

For pipe networks usually encountered, however, the linear laws are in general not valid. Typically the flow-head relationship is of a form

$$I_i = c(V_i - V_j)^\gamma \tag{1.21}$$

where the index γ lies between 1·5 and 2. Even now it would still be possible to write relationships in for the form (1.18) noting, however, that the matrices k^e are no longer an array of constants but are known functions of $\{V\}$. The final equations can once again be assembled but their form will be non-linear and in general iterative techniques of solution will be needed.

Finally it is perhaps of interest to mention the more general form of an electric network subject to an alternating current. It is customary to write the relationships between the current and voltage in complex form with the resistance being replaced by complex impedance. Once again the standard forms of (1.18) to (1.20) will be obtained but with each quantity divided into real and imaginary parts.

Identical solution procedures can be used if the equality of the real and imaginary quantities is considered at each stage. Indeed with modern digital computers it is possible to use standard programming making use of facilities available for dealing with complex numbers. Reference to some problems of this class will be made in a later chapter dealing with vibration problems.

1.6 The General Pattern

To consolidate the concepts discussed in this chapter an example will be considered. This is shown in Fig. 1.4(*a*) where five discrete elements are inter-connected. These may be of structural, electrical, or any other linear type. In the solution:

The first step is the determination of element properties from the geometric material and loading data. For each element the stiffness matrix as well as the corresponding nodal loads are found in the form of Eq. (1.3). Each element has its own identifying number and specified nodal connection.

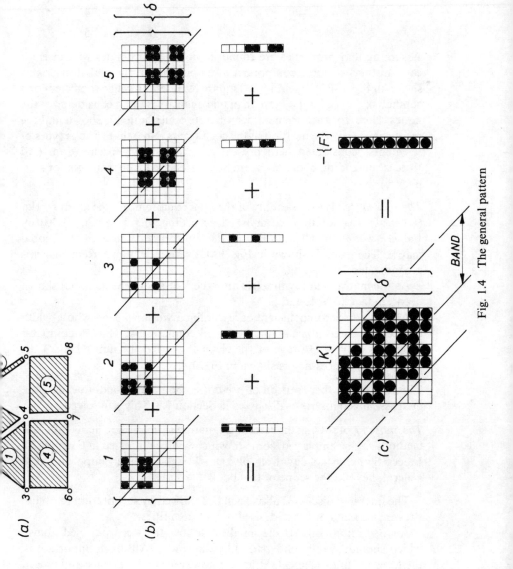

Fig. 1.4   The general pattern

For example:

element	1	connection	1	3	4	
	2		1	4	2	
	3		2	5		
	4		3	6	7	4
	5		4	7	8	5

Assuming that properties are found in global co-ordinates we can enter each stiffness or force component in its position of the global matrix as shown in Fig. 1.4(*b*). Each shaded square represents a single coefficient or a submatrix of type $[k_{ij}]$ if more than one quantity is being considered at the nodes. Here, for each element, its separate contribution is shown and the reader can verify the position of the coefficients. Note that various types of 'elements' considered here present no difficulty in specification. (All 'forces', including nodal ones, are here associated with elements for simplicity.)

The second step is the assembly of the final equations of type given by Eq. (1.12). This is simply accomplished according to rule of Eq. (1.13) by *simple addition* of all numbers in the appropriate space of the global matrix. The result is shown in Fig. 1.4(*c*) where the non zero coefficients are indicated by shading.

As the matrices are symmetric only the half above the diagonal shown needs, in fact, to be found.

All the non-zero coefficients are confined within a *band* whose width can be calculated *a priori* for the nodal connections. Thus in computer programs only the storage of the elements within the upper half of the band width is necessary as shown in Fig. 1.4(*c*).

The third step is the insertion of prescribed boundary conditions into the final assembled matrix as discussed in Section 1.3. This is followed by

The final step of solving the resulting equation system. Here many different methods can be employed, some of which will be discussed in Chapter 20. Indeed the subject of equation solving—though extremely important, is in general, beyond the scope of this book.

The final step discussed above will be followed by substitution to obtain stresses, currents or other desired *output* quantities.

All operations of network analysis follow the steps outlined above, which should be fully understood by the reader. Although important to the topic of 'finite elements' they are however, not its essence and indeed are well known and always applicable in discrete structural or network analysis. *The remainder of this book will be concerned with the method by which continuous media can, approximately, be represented by equivalent discrete elements.* If this can be achieved the framework now presented will allow the actual analysis to be carried out.

References

1. S. P. TIMOSHENKO and D. H. YOUNG, *Theory of Structures*, 2nd ed., McGraw-Hill, 1965.
2a. R. K. LIVESLEY, *Matrix Methods in Structural Analysis*, Pergamon Press, 1964.
2b. J. S. PRZEMIENIECKI, *Theory of Matrix Structural Analysis*, McGraw-Hill, 1968.
2c. H. C. MARTIN, *Introduction to Matrix Methods of Structural Analysis*, McGraw-Hill, 1966.
2d W. M. JENKINS, *Matrix and Digital Computer Methods in Structural Analysis*, McGraw-Hill, 1969.
3. M. J. TURNER, R. W. CLOUGH, H. C. MARTIN, and L. J. TOPP, 'Stiffness and deflection analysis of complex structures', *J. Aero. Sci.*, **23**, 805–23, 1956.
4. N. A. PAYNE and B. IRONS, Private communication, 1963.

2. Finite Elements of an Elastic Continuum—Displacement Approach

2.1 Introduction

In many phases of engineering the solution of stress and strain distributions in elastic continua is required. Special cases of such problems may range from two-dimensional plane stress or strain distributions, axi-symmetrical solids, plate bending, and shells, to fully three-dimensional solids. In all cases the number of interconnections between any 'finite element' isolated by some imaginary boundaries and the neighbouring elements is infinite. It is therefore difficult to see at first glance how such problems may be discretized in the same manner as was described in the preceding chapter for simpler structures. The difficulty can be overcome (and the approximation made) in the following manner:

(a) The continuum is separated by imaginary lines or surfaces into a number of 'finite elements'.

(b) The elements are assumed to be interconnected at a discrete number of nodal points situated on their boundaries. The displacements of these nodal points will be the basic unknown parameters of the problem, just as in the simple structural analysis.

(c) A set of functions is chosen to define uniquely the state of displacement within each 'finite element' in terms of its nodal displacements.

(d) The displacement functions now define uniquely the state of strain within an element in terms of the nodal displacements. These strains, together with any initial strains and the constitutive properties of the material will define the state of stress throughout the element and, hence, also on its boundaries.

(e) A system of forces concentrated at the nodes and equilibrating the boundary stresses and any distributed loads is determined, resulting in a stiffness relationship of the form of Eq. (1.3).

16

Once this stage has been reached the solution procedure can follow the standard structural routine described earlier.

Clearly a series of approximations has been introduced. Firstly, it is not always easy to ensure that the chosen displacement functions will satisfy the requirement of displacement continuity between adjacent elements. Thus, the compatibility condition on such lines may be violated (though within each element it is obviously satisfied due to uniqueness of displacements implied in their continuous representation). Secondly, by concentrating the equivalent forces at the nodes, equilibrium conditions are satisfied in the overall sense only. Local violation of equilibrium conditions within each element and on its boundaries will usually arise.

The choice of element shape and of the form of the displacement function for specific cases leaves much choice to ingenuity and skill of the engineer, and obviously the degree of approximation which can be achieved will much depend on these factors.

The approach outlined here is known as the displacement formulation.[1,2]

So far, the process described is justified only intuitively, but what in fact has been suggested is equivalent to the minimization of the total potential energy of the system in terms of a prescribed displacement field. If this displacement field is defined in a suitable way, then convergence to the correct result must occur. The process is then equivalent to the well-known Ritz procedure. This equivalence will be proved in a later section of this chapter where also a discussion of the necessary convergence criteria will be made.

The recognition of the equivalence of the finite element method with a minimization process was late.[3,2] However, Courant in 1943[4] and Prager and Synge[5] in 1947 proposed methods in essence identical. This broader basis of the method will permit applications to be extended to almost all problems where a variational formulation is possible. Some of such problems of non-structural type will be discussed in this book.

2.2 Direct Formulation of Finite Element Characteristics

The 'prescriptions' for deriving the characteristics of a 'finite element' of a continuum, which were outlined in general terms, will now be presented in more detailed mathematical form.

It is desirable to obtain results in a general form applicable to any situation, but to avoid introducing conceptual difficulties the general relations will be illustrated with a very simple example of plane stress analysis of a thin slice. In this a division of the region into triangular shape elements is used as shown in Fig. 2.1. Relationships of general validity will be printed in bold type, and those referring to the particular example in normal type. Again, matrix notation will be implied.

2.2.1 *Displacement function.* A typical finite element, e, is defined by nodes, i, j, m, etc., and straight line boundaries. Let the displacements at any point within the element be defined as a column vector, $\{f(x, y)\}$

$$\begin{Bmatrix} u \\ v \end{Bmatrix} = \{\mathbf{f}\} = [\mathbf{N}]\{\boldsymbol{\delta}\}^e = [\mathbf{N}_i, \mathbf{N}_j, \mathbf{N}_m \ldots] \begin{Bmatrix} \delta_i \\ \delta_j \\ \delta_m \\ \vdots \end{Bmatrix} \tag{2.1}$$

$N_i = 1$
and 0 at all other nodal points

in which the components of $[N]$ are in general functions of position and $\{\delta\}^e$ represents a listing of nodal displacements for a particular element.

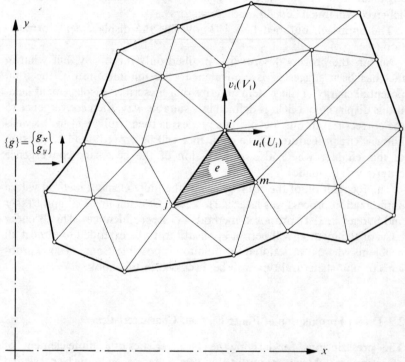

Fig. 2.1   A plane stress region divided into finite elements

In the case of plane stress for instance

$$\{f\} = \begin{Bmatrix} u(x, y) \\ v(x, y) \end{Bmatrix}$$

$$N_i = \frac{1}{2A} \left[a_i + b_i x + c_i y \right] \quad , \quad \begin{aligned} a_i &= x_j y_m - x_m y_j \\ b_i &= y_j - y_m \end{aligned}$$

$$c_i = x_m - x_j$$

represents horizontal and vertical movements of a typical point within the element and

$$\{\delta_i\} = \begin{Bmatrix} u_i \\ v_i \end{Bmatrix}$$

$$2A = \begin{vmatrix} 1 & x_i & y_i \\ 1 & x_j & y_j \\ 1 & x_m & y_m \end{vmatrix}$$

the corresponding displacements of a node i.

The functions N_i, N_j, N_m have to be so chosen as to give appropriate nodal displacements when the co-ordinates of the appropriate nodes are inserted in Eq. (2.1). Clearly, in general

$$N_i(x_i, y_i) = I \quad \text{(identity matrix)}, \qquad (N_i)_{x_i, y_i} = \begin{bmatrix} 1 & 0 \\ 0 & 1 \end{bmatrix}$$

while

$$N_i(x_j, y_j) = N_i(x_m, y_m) = 0 \text{ etc.},$$

which is simply satisfied by suitable linear functions of x and y. Details of these will be shown in the appropriate later chapter.

The functions $[N]$ will be called *shape functions* and will be seen later to play a paramount role in finite element analysis.

2.2.2 *Strains*. With displacements known at all points within the element the 'strains'† at any point can be determined. These will always result in a relationship which can be written in matrix notation as

$$\{\varepsilon\} = [\mathbf{B}]\{\delta\}^e. \tag{2.2}$$

For the plane stress case the relevant strains of interest are those occurring in the plane and are defined in terms of the displacements by well-known relations[6]—

$$\{\varepsilon\} = \begin{Bmatrix} \varepsilon_x \\ \varepsilon_y \\ \gamma_{xy} \end{Bmatrix} = \begin{Bmatrix} \dfrac{\partial u}{\partial x} \\ \dfrac{\partial v}{\partial y} \\ \dfrac{\partial u}{\partial y} + \dfrac{\partial v}{\partial x} \end{Bmatrix}.$$

From the equation Eq. (2.1), with the shape functions N_i, N_j, and N_m already determined, the matrix $[B]$ will easily be obtained. If the linear form of these functions is adopted then, in fact, the strains will be constant throughout the element.

2.2.3 *Stresses*. In general, the material within the element boundaries may be subjected to initial strains such as may be due to temperature

† Strains in this context are generally internal distortions such as, for example, curvatures in a plate problem.

changes, shrinkage, crystal growth, and so on. If such strains are denoted by $\{\varepsilon_0\}$ then the stresses will be caused by the difference between the actual and initial strains.

In addition it is convenient to assume that at the outset of analysis the body is stressed by some known system at initial residual stresses $\{\sigma_0\}$ which for instance could be measured but the prediction of which without the full knowledge of the material's history is impossible. These stresses can simply be added on to the general definition. Thus, assuming general elastic behaviour, the relationship between stresses and strains will be linear and of the form

$$\{\sigma\} = [\mathbf{D}](\{\varepsilon\} - \{\varepsilon_0\}) + \{\sigma_0\} \tag{2.3}$$

where $[D]$ is an elasticity matrix containing the appropriate material properties.

Again, for the particular case of plane stress three components of stress corresponding to the strains already defined have to be considered. These are, in familiar notation

[handwritten: for plane strain $\varepsilon_z \neq 0$, $\varepsilon_z = 0 = \gamma_{xz} = \gamma_{yz} = 0$]

$$\{\sigma\} = \begin{Bmatrix} \sigma_x \\ \sigma_y \\ \tau_{xy} \end{Bmatrix}$$

and the $[D]$ matrix will be simply obtained from the usual isotropic stress-strain relationship[6]

[handwritten: $\varepsilon_z = \dfrac{1}{E}\left[\sigma_z - \nu(\sigma_x + \sigma_y)\right]$]

$$\varepsilon_x - (\varepsilon_x)_0 = \frac{1}{E}\sigma_x - \frac{\nu}{E}\sigma_y,$$

$$\varepsilon_y - (\varepsilon_y)_0 = -\frac{\nu}{E}\sigma_x + \frac{1}{E}\sigma_y,$$

$$\gamma_{xy} - (\gamma_{xy})_0 = \frac{2(1+\nu)}{E}\tau_{xy},$$

i.e., on solving,

[handwritten: plane stress $\varepsilon_z = 0$, $\gamma_{xz} = \gamma_{yz} = 0$]

$$[D] = \frac{E}{1-\nu^2}\begin{bmatrix} 1 & \nu & 0 \\ \nu & 1 & 0 \\ 0 & 0 & (1-\nu)/2 \end{bmatrix}.$$

2.2.4 *Equivalent nodal forces.* Let

$$\{\mathbf{F}\}^e = \begin{Bmatrix} \mathbf{F}_i \\ \mathbf{F}_j \\ \mathbf{F}_m \\ \vdots \end{Bmatrix}$$

define the nodal forces which are equivalent statically to the boundary stresses and distributed loads on the element. Each of the forces $\{\mathbf{F}_i\}$

must contain the same number of components as the corresponding nodal displacement $\{\delta_i\}$ and be ordered in the appropriate, corresponding directions.

The distributed loads $\{\mathbf{p}\}$ are defined as those acting on a unit volume of material within the element with directions corresponding to those of the displacements $\{\mathbf{f}\}$ at that point.

In the particular case of plane stress the nodal forces are, for instance

$$\{F_i\} = \begin{Bmatrix} U_i \\ V_i \end{Bmatrix}$$

with components U and V corresponding to the directions of u and v displacements, and the distributed load is

$$\{\mathbf{p}\} = \begin{Bmatrix} X \\ Y \end{Bmatrix}$$

in which X and Y are the 'body force' components.

To make the nodal forces statically equivalent to the actual boundary stresses and distributed loads, the simplest procedure is to impose an arbitrary (virtual) nodal displacement and to equate the external and internal work done by the various forces and stresses during that displacement.

Let such a virtual displacement be $\mathbf{d}\{\delta\}^e$ at the nodes. This results, by Eqs. (2.1) and (2.2), in displacements and strains within the element equal to

$$\mathbf{d}\{\mathbf{f}\} = [\mathbf{N}]\mathbf{d}\{\delta\}^e \text{ and } \mathbf{d}\{\boldsymbol{\varepsilon}\} = [\mathbf{B}]\mathbf{d}\{\delta\}^e \tag{2.4}$$

respectively.

The work done by the nodal forces is equal to the sum of the products of the individual force components and corresponding displacements, i.e., in matrix language

$$(\mathbf{d}\{\delta\}^e)^{\mathrm{T}} \cdot \{\mathbf{F}\}^e. \tag{2.5}$$

Similarly, the internal work per unit volume done by the stresses and distributed forces is

$$\mathbf{d}\{\boldsymbol{\varepsilon}\}^{\mathrm{T}}\{\boldsymbol{\sigma}\} - \mathbf{d}\{\mathbf{f}\}^{\mathrm{T}}\{\mathbf{p}\} \tag{2.6}$$

or†

$$(\mathbf{d}\{\delta\}^e)^{\mathrm{T}}([\mathbf{B}]^{\mathrm{T}}\{\boldsymbol{\sigma}\} - [\mathbf{N}]^{\mathrm{T}}\{\mathbf{p}\}). \tag{2.7}$$

† Note that by rules of matrix algebra for transpose of products
$$([A][B])^{\mathrm{T}} = [B]^{\mathrm{T}}[A]^{\mathrm{T}}.$$

Equating the external work with the total internal work obtained by integrating over the volume of the element we have

$$(\mathbf{d}\{\boldsymbol{\delta}\}^e)^{\mathrm{T}}\{\mathbf{F}\}^e = (\mathbf{d}\{\boldsymbol{\delta}\}^e)^{\mathrm{T}}\left(\int [\mathbf{B}]^{\mathrm{T}}\{\boldsymbol{\sigma}\}\ \mathbf{d(vol)} - \int [\mathbf{N}]^{\mathrm{T}}\{\mathbf{p}\}\ \mathbf{d(vol)}\right). \quad (2.8)$$

As this relation is valid for any value of the virtual displacement, the equality of the multipliers must exist. On substitution of Eqs. (2.2) and (2.3) we have, therefore,

$$\{\mathbf{F}\}^e = \left(\int [\mathbf{B}]^{\mathrm{T}}[\mathbf{D}][\mathbf{B}]\ \mathbf{d(vol)}\right)\{\boldsymbol{\delta}\}^e - \int [\mathbf{B}]^{\mathrm{T}}[\mathbf{D}]\{\varepsilon_0\}\ \mathbf{d(vol)} +$$

$$+ \int [\mathbf{B}]^{\mathrm{T}}\{\boldsymbol{\sigma}_0\}\ \mathbf{d(vol)} - \int [\mathbf{N}]^{\mathrm{T}}\{\mathbf{p}\}\ \mathbf{d(vol)}. \quad (2.9)$$

This relation will be recognized as one typical of characteristics of any structural element in the form described in Chapter 1 by Eq. (1.3). The stiffness matrix becomes

$$[\mathbf{k}]^e = \int [\mathbf{B}]^{\mathrm{T}}[\mathbf{D}][\mathbf{B}]\ \mathbf{d(vol)}, \quad (2.10)$$

nodal forces due to distributed loads are

$$\{\mathbf{F}\}_p^e = -\int [\mathbf{N}]^{\mathrm{T}}\{\mathbf{p}\}\ \mathbf{d(vol)}, \quad (2.11)$$

and those due to initial strain are

$$\{\mathbf{F}\}_{\varepsilon_0}^e = -\int [\mathbf{B}]^{\mathrm{T}}[\mathbf{D}]\{\varepsilon_0\}\ \mathbf{d(vol)}. \quad (2.12)$$

Due to initial stresses present at the outset of the analysis nodal forces contributed are

$$\{\mathbf{F}\}_{\sigma_0}^e = \int [\mathbf{B}]^{\mathrm{T}}\{\boldsymbol{\sigma}_0\}\ \mathbf{d(vol)}. \quad (2.13)$$

If the initial stress system is self equilibrating as must be the case with normal residual stresses then the forces given by Eq. (2.13) are identically zero after assembly. Thus frequently evaluation of this force component is omitted. However, if for instance a machine part is manufactured out of a block in which residual stresses are present or if an excavation is made in rock where known tectonic stresses exist a removal of material will cause a force imbalance which results from the above term.

For the particular example of the plane stress triangular element these characteristics will be obtained by the appropriate substitution. It has already been noted that the $[B]$ matrix in that example was not dependent on the co-ordinates, hence the integration will become particularly simple.

The interconnection and solution of the whole assembly of the elements follow the simple structural procedures outlined in Chapter 1. In general, external concentrated forces may exist at the nodes and the matrix

$$\{\mathbf{R}\} = \begin{Bmatrix} R_1 \\ R_2 \\ \vdots \\ R_n \end{Bmatrix} \tag{2.14}$$

will be added to the consideration of equilibrium at the nodes.

A note perhaps should be added here concerning elements near the boundary. If, at the boundary, displacements are specified, no special problem arises. Consider, however, the boundary as subject to a distributed external loading, say $\{\mathbf{g}\}$ per unit area. A loading term on the nodes of the element which has a boundary face will now have to be added. By the virtual work consideration, this will simply result in

$$\{\mathbf{F}\}_b^e = -\int [\mathbf{N}]^{\mathrm{T}}\{\mathbf{g}\} \, \mathbf{d(area)} \tag{2.15}$$

surface tractin

with the integration taken over the boundary area of the element. It will be noted that $\{\mathbf{g}\}$ must have the same number of components as $\{\mathbf{f}\}$ for the above expression to be valid.

Such a boundary element is shown again for the special case of plane stress in Fig. 2.1. An integration of this type is seldom explicitly carried out. Often by 'physical intuition' the analyst will consider the boundary loading to be represented simply by concentrated loads acting on the boundary nodes and calculate these by direct static procedures. In the particular case discussed the results will be identical.

Once the nodal displacements have been determined by solution of the overall 'structural' type equations, the stresses at any point of the element can be found from the relations in Eqs. (2.2) and (2.3) giving

$$\{\boldsymbol{\sigma}\} = [\mathbf{D}][\mathbf{B}]\{\boldsymbol{\delta}\}^e - [\mathbf{D}]\{\boldsymbol{\varepsilon}_0\} + \{\boldsymbol{\sigma}_0\} \tag{2.16}$$

in which the typical terms of the relationship of Eq. (1.4), p. 3, will be immediately recognized, the element stress matrix being

$$[\mathbf{S}]^e = [\mathbf{D}][\mathbf{B}]. \tag{2.17}$$

To this the stresses

$$\{\boldsymbol{\sigma}_{\varepsilon_0}\} = -[\mathbf{D}]\{\boldsymbol{\varepsilon}_0\} \quad \text{and} \quad \{\boldsymbol{\sigma}_0\} \tag{2.18}$$

have to be added.

The absence of the term of stresses due to distributed loading $\{\sigma\}_p^e$ needs a comment. It is due to the fact that the internal equilibrium within any element has not been considered, and only overall equilibrium conditions were established.

2.2.5 *Generalized nature of displacements, strains, and stresses.* The meaning of displacements, strains, and stresses in the illustrative case of plane stress was obvious. In many other applications, shown later in this book, this terminology may be applied to other, less obvious, quantities. For example, in considering plate elements the 'displacement' may be characterized by the lateral deflection and the slopes of the plate at a particular point. The 'strains' will then be defined as the curvatures of the middle surface and the 'stresses' as the corresponding internal bending moments.

All the expressions derived here are generally valid provided the sum product of displacement and corresponding load components represents truly the external work done, while that of the 'strain' and corresponding 'stress' components results in the total internal work.

2.3 Generalization to the Whole Region—Internal Nodal Force Concept Abandoned

In the preceding section the virtual work principle was applied to a single element and the concept of equivalent nodal force was retained. The assembly principle apparently followed the conventional, direct equilibrium, approach.

The idea of nodal forces contributed by elements and replacing the continuous interaction is a conceptual difficulty although it has a considerable appeal to 'practical' engineers and does at times allow an interpretation which otherwise would not be obvious to the more rigorous mathematician. There is, however, no need to consider each element individually and the reasoning of the previous section may be applied directly to the whole continuum.

Equation (2.1) can be interpreted as applying to the whole structure, that is,

$$\{\mathbf{f}\} = [\mathbf{\bar{N}}]\{\boldsymbol{\delta}\} \tag{2.19}$$

in which $\{\boldsymbol{\delta}\}$ list all the nodal points and

$$\mathbf{\bar{N}}_i = \mathbf{N}_i^e \tag{2.20}$$

when the point concerned is within a particular element e and i is a point associated with that element. If point i does not occur within the element

$$\mathbf{\bar{N}}_i = 0. \tag{2.21}$$

Matrix $[\bar{\mathbf{B}}]$ will follow a similar definition and the virtual work principle will be now applied to the whole structure. Interelement forces no longer need be considered and external virtual work during any virtual displacement of all nodes $\mathbf{d}\{\delta\}$ becomes

$$\mathbf{d}\{\delta\}^T\{\mathbf{R}\} - \int_V \mathbf{d}\{\mathbf{f}\}^T\{\mathbf{p}\} \, \mathbf{d}(\text{vol}) - \int_S \mathbf{d}\{\mathbf{f}\}^T\{\mathbf{g}\} \, \mathbf{d}(\text{area}) \qquad (2.22)$$

while the internal virtual work is

$$\int_V \mathbf{d}\{\boldsymbol{\varepsilon}\}^T\{\sigma\} \, \mathbf{d}(\text{vol}) \qquad (2.23)$$

where the integrals are now taken over the *whole region*. On substitution of

$$\mathbf{d}\{\mathbf{f}\} = [\bar{\mathbf{N}}] \, \mathbf{d}\{\delta\} \quad \text{and} \quad \mathbf{d}\{\boldsymbol{\varepsilon}\} = [\bar{\mathbf{B}}] \, \mathbf{d}\{\delta\} \qquad (2.24)$$

together with the constitutive relation (2.3) we have immediately on equating the internal and external virtual work

$$[\mathbf{K}]\{\delta\} + \{\mathbf{F}\}_p + \{\mathbf{F}\}_b + \{\mathbf{F}\}_{\varepsilon_0} + \{\mathbf{F}\}_{\sigma_0} - \{\mathbf{R}\} = 0. \qquad (2.25)$$

Typical term of the 'stiffness' matrix becomes

$$[\mathbf{K}_{ij}] = \int [\bar{\mathbf{B}}]_i [\mathbf{D}] [\bar{\mathbf{B}}_j] \, \mathbf{d}(\text{vol}) \qquad (2.26)$$

with the integral being taken over the whole region.

Considering, however, the relationship between $[\bar{B}]_i$ and $[B]_i$ it is immediately obvious that

$$[\mathbf{K}_{ij}] = \sum [\mathbf{k}_{ij}]^e \qquad (2.27)$$

where the element contributions have been evaluated individually according to the prescriptions of the previous section.

The same can easily be shown to be true of the various 'force' components arising in Eq. (2.25).

Thus the assembly rule as well as the whole derivation has been achieved without involving the concept of 'interelement forces'. In the remainder of this chapter the element superscript will be dropped unless specifically needed. Also no differentiation between element and system shape functions will be made.

However, an important point arises immediately. In considering the virtual work for the whole system (Eq. 2.23) and equating this to the sum of the element contributions it is implicitly assumed that no discontinuity between adjacent elements develops. If such a discontinuity developed a contribution equal to the work done by the stresses in the separations would have to be added.

Thus the displacement field defined by the shape functions has to be such that only finite strains exist on the interfaces, i.e., displacement continuity must exist to make the general equations valid. More will be said about this necessary condition later.

2.4 Displacement Approach as a Minimization of Total Potential Energy

The principle of virtual displacements used in the previous sections ensured satisfaction of equilibrium conditions within the limits prescribed by the assumed displacement pattern. Only if the virtual work equality for all, arbitrary, variations of displacement were ensured (prescribing only the boundary conditions) would the equilibrium be complete.

If the number of parameters of $\{\delta\}$ which prescribes the displacement increases without limit then ever closer approximation of all equilibrium conditions can be ensured.

The virtual work principle can be restated in a different form. Equating Eqs. (2.22) and (2.23) we can write

$$\int d\{\varepsilon\}^{T}\{\sigma\}\, d(\text{vol}) - \left[d\{\delta\}^{T}R + \int d\{f\}^{T}\{p\}\, d(\text{vol}) \right.$$
$$\left. + \int d\{f\}^{T}\{g\}\, d(\text{area}) \right] = 0. \qquad (2.28)$$

The first term of the above equation will be recognized as the variation of the *strain energy*, U, of the structure while the second is the variation of the *potential energy of the external loads*, W.†

Thus instead of Eq. (2.28) we can write simply

$$d(U + W) = d(\chi) = 0 \qquad (2.29)$$

in which the quantity χ is called the *total potential energy*.

The above statement means that for equilibrium to be ensured the *total potential energy must be stationary* for variations of admissible displacements. The finite element equations derived in the previous section (2.25) are simply the statements of this variation with respect to displacements constrained to a finite number of parameters $\{\delta\}$ and could be written as

$$\frac{\partial\chi}{\partial\{\delta\}} = \left\{ \begin{array}{c} \dfrac{\partial\chi}{\partial\delta_1} \\[2mm] \dfrac{\partial\chi}{\partial\delta_2} \\[1mm] \vdots \end{array} \right\} = 0. \qquad (2.30)$$

† Providing the external loads are constant or derivable from a potential permitting the expressions to be interpreted as complete differentials.

It can be shown that in elastic situations the total potential energy is not only stationary but is a minimum.[7] *Thus the finite element process seeks such a minimum within the constraint of an assumed displacement pattern.*

The greater the degrees of freedom, the more closely will the solution approximate to the true one ensuring complete equilibrium, providing the true displacement can, in the limit, be approximated. The necessary convergence conditions for the finite element process could thus be derived. Discussion of these will, however, be deferred to a later section.

It is of interest to note that if true equilibrium requires an absolute minimum of the total potential energy, χ an approximate finite element solution by displacement approach will always provide an approximate χ greater than the correct one. *Thus a bound on the value of the total potential energy is always achieved.*

If the function χ could be specified, *a priori*, then the finite element equations could be derived directly by differentiation specified by Eq. (2.30).

If we substitute in Eq. (2.28) the elastic, constitutive, relation (2.3) and further assume the loads not to vary with displacements we can integrate with respect to displacements and strains and obtain

$$\left[\frac{1}{2}\int \{\varepsilon\}^T[D]\{\varepsilon\}\, d(\text{vol}) - \int \{\varepsilon\}^T[D]\{\varepsilon_0\}\, d(\text{vol}) + \int \{\varepsilon\}^T\{\sigma_0\}\, d(\text{vol})\right] -$$

$$-\left[\{\delta\}^T\{R\} + \int \{f\}^T\{p\}\, d(\text{vol}) + \int \{f\}^T\{g\}\, d(\text{area})\right] = \chi. \quad (2.31)$$

In this the first bracketed term explicitly represents U, and the second W. Indeed expressions for total potential energy can usually be written down directly and often are a more convenient starting point of the finite element analysis. The reader is urged, as an exercise, to obtain the explicit finite element expressions of the previous section by starting from Eq. (2.31) and differentiating with respect to a displacement pattern prescribed by Eq. (2.19).

The well-known Rayleigh[8]–Ritz[9] process of approximation frequently used in elastic analysis uses precisely this approach. The total potential energy expression is formulated and the displacement pattern is assumed to vary with a finite set of undetermined parameters. A set of simultaneous equations minimizing the total potential energy with respect to these parameters is set up. Thus the finite element process as described so far is identically the Rayleigh–Ritz procedure. The difference is only in the manner in which the displacements are prescribed. In the Ritz process these are usually specified by expressions valid throughout the whole region thus leading to simultaneous equations in which no banding occurs and the coefficient matrix is full. In the finite element process this specification is piecewise, each nodal parameter influencing only adjacent elements, and thus a sparse and usually banded matrix of coefficients is found.

By its nature the conventional Ritz process is limited to relatively simple geometrical shapes of the total region while this limitation only occurs in finite element analysis in the element itself. Thus complex, realistic, configurations can be assembled from relatively simple element shapes.

A further difference in kind is in the usual association of the undetermined parameter with a particular nodal displacement. This allows a simple physical interpretation invaluable to an engineer. Doubtless much of the popularity of the finite element process is due to this fact.

2.5 Convergence Criteria

The assumed shape functions limit the infinite degrees of freedom of the system, and the true minimum of the energy may never be reached, irrespective of the fineness of subdivision. To ensure convergence to the correct result certain simple requirements have to be satisfied. Obviously, for instance, the displacement function should be able to represent the true displacement distribution as closely as possible. It will be found that this is not so if the chosen functions are such that straining of an element is possible when this is subject to rigid body displacements. Thus, the first criterion the displacement function must obey is as follows.

Criterion 1. The displacement function chosen should be such that it does not permit straining of an element to occur when the nodal displacements are caused by a rigid body displacement.

This self-evident condition can be violated easily if certain types of function are used; care must therefore be taken in the choice of displacement functions.

A second criterion stems from the same requirements. Clearly, as elements get smaller nearly constant strain conditions will prevail in them. If, in fact, constant strain conditions exist, it is most desirable for good accuracy that a finite size element is able to reproduce these exactly. It is possible to formulate functions which satisfy the first criterion but at the same time require a strain variation throughout the element when the nodal displacements are compatible with a constant strain solution. Such functions will, in general, not show a good convergence to an accurate solution and cannot, even in the limit, represent the true strain distribution. The second can therefore be formulated as

Criterion 2. The displacement function has to be of such a form that if nodal displacements are compatible with a constant strain condition such constant strain will in fact be obtained. (In this context again a generalized 'strain' definition is implied.)

It will be observed that Criterion 2 in fact incorporates the requirement of Criterion 1, as rigid body displacements are a particular case of constant strain—with a value of zero. This criterion was first stated by Bazeley et al.[10] in 1965.†

Lastly, as already mentioned in section 2.3, it is implicitly assumed in the derivation presented that no contribution to the virtual work arises at element interfaces. It therefore appears necessary that the following criterion be included:

Criterion 3. The displacement functions should be so chosen that the strains at interface between elements are finite (even though indeterminate).

This criterion implies a certain continuity of displacements between elements. In the case of strains being defined by first derivatives, as in the plane example quoted here, the displacements only have to be continuous. If, however, as in the plate and shell problems, the 'strains' are defined by second derivatives of deflections, first derivatives of these have also to be continuous.[2]

The above criteria are mathematically included in a statement of 'functional completeness' and the reader is referred for full mathematical discussion elsewhere.[11-15] The 'heuristic' proof of the convergence requirements given here is sufficient for practical purposes in all but the most pathological cases.

2.6 Displacement Functions with Discontinuity between Elements

In some cases considerable difficulty is experienced in finding displacement functions for an element which will automatically be continuous along the whole interface between adjacent elements.

As already pointed out, the discontinuity of displacement will cause infinite strains at the interfaces, a factor ignored in the formulation presented because the energy contribution is limited to the elements themselves.

However, if, *in the limit*, as the size of the subdivision decreases continuity is restored, then the formulation already obtained will still tend to the correct answer. This condition is indeed often reached if

(*a*) a constant strain condition automatically ensures displacement continuity,

(*b*) the constant strain criterion of the previous section is satisfied.

† Strictly both criteria have to be satisfied in the limit as element size tends to zero. Their imposition on a *finite* element is, in practice however, advantageous.

In some of the problems dealt with in this book 'discontinuous' displacement functions of this type will be used with success.

Now, however, bounds on the functional will no longer be available.

2.7 Bound on Strain Energy in a Displacement Formulation

While the approximation obtained by the finite element displacement approach always overestimates the true value of χ, the total potential energy (the absolute minimum corresponding to the exact solution), this is not directly useful in practice. It is, however, possible to obtain a more useful limit in special cases.

Consider in particular the problem in which no 'initial' strains or initial stresses exist. Now by principle of energy conservation the strain energy will be equal to the work done by the external loads which increase uniformly from zero.[16] This work done is equal to $-\frac{1}{2}W$ where W is the potential energy of the loads.

Thus

$$U + \tfrac{1}{2}W = 0 \tag{2.32}$$

or

$$\chi = U + W = -U \tag{2.33}$$

whether exact or approximate displacement field is assumed.

Thus in the above case the approximate solution always *underestimates* the value of U and a displacement solution is frequently referred to as the *lower bound solution*.

If only one external concentrated load R is present the strain energy bound immediately informs us that the deflection under this load has been underestimated (as $U = \frac{1}{2}W = \frac{1}{2}R\delta$). In more complex loading cases the usefulness of this bound is limited as neither deflections nor stresses, i.e., the quantities of real engineering interest, can be bounded.

It is important to remember that this bound on strain energy is only valid in the absence of any initial stresses or strains.

The expression for U in this case can be obtained from Eq. (2.31) as

$$U = \tfrac{1}{2} \int \{\varepsilon\}^{\mathrm{T}}[D]\{\varepsilon\}\, \mathrm{d\ vol}$$

which becomes by Eq. (2.2) simply

$$U = \tfrac{1}{2}\{\delta^{T}\}\left[\int [B]^{\mathrm{T}}[D][B]\, \mathrm{d\ vol}\right]\{\delta\} = \tfrac{1}{2}\{\delta\}^{T}[K]\{\delta\}$$

a 'quadratic' matrix form in which $[K]$ is the 'stiffness' matrix previously discussed.

The above energy expression is always positive from physical considerations. It follows therefore that the matrix $[K]$ occurring in all the finite element assemblies is not only symmetric but is 'positive definite' (a property defined in fact by the requirements that the quadratic form should always be greater or equal to zero).

This feature is of importance when the numerical solution of the simultaneous equations involved is considered as simplifications arise in the case of 'symmetric positive definite' equations.

2.8 Direct Minimization

The fact that the finite element approximation reduces to the problem of minimizing the total potential energy χ defined in terms of a finite number of nodal parameters led us to formulation of the simultaneous set of equations given symbolically by Eq. (2.30). This is the most usual and convenient approach especially in linear solutions but other search procedures, now well developed in the field of optimization, could be used to estimate the lowest value of χ. In this text we shall continue with the simultaneous equation process but the interested reader could well bear the alternative possibilities in mind.[17,18]

References

1. R. W. CLOUGH, 'The finite element in plane stress analysis', *Proc. 2nd A.S.C.E. Conf. on Electronic Computation*, Pittsburgh Pa., Sept. 1960.
2. R. W. CLOUGH, 'The finite element method in structural mechanics', chapter 7 of *Stress Analysis*, ed. O. C. Zienkiewicz and G. S. Holister, Wiley, 1965.
3. J. SZMELTER, 'The energy method of networks of arbitrary shape in problems of the theory of elasticity', *Proc. I.U.T.A.M., Symposium on Non-Homogeneity in Elasticity and Plasticity*, ed. by W. Olszak, Pergamon Press, 1959.
4. R. COURANT, 'Variational methods for the solution of problems of equilibrium and vibration', *Bull. Am. Math. Soc.*, **49**, 1–23, 1943.
5. W. PRAGER and J. L. SYNGE, 'Approximation in Elasticity based on the concept of function space', *Quart. Appl. Math.*, **5**, 241–69, 1947.
6. S. TIMOSHENKO and J. N. GOODIER, *Theory of Elasticity*, 2nd ed., McGraw-Hill, 1951.
7. K. WASHIZU, *Variational methods in elasticity and plasticity*, Pergamon Press, 1968.
8. J. W. STRUTT (Lord Rayleigh), 'On the theory of resonance', *Trans. Roy. Soc.* (London), **A161**, 77–118, 1870.
9. W. RITZ, 'Über eine Methode zur Lösung gewissen Variations—Probleme der mathematischen Physik', *J. Reine und Angew. Math.*, **135**, 1–61, 1909.
10. G. P. BAZELEY, Y. K. CHEUNG, B. M. IRONS, and O. C. ZIENKIEWICZ, 'Triangular elements in bending—conforming and non-conforming solutions', *Proc. Conf. Matrix Methods in Struct. Mech.*, Air Force Inst. Techn. Wright Patterson A.F. Base Ohio, 1965.
11. S. G. MIKHLIN, *The problem of the minimum of a quadratic functional*, Holden-Day, 1966.

12. W. M. JOHNSON and R. W. MCLAY, 'Convergence of the finite element method in the theory of elasticity', *J. Appl. Mech. Trans. Am. Soc. Mech. Eng.*, 274–278, 1968.
13. S. W. KEY, *A convergence investigation of the direct stiffness method*, Ph.D. thesis, Univ. of Washington, 1966.
14. T. H. H. PIAN, PING TONG, 'The convergence of finite element method in solving linear elastic problems', *Int. J. Solids Struct.*, 3, 865–80, 1967.
15. E. R. DE ARRANTES OLIVEIRA, 'Theoretical foundations of the finite element method', *Int. J. Solids Struct.*, 4, 929–52, 1968.
16. B. FRAEIJS DE VEUBEKE, 'Displacement and equilibrium models in the finite element method', Chapter 9 of *Stress Analysis*, ed. O. C. Zienkiewicz and G. S. Holister, Wiley, 1965.
17. R. L. FOX and E. L. STANTON, 'Developments in structural analysis by direct energy minimization', *Jn. A.I.A.A.*, 6, 1036–44, 1968.
18. F. K. BOGNER, R. H. MALLETT, M. D. MINICH and L. A. SCHMIT, 'Development and evaluation of energy search methods in non-linear structural analysis', *Proc. Conf. Matrix Methods in Struct Mech.*, Air Force Inst. Techn., Wright Patterson A.F. Base, Ohio, 1965.

3. Generalization of the Finite Element Concepts

3.1 General Variational Problems

The problems of applied physics encountered in engineering can be specified in one of two ways.[1] In the first differential equations governing the behaviour of a typical, infinitesimal, region are given. In the second a variational, extremum, principle valid over the whole region is postulated and the correct solution is the one minimizing some quantity χ which is defined by suitable integration of the unknown quantities over the whole domain. Such an integral quantity as χ which is a function of unknown functions is known as a 'functional'.

The two approaches are mathematically equivalent, an exact solution of one being the solution of the other. *Either* can be taken as the basic formulation though the differential equation approach is probably more usual. Purely mathematical and manipulative transition from one to the other form is possible—and this is the subject of many texts on variational methods.[2-4]

Differences arise in the approximate solution procedures and while some—such as finite difference techniques[5,6] approach the solution of differential equations directly by approximating to those in a discrete manner, others, like Ritz's process and its variant, the finite element method, prefer to deal directly with an approximate minimization of the functional.

In the previous chapter it has been shown how the problem of determining a displacement distribution through a structure is approached via the minimization of total potential energy defined as a 'functional' of the displacements. The finite element process was demonstrated to be equivalent to an approximate minimization with respect to nodal displacements. In this section the problem will be restated in a general form.

Let the physical (or purely mathematical) formulation of the problem require the minimization of a functional χ over a certain domain.

χ is defined as some integral over the domain V and part of its boundary

33

34   FINITE ELEMENT METHOD IN ENGINEERING SCIENCE

S in which the unknown function, $\{\phi\}$, or its derivatives appear, that is,

$$\chi = \int_V f\left(\{\phi\}, \frac{\partial}{\partial x}\{\phi\}\dots\right) dV + \int_S g\left(\{\phi\}, \frac{\partial}{\partial x}\{\phi\}\dots\right) dS. \quad (3.1)$$

Let the region be divided into smaller parts, subregions, which we shall call elements, and let the function which we are trying to determine be described in each element as

$$\{\phi\} = [N]\{\Phi\}^e. \quad (3.2)$$

In this $\{\Phi\}^e$ may list nodal values of the function associated with the element or simply *some parameters* characteristic of it. Curly brackets are put round the unknown function to show that it may be a vector—as indeed was the case in example of Chapter 2, $[N]$ as before is a listing of shape function of the co-ordinates only.

To minimize the functional χ with respect to the total number of parameters $\{\Phi\}$ associated with the whole domain we must write a system of equations

$$\frac{\partial \chi}{\partial \{\Phi\}} = \left\{ \begin{array}{c} \dfrac{\partial \chi}{\partial \Phi_1} \\[2mm] \dfrac{\partial \chi}{\partial \Phi_2} \\[1mm] \vdots \end{array} \right\} = 0. \quad (3.3)$$

If it is true to say that the total functional is equal to the sum of the contributions of each element, that is,

$$\chi = \sum \chi^e \quad (3.4)$$

then a typical equation becomes

$$\frac{\partial \chi}{\partial \Phi_n} = \sum \frac{\partial \chi^e}{\partial \Phi_n} = 0 \quad (3.5)$$

with summation over all elements. The rule for the assembly of a general minimizing set of equations is thus available.

In the special case where χ is a *quadratic* functional of $\{\phi\}$ and its derivatives we shall find that we can always write the element derivatives in a linear form as

$$\frac{\partial \chi^e}{\partial \{\Phi\}^e} = [k]^e\{\Phi\}^e + \{F\}^e \quad (3.6)$$

in which $[k]^e$ and $\{F\}^e$ are matrices of constants. Now the minimizing set of Eqs. (3.3) can be simply written as

$$\frac{\partial \chi}{\partial \{\Phi\}} = [K]\{\Phi\} + \{F\} = 0 \quad (3.7)$$

in which

$$[K_{ij}] = \sum [k_{ij}]^e \qquad (3.8)$$

$$\{F_i\} = \sum \{F_i\}^e \qquad (3.9)$$

with summations over all elements, precisely as in the standard structural/network assembly process of Chapters 1 and 2.

3.2 Convergence Criteria

The function approximation given by Eq. (3.1) must obey certain completeness rules to enable convergence of results to be achieved as the subdivision into ever smaller elements is attempted.

First, as the element size decreases, the functions f and g of the integral (3.1) must tend to be single valued and well behaved in physical problems. Thus it is necessary that the following criterion should be satisfied.

Criterion 1. The element shape functions $[N]$ must be such that with a suitable choice of $\{\Phi\}^e$ any constant values of $\{\phi\}$ or its derivatives present in the functional χ should be able to be represented in the limit as element size decreases to zero.

Second, the validity of summation implied in Eq. (3.4) must be preserved, and unless special surface integrals are added for the inter-element boundaries[7] we must make sure that terms like f and g remain finite there. This is achieved if the highest derivatives of ϕ occurring in these expressions are finite which leads to

Criterion 2. The element shape functions $[N]$ have to be so chosen that at element interfaces $\{\phi\}$ and its derivatives, of one order less than that occurring in expressions f and g which define the functional, are continuous.

This criterion can be simply explained if one imagines the elements to be separated by an extremely narrow layer which has to be included in the integrals defining χ and in which there occurs a smooth transition of the unknown function between values given in adjacent elements. If in the limit, as the width of this transition zone tends to zero, its contribution to χ vanishes then Eq. (3.4) is true.

In Fig. 3.1 such an imaginary transition zone between two elements is shown. Let us assume that ϕ, a scalar function, is defined in such a way that on the interface the values obtained for it from the two elements are identical. Figure 3.1(a) shows a possible plot of the transition for which it will be seen that its slope is discontinuous, indeterminate, but taking up finite value in the transition zone (Fig. 3.1(b)). Plotting similarly the second derivative it will be noted that this becomes very large in the transition (Fig. 3.1(c)) and in fact tends to infinity as its width decreases.

The continuity of ϕ alone is thus sufficient to ensure no contribution to χ from the inter-element zone if the definition of this involves only the first derivative. If the second derivative should be present in this function, however, an indeterminate contribution (due to an infinite quantity multiplied by zero area) would occur and validity of Eq. (3.4) could not be guaranteed.

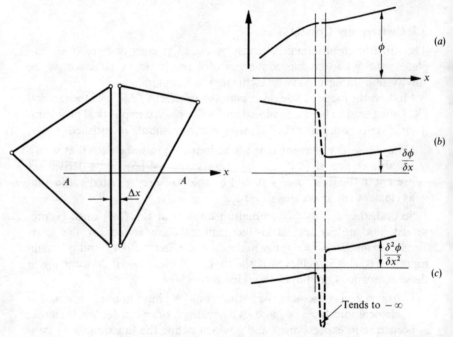

Fig. 3.1   An inter-element zone showing how continuous function ϕ may lead to infinity of second derivative as $\Delta x \to 0$

The two criteria presented generalize the more special ones obtained for displacement formulation in section 2.5.

By convergence in the above discussion we imply that errors in determination of the true χ disappear when the size of the elements becomes infinitely small. It is, however, sometimes important to say that the approximation given by one mesh is a definite improvement on that of another. In the sense of determining χ this statement is obviously true if the shape of the function defined for the first mesh (by Eq. 3.2) is such that it *includes all the shapes* of the second mesh. In general if the elements of the first mesh are derived by subdividing the elements of the coarser mesh this will be the case and in such subdivision a monotonic convergence of χ can occur. This principle was first stated by Melosh in 1963.[8]

elasticity

3.3 Nodeless Variables

$$\epsilon = \frac{\sigma}{E} = \frac{30 \times 10^3}{30 \times 10^6} = 0.001$$

It is of importance to remind the reader that in defining the element shape functions by Eq. (3.2) it was stated that $\{\Phi\}^e$ listed either the nodal values of the unknown functions or simply *some parameters* associated with the element.

To ensure continuity of the function between the elements as required by the second convergence criterion (section 3.2) and indeed to underline the physical significance of the problem it is usual to focus attention on the nodal values. It is always possible, however, to add some modes of function variation which for instance, by yielding zero values at element boundary, do not disturb continuity and to multiply these by some parameter with respect to which the functional is to be minimized. Such nodeless parameters may improve the accuracy of representation and may on occasion be useful.[9]

As, in general, such parameters are only associated with one element at a time they can be minimized before assembly and eliminated from the element matrices.

A particular form of nodeless variable is the well-known Lagrange multiplier.[3]

This occurs if some additional constraint is imposed on the function ϕ which is not implied either in the boundary conditions or in the shape functions proposed. Let this constraint be *a matrix of constraints*

$$G(\{\phi\}) = 0. \tag{3.10}$$

The solution now requires the minimization of†

$$\chi^* = \chi + \lambda G \tag{3.11}$$

and λ is a typical, additional parameter. If a series of such conditions are imposed we minimize

$$\chi^* = \chi + \sum_{i=1}^{i=s} \lambda_i G_i. \tag{3.12}$$

Now λ_i will be additional parameters of the problem which in practice may again be associated with elements or inter-element surfaces. Use of such Lagrange multipliers will be indicated later.

It is of interest here to note the form of the equations which will result in a typical case when the functional is quadratic (see Eq. (3.1)) and Lagrange multipliers are applied on a series of *linear* constraints of Φ.

---

† The proof of the above statement is given in books on variational calculus. This is fairly obvious as $\partial \chi^* / \partial \lambda = G$ simply and hence the constraint is obtained as a minimizing condition. Further $\chi^* = \chi$ at the extremum as $G = 0$. (A physical meaning of λ can often be obtained as $\lambda = \partial \chi^* / \partial G$.)

Now we can generally write

$$\chi = \tfrac{1}{2}\{\Phi\}^{\mathrm{T}}[K]\{\Phi\} + \{F\}^{\mathrm{T}}\{\Phi\} \tag{3.13}$$

in terms of the nodal parameters, where $[K]$ is a symmetric matrix.

The linear constraints can be now expressed in place of Eq. (3.10) by a matrix form

$$[G]\{\Phi\} = 0 \tag{3.14}$$

where $[G]$ is a matrix of constants. Introducing the Lagrange multipliers $\{\lambda\}$ as a vector equal in number with the ~~columns~~ rows of $[G]$ (i.e. the number of constraints) we have

$$\chi = \tfrac{1}{2}\{\Phi\}^{\mathrm{T}}[K]\{\Phi\} + \{F\}^{\mathrm{T}}\{\Phi\} + ([G]\{\Phi\})^{\mathrm{T}}\{\lambda\}. \tag{3.15}$$

Setting up the set of minimizing equations in the manner of Eq. (3.6) but treating both sets of unknowns we have

$$\left\{\begin{array}{c} \dfrac{\partial \chi}{\partial \{\Phi\}} \\[2mm] \dfrac{\partial \chi}{\partial \{\lambda\}} \end{array}\right\} = \begin{bmatrix} [K], & [G]^{\mathrm{T}} \\[2mm] [G], & 0 \end{bmatrix} \left\{\begin{array}{c} \{\Phi\} \\[2mm] \{\lambda\} \end{array}\right\} + \left\{\begin{array}{c} \{F\} \\[2mm] 0 \end{array}\right\} = 0. \tag{3.16}$$

Two factors are of note. Firstly the equation system remains symmetric—a desirable fact in the usual solution systems adopted (Ch. 20). Secondly, zeros occur on the diagonal causing sometimes solution difficulties.

In this text little use of Lagrange multipliers will be made directly but their use is increasing in situations where constraints have to be introduced. A typical situation here may for instance be a finite element formulation which violates continuity conditions. These conditions can be introduced as constraints on the parameters and a correct solution obtained. It is perhaps puzzling that such constraints apparently introduce an increased number of parameters.

3.4 Alternative Approaches to Finite Element Formulation

While approximate minimization of a 'functional' is the most widely accepted means of arriving at a finite element representation it is by no means the sole approach possible. In the early structural work, for instance, a purely physical model was created and although mathematical reservations could be made about the validity and convergence of some approaches proposed, good engineering answers were often obtained.

Quite apart from such approaches it is possible to arrive mathematically at finite element approximation directly from *the differential equations governing the problem.* Such approaches will be outlined here. The possible advantage of such methods is that:

(*a*) The search for a 'functional' equivalent to the known differential equation is made unnecessary.
(*b*) That the methods can be extended to a range of problems for which a 'functional' may not exist, or has not been discovered.[10]

Let us consider a problem of solving approximately a set of differential equations which the unknown function $\{\phi\}$ has to satisfy in the region V. We shall write the governing equation as

$$A(\{\phi\}) = 0 \qquad (3.17)$$

and its boundary condition as

$$C(\{\phi\}) = 0, \qquad (3.18)$$

this having to be satisfied on boundary S.

If a trial function which satisfies the boundary conditions is written in the general form

$$\{\phi\}_a = [N]\{\Phi\} \qquad (3.19)$$

in which, as before, $[N]$ are prescribed functions of co-ordinates and $\{\Phi\}$ is a set of n parameters, then in general

$$A(\{\phi\}_a) = R \neq 0. \qquad (3.20)$$

The best solution will be one which in some sense reduces the residual R to a least value at all points of V.[1]

An obvious way to achieve this is to make use of the fact that if R is identically zero everywhere, then

$$\int_V WR \, dV = 0 \qquad (3.21)$$

where W is any function of the co-ordinates. If the number of unknown parameters $\{\Phi\}$ is n then if n, linearly independent, functions W_i are chosen we can write a suitable number of simultaneous equations as

$$\int_V W_i R \, dV = \int W_i A([N]\{\Phi\}) \, dV = 0 \qquad (3.22)$$

from which $\{\Phi\}$ can be found. These processes are known as *weighted residual methods* and W_i is the *weighting function*. Depending on the choice of the weighting function different classical approaches can be rediscovered.

Point collocation. $W_i = 1$ at some point, i, and zero everywhere else. This is in fact equivalent to satisfying the differential, governing, equation at n separate points.

Subdomain collocation. $W_i = 1$ over a particular subdomain and zero elsewhere. This is equivalent to making the integral zero over a number of subdomains sufficient to give the necessary number of simultaneous equations.

Galerkin process. $W_i = N_i$, i.e., the weighting function is made equal to the shape function defining the approximation. This process leads in general to the *best approximation.*

If any of the above processes are used with Eq. (3.19) which defines the approximate representation element by element, then the typical features of the finite element approach will be rediscovered.

In the first place the simultaneous equations will be banded as the influence of any one parameter extends only to elements neighbouring a nodal point.

Secondly, the integrals can be evaluated (assuming no inter-element contribution as before) over each element independently, and then summed to give the total contribution.

Clearly the assembly rules of the coefficients will be the same as in the structural process if the operator A is linear (vide Eq. (1.14)).

One disadvantage of the above formulation immediately appears. In the integrals of the weighted residual process the differential operator A appears directly and in this, higher order of differentials generally exist than in the variational functional χ. Thus, to avoid contributions from the 'inter-element region' (see 3.2) a *higher order of continuity has to be implied in the shape function definition.* This is a serious matter as the choice of shape function becomes severely limited and may pose insurmountable difficulties.†

To overcome this difficulty it is possible sometimes to transform the integrals of relation (3.22) using integration by parts (or its more general forms of Green's or Stokes' transformations). If this transformation is accomplished in the general form then no restrictions are implied and if a lower order of integrals results continuity requirements of these only need to be satisfied.

In the preceding presentation it has been assumed that the chosen approximation to the unknown function, Eq. (3.19), automatically satisfied the boundary conditions. It is in general preferable to lift this assumption and *formulate the equation in a general form imposing the boundary conditions in the final stage precisely* in the same manner as say the prescribed displacements and boundary forces were imposed on a structure after completion of the stiffness assembly.

† It will be shown later how the very wide choice of functions which ensure continuity of the variable only becomes restricted if the continuity of slope is additionally prescribed. Continuity of second derivatives is only possible in most restricted cases.

3.5 An Example—Poisson Equation

To consolidate some of the ideas of the preceding sections let us consider a purely mathematical problem of solving a partial differential equation

$$\frac{\partial^2 \phi}{\partial x^2} + \frac{\partial^2 \phi}{\partial y^2} + C = 0 \tag{3.23}$$

in a certain region V subject to prescribed values of $\phi = \phi_b$ on the boundary (see Fig. 3.2a).

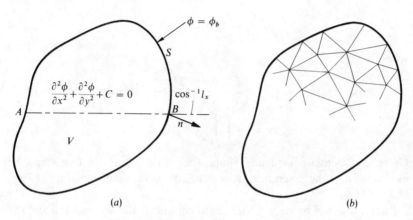

Fig. 3.2   The weighted residual process

It can be shown that mathematically this is equivalent to finding a function ϕ which satisfies the boundary conditions and minimizes

$$\chi = \int \int_V \left[\frac{1}{2}\left(\frac{\partial \phi}{\partial x}\right)^2 + \frac{1}{2}\left(\frac{\partial \phi}{\partial y}\right)^2 - C\phi \right] dx\, dy. \tag{3.24}$$

Further, for the approximate solution we shall assume the region to be divided into finite elements (Fig. 3.2b) in each of which

$$\phi = [N_i, N_j, \ldots] \left\{ \begin{matrix} \phi_i \\ \phi_j \end{matrix} \right\} = [N]\{\phi\}^e, \tag{3.25}$$

where $\{\phi\}^e$ represents a list of parameters which in this case are simply the values of ϕ at the element nodes.

3.5.1 *Minimization of the functional.* Assuming that $[N]$ has been so specified that ϕ is continuous between elements then Eq. (3.4) is satisfied and we can confine our attention to a typical element.

$$\{\phi\} = [N_i \quad N_j \quad \cdots \quad] \begin{Bmatrix} \Phi_i \\ \Phi_j \\ \vdots \end{Bmatrix}$$

Substituting (3.25) into (3.24) integrated over element area we have

$$\frac{\partial \chi^e}{\partial \phi_i} = \int\int_{V^e} \left[\frac{\partial \phi}{\partial x} \frac{\partial}{\partial \overline{\Phi}_i}\left(\frac{\partial \phi}{\partial x}\right) + \frac{\partial \phi}{\partial y}\frac{\partial}{\partial \overline{\Phi}_i}\left(\frac{\partial \phi}{\partial y}\right) - C\frac{\partial \phi}{\partial \overline{\Phi}_i} \right] dx \, dy$$

$$= \int\int_{V^e} \left[\left(\frac{\partial N_i}{\partial x}\overline{\Phi}_i + \frac{\partial N_j}{\partial x}\phi_j + \cdots \right)\frac{\partial N_i}{\partial x} \right.$$

$$\left. + \left(\frac{\partial N_i}{\partial y}\phi_i + \frac{\partial N_j}{\partial y}\phi_j + \cdots\right)\frac{\partial N_i}{\partial y} - CN_i \right] dx \, dy$$

Interchange order of derivative since φ is continuous

$$\frac{\partial}{\partial \overline{\Phi}_i}\left(\frac{\partial \phi}{\partial x}\right) = \frac{\partial N_i}{\partial x}$$

$$\frac{\partial}{\partial \overline{\Phi}_i}\left(\frac{\partial \phi}{\partial x}\right) = \frac{\partial}{\partial x}\left(\frac{\partial \phi}{\partial \overline{\Phi}_i}\right)$$

or

$$\frac{\partial \chi^e}{\partial \{\phi\}^e} = [k]^e \{\phi\}^e + \{F\}^e \tag{3.26}$$

where

$$k_{ij} = \int\int_{V^e} \left(\frac{\partial N_i}{\partial x}\frac{\partial N_j}{\partial x} + \frac{\partial N_i}{\partial y}\frac{\partial N_j}{\partial y}\right) dx \, dy \tag{3.27}$$

$$F_i = -\int\int_{V^e} CN_i \, dx \, dy. \tag{3.28}$$

Given the element form and shape functions the above terms can be evaluated and the assembled system of equations determined as in Eqs. (3.7) to (3.9).

Substitution of boundary conditions completes the formulation and the linear system of equations yields the solution.

3.5.2 *Weighted residual processes.* The typical equation which now has to be formulated is, by (3.22) and (3.23)

1st order derivative should be continuous ⟹ by restrict

$$\int\int_V W_i \left[\frac{\partial^2 \phi}{\partial x^2} + \frac{\partial^2 \phi}{\partial y^2} + C\right] dx \, dy = 0 \tag{3.29}$$

in which ϕ is given by Eq. (3.25). In the form given above the integral would require continuity of slopes at all interface regions to avoid infinities in the second differentials. If we want to avoid this restriction a transformation by partial integration can be used. Thus, for instance

$$\int\int_V W_i \frac{\partial^2 \phi}{\partial x^2} dx \, dy \equiv \int_S \left| W_i \frac{\partial \phi}{\partial x}\right|_A^B dy - \int\int_V \frac{\partial W_i}{\partial x}\frac{\partial \phi}{\partial x} dx \, dy$$

∫v du = uv| − ∫u dv

v = W_i

u = ∂φ/∂x

$$\equiv \oint_S W_i \frac{\partial \phi}{\partial x}l_x \, dS - \int\int_V \frac{\partial W_i}{\partial x}\frac{\partial \phi}{\partial x} dx \, dy \tag{3.30}$$

now W has to be continuous

in which l_x is the direction cosine of the outward normal (Fig. 3.2) and the x direction, and integral S is taken over the whole boundary.

Equation (3.29) can now be written, using the same type of integration on the second term, as

$$\int\int_V \left[\frac{\partial W_i}{\partial x}\frac{\partial \phi}{\partial x} + \frac{\partial W_i}{\partial y}\frac{\partial \phi}{\partial y} - W_i C\right] dx\, dy$$

$$-\oint_S W_i \left(\frac{\partial \phi}{\partial x} l_x + \frac{\partial \phi}{\partial y} l_y\right) dS. \qquad (3.31)$$

The first term integrated in V does not contain inter-element contributions providing ϕ is continuous. However, now a restriction on the weighting function W_i has to be made. This must itself be continuous and the type of function used in point or subdomain collocations is excluded. However, the Galerkin process or indeed any other one in which W_i is continuous is permissible.

To pursue the example further we shall use the Galerkin process with

$$W_i = N_i \qquad (3.32)$$

and the element contribution to the integrals of Eq. (3.31) can be written making now explicit use of relation (3.25) as

$$\sum_{j=0}^{n} k_{ij}^e \phi_j + \{F_i\} - \int_S N_i \left(\frac{\partial \phi}{\partial x} l_x + \frac{\partial \phi}{\partial y} l_y\right) dS. \qquad (3.33)$$

In the above, the expressions for k_{ij}^e and F_i are in fact, perhaps not fortuitously, identical to those given by Eq. (3.28) where the variational process was used. On summing contributions from all elements the same system of equations arises as before, with the exception of the integral taken over the external surface. It will be immediately seen that this integral does not contribute anything to the equations at internal boundary points (i.e., when point i does not lie on the boundary). When the points i in fact lie on the boundary on which prescribed values ϕ_b operate this integral is not known but the boundary condition imposed provides the necessary conditions for solving for all the nodal values.

In this example identical results were achieved by using weighted residual and variational approaches.†[11] If, however, different weighting functions were used this identity would disappear. The fact that a direct approach, not requiring any knowledge of variational calculus, resulted in the same final formulation may be in itself of interest to some readers and provide a convenient alternative.

It is of interest perhaps to remark that the surface integral of Eq. (3.31) has a certain physical significance. It represents in fact a weighted boundary integral of the flux, $\partial \phi/\partial n$, as

$$\int W_i \left(\frac{\partial \phi}{\partial x} l_x + \frac{\partial \phi}{\partial y} l_y\right) dS = \int W_i \frac{\partial \phi}{\partial n} dS. \qquad (3.34)$$

† The Galerkin process will always result in this identity providing a quadratic functional exists.

The boundary conditions sometimes specify this rather than the actual ϕ_b values. In such cases the direct Galerkin approach would still yield the correct answer but the functional would have to be modified by addition of certain boundary terms (as will be done in Chapter 15).

3.6 A Further Example—Viscous Flow Equations

The operator of the general differential equation (3.17) need not necessarily deal with a single variable. A set of simultaneous differential equations can similarly be described. Consider for instance the equations governing plane steady state flow of a viscous, incompressible fluid in which the inertia terms are considered negligible. The unknowns, p, pressure and u, v the velocity components in x and y directions are related by two equilibrium equations (Stokes equations arising from the more general Navier–Stokes equation)[12]

$$X - \frac{\partial p}{\partial x} + \mu\left(\frac{\partial^2 u}{\partial x^2} + \frac{\partial^2 u}{\partial y^2}\right) = 0,$$

$$Y - \frac{\partial p}{\partial y} + \mu\left(\frac{\partial^2 v}{\partial x^2} + \frac{\partial^2 v}{\partial y^2}\right) = 0,$$

(3.35)

in which X, Y are body forces per unit volume into the viscosity. The third relation necessary between the three variables is supplied by the continuity requirement

$$\frac{\partial u}{\partial x} + \frac{\partial v}{\partial y} = 0.$$

(3.36)

Let us write again in terms of nodal parameters

$$p = [N]\{\bar{p}\}, \qquad u = [N]\{\bar{U}\}, \qquad v = [N]\{\bar{V}\},$$

(3.37)

where $[N]$ are shape functions guaranteeing continuity of the variable only. Using the Galerkin weighted residual process we can write for a point i three sets of equations. The first is given by

$$\int_V N_i\left[X - \frac{\partial p}{\partial x} + \mu\left(\frac{\partial^2 u}{\partial x^2} + \frac{\partial^2 u}{\partial y^2}\right)\right] dV = 0.$$

(3.38)

Using integration by parts on the last two terms in the manner of Eq. (3.30), etc., this reduces to

$$\int_V \left[N_i\left(X - \frac{\partial p}{\partial x}\right) - \mu\frac{\partial N_i}{\partial x}\frac{\partial u}{\partial x} - \mu\frac{\partial N_i}{\partial y}\frac{\partial u}{\partial y}\right] dV$$

$$+ \int_S \mu N_i \frac{\partial u}{\partial n}\, dS = 0. \quad (3.39)$$

Substituting the definitions (3.37) we have for the first term

$$\int_V \left[N_i X - N_i \frac{\partial [N]}{\partial x} \{p\} - \left(\mu \frac{\partial N_i}{\partial x} \frac{\partial [N]}{\partial x} + \mu \frac{\partial N_i}{\partial y} \frac{\partial [N]}{\partial y} \right) \{u\} \right] dV \quad (3.40)$$

The second equation is of similar form and obtained from the above by interchanges x, y and u, v.

The last equation arising from the continuity equation (3.36) is simply

$$\int_V N_i \left(\frac{\partial u}{\partial x} + \frac{\partial v}{\partial y} \right) dV = \int_V \left[N_i \left(\frac{\partial [N]}{\partial x} \{u\} + \frac{\partial [N]}{\partial y} \{v\} \right) \right] dV = 0. \quad (3.41)$$

Grouping all the variables referring to a point as

$$\{\Phi_i\} = \begin{Bmatrix} u_i \\ v_i \\ p_i \end{Bmatrix} \quad (3.42)$$

the standard form of assembled equation

$$[K]\{\Phi\} + \{F\} = 0 \quad (3.43)$$

will once again be found in which, again subdividing the contribution from each element, we have

$$[k_{ij}]^e = - \int_{V^e} \mu \begin{bmatrix} \dfrac{\partial N_i}{\partial x} \cdot \dfrac{\partial N_j}{\partial x} + \dfrac{\partial N_i}{\partial y} \cdot \dfrac{\partial N_j}{\partial y}, & 0 & , \dfrac{1}{\mu} N_i \dfrac{\partial N_j}{\partial x} \\ 0 & , \dfrac{\partial N_i}{\partial x} \cdot \dfrac{\partial N_j}{\partial x} + \dfrac{\partial N_i}{\partial y} \cdot \dfrac{\partial N_j}{\partial y}, & \dfrac{1}{\mu} N_i \dfrac{\partial N_j}{\partial y} \\ \dfrac{1}{\mu} N_i \dfrac{\partial N_j}{\partial x} & , \dfrac{1}{\mu} N_i \dfrac{\partial N_j}{\partial y} & , 0 \end{bmatrix} dV$$

$$(3.44)$$

The boundary term of equation (3.39) disappears on external boundaries with prescribed u values as $N_i = 0$ there. Where $\partial u / \partial n$ is prescribed it appears as an appropriate term of the vector $\{F\}$ in equation (3.43). Thus

$$\{F_i\}^e = \int_{V^e} N_i \begin{Bmatrix} X \\ Y \\ 0 \end{Bmatrix} dV + \int_{S^e} N_i \mu \begin{Bmatrix} \dfrac{\partial u}{\partial n} \\ \dfrac{\partial v}{\partial n} \\ 0 \end{Bmatrix} dS \quad (3.45)$$

In the above the surface integral is only taken on external boundaries where $\partial u/\partial n$ or $\partial v/\partial n$ is specified. If u and v are given there the equations are not formed in boundary points.

Although a standard form of a finite element relationship has been established simply, it is of interest to note that the element ('stiffness') matrices are no longer symmetric. This complicates the computer storage and solution processes, and also points to the fact that a quadratic form of the functional no longer exists here. A somewhat simpler flow problem leading to such unsymmetric matrices was tackled by Doctors.[13]

An alternative approach to the above problem could be pursued by introducing a stream function concept. If we define

$$u = -\frac{\partial \theta}{\partial y}, \qquad v = \frac{\partial \theta}{\partial x} \tag{3.46}$$

then Eq. (3.36) is identically satisfied and we are left with two governing equations:

$$
\begin{aligned}
X - \frac{\partial p}{\partial x} + \mu\left(\frac{\partial^2}{\partial x^2} + \frac{\partial^2}{\partial y^2}\right)\left(-\frac{\partial \theta}{\partial y}\right) &= 0, \\
Y - \frac{\partial p}{\partial y} + \mu\left(\frac{\partial^2}{\partial x^2} + \frac{\partial^2}{\partial y^2}\right)\left(\frac{\partial \theta}{\partial x}\right) &= 0.
\end{aligned}
\tag{3.47}
$$

Differentiating the first with respect to y and second with respect to x and subtracting, p is eliminated and only one equation is left.

$$\mu\left(\frac{\partial^2}{\partial x^2} + \frac{\partial^2}{\partial y^2}\right)\left(\frac{\partial^2 \theta}{\partial x^2} + \frac{\partial^2 \theta}{\partial y^2}\right) + \frac{\partial Y}{\partial x} - \frac{\partial X}{\partial y} = 0. \tag{3.48}$$

A similar process of approximate formulation as before can be adopted and the reader can perform this as an exercise. He will find that now symmetric element matrices arise and indeed the formulation will be very similar to that discussed in the chapter on plate bending. The shape function now, however, will have to satisfy continuity of first derivatives between elements as second order differentials occur in the various integrals. Such problems have been dealt with in an axi-symmetric context by Atkinson et al.[14] from the basis of a variational form given in Chapter 15, p. 317.

These examples have been introduced to illustrate the general applicability of the method. The particular problem discussed here, however, is of some considerable engineering interest and much work in the solution of the Navier–Stokes equation is currently in progress. In the illustration, to linearize the equations, the dynamic terms

$$u\frac{\partial u}{\partial x}+v\frac{\partial u}{\partial y},\ u\frac{\partial v}{\partial x}+v\frac{\partial v}{\partial y}$$

have been omitted from the two Eqs. (3.35) respectively. Their retention is obviously possible but then it will be found that the resulting equations of the general form (3.43) are non-linear, $[K]$ being dependent itself on the velocities. The derivation is too complex to be discussed in detail here but the reader could consider extension of the non-linear techniques of Chapter 18 to be applicable here.

3.7 Concluding Remarks

In addition to generalizing the finite element concept to that of approximately solving a variational problem, the alternative of proceeding directly by approximating to the differential expression was presented. Both procedures open up many, as yet unexplored, fields of application. Some general ideas in similar context are given by Oden.[15] Other uses of finite element process, such as minimization of the root mean square value of errors, can easily be envisaged.

References
1. S. H. CRANDALL, *Engineering Analysis*, McGraw-Hill, 1956.
2. K. WASHIZU, *Variational methods in elasticity and plasticity*, Pergamon Press, 1968.
3. R. WEINSTOCK, *Calculus of variations*, McGraw-Hill, 1952.
4. P. N. BERG, 'Calculus of variations', in *Handbook of Engineering Mechanics* Chapter 16, ed. W. Flügge, McGraw-Hill, 1962.
5. R. V. SOUTHWELL, *Relaxation methods in theoretical physics*, Oxford Univ. Press, 1946.
6. G. E. FORSYTHE and W. R. WASOW, *Finite difference methods for partial differential equations*, J. Wiley & Sons, 1960.
7. T. H. H. PIAN and P. TONG, 'Basis of finite element methods for solid continua', *Int. J. Num. Meth. in Eng.*, **1**, 3–28, 1969.
8. R. J. MELOSH, 'Basis for derivation of matrices for the direct stiffness method', *J.A.I.A.A.*, **1**, 1631–7, 1963.
9. T. H. H. PIAN, 'Derivation of Element Stiffness Matrices', *J.A.I.A.A.*, **2**, 576–7, 1964.
10. I. STAKGOLD, *Boundary value problems in Mathematics and Physics*, Macmillan, N.Y., 1966.
11. B. A. SZABO and G. C. LEE, 'Derivation of stiffness matrices for problems in plane elasticity by Galerkin method', *Int. J. Num. Meth. Eng.*, **1**, 301–10, 1969.
12. P. A. LAGERSTROM and I. D. CHANG, 'Flow at low Reynolds numbers', Chapter 81, *Handbook of Eng. Mech.*, ed. W. Flügge, McGraw-Hill, 1962.
13. L. J. DOCTORS, 'An Application of the finite element technique for boundary value problems of potential flow', *Int. J. Num. Meth. Eng.*, **2**, 243–52, 1970.
14. B. ATKINSON, M. P. BROCKLEBANK, C. C. M. CARD, and J. M. SMITH, 'Low Reynolds number developing flows', *A.I. Ch. Eng. J.*, **15**, 548–53, 1969.
15. J. T. ODEN, 'A general theory of finite elements': I 'Topological considerations' pp. 205–21; II 'Applications' pp. 247–60; *Int. J. Num. Meth. Eng.*, **1**, 1969.

4. Plane Stress and Plane Strain

4.1 Introduction

Two-dimensional elastic problems were the first successful examples of the application of the finite element method.[1,2] Indeed, we have already used this situation to illustrate the basis of the finite element formulation in Chapter 2 where the general relationships were derived. These basic relationships are given in Eqs. (2.1), (2.2), (2.3), (2.9), (2.10), and (2.16) and for quick reference are summarized in Appendix II.

In this chapter the particular relationships for the problem in hand will be derived in more detail, and illustrated by suitable practical examples, a procedure that will be followed throughout the remainder of the book.

Only the simplest, triangular, element will be discussed in detail but the basic approach is general. More elaborate elements to be discussed in later chapters would be introduced to the same problem in an identical manner.

The reader not familiar with the applicable basic definitions of elasticity is referred to elementary texts on the subject, in particular to the text by Timoshenko and Goodier,[3] whose notation will be widely used here.

In both problems of plane stress and plane strain the displacement field is uniquely given by the u and v displacements in directions of the cartesian, orthogonal x and y axes.

Again, in both, the only strains and stresses that have to be considered are the three components in the x–y plane. In the case of *plane stress*, by definition, all other components of stress are zero and therefore give no contribution to internal work. In *plane strain* the stress in a direction perpendicular to the x–y plane is not zero. However, by definition, the strain in that direction is zero, and therefore no contribution to internal work is made by this stress, which can in fact be explicitly evaluated from the three main stress components, if desired, at the end of all computation.

4.2 Element Characteristics

4.2.1 *Displacement functions.* Figure 4.1 shows the typical triangular element considered, with nodes i, j, m numbered in an anti-clockwise order.

The displacements of a node have two components

$$\{\delta_i\} = \begin{pmatrix} u_i \\ v_i \end{pmatrix} \tag{4.1}$$

and the six components of element displacements are listed as a vector

$$\{\delta\}^e = \begin{Bmatrix} \delta_i \\ \delta_j \\ \delta_m \end{Bmatrix}. \tag{4.2}$$

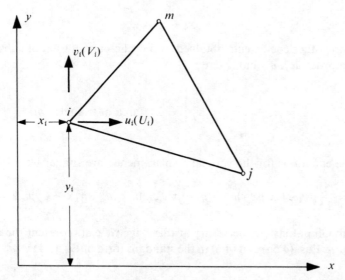

Fig. 4.1   An element of a continuum in plane stress or plane strain

The displacements within an element have to be uniquely defined by these six values. The simplest representation is clearly given by two linear polynomials

$$\begin{aligned} u &= \alpha_1 + \alpha_2 x + \alpha_3 y, \\ v &= \alpha_4 + \alpha_5 x + \alpha_6 y. \end{aligned} \tag{4.3}$$

The six constants α can be evaluated easily by solving the two sets of three simultaneous equations which will arise if the nodal co-ordinates are inserted and the displacements equated to the appropriate nodal displacements. Writing, for example,

$$\begin{aligned} u_i &= \alpha_1 + \alpha_2 x_i + \alpha_3 y_i \\ u_j &= \alpha_1 + \alpha_2 x_j + \alpha_3 y_j \\ u_m &= \alpha_1 + \alpha_2 x_m + \alpha_3 y_m \end{aligned} \tag{4.4}$$

we can easily solve for α_1, α_2, and α_3 in terms of the nodal displacements u_i, u_j, u_m and obtain finally

$$u = \frac{1}{2\Delta}\{(a_i+b_ix+c_iy)u_i+(a_j+b_jx+c_jy)u_j+(a_m+b_mx+c_my)u_m\} \quad (4.5a)$$

in which

$$a_i = x_jy_m-x_my_j$$
$$b_i = y_j-y_m = y_{jm} \quad (4.5b)$$
$$c_i = x_m-x_j = x_{mj}$$

with the other coefficients obtained by a cyclic permutation of subscripts in the order, i, j, m, and where

$$2\Delta = \det \begin{vmatrix} 1 & x_i & y_i \\ 1 & x_j & y_j \\ 1 & x_m & y_m \end{vmatrix} = 2 \quad \text{(area of triangle } ijm\text{).} \quad (4.5c)$$

As the equations for the vertical displacement v are similar we also have

$$v = \frac{1}{2\Delta}\{(a_i+b_ix+c_iy)v_i+(a_j+b_jx+c_jy)v_j+(a_m+b_mx+c_my)v_m\}. \quad (4.6)$$

Though not strictly necessary at this stage we can represent the above relations Eqs. (4.5a) and (4.6) in the standard form of Eq. (2.1)

$$\{f\} = \left\{ \begin{matrix} u \\ v \end{matrix} \right\} = [N]\{\delta\} = \overset{2\times2}{[IN'_i, IN'_j, IN'_m]}\{\delta\}^e \quad (4.7)$$

with I a two by two identity matrix, and

$$N'_i = (a_i+b_ix+c_iy)/2\Delta \quad \text{etc.} \quad (4.8)$$

Note: if co-ordinates are taken from the centroid of the element then $x_i+x_m+x_j = y_i+y_j+y_m = 0$ and $a_i = 2\Delta/3 = a_j = a_m$.

The chosen displacement function automatically guarantees continuity of displacements with adjacent elements because the displacements vary linearly along any side of the triangle and, with identical displacement imposed at the nodes, the same displacement will clearly exist all along an interface.

4.2.2 *Strain (total).* The total strain at any point within the element can be defined by its three components which contribute to internal work.

$$\{\varepsilon\} = \left\{ \begin{array}{c} \varepsilon_x \\ \varepsilon_y \\ \gamma_{xy} \end{array} \right\} = \left\{ \begin{array}{c} \dfrac{\partial u}{\partial x} \\ \dfrac{\partial v}{\partial y} \\ \dfrac{\partial u}{\partial y} + \dfrac{\partial v}{\partial x} \end{array} \right\}. \tag{4.9}$$

Using Eqs. (4.7) or (4.5a) *and* (4.6) we have

$$\{\varepsilon\} = \begin{bmatrix} \dfrac{\partial N'_i}{\partial x} & 0 & \dfrac{\partial N'_j}{\partial x} & 0 & \dfrac{\partial N'_m}{\partial x} & 0 \\ 0 & \dfrac{\partial N'_i}{\partial y} & 0 & \dfrac{\partial N'_j}{\partial y} & 0 & \dfrac{\partial N'_m}{\partial y} \\ \dfrac{\partial N'_i}{\partial y} & \dfrac{\partial N'_i}{\partial x} & \dfrac{\partial N'_j}{\partial y} & \dfrac{\partial N'_j}{\partial x} & \dfrac{\partial N'_m}{\partial y} & \dfrac{\partial N'_m}{\partial x} \end{bmatrix} \left\{ \begin{array}{c} u_i \\ v_i \\ u_j \\ v_j \\ u_m \\ v_m \end{array} \right\}$$

$$= \frac{1}{2\Delta} \begin{bmatrix} b_i & 0 & b_j & 0 & b_m & 0 \\ 0 & c_i & 0 & c_j & 0 & c_m \\ c_i & b_i & c_j & b_j & c_m & b_m \end{bmatrix} \{\delta\}^e \tag{4.10}$$

which defines the matrix $[B]$ of Eq. (2.2) explicitly.

It will be noted that in this case the $[B]$ matrix is independent of the position within the element, and hence the strains are constant throughout it. Obviously, the criterion of constant strain mentioned in Chapter 2 is satisfied by the shape functions.

4.2.3 *Initial strain* (*thermal strain*). 'Initial' strains, that is strains which are independent of stress, may be due to many causes. Shrinkage, crystal growth or, most frequently, temperature changes will, in general, result in an initial strain vector.

$$\{\varepsilon_0\} = \left\{ \begin{array}{c} \varepsilon_{x0} \\ \varepsilon_{y0} \\ \gamma_{xy0} \end{array} \right\}. \tag{4.11}$$

Although this initial strain may, in general, depend on the position within the element, it will usually be defined by average, constant, values. This is consistent with the constant strain conditions imposed by the prescribed displacement function.

Thus, for the case of *plane stress* in an isotropic material in an element subject to a temperature rise θ^e with a coefficient of thermal expansion α, we will have, for instance,

$$\{\varepsilon_0\} = \begin{Bmatrix} \alpha\theta^e \\ \alpha\theta^e \\ 0 \end{Bmatrix} \tag{4.12}$$

as no shear strains are caused by a thermal dilatation.

In *plane strain* the situation is more complex. The presumption of plane strain implies that stresses perpendicular to the x–y plane will develop due to thermal expansion even without the three main stress components, and hence the initial strain will be affected by the elastic constants.

It will be shown that in such a case

$$\{\varepsilon_0\} = (1+v) \begin{Bmatrix} \alpha\theta^e \\ \alpha\theta^e \\ 0 \end{Bmatrix} \tag{4.13}$$

where v is the Poisson's ratio.

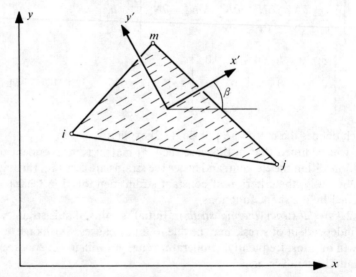

Fig. 4.2   An element of a stratified (transversely-isotropic) material

Anisotropic materials present special problems, since the coefficients of thermal expansion may vary with direction. Let x' and y' in Fig. 4.2 show the principal directions of the material. The initial strain due to thermal expansion becomes, with reference to these co-ordinates for plane stress

$$\{\varepsilon_0\}' = \begin{Bmatrix} \varepsilon_{x'0} \\ \varepsilon_{y'0} \\ \gamma_{x'y'0} \end{Bmatrix} = \begin{Bmatrix} \alpha_1\theta^e \\ \alpha_2\theta^e \\ 0 \end{Bmatrix} \tag{4.14}$$

where α_1 and α_2 are the expansion coefficients referred to the x' and y' axes respectively.

To obtain the strain components in the x, y system it is necessary to use an appropriate strain transformation matrix $[T]$ giving

$$\{\varepsilon_{0'}\} = [T]^T\{\varepsilon_0\}. \tag{4.15}$$

With the β as defined in Fig. 4.2 it is easily verified that

$$[T] = \begin{bmatrix} \cos^2\beta & \sin^2\beta & -2\sin\beta\cos\beta \\ \sin^2\beta & \cos^2\beta & 2\sin\beta\cos\beta \\ \sin\beta\cos\beta & -\sin\beta\cos\beta & \cos^2\beta-\sin^2\beta \end{bmatrix}.$$

Thus, $\{\varepsilon_0\}$ can be simply evaluated. It will be noted that no longer is the shear component of strain equal to zero in the x–y co-ordinates.

4.2.4 *Elasticity matrix.* The matrix $[D]$ of the relation Eq. (2.3)

$$\{\sigma\} = \begin{Bmatrix} \sigma_x \\ \sigma_y \\ \tau_{xy} \end{Bmatrix} = [D] \left(\begin{Bmatrix} \varepsilon_x \\ \varepsilon_y \\ \gamma_{xy} \end{Bmatrix} - \{\varepsilon_0\} \right) \tag{4.16}$$

can be explicitly stated for any material (excluding here $\{\sigma_0\}$ which is simply additive).

Plane stress—isotropic material. For plane stress in an isotropic material we have, by definition,

$$\varepsilon_x = \sigma_x/E - v\sigma_y/E + \varepsilon_{x0}$$
$$\varepsilon_y = -v\sigma_x/E + \sigma_y/E + \varepsilon_{y0} \tag{4.17}$$
$$\gamma_{xy} = 2(1+v)\tau_{xy}/E + \varepsilon_{xy0}.$$

Solving the above for the stresses, we obtain matrix $[D]$ as

$$[D] = \frac{E}{1-v^2} \begin{bmatrix} 1 & v & 0 \\ v & 1 & 0 \\ 0 & 0 & (1-v)/2 \end{bmatrix} \tag{4.18}$$

in which E is the elastic modulus and v is the Poisson's ratio.

Plane strain—isotropic material. In this case a normal stress σ_z exists in addition to the three other stress components. For the special case of isotropic thermal expansion we have

$$\varepsilon_x = \sigma_x/E - v\sigma_y/E - v\sigma_z/E + \alpha\theta^e$$
$$\varepsilon_y = -v\sigma_x/E + \sigma_y/E - v\sigma_z/E + \alpha\theta^e \tag{4.19}$$
$$\gamma_{xy} = 2(1+v)\tau_{xy}/E.$$

but in addition

$$\varepsilon_z = 0 = -v\sigma_x/E - v\sigma_y/E + \sigma_z/E + \alpha\theta^e.$$

On eliminating σ_z and solving for the three remaining stresses we obtain the previously quoted expression for the initial strain Eq. (4.13), and by comparison with Eq. (4.16), the matrix $[D]$

for plane strain

$$[D] = \frac{E(1-v)}{(1+v)(1-2v)} \begin{bmatrix} 1 & v/(1-v) & 0 \\ v/(1-v) & 1 & 0 \\ 0 & 0 & (1-2v)/2(1-v) \end{bmatrix}. \qquad (4.20)$$

Anisotropic materials. For a completely anisotropic material, 21 independent elastic constants are *mostly* necessary to define completely the three-dimensional stress-strain relationship.[4, 5]

If two-dimensional analysis is to be applicable a symmetry of properties must exist, implying at most six independent constants in the $[D]$ matrix. Thus, it is always possible to write

$$[D] = \begin{bmatrix} d_{11} & d_{12} & d_{13} \\ & d_{22} & d_{23} \\ (\text{sym}) & & d_{33} \end{bmatrix} \qquad (4.21)$$

to describe the most general two-dimensional behaviour. (The necessary symmetry of the $[D]$ matrix follows from the general equivalent of the Maxwell-Betti reciprocal theorem and is a consequence of invariant energy irrespective of the path taken to reach a given strain state.)

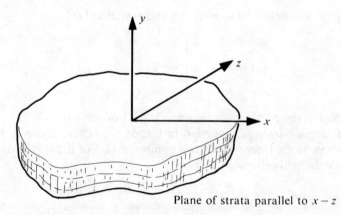

Plane of strata parallel to $x - z$

Fig. 4.3   A stratified (transversely-isotropic) material

A case of particular interest in practice is that of a 'stratified' or transversely-isotropic material in which a rotational symmetry of properties exists within the plane of the strata. Such a material possesses only five independent elastic constants.

The general stress-strain relations give in this case, following the notation of Lekhnitskii,[4] and taking now the y axis as perpendicular to the strata (neglecting initial strain), Fig. 4.3.

$$\varepsilon_x = \sigma_x/E_1 - v_2\sigma_y/E_2 - v_1\sigma_z/E_1$$
$$\varepsilon_y = v_2\sigma_x/E_2 + \sigma_y/E_2 - v_2\sigma_z/E_2$$
$$\varepsilon_z = -v_1\sigma_x/E_1 - v_2\sigma_y/E_2 + \sigma_z/E_1 \qquad (4.22)$$
$$\gamma_{xz} = \{2(1+v_1)/E_1\}\tau_{xz}$$
$$\gamma_{xy} = \frac{1}{G_2}\tau_{xy}$$
$$\gamma_{yz} = \frac{1}{G_2}\tau_{yz}$$

in which the constants E_1, v_1 (G_1 is dependent) are associated with the behaviour in plane of the strata and E_2, G_2, v_2 with a direction normal to these.

The $[D]$ matrix in two-dimensions becomes now, taking

$$\frac{E_1}{E_2} = n \quad \text{and} \quad \frac{G_2}{E_2} = m$$

$$[D] = \frac{E_2}{(1-nv_2^2)}\begin{bmatrix} n & nv_2 & 0 \\ nv_2 & 1 & 0 \\ 0 & 0 & m(1-nv_2^2) \end{bmatrix} \qquad (4.23)$$

for plane stress, or

$$D = \frac{E_2}{(1+v_1)(1-v_1-2nv_2^2)}$$

$$\begin{bmatrix} n(1-nv_2^2) & nv_2(1+v_1) & 0 \\ nv_2(1+v_1) & (1-v_1^2) & 0 \\ 0 & 0 & m(1+v_1)(1-v_1-2nv_2^2) \end{bmatrix} \qquad (4.24)$$

for plane strain.

When, as in Fig. 4.2, the direction of strata is inclined to the x-axis then to obtain the $[D]$ matrices in the universal co-ordinates a transformation is necessary. Taking $[D']$ as relating the stresses and strains in the inclined co-ordinate system (x', y') it is easy to show that

$$[D] = [T][D'][T]^T \tag{4.25}$$

where $[T]$ is the same as given in Eq. (4.15)

If the stress systems $\{\sigma'\}$ and $\{\sigma\}$ correspond to $\{\varepsilon'\}$ and $\{\varepsilon\}$ respectively then by equality of work

$$\{\sigma'\}^T\{\varepsilon'\} = \{\sigma\}^T\{\varepsilon\}$$

or

$$\{\varepsilon'\}^T[D']\{\varepsilon'\} = \{\varepsilon\}^T[D]\{\varepsilon\}$$

from which Eq. (4.25) follows on substitution of Eq. (4.15). (*See also* Chapter 1.)

4.2.5 *The stiffness matrix.* The stiffness matrix of the element *ijm* is defined from the general relationship Eq. (2.10) as

$$[k] = \int [B]^T[D][B]t \, dx \, dy \tag{4.26}$$

where t is the thickness of the element and the integration is taken over the area of the triangle. If the thickness of the element is assumed to be constant, an assumption convergent to the truth as size of elements decreases, then, as neither of the matrices contains x or y we have, simply

$$[k] = [B]^T[D][B]t\Delta \tag{4.27}$$

where Δ is the area of the triangle (defined already by Eq. (3.5)). This form is now sufficiently explicit for computation with the actual matrix operations being left to the computer.

The matrix $[B]$ defined by Eq. (3.10) can be written as

$$[B] = [B_i, B_j, B_m] \quad \text{with} \quad [B_i] = \begin{Bmatrix} b_i & 0 \\ 0 & c_i \\ c_i & b_i \end{Bmatrix} \Big/ 2\Delta, \text{ etc.} \tag{4.28}$$

Now the stiffness matrix can be written in a partitioned form as

$$[k] = \begin{bmatrix} k_{ii} & k_{ij} & k_{im} \\ k_{ji} & k_{jj} & k_{jm} \\ k_{mi} & k_{mj} & k_{mm} \end{bmatrix} \tag{4.29}$$

in which the 2 by 2 submatrices are built up as

$$[k_{rs}] = [B_r]^T[D][B_s]t\Delta. \tag{4.30}$$

This form is often convenient for computation.

4.2.6 *Nodal forces due to initial strain.* These are given directly by the expression Eq. (2.12) which, on performing the integration, becomes

$$\{F\}^e_{\varepsilon 0} = -[B]^T[D][\varepsilon_0]t\Delta, \text{ etc.} \tag{4.31}$$

Partitioning, one can write alternatively

$$\{F_i\}_\varepsilon = -[B_i]^T[D][\varepsilon_0]t\Delta, \text{ etc.} \tag{4.32}$$

These 'initial strain' forces are contributed to the nodes of an element in an unequal manner and require precise evaluation. Similar expressions are derived for initial stress forces.

4.2.7 *Distributed body forces.* In the general case of plane stress or strain each element of unit area in the x–y plane is subject to forces

$$\{p\} = \begin{Bmatrix} X \\ Y \end{Bmatrix}$$

in the direction of the appropriate axes.

Again, by Eq. (2.11), the contribution of such forces to these at each node is given by

$$\{F\}_p^e = -\int [N]^T \begin{Bmatrix} X \\ Y \end{Bmatrix} dx\, dy,$$

or by Eq. (4.7)

$$\{F_i\}_p = -\begin{Bmatrix} X \\ Y \end{Bmatrix}\int N_i\, dx\, dy, \text{ etc.} \tag{4.33}$$

if the body forces X and Y are constant. As N_i is no longer constant the integration has to be carried out explicitly. Some general integration formulae for a triangle are given in Appendix III.

In this special case the calculation will be simplified if the origin of co-ordinates is taken at the centroid of the element. Now

$$\int x\, dx\, dy = \int y\, dx\, dy = 0$$

and on using Eq. (3.8)

$$\{F_i\}_p = -\begin{Bmatrix} X \\ Y \end{Bmatrix}\int a_i\, dx\, dy/2\Delta = -\begin{Bmatrix} X \\ Y \end{Bmatrix} a_i/2$$

or

$$\{F_i\}_p = -\begin{Bmatrix} X \\ Y \end{Bmatrix}\Delta/3 = \{F_j\}_p = \{F_m\}_p \tag{4.34}$$

by relations noted on p. 50.

Explicitly, for the whole element

$$\{F\}_p^e = -\begin{Bmatrix} X \\ Y \\ X \\ Y \\ X \\ Y \end{Bmatrix}\Delta/3 \tag{4.35}$$

which means simply that the total forces acting in x and y direction due to the body forces are distributed to the nodes in three equal parts. This fact corresponds with physical intuition, and was often assumed implicitly.

4.2.8 *Body force potential*. In many cases the body forces are defined in terms of a body force potential ϕ as

$$X = -\frac{\partial\phi}{\partial x}, \qquad Y = -\frac{\partial\phi}{\partial y} \tag{4.36}$$

and this potential, rather than the values of X and Y, is known throughout the region and is specified at nodal points. If $\{\phi\}^e$ lists the three values of the potential associated with the nodes of the element, i.e.,

$$\{\phi\}^e = \begin{Bmatrix} \phi_i \\ \phi_j \\ \phi_m \end{Bmatrix} \tag{4.37}$$

and has to correspond with constant values of X and Y, ϕ must vary linearly within the element. The 'shape function' of its variation will obviously be given by a procedure identical to that used in deriving Eqs. (4.4) to (4.6), and yields

$$\phi = [N'_i, N'_j, N'_m]\{\phi\}^e. \tag{4.38}$$

Thus,

$$X = -\frac{\partial\phi}{\partial x} = -[b_i, b_j, b_m]\{\phi\}^e/2\Delta$$

and

$$Y = -\frac{\partial\phi}{\partial y} = -[c_i, c_j, c_m]\{\phi\}^e/2\Delta. \tag{4.39}$$

The vector of nodal forces due to the body force potential will now replace Eq. (4.35) by

$$\{F\}_p^e = \frac{1}{6} \begin{bmatrix} b_i & b_j & b_m \\ c_i & c_j & c_m \\ b_i & b_j & b_m \\ c_i & c_j & c_m \\ b_i & b_j & b_m \\ c_i & c_j & c_m \end{bmatrix} \{\phi^e\} \tag{4.40}$$

4.2.9 *Evaluation of stresses*. The formulae derived enable the full stiffness matrix of the structure to be assembled, and a solution for displacements to be obtained.

The stress matrix given in general terms in Eq. (2.15) is obtained by the appropriate substitutions for each element.

The stresses are, by the basic assumption, constant within the element. It is usual to assign these to the centroid of the element, and in most of the examples in this chapter this procedure is followed. An alternative consists of obtaining stress values at the nodes by averaging the values in the adjacent elements. Some 'weighting' procedures have been used in this context on an empirical basis but their advantage appears small.

It is usual to arrange for the computer to calculate the principal stresses and their directions of every element.

4.3 Examples—An Assessment of Accuracy

There is no doubt that the solution to plane elasticity problems as formulated in Section 4.2 is, in the limit of subdivision, an exact solution. Indeed at any stage of a finite subdivision it is an approximate solution as, say, a Fourier series solution with a limited number of terms.

As already explained in Chapter 2 the total strain energy obtained during any stage of approximation will be below the true strain energy of the exact solution. In practice it will mean that the displacements, and hence also the stresses, will be underestimated by the approximation in its *general picture*. However, it must be emphasized that this is not necessarily true at every point of the continuum individually; hence the value of such a bound in practice is not great.

What is important for the engineer to know is the order of accuracy achievable in typical problems with a certain fineness of element subdivision. In any particular case the error can be assessed by comparison with known, exact, solutions or by a study of the convergence, using two or more stages of subdivision.

With the development of experience the engineer can assess *a priori* the order of approximation that will be involved in a specific problem tackled with a given element subdivision. Some of this experience will perhaps be conveyed by the examples considered in this book.

In the first place attention will be focused on some simple problems for which exact solutions are available.

Uniform stress field. If the exact solution is in fact that of a uniform stress field then, whatever the element subdivision, the finite element solution will coincide exactly with the exact one. This is an obvious corollary of the formulation, nevertheless it is useful as a first check of written computer programs.

Linearly varying stress field. Here, obviously, the basic assumption of constancy of stress within elements means that solution will be approximate only. In Fig. 4.4 a simple example of a beam subject to constant bending moment is shown with a fairly coarse subdivision. It is readily seen that the axial (σ_y) stress given by the element 'straddles' the exact values and, in fact, if the constant stress values are associated with centroids of the elements and plotted, the best 'fit' line represents the exact stresses.

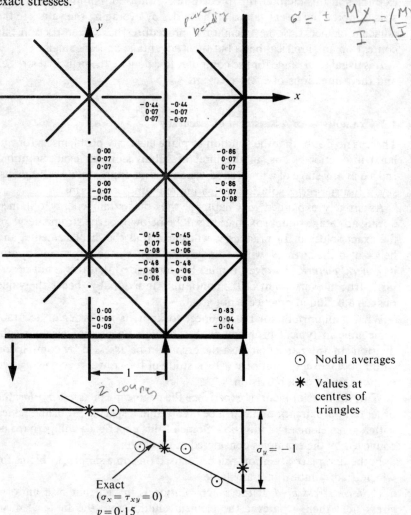

Fig. 4.4   Pure bending of a beam solved by a coarse subdivision into elements of triangular shape. (Values of σ_y, σ_x, and τ_{xy} listed in that order)

The horizontal and shear stress components differ again from the exact values (which are simply zero). Again, however, it will be noted that they oscillate by equal, small amounts around the exact values.

At internal nodes, if the average of stresses of surrounding elements is taken it will be found that the exact stresses are very closely represented. The average at external faces is not, however, so good. The overall improvement in representing the stresses by nodal averages, as shown on Fig. 4.4, is often used in practice for improvement of the approximation.

A weighting of averages near the faces of the structure can further be used for refinement. Without being dogmatic on this point, it seems preferable, when accuracy demands this, simply to use a finer mesh subdivision.

Stress concentration. A more realistic test problem is shown in Figs. 4.5 and 4.6. Here the flow of stress around a circular hole in an isotropic and in an anisotropic stratified material is considered when the stress conditions are uniform.[6] A graded division into elements is used to allow a more detailed study in the region where high stress gradients are expected. The high degree of accuracy achievable can be assessed from Fig. 4.6 where some of the results are compared against exact solutions.[3,7]

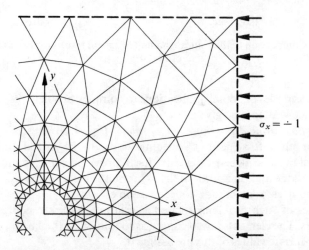

Fig. 4.5 A circular hole in a uniform stress field. (a) isotropic material; (b) stratified (orthotropic) material; $E_x = E_1 = 1$, $E_y = E_2 = 3$, $v_1 = 0.1$, $v_2 = 0$, $G_{xy} = 0.42$

4.4 Some Practical Applications

Obviously, the practical applications of the method are limitless, and indeed at this moment of time the use of the finite element method is superseding experimental technique for plane problems because of its high accuracy, low cost, and versatility. The ease of treatment of material anisotropy, thermal stresses, or body force problems add to its advantages.

———— Exact solution for infinite plate.

o   Finite element solution.

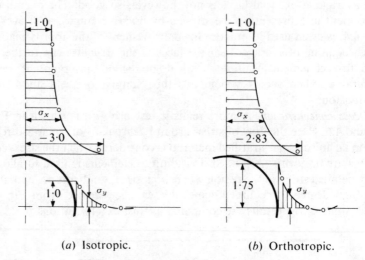

(a) Isotropic.   (b) Orthotropic.

Fig. 4.6   Comparison of theoretical and finite element results for cases (a) and (b)
of Fig. 4.5

A few examples of actual applications to complex problems of engineering practice will now be given.

Stress flow around a reinforced opening (Fig. 4.7). In steel pressure vessels or aircraft structures, openings have to be introduced in the stressed skin. The penetrating duct itself provides some reinforcement round the edge and, in addition, the skin itself is increased in thickness to reduce the stresses due to the concentration effects.

Analysis of such problems treated as cases of plane stress presents no difficulties. The elements are so chosen as to follow the thickness variation, and appropriate values of this are assigned.

The narrow band of thick material near the edge can be represented either by special beam-type elements, or more easily in a standard programme by very thin triangular elements of the usual type, to which appropriate thickness is assigned. The latter procedure was used in the problem shown in Fig. 4.7 which gives some of the resulting stresses near the opening itself. The fairly large extent of the region introduced in the analysis and the grading of the mesh should be noted.

An anisotropic valley subject to tectonic stress[6] (Fig. 4.8). A symmetrical valley subject to a uniform horizontal stress is considered. The material is stratified, hence is 'transversely isotropic', and the direction of strata varies from point to point.

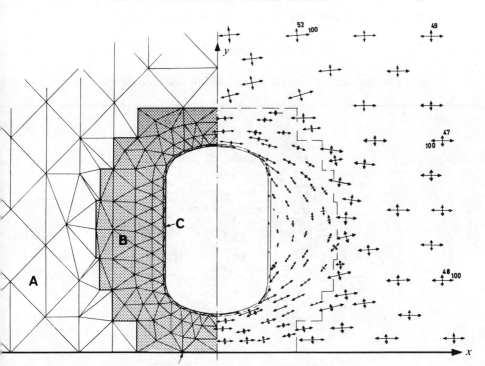

estrained in y direction from movement.

Fig. 4.7 A reinforced opening in a plate. Uniform stress field at a distance from opening $\sigma_x = 100$, $\sigma_y = 50$. Thickness of plate regions A, B, and C is in the ratio of 1:3:23

The stress plot shows the tensile region that develops. This phenomenon is of considerable interest to geologists and engineers concerned with rock mechanics.

A dam subject to external and internal water pressures[8,9] (Fig. 4.9). A buttress dam on a somewhat complex rock foundation is here analysed. The heterogeneous foundation region is subject to plane strain conditions while the dam itself is considered as a plate (plane stress) of variable thickness.

With external and gravity loading no special problems of analysis arise, though perhaps it should be mentioned that it was found worth while to 'automatize' the computation of gravity nodal loads.

When pore pressures are considered, the situation, however, requires perhaps some explanation.

It is well known that in a porous material the water pressure is transmitted to the structure as a *body force* of magnitude

$$X = -\frac{\partial p}{\partial x}, \qquad Y = -\frac{\partial p}{\partial y}$$

and that now the external pressure need not be considered.

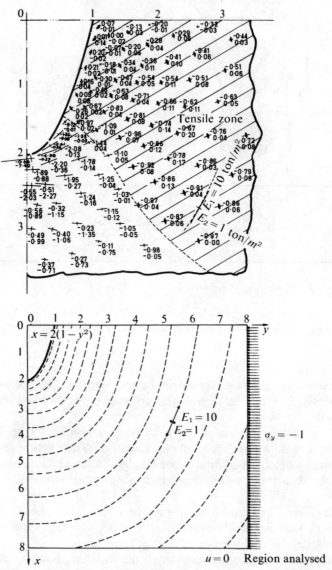

Fig. 4.8   A valley with curved strata subject to a horizontal tectonic stress
(plane strain 170 nodes, 298 elements)

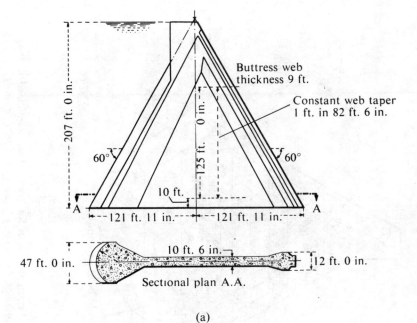

Buttress web
thickness 9 ft.

Constant web taper
1 ft. in 82 ft. 6 in.

207 ft. 0 in.

125 ft. 0 in.

60°   60°

10 ft.

A
121 ft. 11 in.   121 ft. 11 in.

47 ft. 0 in.

10 ft. 6 in.

12 ft. 0 in.

Sectional plan A.A.

(a)

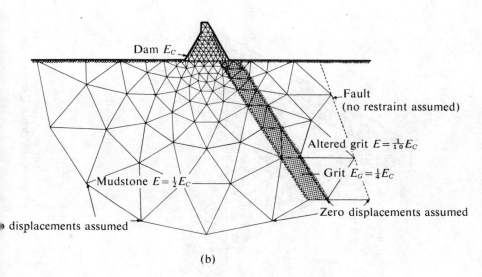

Dam E_C

Fault
(no restraint assumed)

Altered grit $E = \frac{1}{10}E_C$

Grit $E_G = \frac{1}{4}E_C$

Mudstone $E = \frac{1}{2}E_C$

Zero displacements assumed

displacements assumed

(b)

Fig. 4.9 Stress analysis of a buttress dam. Plane stress condition assumed in dam
and plane strain in foundation. (a) The buttress section analysed. (b) Extent of
foundation considered and division into finite elements

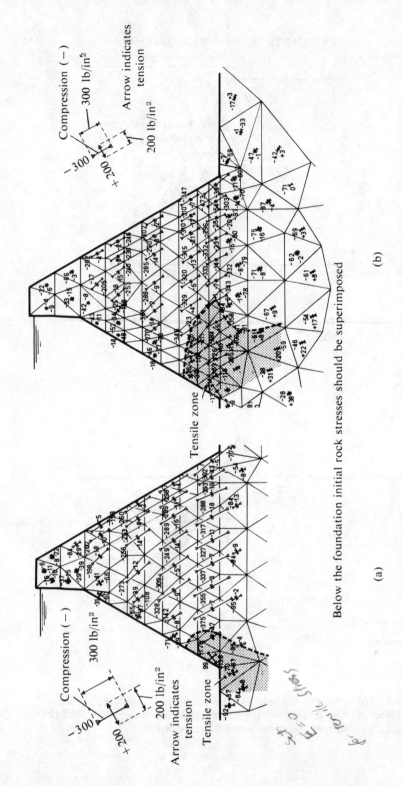

Fig. 4.10 Stress analysis of the buttress dam of Fig. 4.9. Principal stresses for gravity loads combined with water pressures, which are assumed to act (a) as external loads, (b) as body forces due to pore pressure

The pore pressure p is, in fact, now a body force potential, as defined in Eq. (4.36). Figure 4.9 shows the element subdivision of the region and the outline of the dam. Figure 4.10(a) and (b) show the stresses resulting from gravity (applied to the dam only) and due to water pressure assumed to be acting as an external load or, alternatively as an internal pore pressure. Both solutions indicate large tensile regions, but the increase of stresses due to the second assumption is important.

Cracking. The tensile stresses in the previous example will doubtless cause the rock to crack. If a stable situation can develop when such a crack spreads then the dam can be considered safe.

Cracks can be introduced very simply into the analysis by assigning zero elasticity values to chosen elements. An analysis with a wide cracked wedge is shown in Fig. 4.11, where it can be seen that with the extent of the crack assumed no tension within the dam body develops.

A more elaborate procedure for following crack propagation and resulting stress redistribution can be developed and will be discussed later (*see* Chapter 18).

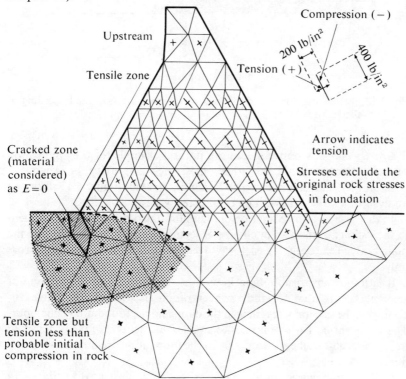

Fig. 4.11 Stresses in a buttress dam. An introduction of a 'crack' modifies stress distribution (same loading as Fig. 4.10(b))

Thermal stresses. As an example of thermal stress computation the same dam is shown under simple temperature distribution assumptions. Results of this analysis are given in Fig. 4.12.

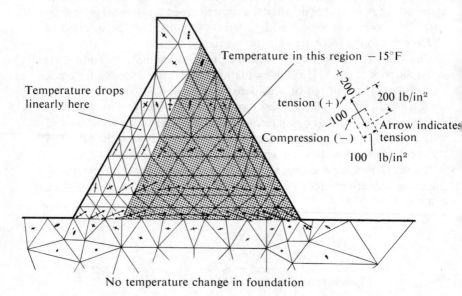

No temperature change in foundation

Fig. 4.12   Stress analysis of a buttress dam. Thermal stresses due to cooling of shaded area by 15°F ($E = 3 \times 10^6$ lb/in², $\alpha = 6 \times 10^{-6}$/deg F)

Gravity dams. A buttress dam is a natural example for the application of finite element methods. Other types, such as gravity dams with or without piers and so on, can also be simply treated. Figure 4.13 shows an analysis of a large dam with piers and crest gates.

In this case an approximation of assuming a two-dimensional treatment in the vicinity of the abrupt change of section, i.e., where the piers join the main body of the dam, is clearly involved, but this leads to localized errors only.

It is important to note here how, in a single solution, the grading of element size is used to study concentration of stress at the cable anchorages, the general stress flow in the dam, and the foundation behaviour. The linear ratio of size of largest to smallest elements is of the order of 30 to 1 (the largest elements occurring in the foundation are not shown in the figure).

Underground power station. This last example illustrated in Figs. 4.14 and 4.15 shows an interesting large-scale application. Here principal stresses are plotted automatically. In this analysis very many different components of $\{\sigma_0\}$, the initial stress, were used due to uncertainty of knowledge about geological conditions. The rapid solution and plot of many results enabled the limits within which stresses vary to be found and an engineering decision arrived at.

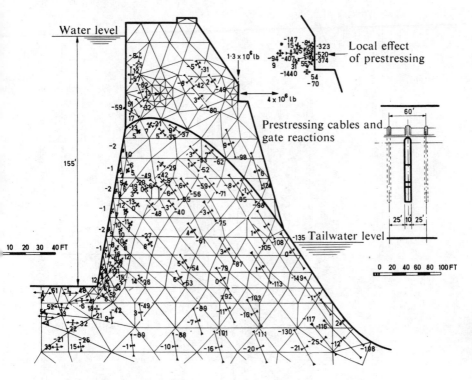

Fig. 4.13   A large barrage with piers and prestressing cables

4.5 Special Treatment of Plane Strain with an Incompressible Material

It will have been noted that the relationship Eq. (4.20) defining the elasticity $[D]$ matrix for an isotropic material breaks down when the Poisson's ratio reaches a value of 0·5 as the factor in the parentheses becomes infinite. A simple way of side-stepping the difficulty presented is to use values of Poisson's ratio approximate to 0·5 but not equal to it. Experience shows, however, that if this is done the approximation of solution deteriorates. An alternative procedure has been suggested by Herrman.[10] This involves the use of a new variational formulation, and readers are referred to his work for details.

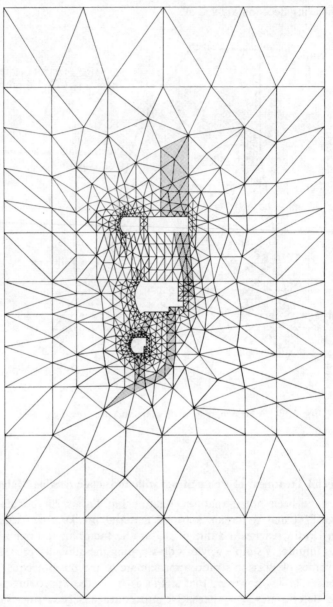

Fig. 4.14   An underground power station. Mesh used in analysis.

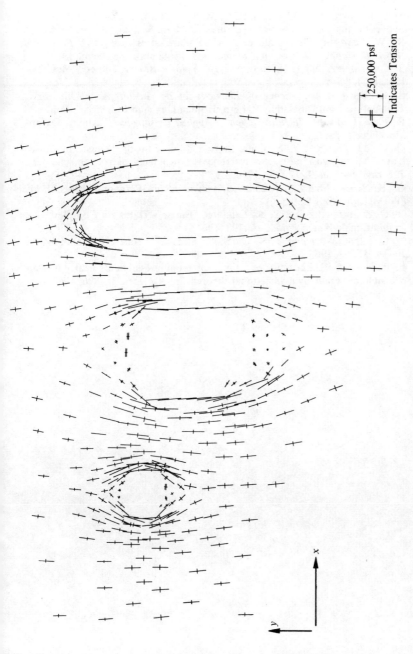

Fig. 4.15 An underground power station. Plot of principal stresses.

References

1. M. J. TURNER, R. W. CLOUGH, H. C. MARTIN, and L. J. TOPP, 'Stiffness and deflection analysis of complex structures', *J. Aero. Sci.*, **23**, 805–23, 1956.
2. R. W. CLOUGH, 'The finite element in plane stress analysis', *Proc. 2nd A.S.C.E. Conf. on Electronic Computation*, Pittsburgh, Pa., Sept. 1960.
3. S. TIMOSHENKO and J. N. GOODIER, *Theory of elasticity*, 2nd ed., McGraw-Hill, 1951.
4. S. G. LEKHNITSKII, *Theory of Elasticity of an Anisotropic Elastic Body*, Translation from Russian by P. Fern, Holden Day, San Francisco, 1963.
5. R. F. S. HEARMON, *An Introduction to Applied Anisotropic Elasticity*, Oxford Univ. Press, 1961.
6. O. C. ZIENKIEWICZ, Y. K. CHEUNG, and K. G. STAGG, 'Stresses in Anisotropic Media with particular reference to problems of rock mechanics', *J. Strain Analysis*, **1**, 172–82, 1966.
7. G. N. SAVIN, *Stress Concentration Around Holes*, Pergamon Press, 1961. (Translation from Russian.)
8. O. C. ZIENKIEWICZ and Y. K. CHEUNG, 'Buttress Dams on Complex rock foundations', *Water Power*, **16**, 193, 1964.
9. O. C. ZIENKIEWICZ and Y. K. CHEUNG, 'Stresses in Buttress Dams', *Water Power*, **17**, 69, 1965.
10. L. R. HERRMAN, 'Elasticity equations for incompressible, or nearly incompressible materials by a variational theorem', *J.A.I.A.A.*, **3**, 1896, 1965.

5. Axi-Symmetric Stress Analysis

5.1 Introduction

The problem of stress distribution in bodies of revolution (axi-symmetric solids) under axi-symmetric loading is of considerable practical interest. The mathematical problems presented are very similar to those of plane stress and plane strain as, once again, the situation is two-dimensional.[1,2] By symmetry, the two components of displacements in any plane section of the body along its axis of symmetry define completely the state of strain and, therefore, the state of stress. Such a cross-section is shown in Fig. 5.1. If r and z denote respectively the radial and axial co-ordinates of a point, with u and v being the corresponding displacements, it can readily be seen that precisely the same displacement functions as those

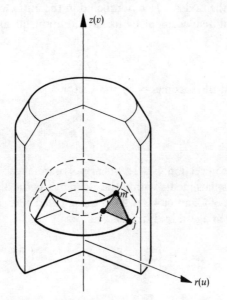

Fig. 5.1   Element of an axi-symmetric solid

73

used in Chapter 4 can be used to define the displacements within the triangular element i, j, m shown.

The volume of material associated with an 'element' is now that of a body of revolution indicated on Fig. 5.1, and all integrations have to be referred to this.

The triangular element is again used mainly for illustrative purposes, the principles developed being completely general.

In plane stress or strain problems it was shown that internal work was associated with three strain components in the co-ordinate plane, the stress component normal to this plane not being involved due to zero values of either the stress or the strain.

In the axi-symmetrical situation any radial displacement automatically induces a strain in the circumferential direction, and as the stresses in this direction are certainly non-zero, this fourth component of strain and of the associated stress has to be considered. Here lies the essential difference in the treatment of the axi-symmetric situation.

The reader will find the algebra involved in this chapter somewhat more tedious than that in the previous one but, essentially, identical operations are once again involved, following the general formulation of Chapter 2.

5.2 Element Characteristics

5.2.1 *Displacement function*. Using the triangular shape of element (Fig. 5.1) with the nodes i, j, m numbered in the anti-clockwise sense, we define the nodal displacement by its two components as

$$\{\delta_i\} = \begin{Bmatrix} u_i \\ v_i \end{Bmatrix} \tag{5.1}$$

and the element displacements by the vector

$$\{\delta\}^e = \begin{Bmatrix} \delta_i \\ \delta_j \\ \delta_m \end{Bmatrix}. \tag{5.2}$$

Obviously, as in section 4.2.1, a linear polynomial can be used to define uniquely the displacements within the element. As the algebra involved is identical to that of Chapter 4 it will not be repeated here. The displacement field is now given again by Eq. (4.7).

$$\{f\} = \begin{Bmatrix} u \\ v \end{Bmatrix} = [IN'_i, IN'_j, IN'_m]\{\delta\}^e$$

with

$$N'_i = (a_i + b_i r + c_i z)/2\Delta, \text{ etc.} \tag{5.3}$$

and I a two-by-two identity matrix. In above

$$a_i = r_j z_m - r_m z_j$$
$$b_i = z_j - z_m = z_{jm} \tag{5.4}$$
$$c_i = r_m - r_j = r_{mj}$$

etc., in cyclic order. Once again Δ is the area of the element triangle.

5.2.2 *Strain (total)*. As already mentioned, four components of strain have now to be considered. These are, in fact, all the non-zero strain components possible in an axi-symmetric deformation. Figure 5.2 illustrates and defines these strains and the associated stresses.

$$\tau_{r\theta} = \tau_{z\theta} = 0$$

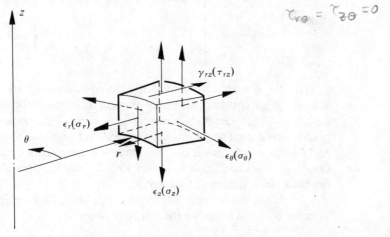

Fig. 5.2 Strains and stresses involved in the analysis of axi-symmetric solids

The strain vector defined below lists the strain components involved and defines them in terms of the displacements of a point. The expressions involved are almost self-evident and will not be derived here. The interested reader can consult a standard elasticity textbook[3] for the full derivation. We have thus

$$\{\varepsilon\} = \begin{Bmatrix} \varepsilon_z \\ \varepsilon_r \\ \varepsilon_\theta \\ \gamma_{rz} \end{Bmatrix} = \begin{Bmatrix} \dfrac{\partial v}{\partial z} \\[2mm] \dfrac{\partial u}{\partial r} \\[2mm] \dfrac{u}{r} \\[2mm] \dfrac{\partial u}{\partial z} + \dfrac{\partial v}{\partial r} \end{Bmatrix}. \tag{5.5}$$

$$\{\varepsilon\} = [B]\{\delta\} \Rightarrow \begin{Bmatrix} \varepsilon_z \\ \end{Bmatrix} = \begin{bmatrix} 0 & \dfrac{\partial N_i}{\partial z} \\ \dfrac{\partial N_i}{\partial r} & 0 \end{bmatrix} \begin{Bmatrix} u_i \\ v_i \\ u_j \\ v_j \end{Bmatrix}$$

Using the displacement functions defined by Eqs. (5.3) and (5.4) we have

$$\{\varepsilon\} = [B]\{\delta\}^e = [B_i, B_j, B_m]\{\delta\}^e$$

in which

$$[B_i] = \begin{bmatrix} 0 & \dfrac{\partial N_i'}{\partial z} \\[2ex] \dfrac{\partial N_i'}{\partial r} & 0 \\[2ex] \dfrac{1}{r} N_i' & 0 \\[2ex] \dfrac{\partial N_i'}{\partial z} & \dfrac{\partial N_i'}{\partial r} \end{bmatrix} = \frac{1}{2\Delta} \begin{bmatrix} 0 & c_i \\[2ex] b_i & 0 \\[2ex] a_i/r + b_i + c_i z/r & 0 \\[2ex] c_i & b_i \end{bmatrix} \quad \text{etc.} \qquad (5.6)$$

With the B matrix now involving the co-ordinates r and z, the strains are no longer constant within an element as in the plane stress or strain case. This strain variation is due to the ε_θ term. If the imposed nodal displacements are such that u is proportional to r then indeed the strains will all be constant. As this is the only state of displacement coincident with a constant strain condition it is clear that the displacement function satisfies the basic criterion of Chapter 2.

5.2.3 *Initial strain (thermal strain).* In general, four independent components of initial strain vector can be envisaged

$$\{\varepsilon_0\} = \begin{Bmatrix} \varepsilon_{z0} \\ \varepsilon_{r0} \\ \varepsilon_{\theta 0} \\ \gamma_{rz0} \end{Bmatrix}. \qquad (5.7)$$

Although this can, in general, be variable within the element, it will be convenient to take the initial strain as constant there.

The most frequently encountered case of initial strain will be that due to a thermal expansion. For an isotropic material we shall have then

$$\{\varepsilon_0\} = \begin{Bmatrix} \alpha\theta^e \\ \alpha\theta^e \\ \alpha\theta^e \\ 0 \end{Bmatrix} \qquad (5.8)$$

where θ^e is the average temperature rise in an element and α is the coefficient of thermal expansion.

A general case of anisotropy need not be considered since axial symmetry would be impossible to achieve under such circumstances. A case of some interest in practice is that of a 'stratified' material, similar to the one discussed in Chapter 2, in which the plane of isotropy is normal to the axis of symmetry (Fig. 5.3). Here, two different expansion co-efficients are possible; one in the axial direction α_z and another in the plane normal to it, α_r.

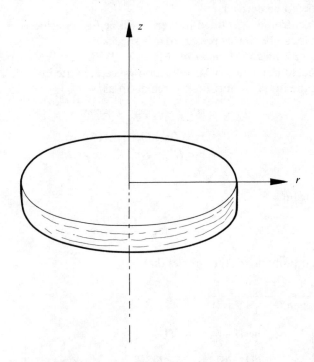

Fig. 5.3 Axi-symmetrically stratified material

Now the initial thermal strain becomes

$$\{\varepsilon_0\} = \begin{Bmatrix} \alpha_z \theta^e \\ \alpha_r \theta^e \\ \alpha_r \theta^e \\ 0 \end{Bmatrix}. \tag{5.9}$$

Practical cases of such 'stratified' anisotropy often arise in laminated or fibreglass construction of machine components.

5.2.4 *Elasticity matrix.* The elasticity matrix $[D]$ linking the strains $\{\varepsilon\}$

and the stresses $\{\sigma\}$ in the standard form

$$\{\sigma\} = \left\{ \begin{array}{c} \sigma_z \\ \sigma_r \\ \sigma_\theta \\ \tau_{rz} \end{array} \right\} = [D](\{\varepsilon\} - \{\varepsilon_0\})$$

needs now to be derived.

The anisotropic, 'stratified' material will be first considered as the isotropic case can be simply presented as a special case.

Anisotropic stratified material (Fig. 5.3). With the z-axis representing the normal to the planes of stratification we can rewrite Eqs. (4.22) (again ignoring the initial strains for convenience) as:

$$\begin{aligned} \varepsilon_z &= \sigma_z/E_2 - v_2\sigma_r/E_2 - v_2\sigma_\theta/E_2 \\ \varepsilon_r &= -v_2\sigma_z/E_2 + \sigma_r/E_1 - v_1\sigma_\theta/E_1 \\ \varepsilon_\theta &= -v_2\sigma_z/E_2 - v_1\sigma_r/E_1 + \sigma_\theta/E_1 \\ \gamma_{zr} &= \tau_{zr}/G_2. \end{aligned} \qquad (5.10)$$

Writing again

$$\frac{E_1}{E_2} = n \quad \text{and} \quad \frac{G_2}{E_2} = m$$

we have, on solving for the stresses that:

$$D = \frac{E_2}{(1+v_1)(1-v_1-2nv_2^2)}$$

$$\begin{bmatrix} 1-v_1^2 & nv_2(1+v_1) & nv_2(1+v_1) & 0 \\ & n(1-nv_2^2) & (v_1+nv_2^2)n & 0 \\ & & n(1-nv_2^2) & 0 \\ \text{symmetric} & & m(1+v_1) \times (1-v_1-2nv_2^2) \end{bmatrix}. \qquad (5.11)$$

Isotropic material. For an isotropic material we can obtain the $[D]$ matrix by taking

$$E_1 = E_2 = E \text{ or } n = 1$$

and

$$v_1 = v_2 = v$$

and using the well-known relationship between the elastic constants

$$\frac{G_2}{E_2} = \frac{G}{E} = m = \frac{1}{2(1+v)}.$$

Substituting in Eq. (5.11) we have now

$$D = \frac{E(1-v)}{(1+v)(1-2v)} \begin{bmatrix} 1 & \dfrac{v}{1-v} & \dfrac{v}{1-v} & 0 \\ & 1 & \dfrac{v}{1-v} & 0 \\ & & 1 & 0 \\ & \text{symmetric} & & \dfrac{1-2v}{2(1-v)} \end{bmatrix}. \quad (5.12)$$

5.2.5 *The stiffness matrix*. The stiffness matrix of the element *ijm* can now be computed according to the general relationship Eq. (2.10). Remembering that the volume integral has to be taken over the whole ring of material we have

$$[k]^e = 2\pi \int [B]^T [D][B] r \, dr \, dz \quad (5.13)$$

with $[B]$ given by Eq. (5.6) and $[D]$ by either Eq. (5.11) or Eq. (5.12), depending on the material.

The integration cannot now be performed as simply as was the case in the plane stress problem because the $[B]$ matrix depends on the co-ordinates. Two possibilities exist: the first that of numerical integration and the second of an explicit multiplication and term-by-term integration.

The simplest approximate procedure is to evaluate $[\bar{B}]$ for a centroidal point

$$\bar{r} = (r_i + r_j + r_m)/3$$

and

$$\bar{z} = (z_i + z_j + z_m)/3.$$

In this case we have simply as a first approximation

$$[k] = 2\pi[\bar{B}]^T[D][\bar{B}]\bar{r}\Delta \quad (5.14)$$

with Δ being the triangle area.

More elaborate numerical integration schemes could be used by evaluating the integrand at several points of the triangle. Such methods will be discussed in detail in Chapter 8. However, it can be shown that if the numerical integration is of such an order that the volume of the element is exactly determined by it, then in the limit of subdivision, the solution will converge to the exact answer.[4] The 'one point' integration suggested here is of such a type, as it is well known that the volume of a

$$\bar{r} = \frac{\iint r \, dr \, dz}{\iint dr \, dz} \qquad \bar{z} = \frac{\iint z \, dr \, dz}{\iint dr \, dz}$$

body of revolution is given exactly by the product of the area and the path swept around by its centroid. With the simple triangular element used here a fairly fine subdivision is in any case needed for accuracy and most practical programs use the simple approximation which, surprisingly perhaps, is in fact sometimes superior to the exact integration. The reason for this is the occurrence of logarithmic terms in the exact formulation. These involve ratios of the type r_i/r_m and, when the element is at a large distance from the axis, such terms tend to unity and evaluation of the logarithm is inaccurate.

If exact integration is required it is convenient to proceed in the following manner.

Again, as in the previous chapter, the stiffness matrix is conveniently split into separate elements (*vide* Eqs. 4.28 to 4.30) giving a typical, two by two, stiffness submatrix as

$$[k_{rs}] = 2\pi \int \int [B_r]^T [D][B_s] r \, dr \, dz. \qquad (5.15)$$

At this stage it is useful to split up the submatrices $[B]$ into constant and variable parts. Thus, for example, we can write

$$[B_i] = [\bar{B}_i] + [B_i'] \qquad (5.16)$$

in which $[\bar{B}_i]$ is the value of $[B_i]$ at the centroid, as used in Eq. (5.14), and the second term accounts for the variation from this value. It will be readily seen that this can be written as

$$[B_i'] = \begin{bmatrix} 0 & 0 \\ 0 & 0 \\ 1 & 0 \\ 0 & 0 \end{bmatrix} \{(a_i + c_i z)/r - (a_i + c_i \bar{z})/\bar{r}\}/2\Delta. \qquad (5.17)$$

Substituting the above expression in Eq. (5.15) and noting that

$$\int [B_i'] r \, dr \, dz = [0]$$

we have

$$[k_{rs}] = [\bar{k}_{rs}] + [k_{rs}'] \qquad (5.18)$$

in which the first term is precisely that given by Eq. (5.14), and the second is a corrective term which is obtained from

$$[k_{rs}'] = \frac{2\pi}{(2\Delta)^2} \begin{bmatrix} 0 & 0 & 1 & 0 \\ 0 & 0 & 0 & 0 \end{bmatrix} [D] \begin{bmatrix} 0 & 0 \\ 0 & 0 \\ 1 & 0 \\ 0 & 0 \end{bmatrix},$$

$$\int \{(a_r + c_r z)/r - (a_r + c_r \bar{z})/\bar{r}\}\{(a_s + c_s z)/r - (a_s + c_s \bar{z})/\bar{r}\} r \, dr \, dz. \qquad (5.19)$$

Handwritten annotations:

$$\bar{r} = \frac{\iint r \, dr \, dz}{\iint dr \, dz}$$

$$[K_{rs}] = 2\pi \iint [\bar{B}_r]^T [D][\bar{B}_s] r \, dr \, dz$$
$$+ 2\pi \iint [\bar{B}_r]^T [D][B_s'] r \, dr \, dz +$$
$$+ 2\pi \iint [B_r']^T [D][\bar{B}_s] r \, dr \, dz$$
$$+ 2\pi \iint [B_r']^T [D][B_s']$$

$$2\pi [\bar{B}_r]^T [D] \iint [B_s'] r \, dr \, dz = 0$$

$$\iint [B_s'] r \, dr \, dz = \begin{bmatrix} 0 & 0 \\ 0 & 0 \\ 0 & 0 \end{bmatrix} \iint [(a_i + c_i z)/r - (a_i + c_i \bar{z})/\bar{r}] r \, dr \, dz$$

$$1^{st}] \quad \iint \left(\frac{a_i}{r}\right) r \, dr \, dz = a_i \iint dr \, dz = \Delta a_i$$

~) $\iint \dfrac{c_i z}{r} r \, dr \, dz = c_i \iint z \, dr \, dz = \bar{z} c_i \Delta$

') $\iint \dfrac{a_i}{r} r \, dr \, dz = \dfrac{a_i}{\bar{r}} \iint r \, dr \, dz = \dfrac{a_i}{\bar{r}} (\bar{r}\Delta) = a_i \Delta$

If the various integrals are written in an abbreviated notation

$\iint \dfrac{c_i z}{r} r \, dr \, dz = $ $\displaystyle\int \dfrac{1}{r} dr \, dz = \Delta \cdot I_1$

$= \dfrac{c_i z}{r} \quad \bar{r} \Delta = c_i \bar{z} \Delta \displaystyle\int \dfrac{z}{r} dr \, dz = \Delta \cdot I_2$ (5.20)

$\displaystyle\int \dfrac{z^2}{r} dr \, dz = \Delta \cdot I_3$

we can finally write simply for the corrective term

$$[k'_{rs}] = \frac{\pi}{2\Delta} \begin{bmatrix} D_{33} & 0 \\ 0 & 0 \end{bmatrix}$$

$$\{a_r a_s(I_1 - 1/\bar{r}) + (a_r c_s + a_s c_r)(I_2 - \bar{z}/\bar{r}) + c_r c_s(I_3 - \bar{z}^2/\bar{r})\}. \quad (5.21)$$

The integrals I_1 to I_3 can be evaluated explicitly in terms of the nodal coordinates.

5.2.6 *External nodal forces.* In the case of two-dimensional problems of the previous chapter the question of assigning of the external loads was so obvious as not to need further comment. In the present case, however, it is important to realize that the nodal forces represent a combined effect of the force acting along the whole circumference of the circle forming the element 'node'. This point was already brought out in the integration of the expressions for the stiffness of an element, such integrations being conducted over the whole ring.

Thus, if $\bar{R}$ represents the radial component of force per unit length of the circumference of a node or a radius r, the external 'force' which will have to be introduced in the computation is

$\begin{bmatrix} 0 & 0 \\ 0 & 0 \\ 0 & 0 \end{bmatrix}$ $\left[\Delta a_i + c_i \bar{z}\Delta - \Delta a_i - c_i \bar{z}\Delta \right] 2\pi r\bar{R}.$

$= 0$

In the axial direction we shall, similarly, have

$$2\pi r\bar{Z}$$

to represent the combined effect of axial forces.

5.2.7 *Nodal forces due to initial strain.* Again, by Eq. (2.9)

$$\{F\}_{\varepsilon_0}^e = -2\pi \int [B]^{\mathrm{T}}[D]\{\varepsilon_0\} r \, dr \, dz \quad (5.22)$$

or partitioning and noting that $\{\varepsilon_0\}$ is constant

$$\{F_i\}_{\varepsilon_0}^e = -2\pi \left(\int [B_i]^{\mathrm{T}} r \, dr \, dz \right) [D]\{\varepsilon_0\}. \quad (5.23)$$

The integration can be performed in a similar manner to that used in the determination of the stiffness.

It will be readily seen that, again, an approximate expression can be used

$$\{\bar{F}_i\}^e_{\varepsilon_0} = -2\pi[\bar{B}_i]^{\mathrm{T}}[D]\{\varepsilon_0\}\bar{r}\Delta \tag{5.24}$$

together with a 'corrective' term. Thus,

$$\{F_i\}^e_{\varepsilon_0} = \{\bar{F}_i\} + \{F'_i\}. \tag{5.25}$$

However, the corrective term will be found to be zero now as

$$\{F'_i\}^e_{\varepsilon_0} = 2\pi\left(\int [B'_i]r\,dr\,dz\right)[D]\{\varepsilon_0\} = 0$$

so that we have in fact exactly

$$\{F'_i\}^e_{\varepsilon_0} = -2\pi[\bar{B}]^{\mathrm{T}}[D]\{\varepsilon_0\}\bar{r}\Delta. \tag{5.26}$$

Initial stress forces are treated in an identical manner.

5.2.8 *Distributed body forces.* Distributed body forces such as those due to gravity (if acting along the z axis), centrifugal force in rotating machine parts or pore pressure, often occur in axi-symmetric problems.

Let such forces be denoted by

$$p = \begin{Bmatrix} R \\ Z \end{Bmatrix} \tag{5.27}$$

per unit volume of material in directions of r and z respectively. By the general Eq. (2.9) we have

$$\{F\}^e_p = -2\pi\int [N]^{\mathrm{T}}\begin{Bmatrix} R \\ Z \end{Bmatrix}r\,dr\,dz$$

or partitioning

$$\{F_i\}^e_p = -2\pi\int \begin{Bmatrix} R \\ Z \end{Bmatrix} N_i r\,dr\,dz. \tag{5.28}$$

Using a co-ordinate shift similar to that of section 3.2.7 it is easy to show that the first approximation, if the body forces are constant, results in

$$\{\bar{F}_i\}^e_p = \{\bar{F}_j\}^e_p = \{\bar{F}_m\}^e_p = -2\pi\begin{Bmatrix} R \\ Z \end{Bmatrix}\bar{r}\Delta/3. \tag{5.29}$$

Although this is not exact the error term will be found to decrease with reduction of element size and, as it is also self-balancing, it will not introduce appreciable inaccuracies. Clearly an exact integration is again possible.

If the body forces are given by a potential similar to that defined in section 4.2.9, i.e.,

$$R = -\frac{\partial\phi}{\partial r}, \qquad Z = -\frac{\partial\phi}{\partial z} \tag{5.30}$$

and if this potential is defined linearly by its nodal values, an expression equivalent to Eq. (4.40) can again be used with the same degree of approximation.

In many problems the body forces vary, proportionately to r. For example in rotating machinery

$$R = \omega^2 \rho r \qquad (5.31)$$

where ω is the angular velocity and ρ the density of the material. Clearly the approximation involved in Eq. (5.29) now deteriorates, and for best results an exact integration is indicated.

4.2.9 *Evaluation of stresses*. The stresses now vary throughout the element as will be appreciated from Eqs. (5.5) and (5.6). It is convenient now to evaluate the average stress at the centroid of the element. The stress matrix resulting from Eqs. (5.6) and (2.3) gives there, as usual

$$\{\bar{\sigma}\}^e = [D][\bar{B}]\{\delta\}^e - [D]\{\varepsilon_0\} + \{\sigma_0\}.$$

It will be found that a certain amount of oscillation of stress values between elements occurs and better approximation can be achieved by averaging nodal stresses.

5.3 Some Illustrative Examples

Test problems such as those of a cylinder under constant axial or radial stress give, as indeed would be expected, solutions which correspond to exact ones. This is again an obvious corollary of the ability of the displacement function to reproduce constant strain conditions.

A problem for which an exact solution is available and in which almost linear stress gradients occur is that of a sphere subject to internal pressure. Figure 5.4(a) shows the centroidal stresses obtained using rather a coarse mesh, and the stress oscillation around the exact values should be noted. (This oscillation becomes even more pronounced at larger values of Poisson's ratio although the exact solution is independent of it.) In Fig. 5.4(b) the very much better approximation obtained by averaging the stresses at nodal points is shown, and in Fig. 5.4(c) a further improvement using a method of averaging is shown. The close agreement with exact solution even for the very coarse subdivision used here shows the accuracy achievable. The displacements at nodes compared with the exact solution are given in Fig. 5.5.

In Fig. 5.6 thermal stresses in the same sphere are computed for a steady-state temperature variation shown. Again, excellent accuracy is demonstrated by comparison with the exact solution.

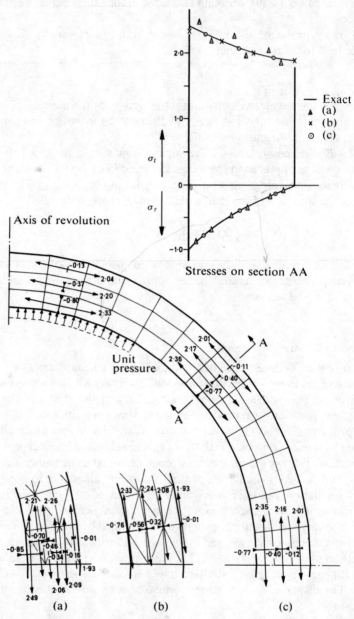

Fig. 5.4   Stresses in a sphere subject to an internal pressure (Poisson's ratio $v = 0.3$). (a) Triangular mesh—centroidal values; (b) Triangular mesh—nodal averages; (c) Quadrilateral mesh obtained by averaging adjacent triangles

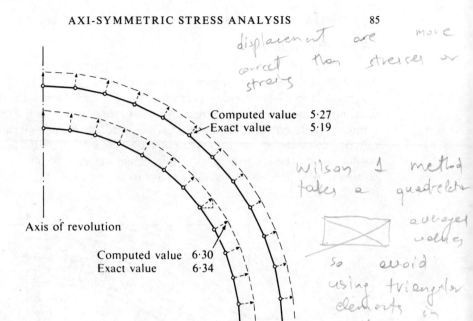

displacement are more correct than stresses or strain

Computed value 5·27
Exact value 5·19

Wilson 1 method takes a quadretta average valles

so avoid using triangular elements in wilson 1 prog-

Axis of revolution

Computed value 6·30
Exact value 6·34

Fig. 5.5 Displacements of internal and external surfaces of sphere under loading of Fig. 5.4

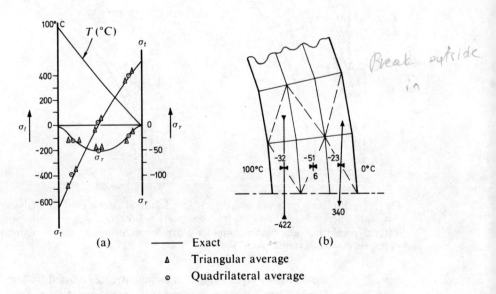

Break outside in

(a)   ——— Exact   (b)
            ▲   Triangular average
            ⊙   Quadrilateral average

Fig. 5.6 Sphere subject to steady-state heat flow (100°C internal temperature, 0° external temperature). (a) Temperature and stress variation on radial section; (b) 'Quadrilateral' averages

5.4 Practical Applications

Two examples of practical application of the programs available for axi-symmetrical stress distribution are given here.

A prestressed concrete reactor pressure vessel. Figure 5.7 shows the stress distribution in a relatively simple prototype pressure vessel. Due to symmetry only one-half of the vessel is analysed, the results given here referring to the components of stress due to an internal pressure. Similar results due to the effect of prestressing cables are readily obtained by putting in the appropriate nodal loads due to these cables.

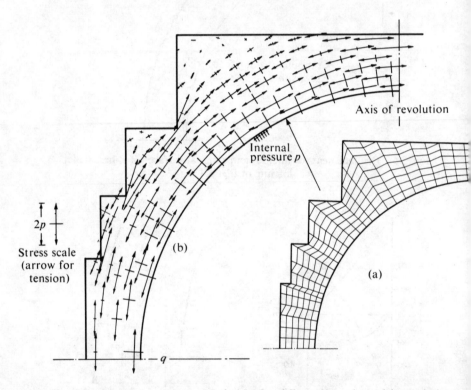

Fig. 5.7   A reactor pressure vessel. (*a*) 'Quadrilateral' mesh used in analysis; this was generated automatically by computer; (*b*) Stresses due to a uniform internal pressure *p* (automatic computer plot). Solution based on quadrilateral averages. Poisson's ratio $v = 0.15$

In Fig. 5.8 contours of equal major principal stresses caused by temperature are shown. The thermal state is due to a steady-state heat conduction and itself was found by the finite element method in a way described in Chapter 15.

Foundation pile. Figure 5.9 shows the stress distribution around a foundation pile penetrating two different strata. This non-homogeneous problem presents no difficulties and is treated by the standard program.

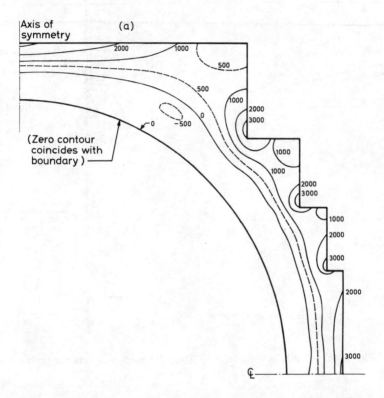

Fig. 5.8 A reactor pressure vessel. Thermal stresses due to steady-state heat conduction. Contours of major principal stress in lb/in^2. (Interior temperature 400°C, Exterior temperature 0°C, $\alpha = 5 \times 10^{-6}/°$C, $E = 2\cdot58 \times 10^6$ lb/in, $v = 0\cdot15$)

5.5 Non-symmetrical Loading

The method described in the present chapter can be extended to deal with non-symmetrical loading. If the circumferential loading variation is expressed in circular harmonics then it is still possible to focus attention on one axial section although the degree of freedom is now increased to three.

Some details of this process are described in Chapter 13. For full description reference (5) should be consulted.

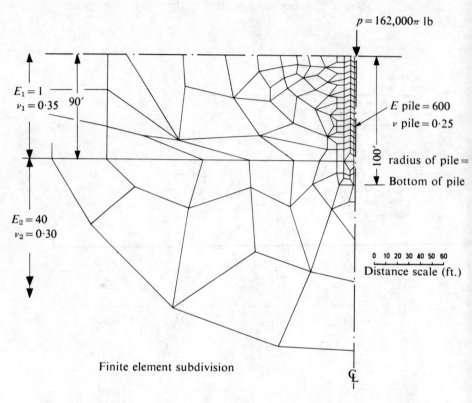

Fig. 5.9(a)   A pile in stratified soil. Irregular mesh and data for problem

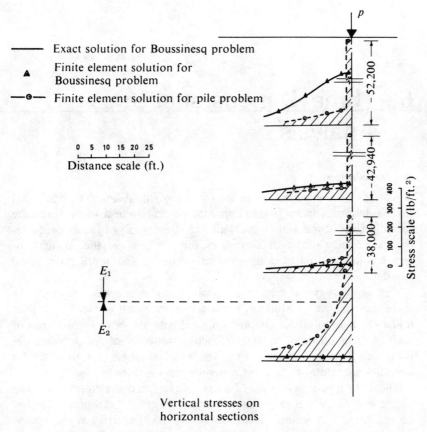

Vertical stresses on
horizontal sections

Fig. 5.9(b) A pile in stratified soil. Plot of vertical stresses on horizontal sections. Solution also plotted for Boussinesq problem obtained by making $E_1 = E_2 = E_{pile}$, and this is compared with exact values

References

1. R. W. CLOUGH, chapter 7, *Stress Analysis*, ed. O. C. Zienkiewicz and G. S. Holister, Wiley, 1965.
2. R. W. CLOUGH and Y. RASHID, 'Finite element analysis of axi-symmetric solids', *Proc. A.S.C.E.*, **91**, EM.1, 71, 1965.
3. S. TIMOSHENKO and J. N. GOODIER, *Theory of Elasticity*, 2nd ed., McGraw-Hill, 1951.
4. B. M. IRONS, Comment on 'Stiffness matrices for sector element' by I. R. Raju and A. K. Rao, *J.A.I.A.A.*, 7, 156–7, 1969.
5. E. L. WILSON, 'Structural analysis of axisymmetric solids', *J.A.I.A.A.*, 3, 2269–74, 1965.

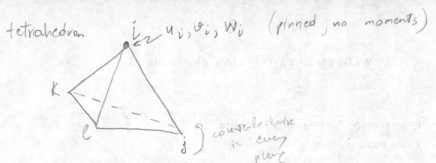

6. Three-Dimensional Stress Analysis

6.1 Introduction

It will have become obvious to the reader by this stage of the book that there is but one further step to apply the general finite element procedure to fully three-dimensional problems of stress analysis. Such problems embrace clearly all the practical cases, though for some, the various two-dimensional approximations give an adequate and more economical 'model'.

The simplest two-dimensional continuum element was a triangle. In three dimensions its equivalent is a tetrahedron, an element with four nodal corners—and this chapter will deal with the basic formulation of such an element. Immediately, a difficulty not encountered previously is presented. It is one of ordering of the nodal numbers and, in fact, of a suitable representation of a body divided into such elements.

The first suggestions for use of the simple tetrahedral element appear to be those of Gallagher et al.[1] and Melosh.[2] Argyris[3,4] elaborated further on the theme and Rashid[5] has shown that with the largest modern computers such a formulation can still be applied to realistic problems.

It is immediately obvious, however, that the number of simple tetrahedral elements which has to be used to achieve a given degree of accuracy has to be very large. This will result in very large numbers of simultaneous equations in practical problems, which may place a severe limitation on the use of the method in practice. Further the band width of the resulting equation system becomes large leading to big computer storage requirements.

To realize the order of magnitude of the problems presented let us assume that the accuracy of triangle in two-dimensional analysis is comparable to that of a tetrahedron in three dimensions. If an adequate stress analysis of a square, two-dimensional region requires a mesh of some $20 \times 20 = 400$ nodes, the total number of simultaneous equations is around 800 given two displacement variables for node. (This is a fairly realistic figure.) The band width of the matrix involves 20 nodes (see chapter on computation), i.e., some 40 variables.

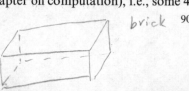

brick

An equivalent three-dimensional region is that of a cube with $20 \times 20 \times 20 = 8000$ nodes. The total number of simultaneous equations is now some 24,000 as three displacement variables have to be specified. Further the band width involves now an interconnection of some $20 \times 20 = 400$ nodes or 1200 variables.

Given that with usual solution techniques the computation effort is roughly proportional to the number of equations and to the square of the band width, the magnitude of the problems can be appreciated. It is not surprising therefore that efforts to improve accuracy by use of complex elements with many degrees of freedom have been strongest in the area of three-dimensional analysis.[6,7,8,9,10] The use and practical application of such elements will be described in the following chapters. However, the presentation of this chapter gives all the necessary ingredients of formulation for three-dimensional elastic problems and so follows directly from the previous ones. Extension to more elaborate elements will be self evident.

6.2 Tetrahedral Element Characteristics

6.2.1 *Displacement functions.* Figure 6.1 illustrates a tetrahedral element i, j, m, p in space defined by the x, y, and z co-ordinates.

The state of displacement of a point is defined by three displacement components, u, v, and w in directions of the three co-ordinates x, y, and z. Thus

$$\{f\} = \begin{Bmatrix} u \\ v \\ w \end{Bmatrix}. \tag{6.1}$$

Just as in a plane triangle where a linear variation of a quantity was defined by its three nodal values, here a linear variation will be defined by the four nodal values. In analogy to Eq. (4.3) we can write, for instance

$$u = \alpha_1 + \alpha_2 x + \alpha_3 y + \alpha_4 z. \tag{6.2}$$

Equating the values of displacement at the nodes we have four equations of the type

$$u_1 = \alpha_1 + \alpha_2 x_i + \alpha_3 y_i + \alpha_4 z_i \text{ etc.} \tag{6.3}$$

from which α_1 to α_4 can be evaluated.

Again, it is possible to write this solution in the form similar to that of

Eq. (4.5) by using a determinant form, i.e.

$$
\begin{aligned}
u = \frac{1}{6V} \Big\{ & (a_i + b_i x + c_i y + d_i z)u_i \\
& + (a_j + b_j x + c_j y + d_j z)u_j \\
& + (a_m + b_m x + c_m y + d_m z)u_m \\
& + (a_p + b_p x + c_p y + d_p z)u_p \Big\}
\end{aligned}
\tag{6.4}
$$

with

$$
6V = \det
\begin{vmatrix}
1 & x_i & y_i & z_i \\
1 & x_j & y_j & z_j \\
1 & x_m & y_m & z_m \\
1 & x_p & y_p & z_p
\end{vmatrix}
\tag{6.5a}
$$

in which, incidentally, the value V represents the volume of the tetrahedron. By expanding the other relevant determinants into their co-factors

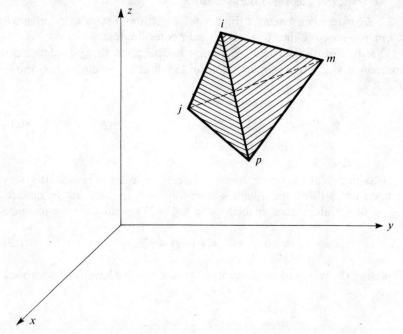

Fig. 6.1   A tetrahedral volume. (Always use a consistent order of numbering, e.g., starting with p count the other nodes in an anti-clockwise order as viewed from p—*pijm* or *mipj* etc.)

we have

$$a_i = \det \begin{vmatrix} x_j & y_j & z_j \\ x_m & y_m & z_m \\ x_p & y_p & z_p \end{vmatrix} , \qquad b_i = -\det \begin{vmatrix} 1 & y_j & z_j \\ 1 & y_m & z_m \\ 1 & y_p & z_p \end{vmatrix} ,$$

$$c_i = \det \begin{vmatrix} x_j & 1 & z_j \\ x_m & 1 & z_m \\ x_p & 1 & z_p \end{vmatrix} , \qquad d_i = -\det \begin{vmatrix} x_j & y_j & 1 \\ x_m & y_m & 1 \\ x_p & y_p & 1 \end{vmatrix} .$$

(6.5b)

with the other constants defined by cyclic interchange of the subscripts in the order p, i, j, m.

The ordering of nodal numbers p, i, j, m must follow a 'right-hand' rule obvious from Fig. 6.1. In this the first three nodes are numbered in an anti-clockwise manner when viewed from the last one.

The element displacement is defined by the twelve displacement components of the nodes as

$$\{\delta\}^e = \begin{Bmatrix} \delta_i \\ \delta_j \\ \delta_m \\ \delta_p \end{Bmatrix}$$

(6.6)

with

$$\{\delta_i\} = \begin{Bmatrix} u_i \\ v_i \\ w_i \end{Bmatrix} \text{etc.}$$

We can write the displacements of an arbitrary point as

$$\{f\} = [IN'_i, \ IN'_j, \ IN'_m, \ IN'_p]\{\delta\}^e$$

(6.7)

with scalars defined as

$$N'_i = (a_i + b_i x + c_i y + d_i z)/6V \text{ etc.}$$

(6.8)

and I being a three by three identity matrix.

Once again the displacement functions used will obviously satisfy continuity requirements on interfaces between various elements. This fact is a direct corollary of the linear nature of the variation of displacements.

6.2.2 *Strain matrix*. Six strain components are relevant in full three-dimensional analysis. The strain matrix can now be defined as

$$
\{\varepsilon\} = \left\{ \begin{array}{c} \varepsilon_x \\ \varepsilon_y \\ \varepsilon_z \\ \gamma_{xy} \\ \gamma_{yz} \\ \gamma_{zx} \end{array} \right\} = \left\{ \begin{array}{c} \dfrac{\partial u}{\partial x} \\[2mm] \dfrac{\partial v}{\partial y} \\[2mm] \dfrac{\partial w}{\partial z} \\[2mm] \dfrac{\partial u}{\partial y}+\dfrac{\partial v}{\partial x} \\[2mm] \dfrac{\partial v}{\partial z}+\dfrac{\partial w}{\partial y} \\[2mm] \dfrac{\partial w}{\partial x}+\dfrac{\partial u}{\partial z} \end{array} \right\}
\tag{6.9}
$$

following the standard notation of Timoshenko's elasticity text. Using Eqs. (6.4) to (6.7) it is an easy matter to verify that

$$
\{\varepsilon\} = [B]\{\delta\}^e = [B_i, B_j, B_m, B_p]\{\delta\}^e
\tag{6.10}
$$

in which

$$
[B_i] = \begin{bmatrix} \dfrac{\partial N_i'}{\partial x} & 0 & 0 \\[2mm] 0 & \dfrac{\partial N_i'}{\partial y} & 0 \\[2mm] 0 & 0 & \dfrac{\partial N_i'}{\partial z} \\[2mm] \dfrac{\partial N_i'}{\partial y} & \dfrac{\partial N_i'}{\partial x} & 0 \\[2mm] 0 & \dfrac{\partial N_i'}{\partial z} & \dfrac{\partial N_i'}{\partial y} \\[2mm] \dfrac{\partial N_i'}{\partial z} & 0 & \dfrac{\partial N_i'}{\partial x} \end{bmatrix} = \frac{1}{6V} \begin{bmatrix} b_i & 0 & 0 \\ 0 & c_i & 0 \\ 0 & 0 & d_i \\ c_i & b_i & 0 \\ 0 & d_i & c_i \\ d_i & 0 & b_i \end{bmatrix}
$$

with other submatrices obtained in a similar manner simply by interchange of subscripts.

Initial strains, such as those due to thermal expansion, can be written in the usual way as a six-component vector which, for example, in an isotropic thermal expansion is simply

$$\{\varepsilon_0\} = \begin{Bmatrix} \alpha\theta^e \\ \alpha\theta^e \\ \alpha\theta^e \\ 0 \\ 0 \\ 0 \end{Bmatrix} \qquad (6.12)$$

with α being the expansion coefficient and θ^e the average element temperature rise.

6.2.3 *Elasticity matrix*. With complete anisotropy the $[D]$ matrix relating the six stress components to the strain components can contain 21 independent constants (*vide* section 4.2.4).

In general, thus,

$$\{\sigma\} = \begin{Bmatrix} \sigma_x \\ \sigma_y \\ \sigma_z \\ \tau_{xy} \\ \tau_{yx} \\ \tau_{zx} \end{Bmatrix} = [D](\{\varepsilon\} - \{\varepsilon_0\}) + \{\sigma_0\}. \qquad (6.13)$$

Although no difficulty presents itself in computation when dealing with such materials, since the multiplication will never be carried out explicitly, it is convenient to recapitulate here the $[D]$ matrix for an isotropic material. This, in terms of the usual elastic constants E (modulus) and v (Poisson's ratio), can be written as

$$[D] = \frac{E(1-v)}{(1+v)(1-2v)}$$

$$\times \begin{bmatrix} 1 & v/(1-v) & v/(1-v) & 0 & 0 & 0 \\ & 1 & v/(1-v) & 0 & 0 & 0 \\ & & 1 & 0 & 0 & 0 \\ & \text{symmetric} & & \dfrac{(1-2v)}{2(1-v)} & 0 & 0 \\ & & & & \dfrac{(1-2v)}{2(1-v)} & 0 \\ & & & & & \dfrac{(1-2v)}{2(1-v)} \end{bmatrix} \cdot \qquad (6.14)$$

6.2.4 *Stiffness, stress, and load matrices.* The stiffness matrix defined by the general relationship Eq. (2.10) can be now explicitly integrated since the strain and stress components are constant within the element.

The general *rs* submatrix of the stiffness matrix will be a three by three matrix defined as

$$[k_{rs}] = [B_r]^{\mathrm{T}}[D][B_s]V \qquad (6.15)$$

where V represents the volume of the elementary tetrahedron.

The nodal forces due to the initial strain become, similarly to Eq. (4.31)

$$\{F\}_{\varepsilon_0}^e = -[B]^{\mathrm{T}}[D]\{\varepsilon_0\}V \qquad (6.16)$$

or partitioning

$$\{F_i\}_{\varepsilon_0}^e = -[B]^{\mathrm{T}}[D]\{\varepsilon_0\}V$$

with similar expression for forces due to initial stresses.

In fact, the similarity with the expressions and results of Chapter 4 is such that further explicit formulation is unnecessary. The reader will find no difficulty in repeating the various steps needed for the formulation of a computer program.

Distributed body forces can once again be expressed in terms of their X, Y, and Z components or in terms of the body-force potential. Not surprisingly, it will once more be found that if the body forces are constant the nodal components of the total resultant are distributed in four equal parts (*vide* Eq. (4.34)).

6.3 Composite Elements with Eight Nodes

The division of a space volume into individual tetrahedra sometimes presents difficulties of visualization and could easily lead to errors in nodal

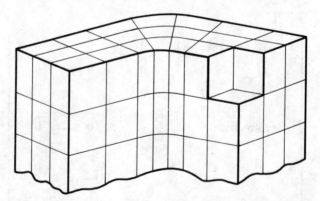

Fig. 6.2   A systematic way of dividing a three-dimensional object into 'brick'-type elements

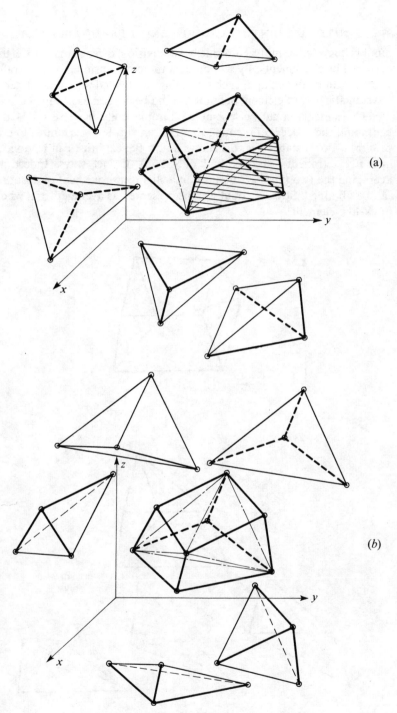

Fig. 6.3 Composite element with eight nodes and its subdivision into five tetrahedra by alternatives (a) or (b)

numbering, etc. A more convenient subdivision of space is into eight-cornered brick elements. By sectioning a three-dimensional body parallel sections can be drawn and, each one being subdivided into quadrilaterals a systematic way of element definition could be devised as in Fig. 6.2.

Such elements could be assembled automatically from several tetrahedra and the process of creating these tetrahedra left to a simple logical program. For instance Fig. 6.3 shows how a typical brick can be divided into five tetrahedra in two (and only two) distinct ways. Indeed by averaging the two types of subdivision a slight improvement of accuracy can be obtained. Stresses could well be presented as averages for a whole brick-like element.

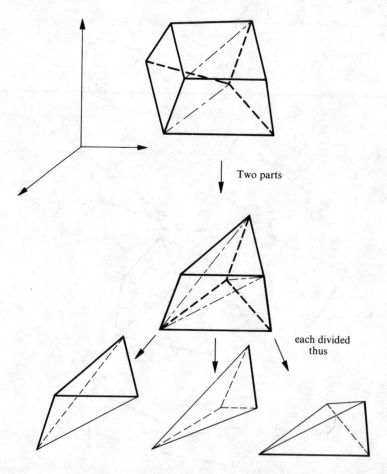

Fig. 6.4   A systematic way of splitting an eight-cornered brick into six tetrahedra

In Fig. 6.4 an alternative subdivision of a brick into six tetrahedra is shown. Here obviously the number of alternatives is very great.

In later chapters it will be seen how the subdivision into such basic bricks can be used effectively with more complex types of elements.

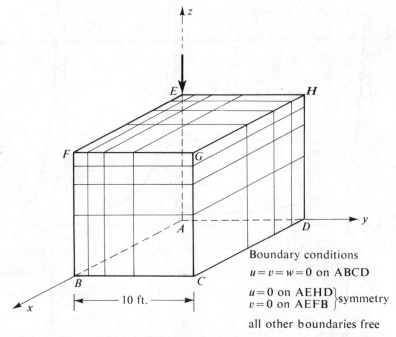

Boundary conditions

$u = v = w = 0$ on ABCD

$u = 0$ on AEHD
$v = 0$ on AEFB $\}$ symmetry

all other boundaries free

Fig. 6.5   The Boussinesq problem as one of three-dimensional stress analysis

6.4 Examples and Concluding Remarks

A simple, illustrative example of application of simple, tetrahedral, elements is shown in Figs. 6.5 and 6.6. Here the well-known Boussinesq problem of an elastic halfspace with a point load is approximated to by analysing a cubic volume of space. Use of symmetry is made to reduce the size of the problem and the boundary displacements are prescribed in a manner shown in Fig. 6.5.[11] As zero displacements were prescribed at a finite distance below the load a correction obtained from the exact expression was applied before executing the plots shown in Fig. 6.6. Comparison of both stresses and displacement appears reasonable although it will be appreciated that the division is very coarse. However, even this trivial problem involved the solution of some 375 equations. More ambitious problems treated with simple tetrahedra are given in references 5 and 11. Figure 6.7, taken from the former, illustrates an analysis of a complex

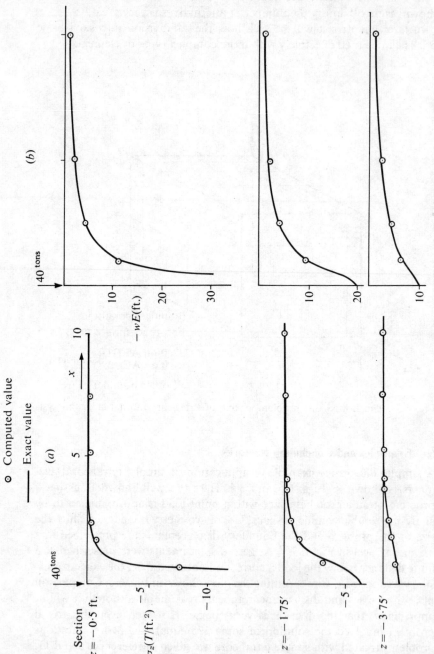

Fig. 6.6   The Boussinesq problem. (a) vertical stresses (σ_z); (b) vertical displacements (w)

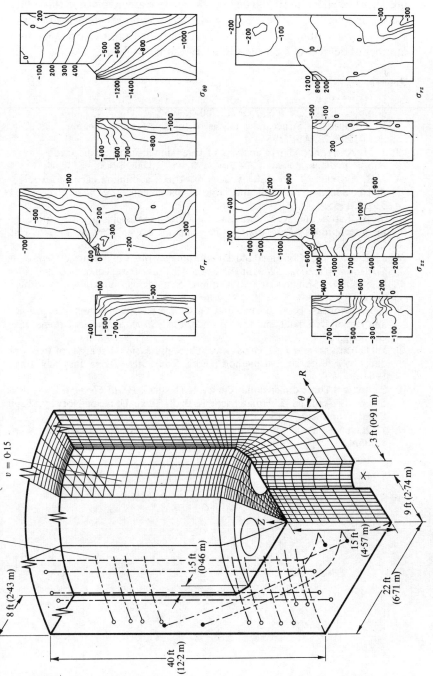

Fig. 6.7 A nuclear pressure vessel analysis using simple tetrahedral elements.[5] Geometry, subdivision and some stress results

pressure vessel. Some 10,000 degrees of freedom are involved in this analysis. In Chapter 9 it will be seen how the use of complex elements permit a sufficiently accurate analysis to be performed with a much smaller total number of degrees of freedom for a very similar problem.

References

1. R. H. GALLAGHER, J. PADLOG, P. P. BIJLAARD, 'Stress analysis of heated complex shapes', *A.R.S. Journal*, 700–7, 1962.
2. R. J. MELOSH, 'Structural analysis of solids', *Proc. Amer. Soc. Civ. Eng.*, **S.T.4**, 205–23, Aug. 1963.
3. J. H. ARGYRIS, 'Matrix analysis of three-dimensional elastic media—small and large displacements', *J.A.I.A.A.*, **3**, 45–51, Jan. 1965.
4. J. H. ARGYRIS, 'Three-dimensional anisotropic and inhomogeneous media—matrix analysis for small and large displacements', *Ingeniour Archiv.*, **34**, 33–55, 1965.
5. Y. R. RASHID and W. ROCKENHAUSER, 'Pressure vessel analysis by finite element techniques', *Proc. Conf. on Prestressed Concrete Pressure Vessels*, Inst. Civ. Eng., 1968.
6. J. H. ARGYRIS, 'Continua and Discontinua', *Proc. Conf. Matrix Methods in Structural Mechanics*, Wright Patterson Air Force Base, Ohio, Oct. 1965.
7. B. M. IRONS, 'Engineering applications of numerical integration in stiffness methods', *J.A.I.A.A.*, **4**, 2035–7, 1966.
8. J. ERGATOUDIS, B. M. IRONS, and O. C. ZIENKIEWICZ, 'Three dimensional analysis of arch dams and their foundations', *Proc. Symp. Arch Dams*, Inst. Civ. Eng., 1968.
9. J. H. ARGYRIS and J. C. REDSHAW, 'Three dimensional analysis of two arch dams by a finite element method', *Proc. Symp. Arch Dams*, Inst. Civ. Eng., 1968.
10. S. FJELD, 'Three dimensional theory of elastics', *Finite Element Methods in Stress Analysis*, ed. I. Holand and K. Bell, Tech. Univ. of Norway, Tapir Press, Trondheim, 1969.
11. J. OLIVEIRA PEDRO, Thesis 1967, Laboratorio Nacional de Engenharia Civil, Lisbon.

7. Element Shape Functions— Some General Families

7.1 Introduction

In the three previous chapters the reader was shown in some detail how linear elasticity problems could be formulated and solved using very simple finite element forms. Although the detailed algebra was concerned with shape functions which arose from triangular and tetrahedral shapes only it should by now be obvious that other element forms could equally well be used. Indeed, once the element and the corresponding shape functions are determined, subsequent operations follow a standard, well-defined path which could be entrusted to an algebraist not familiar with the physical aspects of the problem. It will be seen later that in fact it is possible to program a computer to deal with wide classes of problems by specifying the shape functions only. The choice of these is, however, a matter to which intelligence has to be applied and in which the human factor remains paramount. In this chapter some rules for generation of several families of one-, two-, and three-dimensional elements will be presented.

In the problems of elasticity illustrated in Chapters 4, 5, and 6 the displacement variable was a vector with two or three components and the shape functions were written in a matrix form. They were, however, derived for each component separately and in fact the matrix expressions in these were derived by multiplying a scalar function by an identity matrix (e.g., Eqs. (4.7), (5.3), and (6.7)). We shall therefore concentrate in this chapter on the scalar shape function forms omitting the prime and calling these simply N_i.

The shape functions used in the displacement formulation of elasticity problems were such that to satisfy the convergence criteria of Chapters 2 and 3

  (*a*) the continuity of the unknown only had to occur between elements (i.e., slope continuity is not required)
  (*b*) the function has to allow any arbitrary linear form to be taken so

that the constant strain (constant first derivative) criterion could be observed.

The shape functions described in this chapter will only require the satisfaction of these two criteria. They will be thus applicable to all the problems of the preceding chapters and also to other problems which require only these conditions to be obeyed. For instance all problems of Chapter 15 can use the forms here determined. Indeed they are applicable to any situation where the functional χ (see Chapter 3) is defined by derivatives of the first order only.

The element families discussed will progressively have an increasing number of degrees of freedom. The question may well be asked as to whether any economic or other advantage is gained by increasing thus the complexity of an element. The answer here is not an easy one although it can be stated as a general rule that as the order of an element increases so the total number of unknowns in a problem can be reduced for a given accuracy of representation. Economic advantage requires, however, a reduction of total computations and data preparation effort and this does not follow automatically for a reduced number of total variables as, though equation solving times may be reduced, the time required for element formulation increases.

An overwhelming economic advantage in case of three-dimensional analysis has been already hinted at in the previous chapter on three-dimensional analysis.

The same kind of advantage arises on occasion in other problems but in general the optimum element may have to be determined from case to case.

TWO-DIMENSIONAL ELEMENTS

7.2 Rectangular Elements—Some Preliminary Considerations

Conceptually (especially if the reader is conditioned by education to thinking in the Cartesian co-ordinate system) the simplest element form is that of a rectangle with sides parallel to x and y axes. Consider for instance a rectangle shown in Fig. 7.1 with nodal points numbered 1 to 8, located as shown, and at which the values of the unknown function ϕ form the element parameters. How can suitable shape functions for this element be determined?

Let us first assume that this is expressed in a polynomial form in x and y. To ensure inter-element continuity of ϕ along the top and bottom sides the variation must be linear. Two points at which the function is common between elements lying above or below exist and as two values determine uniquely a linear function its identity all along these sides is ensured with that given by adjacent elements. Use of this fact was already made in specifying linear expansions for a triangle.

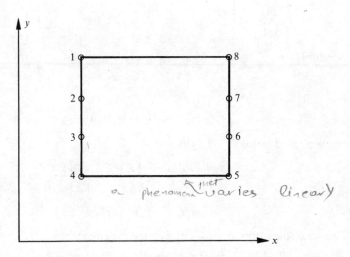

Fig. 7.1   A rectangular element

Similarly if a cubic variation along the vertical sides is assumed continuity will be preserved there as four values determine a unique cubic expansion. Conditions for satisfying the first criterion are now obtained.

To ensure the existence of arbitrary values of first derivative all that is necessary is that all the linear terms of the expansion be retained.

Finally, as eight points are to determine uniquely the variation of the function only eight coefficients of the expansion can be retained and thus we could write

$$\phi = \alpha_1 + \alpha_2 x + \alpha_3 y + \alpha_4 xy + \alpha_5 y^2 + \alpha_6 xy^2 + \alpha_7 y^3 + \alpha_8 xy^3. \qquad (7.1)$$

The choice can in general be made unique by retaining the lowest possible expansion terms though in this case apparently no such choice arises.[†] The reader will easily verify that all the requirements have now been satisfied.

Substituting co-ordinates of the various nodes a set of simultaneous equations will be obtained.

This can be written in exactly the same manner as was done for a

---

† Retention of a higher order term of expansion, ignoring one of lower order, will usually lead to a poorer approximation though still retaining convergence.[1]

triangle in Eq. (4.4) as

$$
\begin{Bmatrix} \phi_1 \\ \vdots \\ \phi_8 \end{Bmatrix} = \begin{bmatrix} 1, x_1, y_1, x_1 y_1, y_1^2, x_1 y_1^2, y_1^3, x_1 y_1^3 \\ \cdot \quad \cdot \quad \cdot \quad \cdot \quad \cdot \quad \cdot \quad \cdot \quad \cdot \quad \cdot \quad \cdot \quad \cdot \\ \cdot \quad \cdot \quad \cdot \quad \cdot \quad \cdot \quad \cdot \quad \cdot \quad \cdot \quad \cdot \quad \cdot \quad \cdot \end{bmatrix} \begin{Bmatrix} \alpha_1 \\ \vdots \\ \alpha_8 \end{Bmatrix} \tag{7.2}
$$

or simply as

$$\{\phi\}^e = [C]\{\alpha\}. \tag{7.3}$$

Formally

$$\{\alpha\} = [C]^{-1}\{\phi\}^e \tag{7.4}$$

and we could write Eq. (7.1) as

$$\phi = [P]\{\alpha\} = [P][C]^{-1}\{\phi\}^e \tag{7.5}$$

in which

$$[P] = [1, x, y, xy, y^2, xy^2, y^3, xy^3]. \tag{7.6}$$

Thus the shape functions for the element defined by

$$\phi = [N]\{\phi\}^e = [N_1, N_2, \ldots, N_8]\{\phi\}^e \tag{7.7}$$

can be found from

$$[N] = [P][C]^{-1}. \tag{7.8}$$

This process, frequently used in practice as it does not involve much ingenuity, has, however, some considerable disadvantages. Occasionally an inverse of $[C]$ may not exist[2] and *always* considerable algebraic difficulty is experienced in obtaining an inverse in general terms suitable for all element geometries. It is therefore worth while to consider whether shape functions, $N_i(x, y)$ can be written down directly. Before doing this some general properties of these functions have to be mentioned.

Inspection of the defining relation, Eq. (7.7) reveals immediately some important characteristics. First, as this expression is valid for all $\{\phi\}^e$

$$N_i = 1$$

at node i and is equal to zero at all other nodes. Further the basic type of variation along boundaries defined for continuity purposes (e.g., linear in x and cubic in y in the above example) must be retained. The typical form of the shape functions for the elements considered is illustrated for two typical nodes isometrically in Fig. 7.2. It is clear that these could have been written down directly as a product of a suitable linear function in x with a cubic in y. The easy solution of this example is not always as obvious but given sufficient ingenuity, a direct derivation of shape function is always recommended.

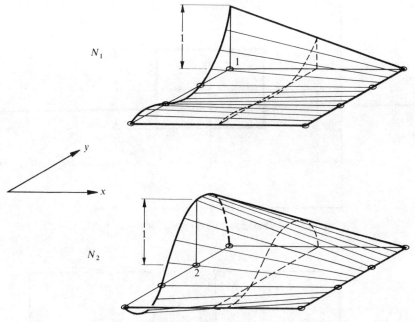

Fig. 7.2   Shape functions for elements of Fig. 7.1

It will be convenient to use normalized co-ordinates in further investigation. Such normalized co-ordinates are shown in Fig. 7.3 and are so chosen that on the faces of the rectangle their values are ±1.

$$\xi = (x - x_c)/a, \qquad d\xi = dx/a,$$
$$\eta = (y - y_c)b, \qquad d\eta = dy/b. \tag{7.9}$$

Once the shape functions are known in the normalized co-ordinates, translation into actual co-ordinates or transformation of the various expressions occurring, for instance, in stiffness derivation is trivial and work can be carried out using these.

7.3 Rectangular Elements—'Serendipity' Family [3,4]

It is usually most convenient to make the functions dependent on nodal values placed on the element boundary. Consider for instance the first three elements of Fig. 7.4. In each a progressively increasing and equal number of nodes is placed on the element boundary. The variation of function on the edges to ensure continuity is linear, parabolic, and cubic in increasing element development.

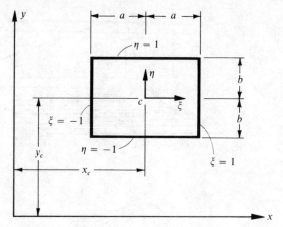

Fig. 7.3   Normalized co-ordinates for a rectangle

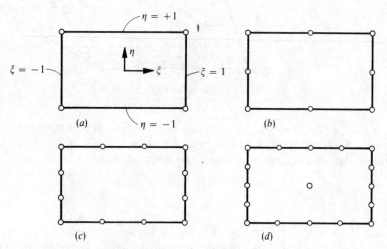

Fig. 7.4   Rectangles of boundary node (Serendipity) family (*a*) linear,
(*b*) quadratic, (*c*) cubic, and (*d*) quartic

To achieve the shape function for the first element it is obvious that a product of the form

$$\tfrac{1}{4}(\xi+1)(\eta+1) \qquad (7.10)$$

gives unity at top right corners where $\xi = \eta = 1$ and zero at all the other corners. Further a linear variation of the shape function of all sides exists and hence continuity is satisfied.

Introducing new variables

$$\xi_0 = \xi\xi_i, \qquad \eta_0 = \eta\eta_i \qquad (7.11)$$

the form

$$N_i = \tfrac{1}{4}(1+\xi_0)(1+\eta_0) \qquad (7.12)$$

allows all shape functions to be written down in one expression.

As a linear combination of these shape functions yields any arbitrary linear variation of ϕ the second convergence criterion is satisfied.

The reader can verify that the following functions satisfy all the necessary criteria for quadratic and cubic members of the family.

'Quadratic' element
   Corner nodes

$$N_i = \tfrac{1}{4}(1+\xi_0)(1+\eta_0)(\xi_0+\eta_0-1). \qquad (7.13)$$

   Mid-side nodes

$$\xi_i = 0, \qquad N_i = \tfrac{1}{2}(1-\xi^2)(1+\eta_0),$$
$$\eta_i = 0, \qquad N_i = \tfrac{1}{2}(1+\xi_0)(1-\eta^2).$$

'Cubic' element
   Corner nodes

$$N_i = \tfrac{1}{32}(1+\xi_0)(1+\eta_0)[-10+9(\xi^2+\eta^2)]. \qquad (7.14)$$

   Mid-side nodes

$$\xi_i = \pm 1 \qquad \text{and} \qquad \eta_i = \pm\tfrac{1}{3}$$
$$N_i = \tfrac{9}{32}(1+\xi_0)(1-\eta^2)(1+9\eta_0)$$

with the remaining mid-side node expression obtained by changing variables.

In the next, quartic, member[5] of this family a central node is added so that all terms of a complete fourth order expansion would be available. This central node adds a shape function $(1-\xi^2)(1-\eta^2)$ which is zero on all outer boundaries.

The above functions have been derived by inspection, and progression to yet higher members is difficult and requires some ingenuity. It is therefore appropriate to name this family 'Serendipity' after the famous princes of Serendip noted for their chance discoveries (Horace Walpole, 1754).

For many practical purposes it may be desirable to devise elements with varying degrees of freedom in ξ and η direction. This may for instance be applicable where, as in a beam, variation of stresses in a particular direction is constrained while being arbitrary in the other direction. Some such element shape functions and indeed others in which the degree of freedom on opposite faces may vary are discussed in reference 2 but the reader can use his ingenuity here.

7.4 Rectangular Elements—Lagrange Family[3, 6, 7]

An easy and systematic method of generating shape functions of any order can be achieved by simple products of appropriate polynomials in the two co-ordinates. Consider an element shown in Fig. 7.5 in which a series of nodes, external and internal, is placed on a regular grid. It is required to determine a shape function for the point indicated by the heavy circle. Clearly a product of a fifth-order polynomial in ξ which has a value of unity at points of the second column of nodes and zero elsewhere with that of a fourth-order polynomial in η having unity on the co-ordinate corresponding to the top row of nodes and zero elsewhere satisfies all the inter-element continuity conditions.

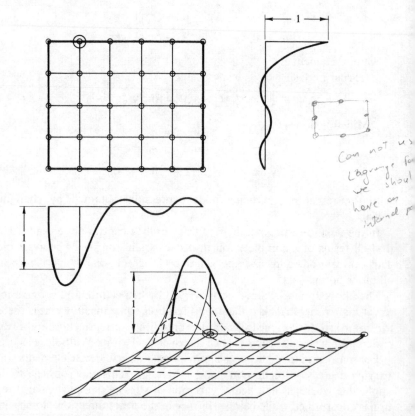

Fig. 7.5   A typical shape function for a Lagrangian element

Polynomials in one co-ordinate having this property are known as Lagrange polynomials and can be written down directly as

$$L_i^n = \frac{(\xi - \xi_1)(\xi - \xi_2)\ldots(\xi - \xi_{i-1})(\xi - \xi_{i+1})\ldots(\xi - \xi_n)}{(\xi_i - \xi_1)(\xi_i - \xi_2)\ldots(\xi_i - \xi_{i-1})(\xi_i - \xi_{i+1})\ldots(\xi_i - \xi_n)} \quad (7.15)$$

and thus if we label the node by its column and node number

$$N_{ij} = L_i^n(\xi)L_j^m(\eta) \quad (7.16)$$

where n and m stand for the number of subdivisions in each direction.

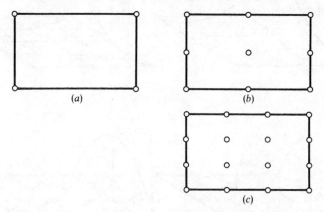

Fig. 7.6   Three elements of the Lagrange family (a) linear, (b) quadratic, and (c) cubic

Figure 7.6 shows a few members of this unlimited family. Though it is easy to generate, the usefulness of this family is limited not only due to a large number of internal nodes present but also due to the poor curve-fitting properties of the higher order polynomials. It will be noticed that the expressions of shape function will contain some very high order terms while omitting some lower ones.

7.5 Internal Nodes and 'Nodeless' Variables

It is instructive to note that both 'serendipity' and 'Lagrangian' elements of Figs. 7.4 and 7.6 are identical in their linear form but differ in the existence of the central node in the quadratic form. The shape functions for the two types of quadratic elements are shown in Fig. 7.7.

On the boundaries of the element the function is uniquely determined by boundary nodes only and hence (although the actual shapes of the first shape function differ internally), on the boundary both are identical. The additional degree of freedom of the Lagrangian type element is represented by adding multiples of the shape which has zero values along

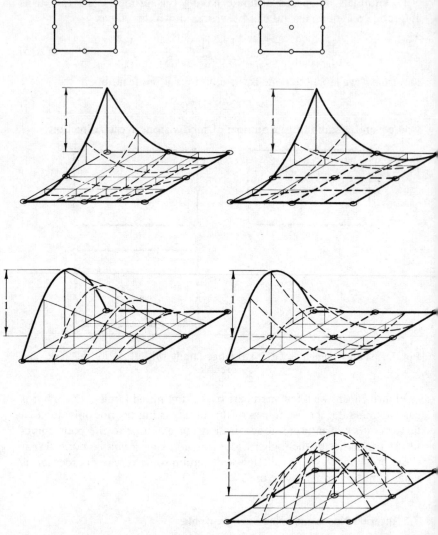

Fig. 7.7   Shape functions for quadratic elements of 'Serendipity' and 'Lagrange' families

all the boundaries. The parameter multiplying that shape is in fact the value of ϕ at the central node.

Now, clearly it would be possible to achieve precisely the same degree of freedom of the first, 'serendipity' type, element by adding the additional shape function which has zero value on all boundaries multiplied by some parameter ϕ^* associated with the element. All the shapes available in the Lagrangian element would again be available but now the multiplying factor obviously does not correspond to any nodal value of ϕ. ϕ^* may be termed a *nodeless variable* associated with the element.

The minimization of the functional with respect to that variable can be treated in precisely the same way as if it were an internal node—but the *physical interpretation* of the quantities such as nodal forces, etc., is no longer obvious. Several such nodeless variables can be associated with any element if desired.

There is usually little advantage in doing this as the additional freedom of the function choosing its best form is constrained on the boundaries.

In the expressions followed so far polynomial terms were used exclusively. This has many advantages—in particular that the linear terms necessary for representing the constant derivative requirements are available. There is no necessity, however, to be so constrained when considering the higher, additional, freedoms.

For instance a function of form

$$\cos \pi\xi/2 \cos \pi\eta/2 \tag{7.17}$$

would be equally suitable in the preceding example giving identically zero on the boundaries.

7.6 Elimination of Internal Variables before Assembly—Substructures

Internal nodes and nodeless variables yield in the usual way the element properties (Chapters 2 and 3)

$$\frac{\partial \chi^e}{\partial \{\phi\}^e} = [k]^e \{\phi\}^e + \{F\}^e. \tag{7.18}$$

As $\{\phi\}^e$ can be subdivided into parts which are common with other elements, $\{\bar{\phi}\}^e$, and others which occur in the particular element only, $\{\bar{\bar{\phi}}\}^e$, we can immediately write

$$\frac{\partial \chi}{\partial \{\bar{\bar{\phi}}\}^e} = \frac{\partial \chi^e}{\partial \{\bar{\bar{\phi}}\}^e} = 0$$

and eliminate these from further consideration. Writing Eq. (7.18) in a partitioned form we have

$$\frac{\partial \chi^e}{\partial \{\phi\}^e} = \left\{ \begin{array}{c} \dfrac{\partial \chi^e}{\partial \{\bar{\phi}\}^e} \\[2ex] \dfrac{\partial \chi^e}{\partial \{\bar{\bar{\phi}}\}^e} \end{array} \right\} = \left\{ \begin{array}{c} \dfrac{\partial \chi^e}{\partial \{\bar{\phi}\}^e} \\[2ex] 0 \end{array} \right\}$$

$$= \begin{bmatrix} [\bar{k}]^e, & [\hat{k}]^e \\[1ex] [\hat{k}]^{e\mathrm{T}}, & [\bar{\bar{k}}]^e \end{bmatrix} \left\{ \begin{array}{c} \{\bar{\phi}\}^e \\[1ex] \{\bar{\bar{\phi}}\}^e \end{array} \right\} + \left\{ \begin{array}{c} \{\bar{F}\}^e \\[1ex] \{\bar{\bar{F}}\}^e \end{array} \right\}. \tag{7.19}$$

From the second set of equations given in above we can write

$$\{\bar{\bar{\phi}}\}^e = -[\bar{k}]^{e-1}([\hat{k}]^{e^T}\{\bar{\phi}\}^e + \{\bar{\bar{F}}\}^e) \tag{7.20}$$

which on substitution yield

$$\frac{\partial \chi^e}{\partial \{\bar{\phi}\}^e} = [k^*]^e\{\bar{\phi}\}^e + \{F^*\}^e \tag{7.21}$$

in which

$$[k^*]^e = [\bar{k}]^e - [\hat{k}]^e[\bar{\bar{k}}]^{e-1}[\hat{k}]^{e^T}$$

and $$\tag{7.22}$$

$$\{F^*\}^e = \{\bar{F}\}^e - [\hat{k}]^e[\bar{\bar{k}}]^{e-1}\{\bar{\bar{F}}\}^e.$$

Assembly of the total region then follows, only considering the element boundary variables, thus giving a considerable saving in the equation-solving effort at the expense of a few additional manipulations carried out at the element stage.

Perhaps a structural interpretation of this elimination is desirable. What in fact is involved is the separation of a part of the structure from its surroundings and determination of its solution separately for any pre-scribed displacements at the interconnecting boundaries. $[k^*]^e$ is now simply the overall stiffness of the separated structure and $\{F^*\}^e$ the equivalent set of nodal forces.

If the triangulation of Fig. 7.8 is interpreted as an assembly of pin-jointed bars the reader will recognize immediately the well-known device of 'substructures' used frequently in structural engineering.

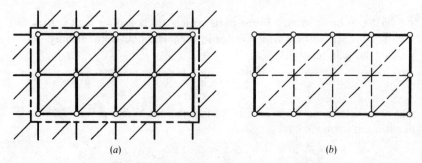

(a)   (b)

Fig. 7.8   Substructure or a complex element

Such a substructure is in fact simply a complex element from which the internal degrees of freedom have been eliminated.

Immediately a new possibility for devising more elaborate, and pre-sumably more accurate, elements is presented.

Let Fig. 7.8(*a*) be interpreted as a continuum field subdivided into triangular elements. The substructure results in fact in one complex element shown in Fig. 7.8(*b*) with a number of boundary nodes.

The only difference from elements derived in previous section is the fact that the unknown ϕ is now not approximated internally by one set of smooth shape functions but by a series of piecewise approximations. This presumably results in a slightly poorer approximation but an economic advantage may arise if the total computation time for such an assembly is saved.

Substructuring is an important device in complex problems particularly where a repetition of complicated components arises.

In simple, small-scale finite element analysis, much improved use of simple triangular elements was found by the use of simple sub-assemblies of the triangles (or indeed tetrahedra). For instance a quadrilateral based on four triangles from which the central node is eliminated was found to give an economic advantage over a direct use of simple triangles, Fig. 7.9. This and other sub-assemblies based on triangles are discussed in detail by Wilson.[8]

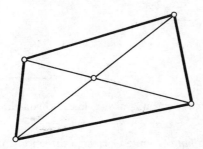

Fig. 7.9   A quadrilateral made up by four simple triangles

7.7 Triangular Element Family

The advantage of an arbitrary triangular shape in approximating to any boundary shape has been amply demonstrated in earlier chapters. Its apparent superiority here over the rectangular shapes needs no further discussion. The question of generating more elaborate elements needs to be further developed.

Consider a series of triangles generated on a pattern indicated in Fig. 7.10. The number of nodes in each member of the family is now such that a complete polynomial expansion, of the order needed for inter-element compatibility, is ensured. This particular feature puts the triangle family in a special privileged position, in which the inversion of the [*C*] matrices (*vide* Eq. (7.3)) will always exist.[2] However, once again a direct generation of shape functions will be preferred—and indeed will be shown to be particularly easy.

Before proceeding further it is convenient to define a special set of normalized co-ordinates for a triangle.

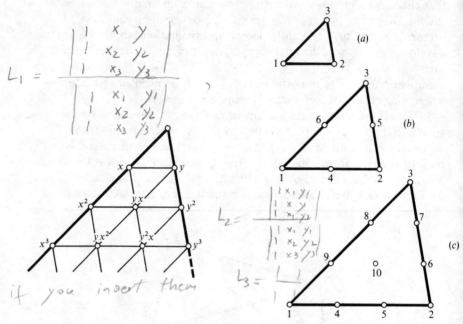

Fig. 7.10   Triangular element family (a) linear, (b) quadratic, and (c) cubic

7.7.1 *Area co-ordinates.*

While Cartesian directions parallel to the sides of a rectangle were a natural choice for that shape, in the triangle these are not convenient.

A convenient set of co-ordinates, L_1, L_2, and L_3 for a triangle 1, 2, 3, Fig. 7.11, is defined by the following linear relation between these and the Cartesian system:

$$x = L_1 x_1 + L_2 x_2 + L_3 x_3$$
$$y = L_1 y_1 + L_2 y_2 + L_3 y_3 \qquad (7.23)$$
$$1 = L_1 + L_2 + L_3.$$

To every set, L_1, L_2, L_3 (which are not independent, but are related by the third equation) corresponds a unique set of Cartesian co-ordinates. At point 1, $L_1 = 1$ and $L_2 = L_3 = 0$, etc. A linear relation between the new and Cartesian co-ordinates implies that contours of L_1 are equally placed straight lines parallel to side 2–3 on which $L_1 = 0$ etc.

Indeed it is easy to see that an alternative definition of the co-ordinate L_1 of a point P is by a ratio of the area of the shaded triangle to that of the total triangle.

$$L_1 = \frac{\text{Area } P23}{\text{Area } 123}. \tag{7.24}$$

Hence the name of area co-ordinates.

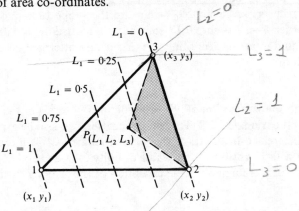

Fig. 7.11   Area co-ordinates

Solving Eq. (7.23) for x and y gives

$$L_1 = (a_1 + b_1 x + c_1 y)/2\Delta$$
$$L_2 = (a_2 + b_2 x + c_2 y)/2\Delta \tag{7.25}$$
$$L_3 = (a_3 + b_3 x + c_3 y)/2\Delta$$

in which

$$\Delta = \tfrac{1}{2} \det \begin{vmatrix} 1 & x_1 & y_1 \\ 1 & x_2 & y_2 \\ 1 & x_3 & y_3 \end{vmatrix} = \text{Area } 123 \tag{7.26}$$

and

$$a_1 = x_2 y_3 - x_3 y_2$$
$$b_1 = y_2 - y_3$$
$$c_1 = x_3 - x_2.$$

The identity of expressions with those derived in Chapter 4 (Eqs. 4.5b, c) is worth remarking upon.

7.7.2 *Shape functions.* For the first element of the series, Fig. 7.10(a), the shape functions are simply the area co-ordinates. Thus

$$N_1 = L_1, \qquad N_2 = L_2, \qquad N_3 = L_3. \qquad (7.27)$$

This is obvious as each individually gives unity at one node, zero at others and varies linearly everywhere.

To derive shape functions for other elements a simple recurrence relation can be derived.[2] Consider a triangle of order n for which shape functions are available—what are the shape functions for a triangle of order $n+1$? Figure 7.12 shows two such triangles with nodes spaced at equal intervals according to the general patterns. For a typical node i we know

$$N_i^n (L_1^n, L_2^n, L_3^n) \qquad (7.28)$$

the shape function of nth order defined in terms of the area co-ordinates of the triangle 1 2 3. This shape function can also be expressed in terms of the area co-ordinates of the larger triangle 1 2* 3* if these can be related. It will then still record a value of unity at node i and at all other nodes of the new triangle with the exception of those along the base 2* 3*.

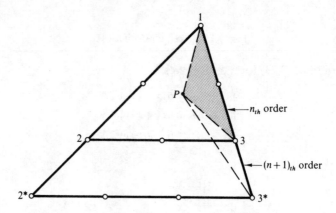

Fig. 7.12   Recurrence generation of shape functions for triangles

It is easy to see that

$$N_i^{n+1} = cL_1^{n+1} N_i^n \qquad (7.29)$$

will be the desired shape function providing c is so scaled as to achieve unity at i, as L_1^{n+1} is zero along the base for the larger triangle. The scaling factor is given by

$$c = \frac{n+1}{l} \qquad (7.30)$$

where l is the number of the 'layer' in which the node $\overset{*}{i}$ lies below i. While the above process will not directly yield shape functions for points on the base these can be obtained by a simple transposition of indices.

The relation between the two sets of co-ordinates is derived by inspection of Fig. 7.12

$$L_2^n = \frac{\text{Area } P13}{\text{Area } 123}, \qquad L_2^{n+1} = \frac{\text{Area } P13^*}{\text{Area } 12^*3^*}$$

therefore

$$L_2^n = \frac{\text{Area } P13}{\text{Area } P13^*} \frac{\text{Area } 12^*3^*}{\text{Area } 123} L_2^{n+1}$$

$$= \left(\frac{n}{n+1}\right)\left(\frac{n+1}{n}\right)^2 L_2^{n+1} = \frac{n+1}{n} L_2^{n+1}. \qquad (7.31a)$$

Similarly

$$L_3^n = \frac{n+1}{n} L_3^{n+1} \qquad (7.31b)$$

and by the fact that $L_1 + L_2 + L_3 = 1$

$$L_1^n = \frac{1}{n}[(n+1)L_1^{n+1} - 1]. \qquad (7.31c)$$

The reader can verify simply the shape functions for the second and third order elements as given below and indeed derive ones of any higher order easily.

Quadratic triangle (Fig. 7.10(b))
For corner nodes

$$N_1 = (2L_1 - 1)L_1, \text{ etc,}$$

mid-side nodes

$$N_4 = 4L_1 L_3, \text{ etc.} \qquad (7.32)$$

Cubic triangle (Fig. 7.10(c))
For corner nodes

$$N_1 = \tfrac{1}{2}(3L_1 - 1)(3L_1 - 2)L_1, \text{ etc,}$$

mid-side nodes

$$N_4 = \tfrac{9}{2} L_1 L_2(3L_1 - 1), \text{ etc,} \qquad (7.33)$$

and for the
internal node

$$N_{10} = 27L_1 L_2 L_3.$$

The last shape again is a function giving zero contribution along boundaries—and will be used in a different context in Chapter 10.

The quadratic triangle appears to have been first derived by Veubeke[9] and used in the context of plane stress analysis by Argyris.[10]

When element matrices have to be evaluated it will follow that we are often faced with integration of quantities defined in terms of area co-ordinates over the triangular region. It is useful to note in this context the following integration expression

$$\int\int_{\Delta} L_1^a L_2^b L_3^c \, dx \, dy = \frac{a!\,b!\,c!}{(a+b+c+2)!} 2\Delta. \tag{7.34}$$

ONE-DIMENSIONAL ELEMENTS

7.8 Linear Elements

So far in this book the continuum was considered in two or three dimensions. 'One-dimensional' members, being of a kind for which exact solutions are generally available, were not treated in the standard finite element manner. In many practical two- or three-dimensional problems such elements do in fact appear in conjunction with the more usual continuum elements—and a unified treatment is desirable. In the context of elastic analysis these elements may represent lines of reinforcement (plane and three-dimensional problems) or sheets of thin lining material in axisymmetric and three-dimensional bodies. In the context of field problems of the type to be discussed in Chapter 15 lines of drains in a porous medium of lesser conductivity can be envisaged.

Once the shape of such a function as displacement is chosen for an element of this kind its properties can be determined, noting, however,

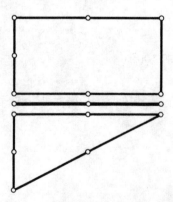

Fig. 7.13   A line element sandwiched between two dimensional elements

that such derived quantities as strain, etc., have to be considered only in one dimension.

Figure 7.13 shows such an element sandwiched between two adjacent cubic-type elements. Clearly for continuity of the function a cubic variation of the unknown with the one variable ξ is all that is required. Thus the shape functions are given directly by the Lagrange polynomial as defined in Eq. (7.15).

THREE-DIMENSIONAL ELEMENTS

7.9 Rectangular Prisms—'Serendipity' Family[4,11,12]

In a precisely analogous way to that given in previous sections equivalent elements of three-dimensional type can be described.

Now, for inter-element continuity the simple rules given previously have to be modified. What is necessary to achieve is that along a whole face of an element the nodal values define a unique variation of the unknown function. With incomplete polynomials, this can be ensured only by inspection.

A family of elements shown in Fig. 7.14 is precisely equivalent to that of Fig. 7.4. Using now three normalized co-ordinates and otherwise following the terminology of section 7.3 we have the following shape functions.

'Linear' element (8 nodes)

$$N_i = \tfrac{1}{8}(1+\xi_0)(1+\eta_0)(1+\zeta_0). \tag{7.35}$$

'Quadratic' element (20 nodes)
  Corner nodes

$$N_i = \tfrac{1}{8}(1+\xi_0)(1+\eta_0)(1+\zeta_0)(\xi_0+\eta_0+\zeta_0-2). \tag{7.36}$$

Typical mid-side node

$$\xi_i = 0, \qquad \eta_i = \pm 1, \qquad \zeta_i = \pm 1$$
$$N_i = \tfrac{1}{4}(1-\xi^2)(1+\eta_0)(1+\zeta_0).$$

'Cubic' elements (32 nodes)
  Corner node

$$N_i = \tfrac{1}{64}(1+\xi_0)(1+\eta_0)(1+\zeta_0)[9(\xi^2+\eta^2+\zeta^2)-19]. \tag{7.37}$$

Typical mid-side node

$$\xi_i = \pm\tfrac{1}{3}, \qquad \eta_i = \pm 1, \qquad \zeta_i = \pm 1$$
$$N_i = \tfrac{9}{64}(1-\xi^2)(1+9\xi_0)(1+\eta_0)(1+\zeta_0).$$

When $\zeta = 1 = \zeta_0$ the above expressions reduce to those of Eqs. (7.12) to (7.14). Indeed such elements of the three-dimensional type can be joined in

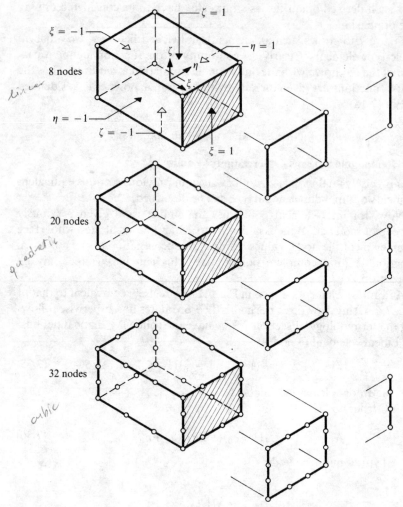

Fig. 7.14   Right prisms of boundary node (Serendipity) family with corresponding sheet and line elements

a comparable manner to sheet or line elements of the appropriate type as
shown in Fig. 7.14.

7.10 Rectangular Prisms—Lagrange Family

Shape function for such elements, illustrated in Fig. 7.15, will be generated
by a direct product of three Lagrange polynomials. Extending the notation of Eq. (7.16) we now have

$$N_{ijl} = L_i^n(\xi)L_j^m(\eta)L_l^k(\zeta).$$ (7.38)

This element again is suggested by Ergatoudis[6] and elaborated upon by Argyris.[7] All the remarks about internal nodes and the limitation of the formulation made in the section 7.4 are applicable here.

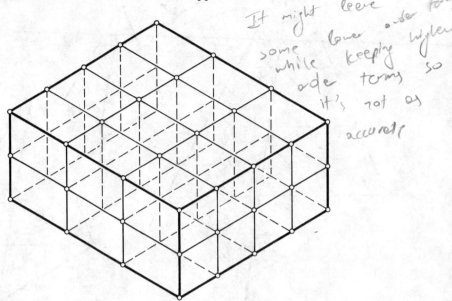

It might leeve some lower order terms while keeping higher order terms so it's not as accurate

Fig. 7.15   Right prism of Lagrange family

7.11 Tetrahedral Elements

The tetrahedral family shown in Fig. 7.16 not surprisingly exhibits properties similar to those of the triangle family.

Firstly, once again complete polynomials in three co-ordinates are achieved at each stage. Secondly, as faces are divided in a manner identical with that of the previous triangles, the same order of polynomial in two co-ordinates in the plane of the face is achieved and element compatibility ensured.

7.11.1 *Volume co-ordinates.* Once again special co-ordinates are introduced defined by (Fig. 7.17):

$$x = L_1x_1 + L_2x_2 + L_3x_3 + L_4x_4$$

$$y = L_1y_1 + L_2y_2 + L_3y_3 + L_4y_4$$

$$z = L_1z_1 + L_2z_2 + L_3z_3 + L_4z_4$$ (7.39)

$$1 = L_1 \quad + L_2 \quad + L_3 \quad + L_4.$$

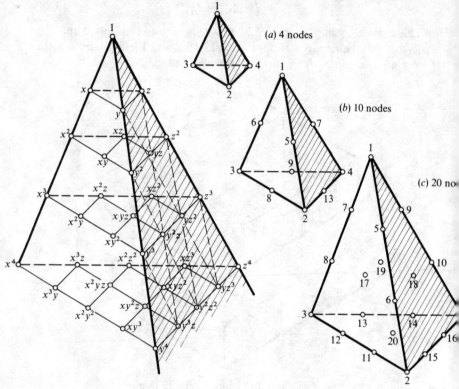

Fig. 7.16   The tetrahedron family (a) linear, (b) quadratic, and (c) cubic

Once again the inversion of above leads to expressions of type (7.25) and (7.26) with the constants which can be identified from Chapter 6 (Eq. 6.5). Once again the physical nature of the co-ordinates can be identified as the ratio of volumes of tetrahedra based on an internal point P in the total volume, e.g., as shown in Fig. 7.17.

$$L_1 = \frac{\text{Volume } P234}{\text{Volume } 1234} \text{ etc.} \tag{7.40}$$

7.11.2 *Shape function.* As the volume co-ordinates vary linearly with the Cartesian ones from unity at one node to zero at the opposite face then shape functions for the linear element, Fig. 7.16, are simply

$$N_1 = L_1, \qquad N_2 = L_2, \text{ etc.} \tag{7.41}$$

Formulae for shape functions of higher order tetrahedra are derived in precisely the same manner as for the triangles by establishing an appropriate recurrence relation. Leaving this to the reader as a suitable exercise we quote the following.

'Quadratic' tetrahedron (Fig. 7.16(b))

For corner nodes

$$N_1 = (2L_1 - 1)L_1, \text{ etc.} \tag{7.42}$$

For mid-side nodes

$$N_5 = 4L_1 L_2, \text{ etc.}$$

'Cubic' tetrahedron

Corner nodes

$$N_1 = \tfrac{1}{2}(3L_1 - 1)(3L_1 - 2)L_1, \text{ etc.} \tag{7.43}$$

Mid-side nodes

$$N_5 = \tfrac{9}{2}L_1 L_2(3L_1 - 1), \text{ etc.}$$

Mid-face nodes

$$N_{18} = 27L_1 L_2 L_3, \text{ etc.}$$

A useful integration formula again may be here quoted

$$\int\!\!\int\!\!\int_{\text{vol.}} L_1^a L_2^b L_3^c L_4^d \, dx \, dy \, dz = \frac{a! \, b! \, c! \, d!}{(a+b+c+d+3)!} \, 6V. \tag{7.44}$$

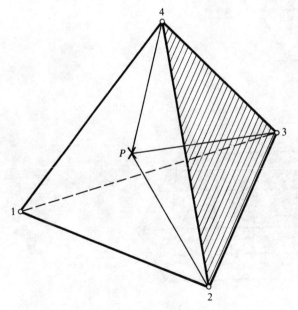

Fig. 7.17   Volume co-ordinates

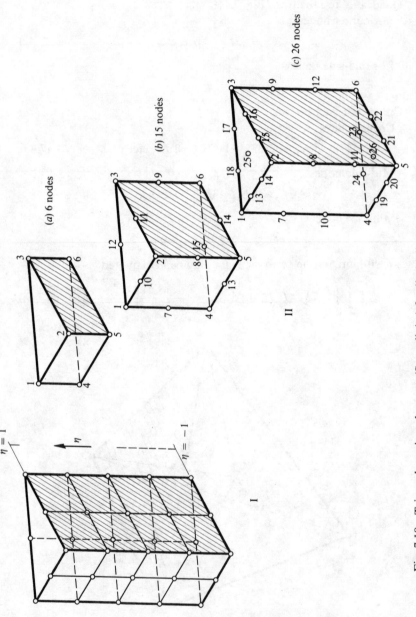

Fig. 7.18   Triangular prism elements (Serendipity) family (*a*) linear, (*b*) quadratic, and (*c*) cubic

7.12 Other Simple Three-dimensional Elements

The possibilities of simple shapes in three dimensions are greater, for obvious reasons, than in two dimensions. A quite useful series of elements can for instance be based on triangular prisms, Fig. 7.18. Here again variants of the product, Lagrange, approach or of the 'Serendipity' type can be distinguished. The first element of both families is identical and indeed the shape functions for it are so obvious as not to need quoting.

For a 'quadratic' element illustrated in Fig. 7.18(b) the shape functions are

Corner nodes $L_1 = \xi_1 = 1$

$$N_1 = \tfrac{1}{2}L_1(2L_1-1)(1+\zeta)-\tfrac{1}{2}L_1(1-\zeta^2). \tag{7.45}$$

Mid-sides of triangles

$$N_5 = 2L_1L_2(1+\zeta), \text{ etc.} \tag{7.46}$$

Mid-sides of rectangle

$$N_8 = L_1(1-\zeta^2), \text{ etc.}$$

Such elements are not purely esoteric but have a practical application as 'fillers' in conjunction with 20 noded parallelepiped elements.

7.13 Concluding Remarks

An unlimited selection of element types has been presented here to the reader—and indeed equally unlimited alternative possibilities exist.[4,12] What of the use of such complex elements in practice? Putting aside the triangle and tetrahedron all the other elements are limited to situations where the real region is of a suitable shape which can be represented as an assembly of right prisms. Such a limitation would be so severe that little practical purpose would have been served by the derivation of such shape functions unless some way could be found of distorting such elements to fit realistic boundaries. In fact, methods for doing this are now available and will be described in the next chapter.

References

1. P. C. DUNNE, 'Complete polynomial displacement fields for finite element methods', *Trans Roy. Aero. Soc.*, **72**, 245, 1968.
2. B. M. IRONS, J. G. ERGATOUDIS, and O. C. ZIENKIEWICZ, Comment on ref. 1, *Trans. Roy. Aero. Soc.*, **72**, 709–11, 1968.
3. J. G. ERGATOUDIS, B. M. IRONS, and O. C. ZIENKIEWICZ, 'Curved, isoparametric, quadrilateral elements for finite element analysis', *Int. J. Solids Struct.*, **4**, 31–42, 1968.

4. O. C. ZIENKIEWICZ et al., 'Iso-parametric and associate elements families for two and three dimensional analysis', Chapter 13, in Finite Element Methods in Stress Analysis, ed. I. Holand and K. Bell, Techn. Univ. of Norway, Tapir Press, Norway, Trondheim, 1969.

5. F. SCOTT, 'A quartic, two dimensional isoparametric element', Undergraduate Project, Univ. of Wales, Swansea, 1968.

6. J. G. ERGATOUDIS, Quadrilateral elements in plane analysis: Introduction to solid analysis, M.Sc. thesis, University of Wales, Swansea, 1966.

7. J. H. ARGYRIS, K. E. BUCK, I. FRIED, G. MARECZEK, and D. W. SCHARPF, 'Some new elements for matrix displacement methods', 2nd Conf. on Matrix Methods in Struct. Mech., Air Force Inst. of Techn., Wright Patterson Base, Ohio, Oct. 1968.

8. W. P. DOHERTY, E. WILSON, and R. L. TAYLOR, Stress Analysis of Axisymmetric Solids utilizing Higher-Order Quadrilateral Finite Elements, Report 69–3, Structural Engineering Laboratory, Univ. of California, Berkeley, Jan. 1969.

9. B. FRAEIJS DE VEUBEKE, 'Displacement and equilibrium models in the finite element method', Chapter 9 of Stress Analysis, ed. O. C. Zienkiewicz and G. S. Holister, J. Wiley & Son, 1965.

10. J. H. ARGYRIS, 'Triangular elements with linearly varying strain for the matrix displacement method', J. Roy. Aero. Soc. Tech. Note, 69, 711–13, Oct. 1965.

11. J. G. ERGATOUDIS, B. M. IRONS, and O. C. ZIENKIEWICZ, 'Three dimensional analysis of arch dams and their foundations', Symposium on Arch Dams, Inst. Civ. Eng., London, 1968.

12. O. C. ZIENKIEWICZ, B. M. IRONS, J. CAMPBELL, and F. SCOTT 'Three Dimensional Stress Analysis', Int. Un. Th. Appl. Mech. Symposium on High Speed Computing in Elasticity, Liége, 1970

8. Curved, Isoparametric Elements and Numerical Integration

8.1 Introduction

In the previous chapter we have shown how some general families of finite elements can be obtained. A progressively increasing number of nodes and hence improved accuracy characterizes each new member of the family and presumably the number of such elements required to obtain an adequate solution decreases rapidly. To ensure that a small number of elements can represent a relatively complex form of the type which is liable to occur in real, rather than academic, problems, simple rectangles and triangles no longer suffice. This chapter is therefore concerned with the subject of distorting such simple forms into others of more arbitrary shape.

Elements of the basic one-, two- or three-dimensional types will be 'mapped' into distorted forms in the manner indicated in Figs. 8.1 and 8.2.

In these figures it is shown that the ξ, η, ζ, or $L_1L_2L_3L_4$ co-ordinates can be distorted to a new, curvilinear set when plotted in a Cartesian space.

Not only can two-dimensional elements be distorted into others in two dimensions but the mapping of these can be taken into three dimensions as indicated by the flat sheet elements of Fig. 8.2 distorting into a three-dimensional space. This principle applies generally, providing some one-to-one correspondence between Cartesian and curvilinear co-ordinates can be established, i.e., once relations of the type

$$\left\{ \begin{array}{c} x \\ y \\ z \end{array} \right\} = f \left\{ \begin{array}{c} \xi \\ \eta \\ \zeta \end{array} \right\} \quad \text{or} \quad f \left\{ \begin{array}{c} L_1 \\ L_2 \\ L_3 \\ L_4 \end{array} \right\} \tag{8.1}$$

can be established.

Once such co-ordinate relationships are known, shape functions can be specified in local co-ordinates and by suitable transformations the element properties established. However, the question of satisfying the convergence criteria by these shape functions needs to be further investigated. It will be shown how with a certain kind of co-ordinate transformation these criteria can be observed.

129

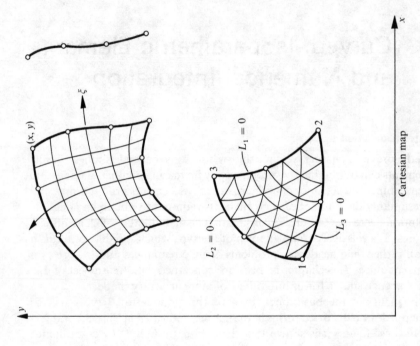

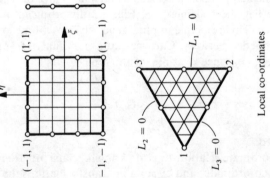

Fig. 8.1　Two dimensional 'mapping' of some elements

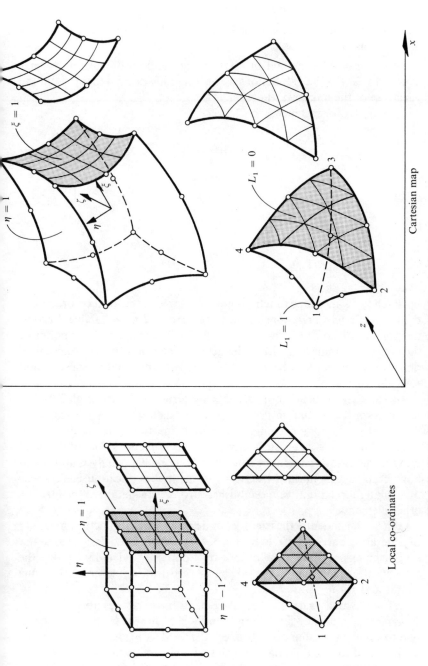

Fig. 8.2 Three dimensional 'mapping' of some elements

CURVILINEAR CO-ORDINATES

8.2 Use of 'Shape Functions' in Establishment of Co-ordinate Transformations

A most convenient method of establishing the co-ordinate transformations is to use the shape functions we have already derived to represent the variation of the unknown function.

If we write, for instance,

$$x = N_1'x_1 + N_2'x_2 + \cdots = [N'] \begin{Bmatrix} x_1 \\ x_2 \\ \vdots \end{Bmatrix}$$

$$y = N_1'y_1 + N_2'y_2 + \cdots = [N'] \begin{Bmatrix} y_1 \\ y_2 \\ \vdots \end{Bmatrix} \qquad (8.2)$$

$$z = N_1'z_1 + N_2'z_2 + \cdots = [N'] \begin{Bmatrix} z_1 \\ z_2 \\ \vdots \end{Bmatrix}$$

in which $[N']$ are shape functions given in terms of the local co-ordinates, then immediately a relationship of the required form is available. Further the points with co-ordinates x_1, y_1, z_1, etc. will lie at appropriate points of the element boundary (as from the general definitions of the shape functions we know that they have a value of unity at the point in question and zero elsewhere).

To each set of local co-ordinates will correspond a set of global Cartesian co-ordinates and in general only one such set. We shall see, however, that a non-uniqueness may arise sometimes with violent distortion.

The concept of using such element shape functions for establishing curvilinear co-ordinates in the context of finite element analysis appears to have been first mentioned by Taig.[1] In his first application basic linear quadrilateral relations were established. Irons [2, 3] generalized the idea for other elements.

Quite independently the exercises of devising various practical methods of generating curved surfaces for purposes of engineering design led to the establishment of similar definitions by Coons,[4, 5] and indeed today the subjects of surface definitions and analysis are drawing closer together due to this activity.

In Fig. 8.3 an actual distortion of elements based on the cubic and quadratic members of the 'serendipity' family is shown. It is seen here that a one-to-one relationship exists between the local (ξ, η) and global (x, y) co-ordinates. If the fixed points are such that a violent distortion occurs then a non-uniqueness may occur in the manner indicated for two situations in

Fig. 8.4. Here at internal points of the distorted element two sets of local co-ordinates are implied in addition to some internal points being mapped outside the element. Care must be taken in practice to avoid such gross distortion.

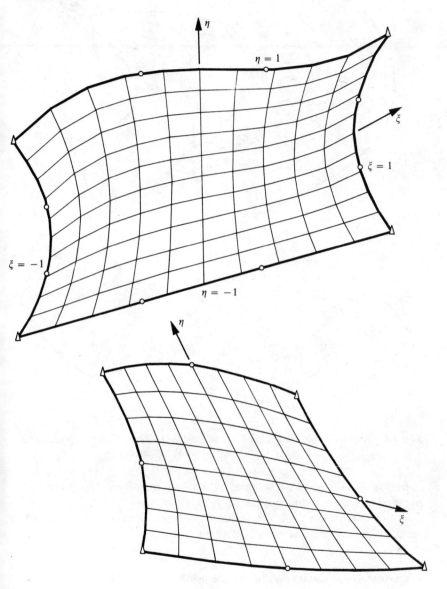

Fig. 8.3   Computer plots of curvilinear co-ordinates for cubic and parabolic elements (reasonable distortion)

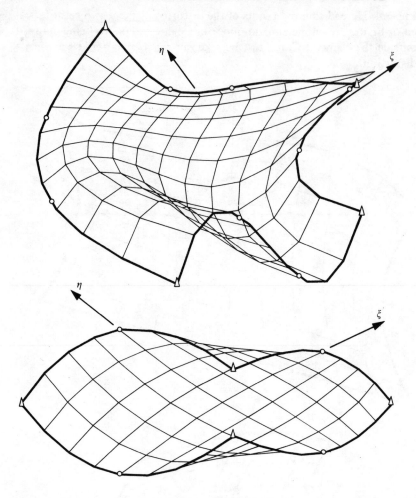

Fig. 8.4   Unreasonable element distortion leading to non-unique mapping, and 'overspill'. Cubic and parabolic elements.

Figure 8.5 shows two examples of a two-dimensional (ξ, η) element mapped into a three-dimensional (x, y, z) space.

In this chapter we shall often refer to the basic element in undistorted, local, co-ordinates as a 'parent' element.

8.3 Geometrical Conformability of Elements

While it was shown that by the use of the shape function transformation each parent element maps uniquely a part of the real object, it is important

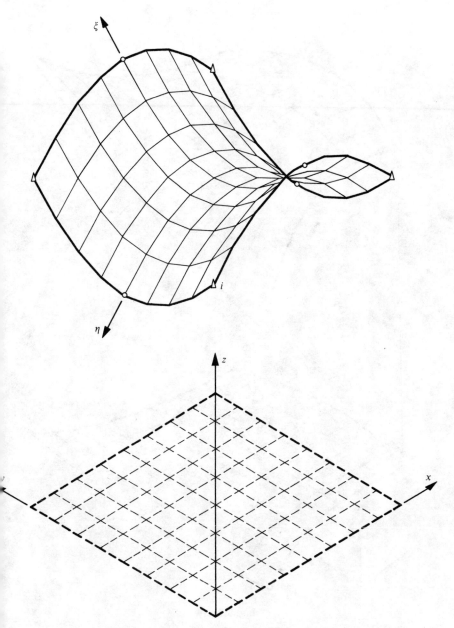

Fig. 8.5   Flat elements (of parabolic type) mapped into three dimensions

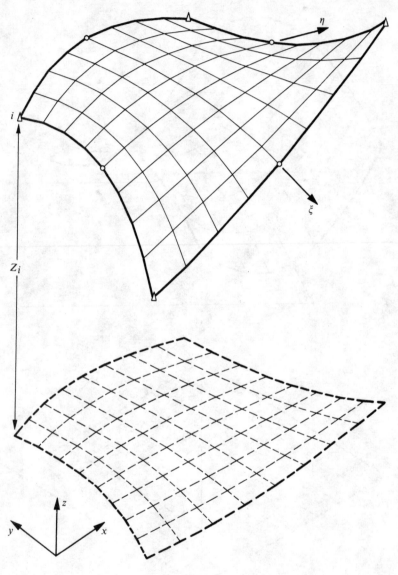

Fig. 8.5 (*cont.*)

that the subdivision of this into the new, curved, elements should leave no gaps. Possibility of such gaps is indicated in Fig. 8.6.

THEOREM 1. *If two adjacent elements are generated from 'parents' in which the shape functions satisfy continuity requirements then the distorted elements will be contiguous.*

This theorem is obvious, as in such cases uniqueness of any function ϕ required by continuity is simply replaced by that of uniqueness of x, y, or z co-ordinate. As adjacent elements are given the same sets of co-ordinates at nodes, continuity is implied.

Nodes of the new distorted elements need not necessarily be placed only at points for which shape functions are specified. Other corresponding sets of nodes can be added on interfaces or boundaries.

8.4 Variation of the Unknown Function within Distorted, Curvilinear, Elements. Continuity Requirements

With the shape of the element now defined by the shape functions $[N']$ the variation of the unknown, ϕ, has to be specified before we can establish element properties. This is most conveniently given in terms of local, curvilinear co-ordinates by the usual expression

$$\phi = [N]\{\phi\}^e \tag{8.3}$$

where $\{\phi\}^e$ lists the nodal values.

THEOREM 2. *If the shape functions $[N]$ used in 8.3 are such that continuity of ϕ is preserved in the parent co-ordinates—then continuity requirements will be satisfied in distorted elements.*

The proof of this theorem follows the same lines as the previous section.

The nodal values may or may not be associated with the same nodes as used to specify the element geometry. For example in Fig. 8.7 the points marked with a circle are used to define the element geometry. We could use the values of the function defined at nodes marked with a square to define the variation of the unknown.

In Fig. 8.7(a) the same points define the geometry and the finite element analysis points. If then

$$[N] = [N'] \tag{8.4}$$

i.e., the shape functions defining geometry and function are the same, the elements will be called *isoparametric*.

We could, however, use only the four corner points to define the variation of ϕ, Fig. 8.7(b). Such an element we shall refer to as *super-para-*

metric, noting that the variation of geometry is more general than that of the actual unknown.

Similarly if for instance we introduce more nodes to define ϕ than are used to define geometry *sub-parametric* elements will result, Fig. 8.7(*c*). Such elements will be found to be more often of use in practice.

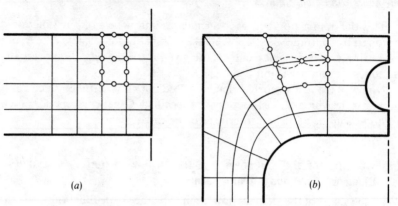

(*a*)

(*b*)

Fig. 8.6   Compatibility requirement in real subdivision of space

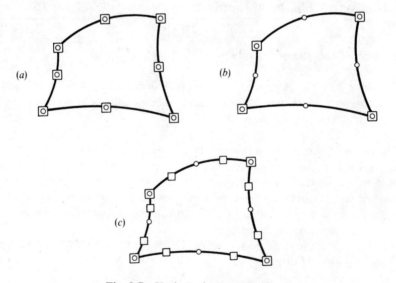

(*a*)

(*b*)

(*c*)

Fig. 8.7   Various element specifications
○ Point at which co-ordinate specified
□ Points at which function parameter specified

    (*a*) isoparametric
    (*b*) super-parametric
    (*c*) sub-parametric

8.5 Satisfaction of the 'Constant Derivative' Criterion

A wide choice of functions could be made separately to define the geometry and variation of ϕ which satisfies continuity criteria. However, the satisfaction of the 'constant strain' criterion of Chapter 2 or of the 'constant derivative' criterion of Chapter 3 imposes some limitation.

We recall that to satisfy convergence it is required that throughout the element any arbitrary constant value of the first derivatives can be obtained with suitable nodal values of ϕ. (This is true for functionals involving only first order derivatives.)

To achieve this

$$\phi = [N]\{\phi\}^e = \sum N_i \phi_i = \alpha_1 + \alpha_2 x + \alpha_3 y + \alpha_4 z$$
$$\text{with } [N] = [N(\xi, \eta, \zeta)] \quad (8.5)$$

must be true for any values of the constants α_{1-4} and suitable $\{\phi\}^e$. In fact at nodes we must have then

$$\phi_i = \alpha_1 + \alpha_2 x_i + \alpha_3 y_i + \alpha_4 z_i \quad (8.6)$$

so that the first equality can be rewritten as

$$[N]\{\phi\}^e = \alpha_1 \sum N_i + \alpha_2 \sum N_i x_i + \alpha_3 \sum N_i y_i + \alpha_4 \sum N_i z_i$$
$$= \alpha_1 + \alpha_2 x + \alpha_3 y + \alpha_4 z. \quad (8.7)$$

This will be always satisfied if

$$\sum N_i = 1$$
$$\sum N_i x_i = x$$
$$\sum N_i y_i = y \quad (8.8)$$
$$\sum N_i z_i = z.$$

For a three-node triangular element

$$\sum N_i x_i = N_i x_i + N_j x_j + N_k x_k$$

$$\sum N_i x_i = \frac{1}{2A}\left(a_i + b_i x + c_i y\right) x_i +$$

The co-ordinate transformation set out in Eq. (8.2) states that

$$\frac{1}{2A}\left(\qquad \right) x_j +$$

$$\sum N_i' x_i = x$$
$$\sum N_i' y_i = y \quad (8.9)$$
$$\sum N_i' z_i = z$$

$$\frac{1}{2}\left(\qquad \right) x_k$$

and hence:

THEOREM 3. *The constant derivative condition will be satisfied for all isoparametric elements providing* $\Sigma N_i = 1$.†

It can be shown that in fact the same requirement is necessary and the

† This in stress analysis context simply means that rigid body motions must not cause any strain—a requirement less stringent than that of constant derivatives.

theorem valid for subparametric transformation providing we can express $[N']$ as a linear combination of $[N]$, that is,

$$N'_i = \sum C_{ij} N_j. \tag{8.10}$$

TRANSFORMATIONS

8.6 Evaluation of Element Matrices (Transformation in ξ, η, ζ Co-ordinates)

To perform finite element analysis the matrices defining element properties, e.g., stiffness, etc., have to be found. These will be of the form

$$\int_V [G] \, dV \tag{8.11}$$

in which the expression $[G]$ depends on N or its derivatives with respect to *global co-ordinates*. As an example of this we have the stiffness matrix

$$\int_V [B]^{\mathrm{T}} [D] [B] \, dV \tag{8.12}$$

and associated load vectors

$$\int_V [N]^{\mathrm{T}} \{p\} \, dV. \tag{8.13}$$

For a particular class of elastic problems the matrices of $[B]$ are given explicitly by their components (*vide* the general form of Eqs. (4.1a), (5.6), and (6.11)). Quoting the first of these Eq. (4.1a), valid for plane problems we have

$$[B_i] = \begin{bmatrix} \dfrac{\partial N_i}{\partial x} & 0 \\[2ex] 0 & \dfrac{\partial N_i}{\partial y} \\[2ex] \dfrac{\partial N_i}{\partial y} & \dfrac{\partial N_i}{\partial x} \end{bmatrix}. \tag{8.14}$$

In this the prime used in Chapter 4 has been dropped from the shape functions which are now deemed to be scalar and valid for each component of displacement. Notice also that the above form is *completely general* and valid for all two-dimensional elements of plane problems of elasticity irrespective of the number of nodes (or nodeless variables) attached to an element. A similar situation arises in all the other problems referred to in the book.

To evaluate such matrices we note that two transformations are necessary. In the first place as N_i is defined in terms of local (curvilinear) co-ordinates it is necessary to devise some means of expressing the global derivatives of the type occurring in Eq. (8.14) in terms of local derivatives.

In the second place the element of volume (or surface) over which the integration has to be carried out needs to be expressed in terms of the local co-ordinates with an appropriate change of limits of integration.

Consider for instance the set of local co-ordinates ξ, η, ζ and a corresponding set of global co-ordinates x, y, z. By the usual rules of partial differentiation we can write for instance the ξ derivative as

$$\frac{\partial N_i}{\partial \xi} = \frac{\partial N_i}{\partial x}\frac{\partial x}{\partial \xi} + \frac{\partial N_i}{\partial y}\frac{\partial y}{\partial \xi} + \frac{\partial N_i}{\partial z}\frac{\partial z}{\partial \xi}. \tag{8.15}$$

Performing the same differentiation with respect to the other two co-ordinates and writing in matrix form we have

$$\left\{\begin{array}{c} \dfrac{\partial N_i}{\partial \xi} \\[2ex] \dfrac{\partial N_i}{\partial \eta} \\[2ex] \dfrac{\partial N_i}{\partial \zeta} \end{array}\right\} = \left[\begin{array}{ccc} \dfrac{\partial x}{\partial \xi}, & \dfrac{\partial y}{\partial \xi}, & \dfrac{\partial z}{\partial \xi} \\[2ex] \dfrac{\partial x}{\partial \eta}, & \dfrac{\partial y}{\partial \eta}, & \dfrac{\partial z}{\partial \eta} \\[2ex] \dfrac{\partial x}{\partial \zeta}, & \dfrac{\partial y}{\partial \zeta}, & \dfrac{\partial z}{\partial \zeta} \end{array}\right] \left\{\begin{array}{c} \dfrac{\partial N_i}{\partial x} \\[2ex] \dfrac{\partial N_i}{\partial y} \\[2ex] \dfrac{\partial N_i}{\partial z} \end{array}\right\} = [J]\left\{\begin{array}{c} \dfrac{\partial N_i}{\partial x} \\[2ex] \dfrac{\partial N_i}{\partial y} \\[2ex] \dfrac{\partial N_i}{\partial z} \end{array}\right\}. \tag{8.16}$$

In the above, the left-hand side can be evaluated as the functions N_i are specified in local co-ordinates. Further as x, y, z are explicitly given by the relation defining the curvilinear co-ordinates (Eq. (8.2)), the matrix $[J]$, can be found explicitly in terms of the local co-ordinates. This matrix is known as the *Jacobian matrix*.

To find now the global derivatives we invert $[J]$ and write

$$\left\{\begin{array}{c} \dfrac{\partial N_i}{\partial x} \\[2ex] \dfrac{\partial N_i}{\partial y} \\[2ex] \dfrac{\partial N_i}{\partial z} \end{array}\right\} = [J]^{-1}\left\{\begin{array}{c} \dfrac{\partial N_i}{\partial \xi} \\[2ex] \dfrac{\partial N_i}{\partial \eta} \\[2ex] \dfrac{\partial N_i}{\partial \zeta} \end{array}\right\}. \tag{8.17}$$

In terms of the shape function defining the co-ordinate transformation $[N']$, (which as we have seen are only identical with the shape func-

[Handwritten margin notes:]

ylindrical Coord

$x = r\cos\theta$

$y = r\sin\theta$

$z = z$

$$J = \begin{bmatrix} \dfrac{\partial x}{\partial r} & \dfrac{\partial y}{\partial r} & \dfrac{\partial z}{\partial r} \\[2ex] \dfrac{\partial x}{\partial \theta} & \dfrac{\partial y}{\partial \theta} & \dfrac{\partial z}{\partial \theta} \\[2ex] \dfrac{\partial x}{\partial z} & \dfrac{\partial y}{\partial z} & \dfrac{\partial z}{\partial z} \end{bmatrix}$$

tions $[N]$ when isoparametric formulation is used) we have

$$[J] = \begin{bmatrix} \sum \dfrac{\partial N'_i}{\partial \xi} x_i, & \sum \dfrac{\partial N'_i}{\partial \xi} y_i, & \sum \dfrac{\partial N'_i}{\partial \xi} z_i \\[2mm] \sum \dfrac{\partial N'_i}{\partial \eta} x_i, & \sum \dfrac{\partial N'_i}{\partial \eta} y_i, & \sum \dfrac{\partial N'_i}{\partial \eta} z_i \\[2mm] \sum \dfrac{\partial N'_i}{\partial \zeta} x_i, & \sum \dfrac{\partial N'_i}{\partial \zeta} y_i, & \sum \dfrac{\partial N'_i}{\partial \zeta} z_i \end{bmatrix}$$

$$= \begin{bmatrix} \dfrac{\partial N'_1}{\partial \zeta} & \dfrac{\partial N'_2}{\partial \zeta} & \cdots \\[2mm] \dfrac{\partial N'_1}{\partial \eta} & \dfrac{\partial N'_2}{\partial \eta} & \cdots \\[2mm] \dfrac{\partial N'_1}{\partial \zeta} & \dfrac{\partial N'_2}{\partial \zeta} & \cdots \end{bmatrix} \begin{bmatrix} x_1 & y_1 & z_1 \\ x_2 & y_2 & z_2 \\ \vdots & \vdots & \vdots \end{bmatrix}. \qquad (8.18)$$

Handwritten annotations (left margin):

$$J = \begin{bmatrix} \cos\theta & \sin\theta & 0 \\ -r\sin\theta & r\cos\theta & 0 \\ 0 & 0 & 1 \end{bmatrix}$$

$$|J| = r$$

$$dx\,dy\,dz = (r)\,dr\,d\theta\,dz$$

To transform the variables and the region with respect to which the integration is made a standard process will be used which involves the determinant of $[J]$. Thus for instance a volume element

$$dx\,dy\,dz = \det [J]\,d\xi\,d\eta\,d\zeta. \qquad (8.19)$$

This type of transformation is valid irrespective of the number of co-ordinates used. For its justification the reader is referred to standard mathematical texts. A particularly lucid account of this is given by Murnaghan.[6]† (See also Appendix 5)

Assuming that the inverse of $[J]$ can be found we have now reduced the evaluation of the element properties to that of finding integrals of the form of Eq. (8.11).

More explicitly we can write this as

$$\int_{-1}^{1} \int_{-1}^{1} \int_{-1}^{1} [G(\xi, \eta, \zeta,)]\,d\xi\,d\eta\,d\zeta \qquad (8.20)$$

if the curvilinear co-ordinates are of the normalized type based on the right prism. Indeed the integration *is carried out within such a prism* and not in the complicated distorted shape, thus accounting for the simple integration limits. One- and two-dimensional problems similarly will

---

† The determinant of the Jacobian matrix is known in literature simply as 'the Jacobian' and is often written as

$$\det [J] \equiv \frac{\partial(x, y, z,)}{\partial(\xi, \eta, \zeta)}.$$

Handwritten annotation (bottom):

$$\frac{\partial}{\partial \xi}(x) = \frac{\partial}{\partial \xi}\left(\sum N_i x_i \right) = \sum \frac{\partial N_i}{\partial \xi} x_i$$

result in integrals with respect to one or two co-ordinates within simple limits.

While the limits of the integration are simple in the above case, unfortunately the explicit form of $[G]$ is not. Excepting the simplest elements, algebraic integration usually defies our mathematical skill, and numerical integration has to be resorted to. This, as will be seen from later sections, is not a severe penalty and has the advantage that algebraic errors are more easily avoided and that general programs, not tied to a particular element, can be written for various classes of problems. Indeed in such numerical calculations the inverses of $[J]$ are never explicitly found.

8.7 Element Matrices. Area and Volume Co-ordinates

The general relationship, Eq. (8.2) for co-ordinate mapping and indeed all the following theorems are equally valid for any set of local co-ordinates and could relate the local L_1, $L_2 \cdots$ co-ordinates, used for triangles and tetrahedra in the previous chapter, to the global Cartesian ones.

Indeed most of the discussion of the previous chapter is valid if we simply rename the local co-ordinates suitably. However, two important differences arise.

The first concerns the fact that the local co-ordinates are not independent and in fact number one more than the Cartesian system. The matrix $[J]$ would apparently therefore become rectangular and would not possess an inverse. The second is simply the difference of integration limits which have to correspond with a triangular or tetrahedral 'parent'.

The simplest, though perhaps not the most elegant, way out of the first difficulty is to consider the last variable as a dependent one. Thus for example we can introduce formally in case of the tetrahedra

$$
\begin{aligned}
\xi &= L_1 \\
\eta &= L_2 \\
\zeta &= L_3 \\
1 - \xi - \eta - \zeta &= L_4
\end{aligned}
\tag{8.21}
$$

(by definition of previous chapter) and thus preserve without change Eq. (8.18) and all the equations up to Eq. (8.19).

As the functions N_i are given in fact in terms of L_1, L_2, etc., we must observe that

$$
\frac{\partial N_i}{\partial \xi} = \frac{\partial N_i}{\partial L_1}\frac{\partial L_1}{\partial \xi} + \frac{\partial N_i}{\partial L_2}\frac{\partial L_2}{\partial \xi} + \frac{\partial N_i}{\partial L_3}\frac{\partial L_3}{\partial \xi} + \frac{\partial N_i}{\partial L_4}\frac{\partial L_4}{\partial \xi}.
\tag{8.22}
$$

On using Eq. (8.21) this becomes simply

$$\frac{\partial N_i}{\partial \xi} = \frac{\partial N_i}{\partial L_1} - \frac{\partial N_i}{\partial L_4}$$

with the other derivatives obtainable by similar expressions.

The integration limits of Eq. (8.20) now change, however, to correspond with the tetrahedron limits. Typically

$$\int_0^1 \int_0^{1-\eta} \int_0^{1-\eta-\zeta} [G(\xi, \eta, \zeta)] \, d\xi \, d\eta \, d\zeta. \tag{8.23}$$

The same procedure clearly will apply in case of triangular co-ordinates.

It must be noted that once again the expression $[G]$ will necessitate numerical integration which, however, is carried out over the simple, un-distorted, parent region whether this be triangular or tetrahedral.

Finally it should be remarked that any of the elements given in the previous section are capable of being mapped. In some, such as the tri-angular prism, both area and rectangular co-ordinates are used, Fig. 8.8. The remarks regarding the dependence of co-ordinates apply once again with regard to the former but the processes of the present section should make procedures clear.

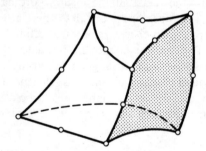

Fig. 8.8   A distorted triangular prism

NUMERICAL INTEGRATION

8.8 Numerical Integration—One-dimensional

Already in Chapter 5 dealing with a relatively simple problem of axi-symmetric stress distribution and simple triangular elements it was noted that exact integration of expressions for element matrices could be trouble-some. There, as well as in the more complex distorted element, numerical integration is essential.

Some principles of numerical integration will be summarized here together with tables of convenient numerical coefficients.

To find numerically the integral of a function of one variable we can proceed in one of two basic ways.[7,8]

Newton-Cotes Quadrature.† In the first, points at which the function is to be found are determined *a priori*—usually at equal intervals—and a polynomial passed through the values of the function at these points and exactly integrated, Fig. 8.9(*a*).

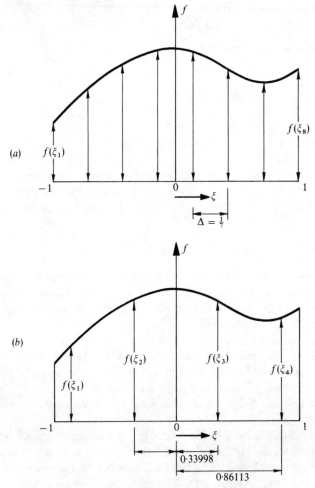

Fig. 8.9   Newton-Cotes (a) and Gauss (b) integrations. Each integrates exactly a seventh order polynomial (i.e., error $0(\Delta^8)$)

As '*n*' values of the function define a polynomial of degree $n-1$, the errors will be of the order $0(\Delta)^n$ where Δ is the point spacing. This leads to

† 'Quadrature' is a term used alternatively to 'Numerical Integration'.

the well-known Newton-Cotes 'quadrature' formulae. The integrals can be written as

$$I = \int_{-1}^{1} f(\xi)\, d\xi = \sum_{1}^{n} H_i f(\xi_i) \tag{8.24}$$

for range of integration between -1 and $+1$, Fig. 8.9(a). For example if $n = 1$,

$$I = f(-1) + f(1). \tag{8.25}$$

The well known trapezoidal rule, $n = 2$;

$$I = \tfrac{1}{3}[f(-1) + 4f(0) + f(1)]. \tag{8.26}$$

The Simpson 'one third' rule, $n = 3$;

$$I = \tfrac{1}{4}[f(-1) + 3f(-\tfrac{1}{3}) + 3f(\tfrac{1}{3}) + f(1)]. \tag{8.27}$$

Formulae for n up to 20 are given by Kopal.[8]

Gauss quadrature. If in place of specifying the position of sampling points *a priori*, we allow these to be located at points to be determined so as to achieve for best accuracy, presumably for a given number of sampling points an increased accuracy can be obtained. Indeed if we consider again that

$$I = \int_{-1}^{1} f(\xi)\, d\xi = \sum_{1}^{n} H_i f(\xi_i) \tag{8.28}$$

and assume again a polynomial expression it is easy to see that for n sampling points we have $2n$ unknowns (f_i and ξ_i) and hence a polynomial of degree $2n - 1$ could be constructed and exactly integrated, Fig. 8.9(b). The error thus is of order $0(\Delta)^{2n}$.

The simultaneous equations involved are difficult to solve, but some mathematical manipulation[7] will show that the solution can be obtained explicitly in terms of Legendre polynomials. Thus this particular process is frequently known as Gauss-Legendre quadrature.

Table 8.1 shows the positions and weighting coefficients for Gaussian integration.

For purposes of finite element analysis the complex calculations are involved in determining the values of f, the function to be integrated. Thus the Gauss processes, requiring the least number of such evaluations are ideally suited and from now on will be exclusively used.

Other expressions for integration functions of the type

$$I = \int_{-1}^{1} w(\xi) f(\xi)\, d\xi = \sum_{1}^{n} H_i f(\xi_i) \tag{8.29}$$

can be derived for prescribed forms of $w(\xi)$ again integrating up to a certain order of accuracy a polynomial expansion of $f(\xi)$.[7]

TABLE 8.1
ABSCISSAE AND WEIGHT COEFFICIENTS OF THE GAUSSIAN QUADRATURE FORMULA

$$\int_{-1}^{1} f(x)\ \mathrm{d}x = \sum_{j=1}^{n} H_i f(a_j),$$

$\pm a$	H
$n = 2$	
0·57735 02691 89626	1·00000 00000 00000
$n = 3$	
0·77459 66692 41483	0·55555 55555 55556
0·00000 00000 00000	0·88888 88888 88889
$n = 4$	
0·86113 63115 94053	0·34785 48451 37454
0·33998 10435 84856	0·65214 51548 62546
$n = 5$	
0·90617 98459 38664	0·23692 68850 56189
0·53846 93101 05683	0·47862 86704 99366
0·00000 00000 00000	0·56888 88888 88889
$n = 6$	
0·93246 95142 03152	0·17132 44923 79170
0·66120 93864 66265	0·36076 15730 48139
0·23861 91860 83197	0·46791 39345 72691
$n = 7$	
0·94910 79123 42759	0·12948 49661 68870
0·74153 11855 99394	0·27970 53914 89277
0·40584 51513 77397	0·38183 00505 05119
0·00000 00000 00000	0·41795 91836 73469·
$n = 8$	
0·96028 98564 97536	0·10122 85362 90376
0·79666 64774 13627	0·22238 10344 53374
0·52553 24099 16329	0·31370 66458 77887
0·18343 46424 95650	0·36268 37833 78362
$n = 9$	
0·96816 02395 07626	0·08127 43883 61574
0·83603 11073 26636	0·18064 81606 94857
0·61337 14327 00590	0·26061 06964 02935
0·32425 34234 03809	0·31234 70770 40003
0·00000 00000 00000	0·33023 93550 01260
$n = 10$	
0·97390 65285 17172	0·06667 13443 08688
0·86506 33666 88985	0·14945 13491 50581
0·67940 95682 99024	0·21908 63625 15982
0·43339 53941 29247	0·26926 67193 09996
0·14887 43389 81631	0·29552 42247 14753

8.9 Numerical Integration—Rectangular or Right Prism Regions

The most obvious way of obtaining the integral

$$I = \int_{-1}^{1} \int_{-1}^{1} f(\xi, \eta) \, d\xi \, d\eta \tag{8.30}$$

is to first evaluate the inner integral keeping η constant, i.e.,

$$\int_{-1}^{1} f(\xi, \eta) \, d\xi = \sum_{j=1}^{n} H_j f(\xi_j, \eta) = \psi(\eta). \tag{8.31}$$

Evaluating the outer integral in a similar manner, we have

$$\begin{aligned} I = \int_{-1}^{1} \psi(\eta) \, d\eta &= \sum_{i=1}^{n} \psi(\eta_i) \\ &= \sum_{i=1}^{n} H_i \sum_{j=1}^{n} H_j f(\xi_j, \eta_i) \\ &= \sum_{i=1}^{n} \sum_{j=1}^{n} H_i H_j f(\xi_j, \eta_i). \end{aligned} \tag{8.32}$$

For a right prism we have similarly

$$\begin{aligned} I &= \int_{-1}^{1} \int_{-1}^{1} \int_{-1}^{1} f(\xi, \eta, \zeta) \, d\xi \, d\eta \, d\zeta \\ &= \sum_{m=1}^{n} \sum_{j=1}^{n} \sum_{i=1}^{n} H_i H_j H_m f(\xi_i, \eta_j, \zeta_m). \end{aligned} \tag{8.33}$$

In the above the number of integrating points in each direction was assumed to be the same. Clearly this is not necessary and on occasion it may be of advantage to use different numbers in each direction of integration.

It is of interest to note that in fact the double summation can be readily interpreted as a single one over $(n \times n)$ points for a rectangle (or n^3 points for a cube). Thus in Fig. 8.10 we show the nine sampling points which result in exact integrals of order 5 in each direction.

However, we could approach the problem directly and require an exact integration of a fifth-order polynomial in two directions. At any sampling point two co-ordinates and a value of f have to be determined in a weighting formula of type

$$I = \int_{-1}^{1} \int_{-1}^{1} f(\xi, \eta) \, d\xi \, d\eta = \sum_{1}^{m} w_i f(\xi_i, \eta_i). \tag{8.34}$$

There it would appear that only seven points would suffice to obtain the same order of accuracy. Some such formulae for three dimensional bricks have been derived by Irons[9] and used successfully.

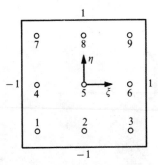

Fig. 8.10   Integrating points for $n = 3$ in a square region. (Exact for polynomial of fifth order in each direction)

8.10 Numerical Integration—Triangular or Tetrahedral Regions

For a triangle, in terms of the area co-ordinates the integrals are of the form

$$I = \int_0^1 \int_0^{1-L_1} f(L_1 L_2 L_3) \, dL_1 \, dL_2. \tag{8.35}$$

Once again we could use n Gauss points and arrive at a summation expression of the type used in previous section. However, the limits of integration now involve the variable itself and it is convenient to use alternative sampling points for the second integration by use of a special Gauss expression for integrals of type given by Eq. (8.29) in which w is a linear function. These have been devised by Radau.[10,11] Table 8.2 shows the weighting constants now required in expressions

$$I = \sum_{i=1}^n \sum_{j=1}^n Wf(L_1, L_2, L_3)$$

in which

$$\begin{aligned}
L_1 &= AI(i) \\
L_2 &= AJ(j)(1-L_1) \\
L_3 &= 1 - L_1 - L_2 \\
W &= AS(i)H(j)(1 - L_1).
\end{aligned} \tag{8.36}$$

Similar expressions could be deduced for a tetrahedron.

Figure 8.11 shows the distribution of integrating points inside triangles for $n = 1$ to 3. It is immediately obvious that these are not evenly (or symmetrically) spaced. Further, the accuracy is not now uniform in L_1, L_2, and L_3 directions. A considerable numerical (and aesthetic) improvement

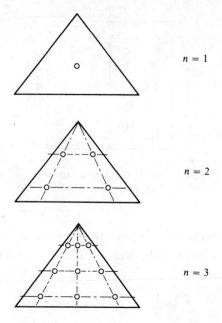

Fig. 8.11   Integrating points for a triangle using Gauss-Radau procedure

TABLE 8.2
GAUSS AND RADAU INTEGRATING CONSTANTS

Number of Integrating Points in Each Direction	$AJ[J]$ $J = 1, n$	$H[J]$ $J = 1, n$	$AI[I]$ $I = 1, n$	$AS[I]$ $I = 1, n$
$n = 1$	0·5	1·0	0·3333333333 (1·0)	0·75 (0·25)
$n = 2$	0·2113248654	0·5	0·1550510257	0·3764030627
	0·7886751346	0·5	0·6449489743 (1·0)	0·5124858262 (0·1111111111)
$n = 3$	0·1127016654	0·2777777778	0·0885879595	0·2204622112
	0·5	0·4444444444	0·4094668644	0·3881934688
	0·8872983346	0·2777777778	0·7876594618 (1·0)	0·3288443200 (0·0625)
$n = 4$	0·0694318442	0·1739274226	0·0571041961	0·1437135608
	0·3300094782	0·3260725774	0·2768430136	0·2813560151
	0·6699905218	0·3260725774	0·5835904324	0·3118265230
	0·9305681558	0·1739274226	0·8602401357 (1·0)	0·2231039011 (0·04)
$n = 5$	0·0469100770	0·1184634425	0·0398098571	0·1007941926
	0·2307653449	0·2393143353	0·1980134179	0·2084506672
	0·5	0·2844444444	0·4379748102	0·2604633916
	0·7692346551	0·2393143353	0·6954642734	0·2426935942
	0·9530899230	0·1184634425	0·9014649142 (1·0)	0·1598203766 (0·277777778)

TABLE 8.3
NUMERICAL INTEGRATION FORMULAS FOR TRIANGLES

Order	Fig.	Error	Points	Triangular Co-ordinates	Weights $2W_k$
Linear		$R = 0(h^2)$	a	$\frac{1}{3}, \frac{1}{3}, \frac{1}{3}$	1
Quadratic		$R = 0(h^3)$	a b c	$\frac{1}{2}, \frac{1}{2}, 0$ $0, \frac{1}{2}, \frac{1}{2}$ $\frac{1}{2}, 0, \frac{1}{2}$	$\frac{1}{3}$ $\frac{1}{3}$ $\frac{1}{3}$
Cubic		$R = 0(h^4)$	a b c d	$\frac{1}{3}, \frac{1}{3}, \frac{1}{3}$ $\frac{11}{15}, \frac{2}{15}, \frac{2}{15}$ $\frac{2}{15}, \frac{11}{15}, \frac{2}{15}$ $\frac{2}{15}, \frac{2}{15}, \frac{11}{15}$	$-\frac{27}{48}$ $\frac{25}{48}$

This formula not recommended due to negative weight and round-off error

Cubic		$R = 0(h^4)$	a b c d e f g	$\frac{1}{3}, \frac{1}{3}, \frac{1}{3}$ $\frac{1}{2}, \frac{1}{2}, 0$ $0, \frac{1}{2}, \frac{1}{2}$ $\frac{1}{2}, 0, \frac{1}{2}$ $1, 0, 0$ $0, 1, 0$ $0, 0, 1$	$\frac{27}{60}$ $\frac{8}{60}$ $\frac{3}{60}$
Quintic		$R = 0(h^6)$	a b c d e f g	$\frac{1}{3}, \frac{1}{3}, \frac{1}{3}$ $\alpha_1, \beta_1, \beta_1$ $\beta_1, \alpha_1, \beta_1$ $\beta_1, \beta_1, \alpha_1$ $\alpha_2, \beta_2, \beta_2$ $\beta_2, \alpha_2, \beta_2$ $\beta_2, \beta_2, \alpha_2$	0·225 0·13239415 0·12593918

with
$\alpha_1 = 0·05971587$
$\beta_1 = 0·47014206$
$\alpha_2 = 0·79742699$
$\beta_2 = 0·10128651$

was obtained by Hammer et al.[12] and a series of these weighted expressions is given in Table 8.3[13] for an expression similar to Eq. (8.34).

It can be verified that the number of points is always just sufficient or larger than that required to obtain a given degree complete polynomials.

Similar extension for tetrahedra could obviously be made. Table 8.4 presents some such formulae based on reference (12).

TABLE 8.4

NUMERICAL INTEGRATION FORMULAS FOR TETRAHEDRA

No.	Order	Fig.	Error	Points	Tetrahedral Co-ordinates	Weights
1	Linear		$R = 0(h^2)$	a	$\frac{1}{4}, \frac{1}{4}, \frac{1}{4}, \frac{1}{4}$	1
2	Quadratic		$R = 0(h^3)$	a b c d	$\alpha, \beta, \beta, \beta$ $\beta, \alpha, \beta, \beta$ $\beta, \beta, \alpha, \beta$ $\beta, \beta, \beta, \alpha$ $\alpha = 0{\cdot}58541020$ $\beta = 0{\cdot}13819660$	$\frac{1}{4}$ $\frac{1}{4}$ $\frac{1}{4}$ $\frac{1}{4}$
3	Cubic		$R = 0(h^4)$	a b c d e	$\frac{1}{4}, \frac{1}{4}, \frac{1}{4}, \frac{1}{4}$ $\frac{1}{3}, \frac{1}{6}, \frac{1}{6}, \frac{1}{6}$ $\frac{1}{6}, \frac{1}{3}, \frac{1}{6}, \frac{1}{6}$ $\frac{1}{6}, \frac{1}{6}, \frac{1}{3}, \frac{1}{6}$ $\frac{1}{6}, \frac{1}{6}, \frac{1}{6}, \frac{1}{3}$	$-\frac{4}{5}$ $\frac{9}{20}$ $\frac{9}{20}$ $\frac{9}{20}$ $\frac{9}{20}$

8.11 Concluding Remarks

In this chapter we have shown how a large number of curvilinear elements can be formulated. The necessity for numerical integration processes led to a description of some of these—for further details the reader is referred to the various texts on Numerical Analysis.

Obviously the numerical integration is approximate. The question as to the necessary degree of approximation needed in practical problems will be discussed in the next chapter as well as the matter of a general organization of programs based on numerical integration.

References

1. I. C. TAIG, *Structural analysis by the matrix displacement method*, Engl. Electric Aviation Report No. SO17, 1961.
2. B. M. IRONS, 'Numerical Integration applied to finite element methods', *Conf. Use of Digital Computers in Struct Eng.*, Univ. of Newcastle, 1966.
3. B. M. IRONS, 'Engineering application of numerical integration in stiffness method', *J.A.I.A.A.*, **14**, 2035–7, 1966.
4. S. A. COONS, *Surfaces for computer aided design of space form*, M.I.T. Project MAC, MAC-TR-41, 1967.
5. A. R. FORREST, *Curves and surfaces for Computer aided design*, Comp. Aided Design Group, Cambridge England, 1968.
6. F. D. MURNAGHAN, *Finite deformation of an elastic solid*, J. Wiley & Son, 1951.
7. F. SCHIED, *Numerical Analysis*, Schaum Series, McGraw-Hill, 1968.
8. Z. KOPAL, *Numerical Analysis*, 2nd ed., Chapman & Hall, 1961.
9. B. M. IRONS, 'Quadrature rules for brick based finite elements', *Int. J. Num. Meth. Eng.*, **3**, 1971.
10. RADAU, *Journ. de. Meth.*, **3**, 283, 1880.
11. R. G. ANDERSON, B. M. IRONS, and O. C. ZIENKIEWICZ, 'Vibration and Stability of Plates using finite elements', *Int. J. Solids Struct.*, **4**, 1031–55, 1968.
12. P. C. HAMMER, O. P. MARLOWE, and A. H. STROUD, 'Numerical integration over simplexes and cones', *Math. Tables Aids Comp.*, **10**, 130–7, 1956.
13. C. A. FELIPPA, 'Refined finite element analysis of linear and non-linear two dimensional structures', *Structures Materials Research Report* No. 66-22, Oct. 1966. Univ. of California, Berkeley.

9. Some Applications of Isoparametric Elements in Two- and Three-Dimensional Stress Analysis

9.1 Introduction

The high order elements introduced in the previous two chapters require some justification. The additional complexity will require more computer time to be spent in their formulation. The question of economics has therefore to be considered.

Figure 9.1 gives a simple example of a cantilever beam to which various elements are applied. In the first and second pairs of results it will be seen that *a dramatic improvement of accuracy arises with the same number of degrees of freedom when complex elements are used.* This does not necessarily result in a proportional decrease of solution time as with complex elements a larger bandwidth will be encountered—nevertheless a considerable saving occurs.

Further, the data preparation is considerably reduced with complex elements. In the examples shown three complex elements replace six and eighteen simple triangles respectively and thus fewer elements have to be specified. Also it is a very simple matter to write into the program a routine which interpolates the positions of mid-side co-ordinates if these sides are straight. Thus the number of co-ordinates needing specification is much smaller.

These points in favour of complex elements can well be countered if efficient automatic mesh generation processes are used—nevertheless the latter will always present more programing difficulty.

On the other side of the picture it will be sometimes seen that the very much reduced number of complex elements may not be adequate to represent all the local geometries of the real problem with the minimum number of elements. In such cases often the balance is in favour of the use of simple formulations.

Probably the most serious economic problem of complex curvilinear elements is the computer time necessary for performing the numerical integrations. Here some economic limit on the accuracy required in this integration must obviously be imposed.

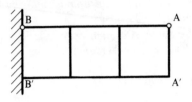

Type of element	Vertical Load of A		Couple at AA'	
	Max. defl. at AA'	Max. stress BB'	Max. defl. at AA'	Max. stress BB'
	0·26	0·19	0·22	0·22
	0·65	0·56	0·67	0·67
	0·53	0·51	0·52	0·55
	0·99	0·99	1·00	1·00
	1·00	1·00	1·00	1·00
EXACT	1·00	1·00	1·00	1·00

Fig. 9.1   A cantilever in plane stress analysed by various elements. Accuracy improvement with higher order elements

9.2 Required Accuracy of Numerical Integration

In the previous chapter it has been indicated how the element matrices can be formed using numerical integration in terms of n Gauss points. The effort of this integration over plane area is roughly proportional to n^2—the number of points at which the function has to be found—while in a three-dimensional situation it is proportional to n^3. The determination of an *adequate minimum number* of Gauss points is thus of some importance.

In this chapter we are concerned with elastic stress analysis and hence the matrix which needs to be evaluated is the stiffness of the element. The following proposition is now made.

Convergence of the finite element process will occur in elastic displacement analysis problems if the integration is sufficient to evaluate exactly the volume of the element.[1,2]

The proof of the above statement is simple. In the limit as the element size decreases we have specified shape functions which give constant strain and stress.

Thus the 'nodal forces' become

$$\{F_i\}^e = \int_{V^e} \{\sigma\}^T [B] \, d \, (\text{vol}) = \{\sigma\}^T \int_{V^e} [B] \, d \, (\text{vol}). \qquad (9.1)$$

As

$$d \, (\text{vol}) = \det [J] \, d\xi \, d\eta \, d\zeta \qquad (9.2)$$

and the matrix $[B]$ is obtained from the first derivatives of N_i multiplied by $[J]^{-1}$, we find that exact integral of Eq. (9.2) provides an exact integral of Eq. (9.1). Examining in detail the form of the Jacobian determinant (which is expressed in terms of the shape function derivatives *vide* Eq. (8.18)) we can determine its order and hence the number of Gauss points required for exact integration.[3]

For example in a two-dimensional quadratic quadrilateral the determinant results in a quadratic expression which requires a two-point Gauss formulation as a minimum. In three-dimensional, quadratic type prisms a cubic expression arises, again exactly integrable by two Gauss points in each direction.

These minima necessary for convergence are not necessarily the best economic compromise. If few elements are used to represent a region a better integration may be worth while, while conversely where a large number of elements has to be used to represent the configuration the lowest necessary order of integration is indicated by economy.

It is clear that computer programs should be so written as to permit the user a choice of the number of integrating points. These should never be less than the minimum necessary for convergence nor more than needed to achieve exact integrals.

In Fig. 9.2 an example of an axi-symmetric problem of a sphere loaded by internal pressure is shown. Here two orders of elements and different numbers of integrating points are used. Results are self explanatory.

Recent work shows that in some situations a considerable *improvement* of element properties can be achieved by using the minimum integrating order. This is due to two causes.

In the first place displacement elements are always too stiff (as shown in Chapter 2) and a reduced integration order reduces the stiffness.

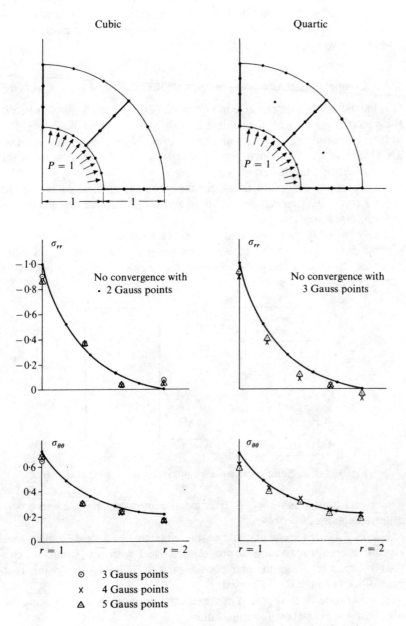

Fig. 9.2   Effect of different integration orders on analysis of a sphere
under internal pressure (cubic and quartic elements)
Solid line shows exact result.

In the second place, by focussing attention on only a few integrating points, the reduced formulation excludes regions where displacement may be over-constrained in order to achieve inter-element compatibility. In Chapter 14 we shall return to the same topic.

9.3 A Computational Advantage of Numerically Integrated Finite Elements[3]

One considerable gain possible in numerically integrated finite elements is the versatility which can be achieved in a single computer program.

It will be observed that for a *given class of problems* the general matrices are always of the same form (*vide* example of Eq. (8.14)) in terms of the shape function and its derivatives.

' To proceed to evaluation of the element properties it is necessary first to *specify the shape function* and its derivatives and second, to *specify the order of integration*.

The computation of element properties thus is composed of three distinct parts as shown in Fig. 9.3. For a *given class of problems* it is only necessary to change the prescription of the shape functions to achieve a variety of possible elements.

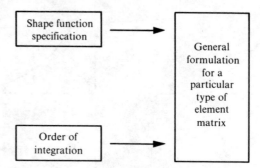

Fig. 9.3   Computation scheme for numerically integrated elements

Conversely the *same shape function* routines can be used in many different classes of problem.

Use of different elements, testing the efficiency of a new element in a given context, or extension of programs to deal with new situations can thus be readily achieved, and considerable algebra (with its inherent possibilities of mistakes) avoided.

The computer is thus placed in the position it deserves, i.e., of being the obedient slave capable of saving routine.

The greatest practical advantage of the use of universal shape function routines is that they can be checked decisively for errors by a simple program. Usually it is sufficient to check that the nodal values are correct

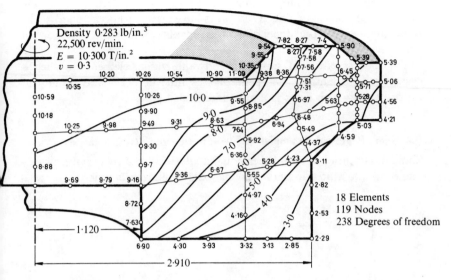

Fig. 9.4   A rotating *disk*—analysed with cubic elements

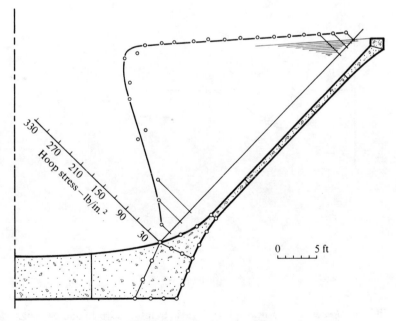

Fig. 9.5   Conical water tank

and that the numbers purporting to be derivatives really are derivatives; this is achieved using simple difference formulae and entering the routine at two closely spaced points. Other tests have been used occasionally. The most interesting is one depending on eigenvalues but its use is somewhat expensive.[4]

The incorporation of simple, exactly integrable, elements in such a system is, incidentally, not penalized as time of exact and numerical integration in such cases is almost identical.

9.4 Some Practical Examples of Two-dimensional Stress Analysis[5-10]

Some possibilities of two-dimensional analysis offered by curvilinear elements are illustrated in the following axi-symmetric examples.

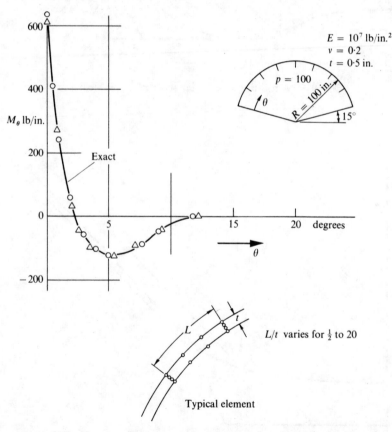

Fig. 9.6 *Encastré*, thin hemispherical shell. Solution with 15 and 24 cubic elements

Rotating disk (Fig. 9.4). Here eighteen elements only are needed to obtain an adequate solution. It is of interest to observe that all mid-side nodes of the cubic elements are generated within a program and need not be specified.

Conical water tank (Fig. 9.5). In this problem again cubic elements are used. It is worth noting that single element thickness throughout is adequate to represent the bending effects in both the thick and thin parts of the container. With simple triangular elements, as we have seen, several layers of elements would have been needed to give an adequate solution.

A hemispherical dome (Fig. 9.6). The possibilities of dealing with shells approached in the previous example are here further exploited to show how a limited number of elements can solve adequately a thin shell problem, with precisely the same program. This type of solution can be further improved upon from the economy viewpoint by making use of the well-known shell assumptions involving a linear variation of displacements across the thickness. Thus the number of degrees of freedom can be reduced. Methods of this kind will be dealt with in detail in Chapter 14.

9.5 Three-dimensional Stress Analysis

In three-dimensional analysis, as was already hinted at in Chapter 6, the complex element presents a considerable economic advantage. Some typical examples are shown here in which the quadratic, serendipity type formulation is used almost exclusively. In all problems integration using *three* Gauss points in each direction was used.

Rotating sphere (Fig. 9.7).[6] This example, in which the stresses due to centrifugal action are compared with exact values, is perhaps a test on the efficiency of highly distorted elements. Seven elements are used here and results show reasonable agreement with exact stresses.

Arch dam in rigid valley. This problem, perhaps a little unrealistic from the engineer's viewpoint, was subject of a study carried out by a committee of the Institution of Civil Engineers and provided an excellent test for a convergence study of three-dimensional analysis. In Fig. 9.8 two subdivisions into quadratic and two into cubic elements are shown. In Fig. 9.9 the convergence of displacements in centre line section is shown, indicating that quite remarkable accuracy can be achieved with even one element.

The comparison of stresses in Fig. 9.10 is again quite remarkable, though showing a greater 'oscillation' with coarse subdivision. The finest subdivision results can be taken as 'exact' from checks by models and alternative methods of analysis.[9]

The above test problems illustrate the general applicability and accuracy. Two further illustrations typical of real situations are included.

Pressure vessel (Fig. 9.11); *An arch dam and its foundations* (Fig. 9.12).

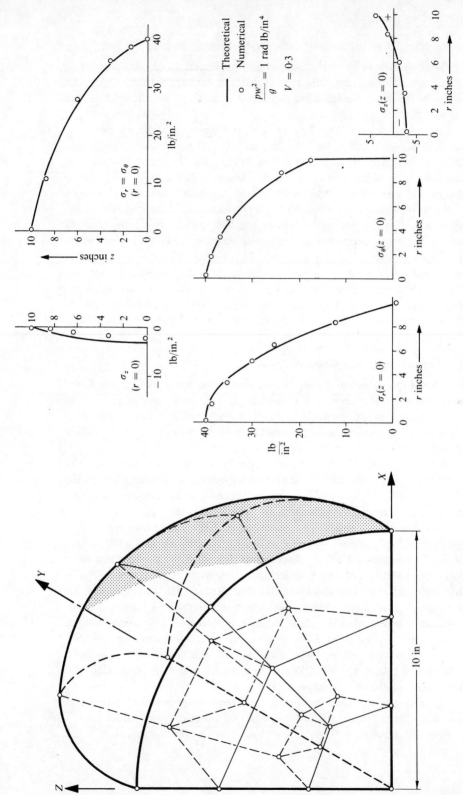

Fig. 9.7 A rotating sphere as a three dimensional problem. 7 parabolic elements. Stresses along $z = 0$ and $r = 0$

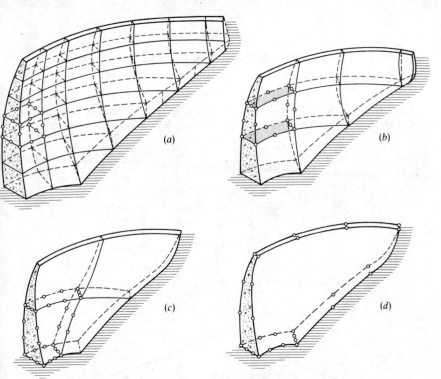

Fig. 9.8 Arch dam in a rigid valley—various element subdivisions

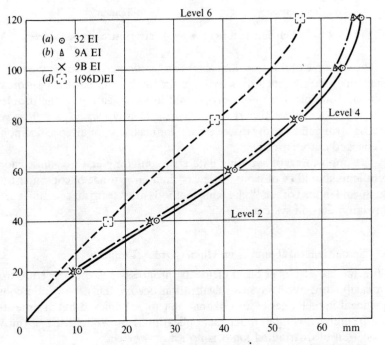

Fig. 9.9 Arch dam in a rigid valley—centre line displacements

Both show subdivisions sufficient to obtain a reasonable engineering accuracy. The pressure vessel, somewhat similar to the one indicated in Chapter 6, Fig. 6.6, shows the very considerable reduction of degrees of freedom possible with the use of more complex elements.

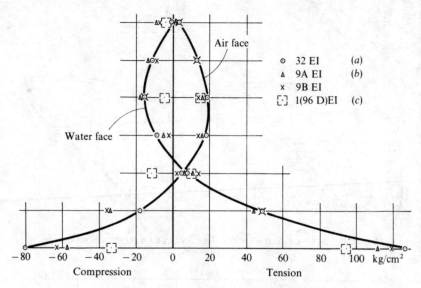

Fig. 9.10   Arch dam in a rigid valley—vertical stresses on centreline

The example of the arch dam shows an 'exploded' isometric view of the elements used obtained directly from the analysis data on an automatic plotter. Such plots are not only helpful in visualization of the problem. They form an essential part of *data correctness checks* as any gross geometric error can be easily discovered. 'Connectivity' of all specified points is checked automatically.

The importance of avoiding data errors in complex three-dimensional problems should be obvious in view of their large usage of computer time. Such, and indeed other,[10] checking methods must form an essential part of any computation system.

9.6 Some General Remarks on Higher Order Elements

With the use of higher order elements, progressively, the departure from an easily conceived physical idealization occurs. This is of little consequence if in fact a better approximation can be achieved but at times this can be embarrassing in practical application. For instance the 'intuitive' allocation of distributed loads is no longer correct.

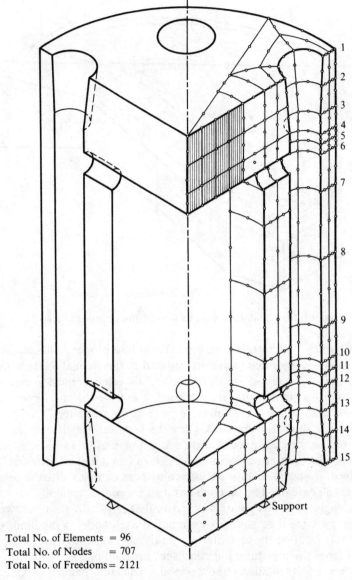

Total No. of Elements = 96
Total No. of Nodes = 707
Total No. of Freedoms = 2121

Fig. 9.11 Three dimensional analysis of a pressure vessel

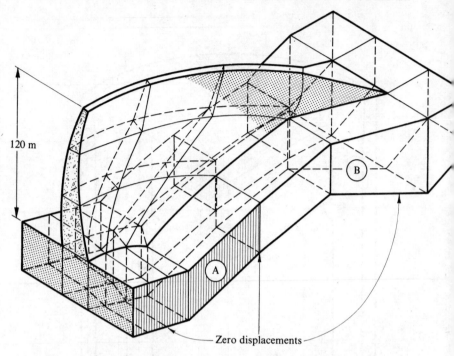

120 m

B

A

Zero displacements

Fig. 9.12(a)   Arch dam with its foundation included in analysis

In Chapter 4, for instance, we have shown how properly allocated, consistent nodal forces due to gravity resulted in three equal loads at nodes of a triangular element (section 4.2.7). This result coincides with 'the obvious'. If a similar allocation is carried out for the two-dimensional series of elements of 'serendipity' type (Fig. 7.4, Chapter 7) we get the distribution shown in Fig. 9.13. Only the first one, for the simplest element of the series, coincides with 'common sense'. In all the others negative allocations at corner nodes exist—a fact not at all 'obvious'.

Indeed, if such elements are curved a more complex distribution yet occurs, and care must be taken to ensure a proper allocation.

The engineer at this point will exclaim that physically the result would still be the same if equal loads were put at each node, in the limit. Certainly this must be the case but in a *finite subdivision* a greater accuracy ensues from the unnatural but consistent distribution.

Surface effects similarly show a non-predictable pattern as given in Fig. 9.14.

The above considerations affect the *interpretation* of inter-element forces in the usual engineering manner and allowance for this has to be made.

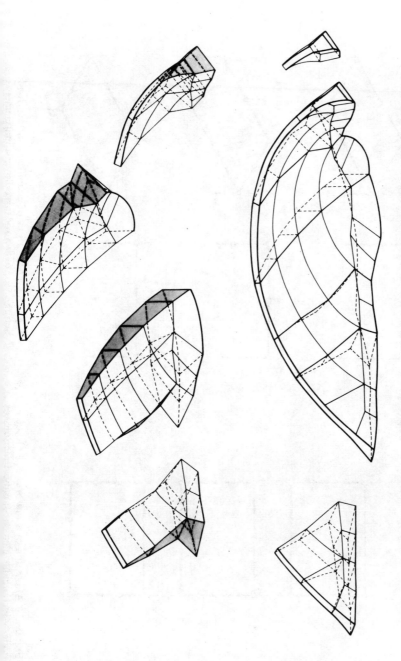

Fig. 9.12(b)   An isometric computer plot of an arch dam. Exploded and assembled views of subdivision.

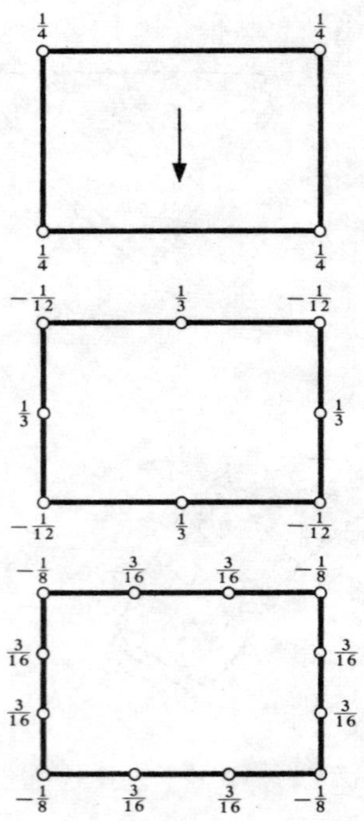

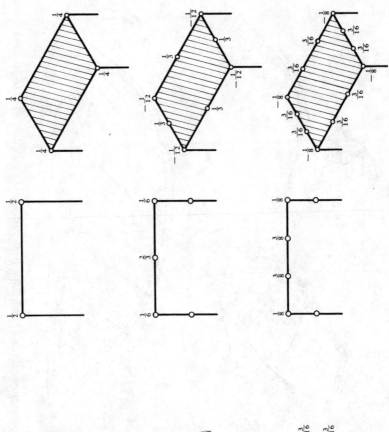

Fig. 9.14   Allocation of a uniform surface load acting on top of two and three dimensional elements

Fig. 9.13   Allocation of a uniform body force to nodes—rectangular element family. Fractions of

Conversely the representation of stresses in regions close to concentrated load singularities suffers and sometimes unexpected stresses in the vicinity of such loads can be indicated. This indeed is not a sign of decreasing accuracy but an indication that an element tries on the average, to represent the true effects in an improved way.

In Fig. 9.15 a qualitative comparison between stress representation achieved in constant and linearly varying strain elements is shown near such a singularity. By trying to achieve a closer approximation to the true stress, the more elaborate element gives improved values at the singularity but may result in an unnatural stress reversal close to it which is not indicated by simpler elements. Clearly appropriate smoothing must be resorted to in such cases and proper account taken in interpretation of results.

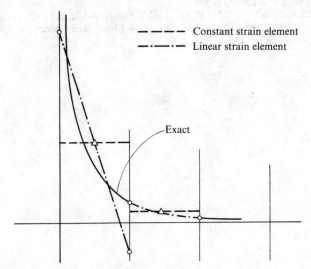

Fig. 9.15   Anomalies which may arise in the vicinity of a concentrated load
with complex elements

References

1. B. M. IRONS, 'Engineering Application of numerical integration in stiffness method', *A.I.A.A.*, **4**, 2035–7, 1966.
2. B. M. IRONS, Comment on 'Stiffness Matrices for sector element' by I. R. Raju and A. K. Rao, *J.A.I.A.A.*., **7**, 156–7, 1969.
3. B. M. IRONS, Discussion, p. 328–31, of *Finite Element Techniques in Structural Mechanics*, ed. H. Tottenham and C. Brebbia, Southampton Univ. Press, 1970.
4. B. M. IRONS, 'Testing and assessing finite elements by an eigenvalue technique', *Proc. Conf. on Recent developments in Stress Analysis, J. Br. Soc. St. An.*, Royal Aero Soc., 1968.

5. O. C. ZIENKIEWICZ, B. M. IRONS, J. ERGATOUDIS, S. AHMAD, and F. C. SCOTT. 'Isoparametric and associated element families for two and three dimensional analysis', *Proc. Course on Finite Element Methods in Stress Analysis* ed. I. Holand and K. Bell, Trondheim Tech. University, 1969.

6. B. M. IRONS and O. C. ZIENKIEWICZ, 'The isoparametric finite element system —a new concept in finite element analysis', *Proc. Conf. Recent Advances in Stress Analysis*, Royal Aero Soc., 1968.

7. J. ERGATOUDIS, B. M. IRONS, and O. C. ZIENKIEWICZ, 'Curved, Isoparametric, "Quadrilateral" elements for finite element analysis', *Int. J. Solids & Struct.*, 4, 31–42, 1968.

8. J. G. ERGATOUDIS, *Isoparametric elements in two and three dimensional analysis*, Ph.D. Thesis, University of Wales, Swansea, 1968.

9. J. ERGATOUDIS, B. M. IRONS, and O. C. ZIENKIEWICZ, 'Three dimensional analysis of arch dams and their foundations', *Symposium on Arch Dams*, Inst. Civ. Eng., London, 1968.

10. O. C. ZIENKIEWICZ, B. M. IRONS, J. CAMPBELL, and F. SCOTT, 'Three Dimensional Stress Analysis' Int. Un. Th. Appl. Mech. Symposium on High Speed Computing in Elasticity, Liége, 1970.

10. Bending of Plates

10.1 Introduction

In all the problems treated in the earlier chapters the basic stress-strain relationships have been given in their exact form, even though the ultimate solution introduced approximations. In the classical theory of plates[1] certain approximations are introduced initially to simplify the problem to two dimensions. Such assumptions concern the linear variation of strains and stresses on lines normal to the plane of the plate. So-called 'exact' solutions of plate theory are therefore only true if these assumptions are valid. This is so when the plates are thin and the deflection small.

In the solutions presented here the starting point will, once again, be based on the classical plate theory assumptions, and the validity of the approximate, numerical treatment must therefore be tested against plate theory solutions. It will also be subject to precisely the same limitations.

The state of deformation of a plate can be described entirely by one quantity. This is the lateral displacement w of the 'middle plane' of the plate. Continuity conditions between elements have now, however, to be imposed not only on this quantity but on its derivatives. This is to ensure that the plate remains continuous and does not 'kink'.† At each node, therefore, three conditions of equilibrium and continuity will usually be imposed.

Determination of suitable shape functions is now much more complex. Indeed, if complete slope continuity is required on the interfaces between various elements, the mathematical and computational difficulties often rise disproportionately fast. It is, however, relatively simple to obtain shape functions which, while preserving continuity of w, may violate the slope continuity between elements, though naturally not at the node where continuity is imposed. If such functions satisfy the 'constant strain' criterion, then convergence may still be found (*vide* Chapter 2). The first part of this chapter will be concerned with such 'non-conforming' shape functions. In the second part new functions are introduced by which continuity can be restored. The solution with such 'conforming' shape

† If 'kinking' occurs the second derivative or curvature becomes infinite and certain infinite terms occur in the energy expression.

171

functions will now give bounds to the correct answer but, on many occasions, will yield an inferior accuracy. For practical usage the methods of the first part of the chapter are often recommended.

The simplest type of element shape is now a rectangle and this will be introduced first. Triangular and quadrilateral elements present some difficulties and will be introduced later; for solutions of plates of arbitrary shape or, for that matter, for dealing with shell problems such elements are essential.

10.2 Displacement Formulation of the Plate Problem

Displacement of a plate, under the usual thin plate theory, is uniquely specified once the deflection, w, is known at all points.

We will write the general form as

$$w = [N]\{\delta\}^e \tag{10.1}$$

in which the shape functions are dependent on Cartesian co-ordinates x, y, and $\{\delta\}^e$ list the element (nodal) parameters.

The generalized 'strains' and 'stresses' have now to be specified in such a way that their scalar product gives the internal work in the manner of Chapter 2. Thus we shall define the 'strain' as (Fig. 10.1)

$$\{\varepsilon\} = \left\{ \begin{array}{c} -\dfrac{\partial^2 w}{\partial x^2} \\[2mm] -\dfrac{\partial^2 w}{\partial y^2} \\[2mm] 2\dfrac{\partial^2 w}{\partial x \partial y} \end{array} \right\}. \tag{10.2}$$

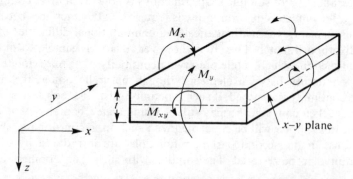

Fig. 10.1   Stress resultants or 'stresses' in plate bending

The corresponding 'stresses' are in fact the usual bending and twisting moments per unit lengths in x and y directions.[1]

$$\{\sigma\} = \begin{Bmatrix} M_x \\ M_y \\ M_{xy} \end{Bmatrix} . \tag{10.3}$$

As true strains and stresses vary linearly across the plate thickness[1] these can be found from such expressions as

$$\sigma_x = \frac{6M_x}{t^2} z, \text{ etc.}$$

where z is measured from the plate mid-plane and t is the thickness of plate.

The product of the expressions (10.2) and (10.3) will be found to correspond exactly to the internal work requirements.

As the strains are now defined by second derivatives the continuity criterion requires that the shape functions be such that both w and its slope normal to the interface between elements be continuous.

The criterion of constant strain requires that any constant arbitrary value of second derivative should be reproducible within the element.

To ensure at least an approximate satisfaction of slope continuity three displacement components are considered as nodal parameters: the first the actual displacement w_n in the z direction, the second a rotation about the x axis $(\theta_x)_n$, and the third a rotation about the y axis $(\theta_y)_n$. Figure 10.2 shows these rotations with their positive directions determined by the right-hand screw rule. Their magnitudes are shown by vectors directed along the axes.

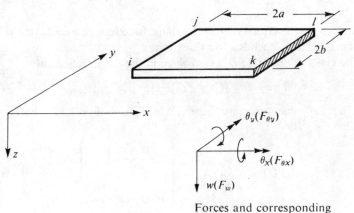

Forces and corresponding displacements

Fig. 10.2 A rectangular plate element

Clearly the slopes of w and the rotation are identical (except for sign) and we can write

$$\{\delta_i\} = \left\{ \begin{array}{c} w_i \\ \theta_{xi} \\ \theta_{yi} \end{array} \right\} = \left\{ \begin{array}{c} w_i \\ -\left(\dfrac{\partial w}{\partial y}\right)_i \\ \left(\dfrac{\partial w}{\partial x}\right)_i \end{array} \right\}. \tag{10.4}$$

The nodal 'forces' corresponding to these displacements can be interpreted as a direct force and two couples

$$\{F_i\} = \left\{ \begin{array}{c} F_{wi} \\ F_{\theta xi} \\ F_{\theta yi} \end{array} \right\} \tag{10.5}$$

as shown in Fig. 10.2.

The stiffness and other element matrices will be obtained in the usual manner by the expressions of Chapter 2 once the $[B]$ matrix has been determined.

From the definitions, Eqs. (10.1) and (10.2) it follows immediately that

$$[B_i] = \left\{ \begin{array}{c} -\dfrac{\partial^2}{\partial x^2}[N_i] \\ -\dfrac{\partial^2}{\partial y^2}[N_i] \\ 2\dfrac{\partial^2}{\partial x\,\partial y}[N_i] \end{array} \right\}. \tag{10.6}$$

Brackets are retained now in the shape functions to denote that this is a matrix quantity dependent on three terms.

The elasticity matrix $[D]$ is involved in the usual definition

$$\{\sigma\} \equiv \{M\} = [D](\{\varepsilon\} - \{\varepsilon_0\}) + \{\sigma_0\}. \tag{10.7}$$

For an *isotropic plate* we have (*vide* Timoshenko and Woinowsky-Krieger,[1] p. 81)

$$[D] = \frac{Et^3}{12(1-v^2)} \begin{bmatrix} 1 & v & 0 \\ v & 1 & 0 \\ 0 & 0 & (1-v)/_2 \end{bmatrix}. \tag{10.8}$$

For an *orthotropic slab* with principal directions of orthotropy coinciding with the x and y axes, four constants are needed to define the behaviour i.e.,

$$[D] = \begin{bmatrix} D_x & D_1 & 0 \\ D_1 & D_y & 0 \\ 0 & 0 & D_{xy} \end{bmatrix}. \tag{10.9}$$

These can be related to the appropriate elastic constants of the material as shown in Timoshenko and Woinowsky-Krieger[1] but it is more convenient to leave them in the above form as the plate theory is often used to solve grillage problems. In such cases the constants must be related to the properties at the grillage. Clearly, for a most complete case of anisotropy, six constants at most will be needed to define $[D]$ since the matrix always has to be symmetric.

10.3 Continuity of Requirement for Shape Function

To ensure the continuity of both w and its normal slope across an interface we must have both w and $\partial w/\partial n$ uniquely defined by values along such an interface.

Consider Fig. 10.3 depicting the side 1–2 of a rectangular element. The normal direction n is in fact that of y and we desire w and $\partial w/\partial y$ to be uniquely determined by values of w, $\partial w/\partial x$, $\partial w/\partial y$ at the nodes lying along this line.

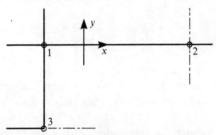

Fig. 10.3 Continuity requirement for normal slopes

Following the principles of Chapter 7 we would write along 1–2

$$w = A_1 + A_2 x + A_3 x^2 + \cdots \tag{10.10}$$

and

$$\frac{\partial w}{\partial y} = B_1 + B_2 x + B_3 x^2 + \cdots \tag{10.11}$$

with a number of constants in each expression just sufficient to determine the expressions by nodal parameters associated with the line.

Thus for instance if only two nodes are present a cubic variation of w would be permissible noting that $\partial w/\partial x$ and w are specified at each. Similarly only a linear or, two term, variation of $\partial w/\partial y$ would be permissible.

Note, however, that a similar exercise could be performed along the y direction preserving continuity of $\partial w/\partial x$ along this.

We thus have along (1–2)

$$\frac{\partial w}{\partial y} \quad \text{(depends on nodal parameters of line 1–2 only)}$$

and along (1–3)

$$\frac{\partial w}{\partial x} \quad \text{(depends on nodal parameters of line 1–3 only).}$$

Differentiating the first with respect to x we have on line 1–2

$$\frac{\partial^2 w}{\partial x\,\partial y} \quad \text{(depends on nodal parameters of line 1–2 only)}$$

and on line 1–3 similarly

$$\frac{\partial^2 w}{\partial y\,\partial x} \quad \text{(depends on nodal parameters of line 1–3 only).}$$

At the common point, 1, an inconsistency arises immediately as we cannot have there

$$\frac{\partial^2 w}{\partial x\,\partial y} = \frac{\partial^2 w}{\partial y\,\partial x}$$

for arbitrary values of parameters at nodes 2 and 3.

It is thus impossible to specify simple polynomial expressions for shape functions ensuring full compatibility when only w and its slopes are prescribed at nodes.[2]

If any functions satisfying the compatibility are found with the three nodal variables, they must be such that at corner nodes they are not continuously differentiable and the cross derivative is not unique. Some such functions are discussed in the second part of this chapter.[3–7]

The above proof has been given for a rectangular element. Clearly the arguments can be extended for any two arbitrary directions of interfaces at the corner node 1.

A way out of this difficulty appears to be obvious. We could specify the cross derivative as one of the nodal parameters. This, for an assembly of rectangular elements, is convenient and indeed permissible. Simple functions of that type have been suggested by Bogner *et al.*[8] and used with some success.

Unfortunately the extension to nodes at which a number of element interfaces meet under different angles, Fig. 10.4, is not in general permissible. Here the continuity of cross derivatives in several sets of orthogonal directions implies in fact a specification of *all second derivatives at a node*.

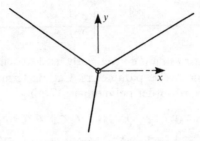

Fig. 10.4   Nodes where elements meet in arbitrary directions

This, however, violates physical requirements if the plate stiffness varies abruptly from element to element as then equality of moments normal to the interfaces cannot be maintained. However, this process has been used with some success in homogeneous plate situations.[9-11]

Indeed Smith, in reference 9 examines the effect of imposing such 'excessive continuities' on several orders of higher derivatives.

The difficulties of finding compatible displacement functions here led to several attempts at ignoring the complete slope continuity while still continuing with the other necessary criteria. Proceeding perhaps, from a naïve but intuitive idea that the imposition of slope continuity at nodes must, in the limit, lead to a complete slope continuity several very successful elements have been developed.[12-15] The convergence of some of these can be demonstrated and proved by other means than those used in Chapters 2 and 3.[4, 16] Conversely it can be shown that under certain circumstances small errors in the convergence limit will exist.[4]

The simplicity and practical use of such elements justifies their special treatment in the following section.

NON-CONFORMING SHAPE FUNCTIONS

10.4 Rectangular Element with Corner Nodes[12, 17, 18]

10.4.1 *Shape functions.* Consider a rectangular element of a plate *ijkl* coinciding with the x, y plane as shown on Fig. 10.2. At each node displacements $\{\delta_n\}$ are introduced. These have three components: the first a displacement in the z direction, w_n, the second a rotation about the x axis, $(\theta_x)_n$, the third a rotation about the y axis $(\theta_y)_n$.

The nodal displacements are defined by Eq. (10.4) while the element displacement will, as usual, be given by the listing of the nodal displacements, now totalling four,

$$\{\delta\}^e = \left\{ \begin{array}{c} \delta_i \\ \delta_j \\ \delta_l \\ \delta_k \end{array} \right\}. \tag{10.12}$$

A polynomial expression is conveniently used to define the shape functions in terms of the twelve parameters. Certain terms must be omitted from a complete fourth-order polynomial. Writing

$$w = \alpha_1 + \alpha_2 x + \alpha_3 y + \alpha_4 x^2 + \alpha_5 xy + \alpha_6 y^2 + \alpha_7 x^3 + \alpha_8 x^2 y$$
$$+ \alpha_9 xy^2 + \alpha_{10} y^3 + \alpha_{11} x^3 y + \alpha_{12} xy^3 \tag{10.13}$$

has certain advantages. In particular, along any $x = $ constant or $y = $ constant line, the displacement w will vary as a cubic. The element boundaries or interfaces are composed of such lines. As a cubic is uniquely defined by four constants, the two end values of slopes and displacements at the ends of the boundaries will therefore define the displacements along this boundary uniquely. As such end values are common to adjacent elements, continuity of w will be imposed all along any interface.

It will be observed that the gradient of w normal to any of the boundaries varies along it in a cubic way. (Consider, for instance, $\partial w / \partial x$ along a line on which x is constant.) As on such lines only two values of the normal slope are defined, the cubic is not specified uniquely and, in general, a discontinuity of normal slope will occur. The function is thus 'non-conforming'.

The constants α_1 to α_{12} can be evaluated by writing down the twelve simultaneous equations linking the values of w and its slopes at the nodes when the co-ordinates take up their appropriate values. For instance

$$w_i = \alpha_1 + \alpha_2 x_i + \alpha_3 y_i + \text{ etc.}$$

$$\left(-\frac{\partial w}{\partial y} \right)_i = \theta_{xi} = \qquad -\alpha_3 \quad + \text{ etc.}$$

$$\left(\frac{\partial w}{\partial x} \right)_i = \theta_{yi} = \qquad \alpha_2 \qquad + \text{ etc.}$$

$$\cdot \quad \cdot \quad \cdot \quad \cdot \quad \cdot \quad \cdot \quad \cdot \quad \cdot \quad \cdot \quad \cdot \quad \cdot \quad \cdot \quad \cdot \quad \cdot$$

Listing all twelve equations we can write, in matrix form,

$$\{\delta\}^e = [C]\{\alpha\} \tag{10.14}$$

where $[C]$ is a twelve by twelve matrix depending on nodal co-ordinates and $\{\alpha\}$ a vector of the twelve unknown constants. Inverting

$$\{\alpha\} = [C]^{-1}\{\delta\}^e. \tag{10.15}$$

This inversion can be carried out by the computer or, if an explicit expression for the stiffnesses, etc., is desired, can be performed algebraically. This was in fact done by Zienkiewicz and Cheung.[12]

It is now possible to write the expression for the displacement within the element in a standard form as

$$\{f\} = w = [N]\{\delta\}^e = [P][C]^{-1}\{\delta\}^e \tag{10.16}$$

where

$$[P] = (1, x, y, x^2, xy, y^2, x^3, x^2y, xy^2, y^3, x^3y, xy^3)$$

An explicit form of the above expression was derived by Melosh.[17] The expressions can be written simply in terms of normalized coordinates of Chapter 8.

Thus we can write for any node

$$[N_i] = \tfrac{1}{8}[(\xi_0 + 1)(\eta_0 + 1)(2 + \xi_0 + \eta_0 - \xi^2 - \eta^2),$$
$$a\xi_i(\xi_0 + 1)^2(\xi_0 - 1)(\eta_0 + 1),$$
$$b\eta_i(\xi_0 + 1)(\eta_0 + 1)^2(\eta_0 - 1)] \tag{10.17}$$

with

$$\xi = (x - x_c)/a, \qquad \eta = (y - y_c)/b$$
$$\xi_0 = \xi \cdot \xi_i, \qquad \eta_0 = \eta \cdot \eta_i.$$

The form of $[B]$ is obtained directly from Eq. (10.13) or from Eq. (10.17) by use of Eq. (10.6). As

$$\{\varepsilon\} = \begin{Bmatrix} -2\alpha_4 & -6\alpha_7 x & -2\alpha_8 y & -6\alpha_{11}xy \\ -2\alpha_6 & -2\alpha_9 x & -6\alpha_{10}y & -6\alpha_{12}xy \\ 2\alpha_5 & +4\alpha_8 x & +4\alpha_9 y & +6\alpha_{11}x^2 & +6\alpha_{12}y^2 \end{Bmatrix}. \tag{10.18}$$

We can write

$$\{\varepsilon\} = [Q]\{\alpha\} = [Q][C]^{-1}\{\delta\}^e; \quad \text{and thus} \quad [B] = [Q][C]^{-1}$$

in which

$$[Q] = \begin{bmatrix} 0 & 0 & 0 & -2 & 0 & 0 & -6x & -2y & 0 & 0 & -6xy & 0 \\ 0 & 0 & 0 & 0 & 0 & -2 & 0 & 0 & -2x & -6y & 0 & -6xy \\ 0 & 0 & 0 & 0 & 2 & 0 & 0 & 4x & 4y & 0 & 6x^2 & 6y^2 \end{bmatrix}. \tag{10.19}$$

It is of interest to remark now that the displacement function chosen does in fact permit a state of constant strain (curvature) to exist† and therefore satisfies the criterion of convergence stated in Chapter 2.

10.4.2 *Stiffness and load matrices.* Standard procedure can now be followed, and it is almost superfluous to recount the details.

By Eq. (2.10) the stiffness matrix relating the nodal *forces* (given by a lateral force and two moments at each node) to the corresponding nodal displacements is

$$[k] = \int \int [B]^{\mathrm{T}}[D][B]\, \mathrm{d}x\, \mathrm{d}y \qquad (10.20)$$

or substituting Eq. (10.18) and taking t as constant within the element,

$$[k] = \{[C]^{-1}\}^{\mathrm{T}}\left(\int \int [Q]^{\mathrm{T}}[D][Q]\, \mathrm{d}x\, \mathrm{d}y\right)[C]^{-1}. \qquad (10.21)$$

The terms not containing x and y have now been removed from the operation of integrating. The term within the integration sign can be multiplied out and integrated explicitly without difficulty, if t is constant.

An explicit expression for the stiffness matrix $[k]$ has been evaluated for the case of an orthotropic material and the result is given in Table 10.1.

The corresponding stress matrix for the internal moments of all the nodes is given in Table 10.2.

The external forces at nodes due to distributed loading can be assigned 'by inspection', allocating specific areas as contributing to any node. However, it is more logical and accurate to use once again the standard expression Eq. (2.9) for such an allocation.

If a distributed loading q is acting per unit area of an element in direction of w then, by Eq. (2.9), the contribution of these forces to each of the nodes is

$$\{F\}_p^e = -\int \int [N]^{\mathrm{T}}q\, \mathrm{d}x\, \mathrm{d}y \qquad (10.22)$$

or by Eq. (10.15)

$$\{F\}_p^e = \{-[C]^{-1}\}^{\mathrm{T}}\int \int [P]^{\mathrm{T}}q\, \mathrm{d}x\, \mathrm{d}y. \qquad (10.23)$$

---

† If α_7 to α_{12} are zero then the 'strain' is constant. By Eq. (10.13) corresponding $\{\delta\}^e$ can be found. As there is a unique correspondence between $\{\delta\}^e$ and $\{\alpha\}$ such a state is therefore unique. All this presumes that $[C]^{-1}$ does in fact exist. The algebraic inversion shows that the matrix $[C]$ is never singular.

TABLE 10.1
STIFFNESS MATRIX FOR A RECTANGULAR ELEMENT
(FIG. 10.3: ORTHOTROPIC MATERIAL)

Stiffness matrix

$$[k] = \frac{1}{60ab}[L]\{D_x[K_1] + D_y[K_2] + D_1[K_3] + D_{xy}[K_4]\}[L]$$

with

$$\begin{Bmatrix} F_i \\ F_j \\ F_k \\ F_l \end{Bmatrix} = [k] \begin{Bmatrix} \delta_i \\ \delta_j \\ \delta_k \\ \delta_l \end{Bmatrix}$$

$K_1 = p^{-2}$

$p^{-2} = \dfrac{b^2}{a^2}$

Symmetrical

60											
0	0										
30	0	20									
30	0	15	60								
0	0	0	0	0							
15	0	10	30	0	20						
−60	0	−30	−30	0	−15	60					
0	0	0	0	0	0	0	0				
30	0	10	15	0	5	−30	0	20			
−30	0	−15	−60	0	−30	30	0	−15	60		
0	0	0	0	0	0	0	0	0	0	0	
15	0	5	30	0	10	−15	0	10	−30	0	20

$K_2 = p^2$

$p^2 = \dfrac{a^2}{b^2}$

Symmetrical

60											
−30	20										
0	0	0									
−60	30	0	60								
−30	10	0	30	20							
0	0	0	0	0	0						
30	−15	0	−30	−15	0	60					
−15	10	0	15	5	0	−30	20				
0	0	0	0	0	0	0	0	0			
−30	15	0	30	15	0	−60	30	0	60		
−15	5	0	15	10	0	−30	10	0	30	20	
0	0	0	0	0	0	0	0	0	0	0	0

$K_3 =$

Symmetrical

30											
−15	0										
15	−15	0									
−30	0	−15	30								
0	0	0	15	0							
−15	0	0	15	15	0						
−30	15	0	30	0	0	30					
15	0	0	0	0	0	−15	0				
0	0	0	0	0	0	−15	15	0			
30	0	0	−30	−15	0	−30	0	15	30		
0	0	0	−15	0	0	0	0	0	15	0	
0	0	0	0	0	0	15	0	0	−15	−15	0

$$
K_4 = \begin{bmatrix}
84 \\
-6 & 8 \\
6 & 0 & 8 & & & \text{Symmetrical} \\
-84 & 6 & -6 & 84 \\
-6 & -2 & 0 & 6 & 8 \\
-6 & 0 & -8 & 6 & 0 & 8 \\
-84 & 6 & -6 & 84 & 6 & 6 & 84 \\
6 & -8 & 0 & -6 & 2 & 0 & -6 & 8 \\
6 & 0 & -2 & -6 & 0 & 2 & -6 & 0 & 8 \\
84 & -6 & 6 & -84 & -6 & -6 & -84 & 6 & 6 & 84 \\
6 & 2 & 0 & -6 & -8 & 0 & -6 & -2 & 0 & 6 & 8 \\
-6 & 0 & 2 & 6 & 0 & -2 & 6 & 0 & -8 & -6 & 0 & 8
\end{bmatrix}
$$

$$
L = \begin{bmatrix} l & 0 & 0 & 0 \\ 0 & l & 0 & 0 \\ 0 & 0 & l & 0 \\ 0 & 0 & 0 & l \end{bmatrix}, \quad \text{where} \quad l = \begin{bmatrix} 1 & 0 & 0 \\ 0 & 2b & 0 \\ 0 & 0 & 2a \end{bmatrix}
$$

The integral is again evaluated simply. It will now be noted that, in general, all three components of external force at any node will have non-zero values. This is a result which the simple allocation of external loads would have missed. Table 10.3 shows the nodal load vector for a uniform loading q.

If initial strains are introduced into the plate the vector of nodal forces due to such initial strains and the initial stresses can be found in a similar way. It is necessary to remark in this connection that initial strain, such as may be due to a temperature rise, is seldom confined in its effects on curvatures. Usually, direct strains in the plate are introduced additionally, and the complete problem can be solved only by consideration of the plane stress problem as well as that of bending.

10.5 Quadrilateral and Parallelogram Elements

The rectangular element cannot be easily generalized into quadrilateral shape. Transformation of co-ordinates of the type described in Chapter 9 can be performed but unfortunately now it will be found that the constant curvature criterion is violated. As expected such elements behave badly. Only for the case of a parallelogram is it possible to achieve states of constant curvature using exclusively functions of ξ and η.

Such an element is suggested in the discussion to reference 12 and the stiffness matrices have been worked out by Dawe.[14]

A somewhat different set of shape functions was suggested by Argyris.[15]

Table 10.2

Stress Matrix $\left(p = \dfrac{a}{b}\right)$

Rectangular Element of Fig. 10.2 Orthotropic Material

$$
\begin{Bmatrix} M_i \\ M_j \\ M_k \\ M_l \end{Bmatrix}
= \frac{1}{4ab}
\;[\,K\,]\;
\begin{Bmatrix} \delta_i \\ \delta_j \\ \delta_k \\ \delta_l \end{Bmatrix}
$$

	δ_i			δ_j			δ_k			δ_l	
$6p^{-1}D_x+6pD_1$	$-8aD_1$	$8bD_x$	$-6pD_1$	$-4aD_1$	0	$-6p^{-1}D_x$	0	$4bD_x$	0	0	0
$6pD_y+6p^{-1}D_1$	$-8aD_y$	$8bD_1$	$-6pD_y$	$-4aD_y$	0	$-6p^{-1}D_1$	0	$4bD_1$	0	0	0
$-2D_{xy}$	$4bD_{xy}$	$-4aD_{xy}$	$2D_{xy}$	0	$4aD_{xy}$	$2D_{xy}$	$-4bD_{xy}$	0	$-2D_{xy}$	0	0
$-6pD_1$	$4aD_1$	0	$6p^{-1}D_x+6pD_1$	$8aD_1$	$8bD_x$	0	0	0	$-6p^{-1}D_x$	0	$4bD_x$
$-6pD_y$	$4aD_y$	0	$6pD_y+6p^{-1}D_1$	$8aD_y$	$8bD_1$	0	0	0	$-6p^{-1}D_1$	0	$4bD_1$
$-2D_{xy}$	$-4aD_{xy}$	$4bD_{xy}$	$2D_{xy}$	$4aD_{xy}$	0	$2D_{xy}$	0	0	$2D_{xy}$	$-4bD_{xy}$	0
$-6p^{-1}D_x$	0	$-4bD_x$	0	0	0	$6p^{-1}D_x+6pD_1$	$-8aD_1$	$-8bD_x$	$-6pD_1$	$-4aD_1$	0
$-6p^{-1}D_1$	0	$-4bD_1$	0	0	0	$6pD_y+6p^{-1}D_1$	$-8aD_y$	$-8bD_1$	$-6pD_y$	$-4aD_y$	0
$2D_{xy}$	$-4bD_{xy}$	0	$2D_{xy}$	0	0	$-2D_{xy}$	$-4bD_{xy}$	$-4aD_{xy}$	$2D_{xy}$	0	$4aD_{xy}$
0	0	0	$-6p^{-1}D_x$	0	$4bD_x$	$-6pD_1$	$4aD_1$	0	$6p^{-1}D_x+6pD_1$	$8aD_1$	$-8bD_x$
0	0	0	$-6p^{-1}D_1$	0	$4bD_1$	$-6pD_y$	$4aD_y$	0	$6pD_y+6p^{-1}D_1$	$8aD_y$	$-8bD_1$
$-2D_{xy}$	0	0	$2D_{xy}$	$-4bD_{xy}$	0	$2D_{xy}$	0	$4aD_{xy}$	$-2D_{xy}$	$-4bD_{xy}$	$4aD_{xy}$

TABLE 10.3
LOAD MATRIX FOR A RECTANGULAR ELEMENT OF FIG. 10.3
UNDER UNIFORM LOAD q

$$\begin{Bmatrix} F_i \\ F_j \\ F_k \\ F_l \end{Bmatrix} = 4qab \begin{Bmatrix} 1/4 \\ -b/12 \\ a/12 \\ 1/4 \\ b/12 \\ a/12 \\ 1/4 \\ -b/12 \\ -a/12 \\ 1/4 \\ b/12 \\ -a/12 \end{Bmatrix} \qquad F_i = \begin{Bmatrix} F_{wi} \\ F_{\theta xi} \\ F_{\theta yi} \end{Bmatrix}.$$

For a parallelogram the local co-ordinates can be related to the global ones by an explicit expression (Fig. 10.5)

$$\xi = (x - y \cot \alpha)/a$$
$$\eta = y \operatorname{cosec} \alpha / b \qquad (10.24)$$

and all expressions can therefore be also derived directly.

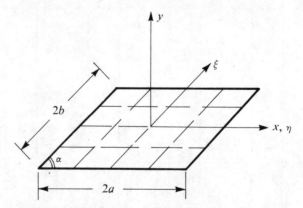

Fig. 10.5   Parallelogram element and skew co-ordinates

10.6 Triangular Element with Corner Nodes

10.6.1 *Shape functions*. At first sight, it would seem that once again a simple polynomial expansion could be used in a manner identical to that of the previous section. As only nine independent movements are imposed, only nine terms of the expansion are permissible. Here, an immediate difficulty arises as the full cubic expansion contains ten terms (Eq. (10.13)) and any omission has to be made rather arbitrarily. To retain a certain symmetry of appearance all ten terms could be retained and two co-efficients made equal (e.g., $\alpha_8 = \alpha_9$) to limit the number of unknowns to nine. Several such possibilities have been investigated but a further, much more serious, problem arises. The matrix corresponding to $[C]$ of Eq. (10.14) becomes singular for certain orientations of the triangle sides. This happens, for instance, when two sides of the triangle are parallel to the x and y axes.

Difficulties of such asymmetry can be avoided by the use of area co-ordinates described in Chapter 8. These are indeed nearly always a natural choice for triangles.

As before we shall use polynomial expansion terms, and it is worth remarking that these are given in area co-ordinates in an unusual form. For instance

$$\alpha_1 L_1 + \alpha_2 L_2 + \alpha_3 L_3$$

gives the three terms of a *complete* linear polynomial and

$$\alpha_1 L_1 L_2 + \alpha_2 L_2 L_3 + \alpha_3 L_3 L_1 + \alpha_4 L_1^2 + \alpha_5 L_2^2 + \alpha_6 L^2$$

gives all the six terms of a quadratic (containing within it the linear terms). The ten terms of a cubic expression are similarly formed by the products of all possible cubic combinations, i.e.,

$$L_1^3, \ L_2^3, \ L_3^3, \ L_1^2 L_2, \ L_3^3 L_3, \ L_3^3 L_1, \ L_1 L_2^2, \ L_2 L_3^2, \ L_3 L_1^2, \ L_1 L_2 L_3.$$

For a nine degree of freedom element any of the above terms can be used in a suitable combination, remembering, however, that only nine independent functions are needed and that constant curvature states have to be obtained. Figure 10.6 shows some functions which are of importance. The first (Fig. 10.6(a)) gives one of three functions representing a simple, unstrained, translation of plate. Obviously these modes must be available.

Further, functions of the type $L_1^2 L_2$ of which there are six in the cubic expression will be found to take up a form similar (though not identical) to Fig. 10.6(b).

Last, a function $L_1 L_2 L_3$ is shown in Fig. 10.6(c) illustrating that this is a purely internal mode with zero values and slopes at all the three corners. This function could thus be useful for a nodeless or internal variable but will not, in isolation, be used as it cannot be prescribed in terms of corner variables. It can, however, be added to any other basic shape in any corner proportion.

The functions of the second kind are therefore of essential interest. They have zero values of w at all corners and indeed always have a zero slope in the direction of one side. A linear combination of two of these (e.g., $L_2^2 L_3$ and $L_2^2 L_1$) will be capable of providing any desired slopes in the x and y directions at one node while maintaining all other slopes at zero.

We shall, however, consider modes of the type

$$L_2^2 L_3 + c L_1 L_2 L_3$$

for an added generality (as the last term does not have a slope contribution at the nodes).

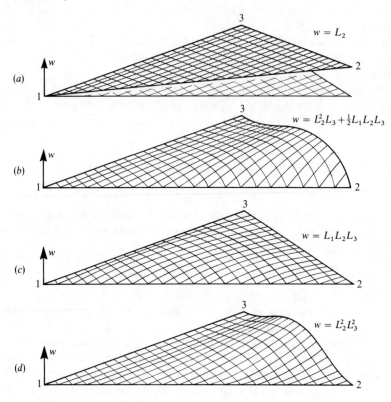

(a) $w = L_2$

(b) $w = L_2^2 L_3 + \frac{1}{2} L_1 L_2 L_3$

(c) $w = L_1 L_2 L_3$

(d) $w = L_2^2 L_3^2$

Fig. 10.6   Some basic functions in area coordinate polynomials

As these modes are the only ones contributing to curvatures it is important to ensure that the general arbitrary state of curvature with zero values of w at nodes is included in a linear combination of six of these functions. In algebraic terms this means that the expression

$$A_1 L_1 L_2 + A_2 L_2 L_3 + \cdots + A_6 L_3^2$$

with any set of values of the coefficients A must be achievable by an appropriate combination of

$$B_1(L_2^2 L_1 + c L_1 L_2 L_3) + B_2(L_1^2 L_2 + c L_1 L_2 L_3) + \cdots$$

with same set of the six constants B. It is possible to show after some algebraic manipulation that this can only be achieved for a value of $c = \frac{1}{2}$. Hence the mode plotted in Fig. 10.6(*b*) is one of the basic ones needed for the generation of shape functions.

We can now describe the displacement of the plate in the form

$$w = \beta_1 L_1 + \beta_2 L_2 + \beta_3 L_3 + \beta_4 (L_1^2 L_1 + \tfrac{1}{2} L_1 L_2 L_3)$$
$$+ \ldots + \beta_9 (L_1^2 L_2 + \tfrac{1}{2} L_1 L_2 L_3) \quad (10.25)$$

and substituting the nodal values of

$$w_i, \quad \theta_{xi} = -\left(\frac{\partial w}{\partial y}\right)_i \quad \text{and} \quad \theta_{yi} = \left(\frac{\partial w}{\partial x}\right)_i$$

the constants and hence the shape functions can be determined.

Explicitly the first result can be written in the form given below for a typical shape function using the definitions of Chapter 7, where

$$b_1 = y_2 - y_3 \qquad c_1 = x_3 - x_2, \text{ etc.}$$

$$[N_1]^{\mathrm{T}} = \left\{ \begin{array}{c} L_1 + L_1^2 L_2 + L_1^2 L_3 - L_1 L_2^2 - L_1 L_3^2 \\ b_3(L_1^2 L_2 + \tfrac{1}{2} L_1 L_2 L_3) - b_2(L_3 L_1^2 + \tfrac{1}{2} L_1 L_2 L_3) \\ c_3(L_1^2 L_2 + \tfrac{1}{2} L_1 L_2 L_3) - c_2(L_3 L_1^2 + \tfrac{1}{2} L_1 L_2 L_3) \end{array} \right\}. \quad (10.26)$$

The other two functions for nodes 2 or 3 are written by a cyclic permutation of suffixes $\overrightarrow{1\text{–}2\text{–}3}$. The element specified by the above function was first $\overleftarrow{\phantom{1\text{–}2\text{–}3}}$ presented in reference 4.

10.6.2 *Stiffness and load matrices*. With the definition of strains of Eq. (10.2) and the general $[B_i]$ matrix of Eq. (10.6) we see that second derivatives of $[N]$ are necessary.

The only new feature is presented by the fact that differentiation with respect to Cartesian co-ordinates needs to be carried out. This is quite easy noting that

$$\frac{\partial}{\partial x} = \frac{\partial L_1}{\partial x} \frac{\partial}{\partial L_1} + \frac{\partial L_2}{\partial x} \frac{\partial}{\partial L_2} + \frac{\partial L_3}{\partial x} \frac{\partial}{\partial L_3} =$$

$$= \frac{1}{2\Delta} \left(b_1 \frac{\partial}{\partial L_1} + b_2 \frac{\partial}{\partial L_2} + b_3 \frac{\partial}{\partial L_3} \right), \text{ etc.} \quad (10.27)$$

All expressions remain polynomial in the area co-ordinates and can be simply integrated using the general expression, Eq. (7.34) of Chapter 7. The explicit final form for stiffness and load matrices is somewhat lengthy and the interested reader will find these in reference 19.

However, it is simpler to program using numerical integration as outlined in Chapter 8. As the stiffness matrix involves only quadratic terms a triangle integrating expression using three points only is exact (*vide* Table 8.3 of Chapter 8) and the actual computer times used in such numerical integration are indistinguishable from those involving explicit expressions.

The 'stress' matrix gives moments which vary linearly. However, as the full cubic terms are not allowed in the expansion this leads to a poor approximation and it is usual to evaluate the moments only at centroids and indeed to use nodal averages for further smoothing.

10.7 Convergence of Non-conforming Elements

The two types of elements outlined in the preceding section violate the continuity of slope conditions and therefore only approximate to the principle of minimization of total potential energy. In the next section results will be shown, however, which demonstrate their practical accuracy. The reader may ask whether convergence will always in fact occur to the 'exact' answer with decreasing subdivision. Although this question is somewhat academic it needs an answer.

With regard to rectangular elements Walz et al.[16] investigated the algorithm obtained by a set of such elements and, by comparing this with expansions of the governing differential equations for the case of homogeneous plates found that such convergence is then guaranteed. It is not reasonable to extend these conclusions beyond this proven case.

The simple triangle again has been shown by Irons[4] to give an exactly convergent solution when the mesh is generated by three sets of equally spaced parallel lines.

The test applied here was simple. If an array of a large number of assembled elements can reproduce an *exact* response to all constant curvature states applied, then, in the limit of subdivision, the plate behaves exactly according to the physical rules applied to an infinitesimal material element. Conversely if such response is *not* available convergence cannot occur.

Indeed, the same test applied to a mesh of type shown in Fig. 10.7 (4 × 4 B), in which the triangles are obtained by drawing two diagonals of a parallelogram, was shown to give some 1·5 per cent error in displacements. Thus here the non-conforming triangle will not converge to the exact solution but to one in which the errors are of that order.

A similar test was also applied to the non-conforming rectangular element in reference 4 and gave the first convergence proof for this element.

For practical engineering purposes in most cases the accuracy obtained by the non-conforming triangle is adequate. Indeed it gives, at most practical subdivisions, results superior to those attainable with equivalent conforming triangles.[4] This may well be due to the fact that the solution now does not follow the energy bounds given in Chapter 2, and has a greater freedom to take up the best shape.

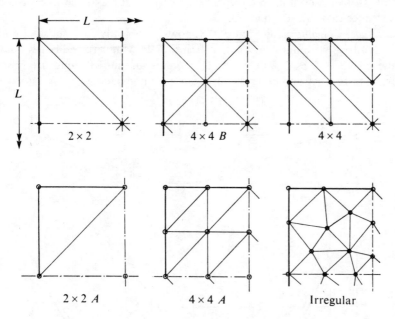

Fig. 10.7   Square plate—element divisions (triangular)

In the derivation of non-conforming elements given here, it was argued that displacement w should at least be continuous and that the slope condition should be satisfied at all points of interconnection. This always resulted in at least a cubic variation of w. If one relaxes some of these requirements, further interesting possibilities develop. For instance, if a triangle with six nodes is taken and degrees of freedom are six prescribed as w at corners and $\partial w/\partial n$ normal slope at midsides, we find that a *complete quadratic* expansion can be determined. This will result in constant moments and curvatures throughout and would produce the *simplest bending element possible* equivalent to the constant strain triangle.

Such an element has been recently derived by Morley [31] who shows that despite the apparently rather serious discontinuities the element is a convergent one and gives an approximation comparable with that attainable with the more complex triangle discussed here.

The problem of stiffness derivation for this element is left to the reader as an exercise.

10.8 Examples of Solution

10.8.1 *Rectangular elements.* A program based on the displacement functions developed in Eq. (10.13) has been prepared and a few simple test problems computed to illustrate the accuracy and the rate of convergence that can be expected.

Square isotropic plate. Figure 10.8 shows graphically the results obtained by loading, with uniform load, a square plate with clamped edges. Only the results of 2 by 2, 4 by 4, and 6 by 6 division into elements are given, but the accuracy and general convergence are convincing.

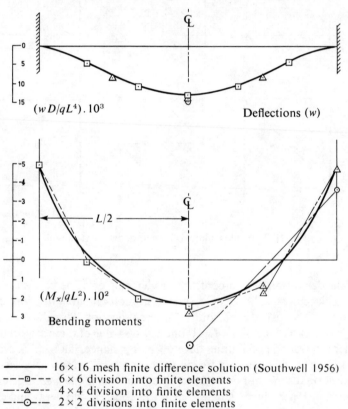

16 × 16 mesh finite difference solution (Southwell 1956)
6 × 6 division into finite elements
4 × 4 division into finite elements
2 × 2 divisions into finite elements

Fig. 10.8   A square plate with clamped edges. Uniform load q. Square elements

The linear distribution of moments tries, as it were, to give the 'best fit' to the exact moment distributions at all stages of the subdivision.

The convergence and accuracy are even more strikingly demonstrated in Table 10.4. In this the central deflections are compared for concentrated and distributed loadings with various edge conditions. With an 8 by 8 division into elements the largest error is of the order of 3 per cent. In all cases convergence appears to occur for all subdivisions.

Cantilever plate. A similar plate, but now supported as a cantilever, gives displacements shown in Fig. 10.9. Here the answers are compared with other numerical and experimental solutions and, once again, good accuracy is apparent.

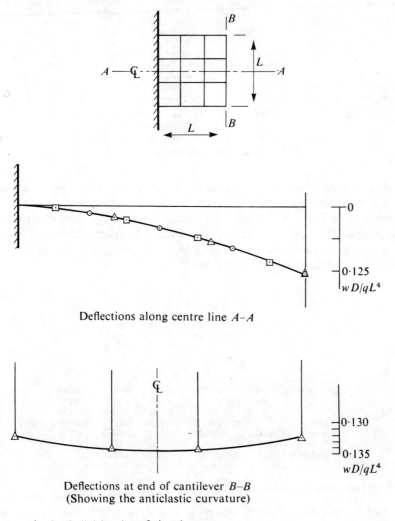

Deflections along centre line *A–A*

Deflections at end of cantilever *B–B*
(Showing the anticlastic curvature)

△ 3 × 3 division into finite elements
▣ 5 × 5 mesh finite difference solution (Livesey & Birchall 1956)
⊙ Experimental values (Dalley 1948)

Fig. 10.9 Loading of a square plate supported as a cantilever (Uniform load *q*)

TABLE 10.4

COMPUTED CENTRAL DEFLECTION OF A SQUARE PLATE FOR
SEVERAL MESHES (RECTANGULAR ELEMENTS)

Mesh	Total No. of nodes	Simply Supported Plate		Clamped Plate	
		α (uniform load)	β (concentrated load)	α (uniform load)	β (concentrated (load)
(2×2)	9	0·003446	0·013784	0·001480	0·005919
(4×4)	25	0·003939	0·012327	0·001403	0·006134
(8×8)	81	0·004033	0·011829	0·001304	0·005803
(12×12)	169	0·004050	0·011715	0·001283	0·005710
(16×16)	289	0·004056	0·011671	0·001275	0·005672
Exact (Timoshenko)		0·004062	0·01160	0·00126	0·00560

$w_{max} = \alpha q L^4/D$ for a uniformly distributed load q;
$w_{max} = \beta P^2/D$ for a central concentrated load P.
(Based on Tocher, J. L., and Kapur, K. K.).[20]

(Subdivision of whole plate given above)

Corner supported plate.[12] A square plate supported by corner columns
has been subjected to various experimental and approximate analytical
solutions. In Table 10.5 results of a finite element analysis are compared
with some other approximate solutions. Even in this case, where the corner
concentration would tend to cause difficulties, reasonable agreement of
both displacements and stresses is apparent.

TABLE 10.5

CORNER SUPPORTED SQUARE PLATE

	Point 1		Point 2	
	w	M_x	w	M_x
Finite element 2×2	0·0126	0·139	0·0176	0·095
4×4	0·0165	0·149	0·0232	0·108
6×6	0·0173	0·150	0·0244	0·109
Marcus	0·0180	0·154	0·0281	0·110
Lee and Ballesteros	0·0170	0·140	0·0265	0·109
Multiplier	qL^4/D	qL^2	qL^4/D	qL^2

Point 1, centre of side: point 2, centre of plate

10.8.2 *Triangular elements—square isotropic plate.* Once again a square
plate is chosen to illustrate the convergence. This is now divided into
different combinations of triangular elements. Some of these are based on
a square network, some are completely irregular. Figure 10.7 shows the
various types of division into elements while Fig. 10.10 illustrates the dis-

placements obtained for various edge and loading conditions. Again, the accuracy and convergence of displacements are good (though perhaps not quite as good as with rectangular elements).

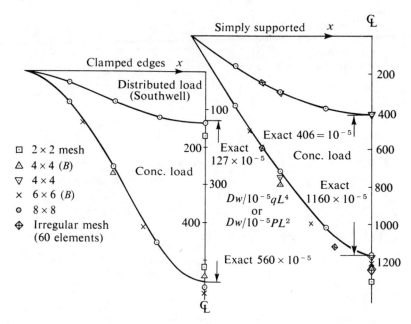

Fig. 10.10 Square plate deflections on centre-line (triangular elements)

Figure 10.11 shows the variation of bending moments on typical centre line sections. If the mean values are used then these moments compare well with exact values. No longer can we say, however, that the linear variation of stresses follow the 'best fit' to the actual stress distribution.

For practical problems it is therefore recommended that attention should be focused at stresses (moments) at centroids of the elements.

Plate with central circular hole. Although for this example no exact solution is available it was chosen to illustrate the versatility of the triangular elements for dealing with perforations and boundaries of any shape.

In Fig. 10.12 the mesh division used is plotted together with the contours of w. In Fig. 10.13, slope contours are compared against a Moire type experimental solution. The agreement of slopes is within limits of experimental error.

10.8.3 *Some practical applications.* The range of practical application of the solution program, particularly the one based on triangular elements,

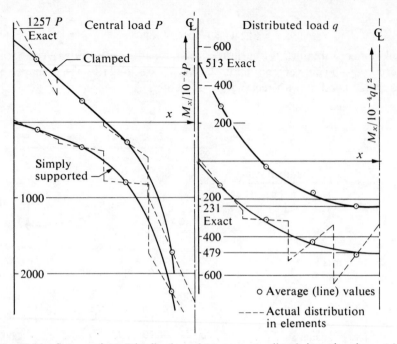

Fig. 10.11 Square plate. Distribution of M_x on centre line (triangular elements)

Fig. 10.12 Square plate with hole. Contours—values of deflections (wD/PL^2). Division into triangular elements shown

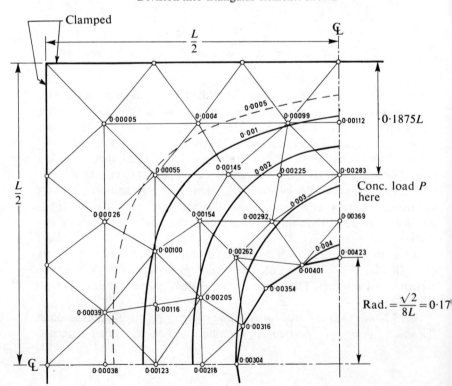

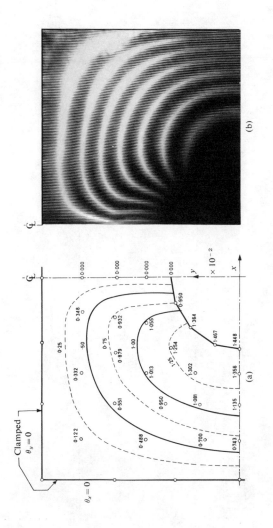

Fig. 10.13   Square plate with hole. Contours of slope ($\theta_Y = \partial W/\partial X . D/PL$)
(a) computed, (b) by Moire fringe experiment (1 fringe $= 0.213 \times 10^{-2}$)

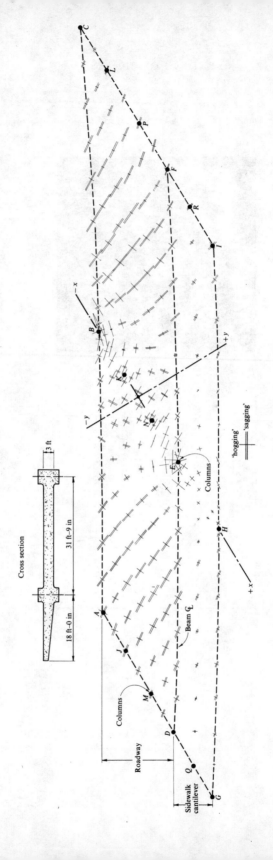

Fig. 10.14 A two span skew bridge with beams and non uniform thickness. Computer plot of principal moments under dead load.

is great. Problems of foundation slabs, bridge decks, or ship hulls can be
treated with ease.

Indeed the problem of bridge structures is one of extensive practical
use and here applications have been very numerous. Figure 10.14 shows an
automatic computer plot of prescribed stresses on a multispan bridge.

In Figs. 10.15 and 10.16 a bridge of more complex shape is illustrated.
Here component contour plots are given as an alternative presentation.
In this example edge beams are present and these have been assumed to
have the same neutral axis as the plate. No difficulty exists in coupling
such beam elements to the plate structure, assembly proceeding on the
usual lines of Chapter 1.

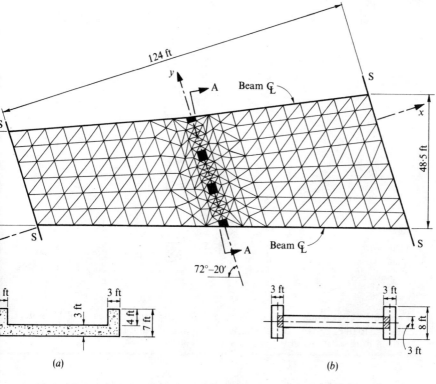

Fig. 10.15   The Castleton bridge. General geometry and detail of finite element
subdivisions: (a) shows the typical actual section, while (b) shows the nature of
idealization involved. The bridge ends are simply supported with no rotational
restraint. Columns taken as artificial slab thickening over black area and given an
elastic vertical restraint. $v = 0.17$

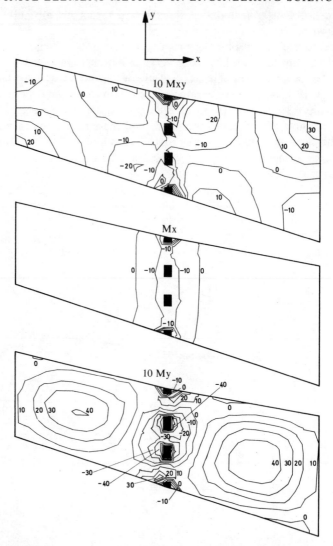

Fig. 10.16   Moment components (ton ft./ft.) for bridge of Fig. 10.15 under a uniform load of 150 lb./sq. ft. Computer plot of contours. Note that most loads are carried in this example by transverse slab bending

CONFORMING SHAPE FUNCTIONS WITH NODAL SINGULARITIES

10.9 General Remarks

It was already seen in section 10.3 that it is impossible to devise a simple polynomial function with only three degrees of nodal freedom which will

be able to satisfy slope continuity requirements. The alternative of imposing curvature parameters at nodes has the disadvantage, however, of
imposing excessive conditions of continuity. Furthermore it is desirable
from many points of view to limit the nodal variables to three quantities
only. These, with a simple physical interpretation, allow the generalization of plate elements to shells to be easily interpreted. Also computational
advantages arise.

The simple alternative is to provide additional shape functions for
which *second-order derivatives have non-unique values at nodes*. Providing
no infinities occur there, convergence is assured.

Such shape functions will be discussed now in the context of triangular
and quadrilateral elements. The simple rectangular shape will be omitted.

10.10 Singular Shape Functions for the Simple Triangular Element

Consider for instance either of the following sets of functions:

$$\varepsilon_{23} = \frac{L_1 L_2^2 L_3^2}{(L_1 + L_2)(L_2 + L_3)}, \text{ etc.} \tag{10.28}$$

or

$$\varepsilon_{23} = \frac{L_1 L_2^2 L_3^2 (1 + L_1)}{(L_1 + L_2)(L_2 + L_3)}, \text{ etc.} \tag{10.29}$$

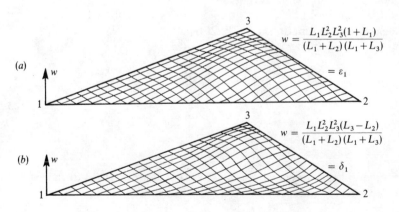

Fig. 10.17   Some singular area co-ordinate functions

Both have the property that along two sides (1–2) and (1–3) of a triangle
(Fig. 10.17), their values and the values of their normal slope are zero. On
the third side (2–3) their value is zero but a normal slope exists. In both its
variation is parabolic. The second function shape is illustrated in Fig.
10.17(a).

Now, all the functions used for definition of the non-conforming triangle (*vide* Eq. (10.25)) were cubic and hence permitted also a parabolic variation of the normal slope which is not uniquely defined by the two, end, nodal values (and hence resulted in the non-conformity). However, if we specify as an additional variable the *normal slope of w* at a mid-side point of each side then by combining the new function ε with the other functions previously given a *unique parabolic variation of the normal slope* along inter-element faces is achieved and a compatible element will result.

Apparently, this can be achieved by adding three such additional degrees of freedom to expression (10.25) and proceeding as there described. This will result in an element shown in Fig. 10.18(a) which has six nodes, three corner ones as before and three additional ones at which only normal slope is specified.

Such an element presents some assembly difficulties as different numbers of degrees of freedom are associated with the nodes.

To avoid the above difficulty the mid-side node degree of freedom can now be constrained. For instance we can assume that the normal slope at the centre point of a line is given as the average of the two slopes at the end of that side. This results in a compatible element with exactly the same degrees of freedom as that described in previous sections, Fig. 10.18(b).

The algebra involved in the generation of suitable shape functions on the lines described here is tedious and will not be given. It is developed most simply on the following lines.

First the normal slopes at mid-sides are calculated from the basic element shape functions (Eq. 10.26)) as

$$\left\{ \begin{array}{c} \left(\dfrac{\partial w}{\partial n}\right)_4 \\[2ex] \left(\dfrac{\partial w}{\partial n}\right)_5 \\[2ex] \left(\dfrac{\partial w}{\partial n}\right)_6 \end{array} \right\} = [Z]\{\delta\}^e. \tag{10.30}$$

Similarly the average values of the corner slopes normal to the sides are calculated for these points from these functions,

$$\left\{ \begin{array}{c} \left(\dfrac{\partial w}{\partial n}\right)_4^a \\[2ex] \left(\dfrac{\partial w}{\partial n}\right)_5^a \\[2ex] \left(\dfrac{\partial w}{\partial n}\right)_6^a \end{array} \right\} = [Y]\{\delta\}^e. \tag{10.31}$$

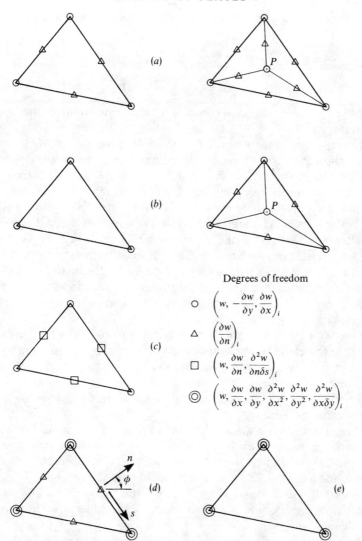

Fig. 10.18   Various conforming triangular elements

Now the contribution of the ε functions to these slopes is added in proportions $\varepsilon_{23} \times \gamma_1$, etc., is simply (as these give unit normal slope)

$$\{\gamma\} = \begin{Bmatrix} \gamma_1 \\ \gamma_2 \\ \gamma_3 \end{Bmatrix}. \qquad (10.32)$$

On combining Eq. (10.26) and the last three relations we have

$$[Y]\{\delta\}^e = [Z]\{\delta\}^e + \{\gamma\} \qquad (10.33)$$

from which it immediately follows on finding γ that

$$w = [N^\circ]\{\delta\}^e + [\varepsilon_{23}, \varepsilon_{31}, \varepsilon_{13}]([Y] - [Z])\{\delta\}^e \qquad (10.34)$$

in which $[N^\circ]$ are the non-conforming shape functions defined previously.

Thus the shape functions are now available from Eq. (10.34).

An alternative way of generating compatible triangles was developed by Clough and Tocher.[3] As shown in Fig. 10.18(a) each element triangle is first divided into three parts based on an internal point P. For each triangle a complete cubic expansion is written involving ten terms. The final expansion is to be expressed in terms of nine conventional degrees of freedom at nodes 1, 2, 3 and normal slopes at nodes 4, 5, 6. As at each corner two triangles have to give the same nodal values, two sets of equations are there provided, i.e., a total of $9 \times 2 + 3 = 21$ equations is thus provided. In addition continuity of displacements and slopes at the centre node P provides an additional six equations and continuity of slopes of internal mid-sides a further three.

Thus we have thirty equations and thirty unknowns which suffice in this case to determine the shape functions explicitly and thus achieve an element with twelve degrees of freedom similar to the one previously outlined.

Constraint of normal slopes on exterior sides leads to an element with nine degrees of freedom.

These elements are achieved at the expense of providing two values of second derivatives at the corners. In the previously discussed set, in fact, the shape functions ε provide an infinite number of derivatives depending on the direction in which the corner is approached.

Indeed the derivation of the Clough and Tocher triangles can be approached by defining an alternative set of ε functions as has been shown in reference 4.

As both types of elements lead to almost identical numerical results the preferable one is that leading to simplified computation. If numerical integration is used (as indeed is strongly recommended for such elements) the form of functions continuously defined over the whole triangle as given in Eqs. (10.28) and (10.29) is advantageous.

10.11 An Eighteen-degree-of-freedom Triangular Element with Conforming Shape Functions

An element which presents a desirable improvement over the type illustrated in Fig. 10.18(a) is shown in Fig. 10.18(c). Here the twelve degrees of freedom are increased to eighteen by considering both the value of w and its cross derivative $\partial^2 w/\partial s\,\partial n$, in addition to the normal slope of $\partial w/\partial n$, at element mid-sides.

Thus an equal number of degrees of freedom is presented at each node giving a computational advantage. Imposition of the continuity of cross derivatives *at mid-sides* does not involve an additional constraint as this indeed must be continuous in physical situations.

The derivation of this element is given by Irons[7] and it will suffice here to say that in addition to the modes already discussed, fourth-order terms of the type illustrated in Fig. 10.6(*d*) and 'twist' function of Fig. 10.17 (*b*) are used. Indeed it can be simply verified that the element contains *all* the fifteen terms of the quartic expansion in addition to the 'singularity' functions.

10.12 Compatible Quadrilateral Elements

Any of the previous triangles can be combined to produce compatible quadrilateral elements with or without internal degrees of freedom. Three such quadrilaterals are illustrated in Fig. 10.19 and in all, no mid-side nodes exist on the external boundaries. This is to avoid the difficulties of assembly already mentioned.

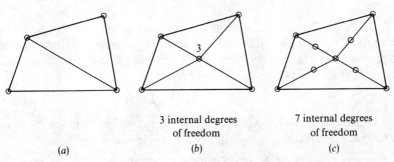

3 internal degrees
of freedom

7 internal degrees
of freedom

(*a*)　　　　　　　(*b*)　　　　　　　(*c*)

Fig. 10.19　Some composite quadrilateral elements

In the first, no internal degrees of freedom are present and indeed no improvement on the comparable triangles is expected. In the following two, 3 and 7 internal degrees of freedom exist respectively. Here normal slope continuity imposed in the last one does not interfere with the assembly, as internal degrees of freedom are in all cases eliminated. Much improved accuracy with these elements has been demonstrated by Clough and Felippa.[21]

An alternative direct derivation of a quadrilateral element was proposed by Sander[5] and Fraeijs de Veubeke.[6,22] This is along the following lines; within a quadrilateral of Fig. 10.20 a complete cubic with ten constants is taken giving the first component of the displacement which is defined by three functions. Thus

$$w = w^a + w^b + w^c$$

and

$$w^a = \alpha_1 + \alpha_2 x + \cdots + \alpha_{10} y^3. \tag{10.35}$$

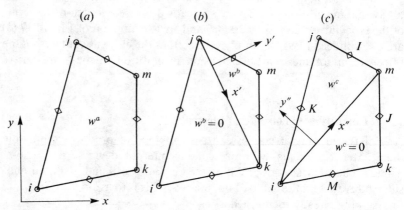

Fig. 10.20 The compatible functions suggested by Fraeijs de Veubeke

The second function w^b is defined in a piecewise manner. In the lower triangle of Fig. 10.20(b) it is taken as zero; in the upper triangle a cubic expression with three constants merges without slope discontinuity into the field of the lower triangle. Thus in *jkm*

$$w^b = \alpha_{11} y'^2 + \alpha_{12} y'^3 + \alpha_{13} x' y'^2 \tag{10.36}$$

in terms of the locally specified co-ordinates x', y'. Similarly for the third function, Fig. 10.20(c), $w^c = 0$ in lower triangle and in *imj*

$$w^c = \alpha_{14} y''^2 + \alpha_{15} y''^3 + \alpha_{16} x'' y''^2. \tag{10.37}$$

The sixteen external degrees of freedom are provided by three usual corner variables and normal mid-side slopes and allow the sixteen constants α_{1-16} to be found by inversion. Compatibility is assured and once again non-unique second derivatives arise at corners.

Again it is possible to constrain the mid-side nodes if desired and thus obtain a twelve-degree-of-freedom element.

The expansion can be found explicitly as shown by Veubeke[22] and a useful element generated.

The element described above cannot be formulated if a corner of the quadrilateral is re-entrant. This is not a serious limitation but needs to be considered on occasion if such an element degenerates to near triangular shape.

10.13 Some Solutions with Conforming Elements

Convergence and accuracy of the various elements described here has been much discussed in the literature. References 3, 4, and 21 are particularly useful in this context.

In Fig. 10.21 convergence of the two simple, but incompatible elements discussed in this chapter is compared with that of three different compatible elements.

— — — —	Incompatible Rectangle	12 degrees of freedom
————————	Incompatible Triangle	9 degrees of freedom
—·—·—·	Compatible Quadrilateral (Veubeke)	16 degrees of freedom
++++++++	Compatible Triangle	9 degrees of freedom
··············	Compatible Quadrilateral (Clough)	12 degrees of freedom (+7 internal)

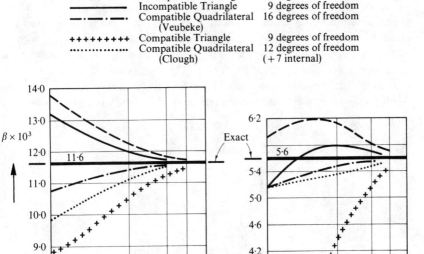

Fig. 10.21 Comparison of various finite element solutions for a square plate under a central load P. n—number of divisions of half edge a. $\beta = w/Pa^2D$

Some remarks are worth making. Firstly the simplest compatible triangle gives a rather poor approximation at coarse subdivision and is at all times worse than its incompatible equivalent.

Further, whilst all compatible elements converge to the exact answer *from below* as they give in this case, by the theorems of Chapter 2, a lower bound, incompatible elements, whilst *usually* converging from above may err on either side.

Finally the excellent results attainable with the Veubeke quadrilateral of Fig. 10.20 and with the quadrilateral of Clough, Fig. 10.19(c), are worth remarking.

CONFORMING SHAPE FUNCTION WITH ADDITIONAL DEGREES OF FREEDOM

10.14 Hermitian Rectangle Shape Function

With a rectangular element of Fig. 10.1 the specification of $\partial^2 w / \partial x\, \partial y$ as a nodal parameter is always permissible as it does not involve 'excessive continuity'. It is easy to show that for such an element polynomial shape functions giving compatibility can be easily determined.

A polynomial expansion involving sixteen constants (equal to the number of nodal parameters) could for instance be written retaining terms which do not produce a higher order variation of w or its normal slope than cubic along the sides. Many alternatives will be present here and some may not produce invertible $[C]$ matrices.

An alternative derivation uses Hermitian polynomials which permit the writing down of suitable functions directly. A Hermitian polynomial

$$H^n_{mi}(x) \tag{10.38}$$

is a polynomial of order $2n + 1$ which gives, when $x = x_i$,

$$\frac{d^k H}{dx^k} = 1, \quad k = m \quad \text{for } m = 0 \text{ to } n$$

and

$$\frac{d^k H}{dx^k} = 0, \quad k \neq m \quad \text{or when } x = x_j.$$

A set of first-order Hermitian polynomials is thus a set of cubics giving shape functions for a linear element ij at the ends of which slopes and values of the function are used as variables.

Figure 10.22 shows such a set of cubics.

It is easy to verify that the following shape functions

$$[N_i] = [H^{(1)}_{0i}(x)H^{(1)}_{0i}(y),\ H^{(1)}_{1i}(x)H^{(1)}_{0i}(y),$$
$$H^{(1)}_{0i}(x)H^{(1)}_{1i}(y),\ H^{(1)}_{1i}(x)H^{(1)}_{1i}(y)] \tag{10.39}$$

correspond to

$$w,\ \frac{\partial w}{\partial y},\ \frac{\partial w}{\partial x},\ \frac{\partial^2 w}{\partial x\, \partial y}$$

taking successively unit values at node i and zero elsewhere.

An element based on these shape functions has been developed by Bogner and Schmit[8] and used with some success.

A development of this type of element to include continuity of higher derivatives is simple and is outlined in reference 9.

In its undistorted form the above elements are, as all rectangles, of very limited applicability.

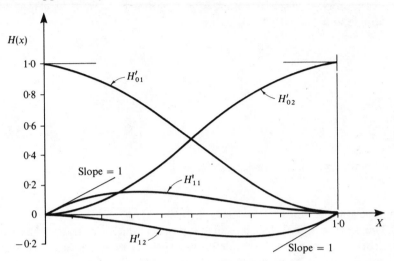

Fig. 10.22   First order Hermitian Functions

10.15 Twenty-one- and eighteen-degree-of-freedom Triangles

If continuity of higher derivatives than the first is accepted at nodes (thus imposing a certain constraint on non-homogeneous situations as explained in section 10.3), the generation of slope and deflection compatible elements presents less difficulty.

Considering as nodal degrees of freedom.

$$w, \quad \frac{\partial w}{\partial x}, \quad \frac{\partial w}{\partial y}, \quad \frac{\partial^2 w}{\partial x^2}, \quad \frac{\partial^2 w}{\partial y^2}, \quad \frac{\partial^2 w}{\partial x \, \partial y}$$

a triangular element will involve at least eighteen degrees of freedom. Now, a complete fifth-order polynomial contains twenty-one terms. If therefore we add three normal slopes at mid-side as additional degrees of freedom a sufficient number of equations appear to exist for which the shape function can be found.

Along any edge we have six quantities determining the variation of w (displacement, slopes (and curvature at corner nodes), i.e., specifying a fifth-order variation. Thus this is uniquely defined and therefore w is continuous between elements.

Similarly $\partial w/\partial n$ is prescribed by five quantities and varies as a fourth-order polynomial. Again this is as required by the deformation and slope continuity between elements.

If we write the complete quintic†

$$w = \alpha_1 + \alpha_2 x + \cdots + \alpha_{21} y^5 \qquad (10.40)$$

we can proceed along the lines of the argument used to develop the rectangle in section 10.4 and write

$$w_1 = \alpha_1 + \alpha_2 x_1 + \qquad\qquad + \alpha_{21} y_1^5$$

$$\left(\frac{\partial w}{\partial x}\right)_1 = \qquad \alpha_2 \qquad\qquad + \alpha_{20} y_1^3$$

$$\vdots \quad = \qquad\qquad\qquad \vdots$$

$$\left(\frac{\partial^2 w}{\partial x^2}\right)_1 = \qquad\qquad + 2\alpha_4 + \cdots + 2\alpha_{19} y_1^2, \text{ etc.}$$

and finally obtain an expression

$$\{\delta\}^e = [C]\{\alpha\} \qquad (10.41)$$

in which $[C]$ is a 21×21 matrix.

The only apparent difficulty in the process which the reader may experience in forming this is the definition of the normal slopes at mid-side nodes. However, if one notes that (Fig. 10.18)

$$\frac{\partial w}{\partial n} = -\sin\phi\,\frac{\partial w}{\partial x} + \cos\phi\,\frac{\partial w}{\partial y} \qquad (10.42)$$

in which ϕ is the angle of a particular side to the x axis the matter of formulation becomes simple.

Indeed it is not easy to determine an explicit inverse of $[C]$ and the stiffness expressions, etc., are evaluated as in Eq.(10.21) by a numerical inversion.

The existence of the mid-side nodes with their single degree of freedom along the sides is an embarrassment. It is possible, however, to constrain these by allowing only a cubic variation of the normal slope along each triangle side. Now, explicitly, the matrix $[C]$ and the degrees of freedom can be reduced to eighteen giving an element illustrated in Fig. 10.18(c) with three corner nodes and eighteen degrees of freedom. This in fact is the more useful element in practice.

Both these elements were described in several publications appearing during 1968 and obviously quite independently arrived at. This 'simultaneous discovery' fact is one of the curiosities of scientific progress and

---

† For this derivation use of simple Cartesian co-ordinates is recommended in preference to area co-ordinates. Symmetry is assured as polynomial is complete.

seems to occur in many fields where the stage for a particular development is reached.

Thus the twenty-one-degree-of-freedom element is described by Argyris,[23] Bell,[10] Bosshard,[24] Irons,[27] and Visser,[25] listing the authors alphabetically.

The reduced, eighteen-degree-of-freedom version is developed by Argyris,[23] Bell,[10] and Cowper et al.[26] An essentially similar but more complicated formulation has been developed by Butlin and Ford.[11]

It is clear that many more elements of this type could be developed and indeed some are suggested in the above references. However, it should always be borne in mind that they involve an inconsistency when non-homogeneous, step, property variation occurs. Further, the existence of higher order derivatives makes it difficult to impose boundary conditions on these and indeed the simple interpretation of energy derivatives as 'nodal forces' disappears. Thus the engineer may still feel a justified preference for the more intuitive formulation previously described despite the fact that very good accuracy has been demonstrated in the many references quoted for these elements.

10.13 Concluding Remarks

A fairly extensive survey of shape functions and the methods of their generation has been included in this chapter. The reason for this is not only the fact that plate bending situations are an important engineering application but that *all the shape functions here presented are applicable to problems in which the functional involves second-order derivatives*. Thus use of these can be made in the context of viscous flow and other physical problems of that type.

Indeed, even two-dimensional stress analysis can, as is well known, be formulated in terms of stress functions and therefore such functionals. As such formulations automatically satisfy the equilibrium conditions an 'upper bound' solution is possible by minimization of 'complementary strain energy'. Such an application was first suggested by Veubeke and Zienkiewicz.[28, 29]

It is for these reasons that many alternative formulations of the plate problem have been here omitted. Some of these are well established[30-36] but involve principles of less general applicability.

In the basic formulation of this chapter the classical theory of thin plates has been followed. The shear deformation of plates has thus not been included. This undoubtedly has some importance in very thick plate situations. Some approximate attempts to include shear deformations are described in references 21, 30, and 31. In this book the subject will be dealt with in a different manner in Chapter 14.

References

1. S. TIMOSHENKO and S. WOINOWSKY-KRIEGER, *Theory of Plates and Shells*, McGraw-Hill, 2nd ed., 1959.

2. B. M. IRONS and K. J. DRAPER, 'Inadequacy of nodal connections in a stiffness solution for plate bending', *J.A.I.A.A.*, **3**, 5, 1965.

3. R. W. CLOUGH and J. L. TOCHER, 'Finite element stiffness matrices for analysis of plates in bending', *Proc. Conf. Matrix Methods in Struct. Mech.*, Air Force Inst. of Tech., Wright Patterson A.F. Base, Ohio, 1965 (October).

4. G. P. BAZELEY, Y. K. CHEUNG, B. M. IRONS, and O. C. ZIENKIEWICZ, 'Triangular elements in bending—conforming and non-conforming solutions', *Proc. Conf. Matrix Methods in Struct. Mech.*, Air Force Inst. of Tech., Wright Patterson A.F. Base, Ohio, 1965 (October).

5. G. SANDER, 'Bornes supérieures et inférieures dans l'analyse matricielle des plaques en flexion-torsion', *Bull. Soc. Royale des Sc. de Liège*, **33**, 456–94, 1964.

6. B. FRAEIJS DE VEUBEKE, 'Bending and Stretching of Plates', *Proc. Conf. Matrix Methods in Struct. Mech.*, Air Force Inst. of Tech., Wright Patterson A.F. Base, Ohio, 1965 (October).

7. B. M. IRONS, 'A conforming quartic triangular element for plate bending', *Int. J. Num. Meth. Eng.*, **1**, 29–46, 1969.

8. F. K. BOGNER, R. L. FOX, and L. A. SCHMIT, 'The generation of interelement—compatible stiffness and mass matrices by the use of interpolation formulae', *Proc. Conf. Matrix Methods in Struct. Mech.*, Air Force Inst. of Tech., Wright Patterson A.F. Base, Ohio, 1965 (October).

9. I. M. SMITH and W. DUNCAN, 'The effectiveness of nodal continuities in finite element analysis of thin rectangular and skew plates in bending', *Int. J. Num. Mech. Eng.*, **2**, 253–8, 1970.

10. K. BELL, 'A refined triangular plate bending element', *Int. J. Num. Meth. Eng.*, **1**, 101–22, 1969.

11. G. A. BUTLIN and R. FORD, 'A compatible plate bending element', *Univ. of Leicester Eng. Dept. report*, 68-15, 1968.

12. O. C. ZIENKIEWICZ and Y. K. CHEUNG, 'The finite element method for analysis of elastic isotropic and orthotropic slabs', *Proc. Inst. Civ. Eng.*, **28**, 471–88, 1964.

13. R. W. CLOUGH, 'The finite element method in structural mechanics', chapter 7 of *Stress Analysis*, ed. O. C. Zienkiewicz and G. S. Holister, J. Wiley, 1965.

14. D. J. DAWE, 'Parallelogram element in the solution of rhombic cantilever plate problems', *J. of Strain Analysis*, **3**, 1966.

15. J. H. ARGYRIS, 'Continua and Discontinua', *Proc. Conf. Matrix Methods in Struct. Mech.*, Air Force Inst. of Tech., Wright Patterson A.F. Base, Ohio, 1965 (October).

16. J. E. WALZ, R. E. FULTON, and N. J. CYRUS, 'Accuracy and Convergence of finite element approximation', *Proc. 2nd Conf. Matrix Methods in Struct. Mech.*, Air Force Inst. of Tech., Wright Patterson A.F. Base, Ohio, 1968.

17. R. J. MELOSH, 'Basis of derivation of matrices for the direct stiffness method', *J.A.I.A.A.*, **1**, 1631–7, 1963.

18. A. ADINI and R. W. CLOUGH, *Analysis of plate bending by the finite element method* and Report to Nat. Sci. Found/U.S.A., G.7337, 1961.

19. Y. K. CHEUNG, I. P. KING, and O. C. ZIENKIEWICZ, 'Slab bridges with arbitrary shape and support conditions—a general method of analysis based on finite elements', *Proc. Inst. Civ. Eng.*, **40**, 9–36, 1968.

20. J. L. TOCHER and K. K. KAPUR, 'Comment on Basis of derivation of matrices for direct stiffness method', *J.A.I.A.A.*, **3**, 1215–16, 1965.

21. R. W. CLOUGH and C. A. FELIPPA, 'A refined quadrilateral element for analysis of plate bending', *Proc. 2nd Conf. Matrix Methods in Struct. Mech.*, Air Force Inst. of Tech., Wright Patterson A.F. Base, Ohio, 1968.

22. B. FRAEIJS DE VEUBEKE, 'A conforming finite element for plate bending', *Int. J. Solids Struct.*, **4**, 95–108, 1968.

23. J. H. ARGYRIS, I. FRIED, and D. W. SCHARPF, 'The TUBA family of plate elements for the matrix displacement method', *The Aeronautical J. R. Ae. S.*, **72**, 701–9, 1968.

24. W. BOSSHARD, 'Ein neues vollverträgliches endliches Element für Plattenbiegung', *Mt. Assoc. Bridge Struct. Eng. Bulletin*, **28**, 27–40, 1968.

25. W. VISSER, *The finite element method in deformation and heat conduction problems*, Dr. W. Dissertation, T.H., Delft, 1968.

26. G. R. COWPER, E. KOSKO, G. M. LINDBERG, and M. D. OLSON, 'Formulation of a new triangular plate bending element', *Trans. Canad. Aero-Space Inst.*, **1**, 86–90, 1968. (See also N.R.C. Aero report LR514, 1968).

27. B. M. IRONS, Comments on 'Complete polynomial displacement fields for finite element method', by P. C. Dunne, *The Aeronautical J.*, R. Ae. S., **72**, 709, 1968.

28. B. FRAEIJS DE VEUBEKE and O. C. ZIENKIEWICZ, 'Strain Energy Bounds. in finite element analysis by slab analogy', *J. Strain Analysis*, **2**, 265–71, 1967.

29. L. S. D. MORLEY, 'The triangular equilibrium element in the solution of plate bending problems', *Aero Quart.*, **19**, p. 149–69, 1968.

30. T. H. H. PIAN, 'Derivation of Element Stiffness Matrices by assumed stress distribution', *A.I.A.A. Int*, **2**, 1332–6, 1964.

31. T. H. H. PIAN and P. TONG, 'Basis of finite element methods for solid continua', *Int. J. Num. Meth. Eng.*, **1**, 3–28, 1969.

32. R. J. ALWOOD and G. M. M. CORNES, 'A polygonal finite element for plate bending problems using the assumed stress approach', *In. J. Num. Meth. Eng.*, **1**, p. 135–50, 1969.

33. R. T. SEVERN and P. R. TAYLOR, 'The finite element method for flexure of slabs where stress distributions are assumed', *Proc. Inst. Civ. Eng.*, **34**, 153–70, 1966.

34. L. R. HERRMANN, 'Finite Element Bending analysis of plates', *Proc. Am. Soc. Eng.*, **93**, EM 5, 1967.

35. B. FRAEIJS DE VEUBEKE, 'An equilibrium model for plate bending', *Int. J. Solid Struct.*, **4**, 447–68, 1968.

36. L. S. D. MORLEY, 'On the constant moment plate bending element', *Journal Strain Analysis*, (to be published).

11. Shells as an Assembly of Flat Elements

11.1 Introduction

A shell is, in essence, a structure which can be derived from a thin plate by initially forming the middle plane to a singly (or doubly) curved surface. Although the same assumptions regarding the transverse distribution of strains and stresses are again valid, the way in which the shell supports external loads is quite different from that of a flat plate. The stress resultants acting parallel to the middle plane of the shell now have components normal to the surface and carry a major part of the load, a fact which explains the economy of shells as load-carrying structures and their well-deserved popularity.

The derivation of detailed governing equations for a curved-shell problem presents many difficulties and, in fact, leads to many alternative formulations, each depending on the approximations introduced. For details of classical shell treatment the reader is referred to standard texts on the subject, e.g., the well-known treatise by Flügge.[1]

In the finite element treatment of shell problems to be described in this chapter the difficulties referred to above are eliminated, at the expense of introducing a further approximation. This approximation is of a physical, rather than mathematical, nature. In this it is assumed that the behaviour of a continuously curved surface can be adequately represented by the behaviour of a surface built up of small, flat, elements.

Intuitively, as the size of the subdivision decreases it would seem that convergence must occur, and indeed experience indicates such a convergence.

An important point, however, must be considered when nodal loads (or masses) are assigned. In previous examples it was advantageous to perform a 'consistent' assignment of such loads and masses to the nodes in order to reproduce more realistically the local effects. Now, to be 'consistent' with the physical effect of replacing a curved surface by a collection of planes it would seem to be just as realistic to concentrate the distributed load as statically equivalent nodal forces. This point is perhaps

best illustrated by the simple problem of an arch ring illustrated in Fig.
11.1. The true problem of a curved arch ring subject to distributed loading
is more realistically approximated to by a segmental arch with equivalent
external static load as indicated in Fig. 11.1(b) rather than by the same
polygonal arch under a uniformly distributed load, Fig. 11.1(c). That this
is so can be verified simply by drawing the appropriate force polygons.

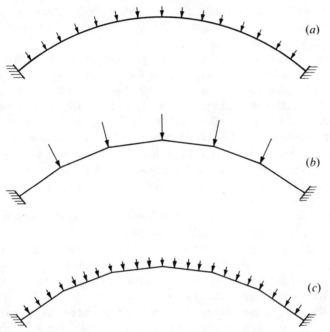

Fig. 11.1   Representation of a curve of an arch by a series of straight lines.
Loading (b) is more 'consistent' than (c)

In a shell, the element will be subject, generally, both to bending and
'in-plane' forces. For a flat element these cause independent deformations,
provided the local deformations are small, and therefore the ingredients
for obtaining the necessary stiffness matrices are available in the material
already covered in this book.

In the division of an arbitrary shell into flat elements only triangular
elements can be used. Although the concept of the use of such elements in
the analysis has been suggested as early as 1961 by Greene et al.,[2] the
success of such analysis was hampered by the lack of a good stiffness
matrix for triangular plate elements in bending.[3-6] The developments
described in Chapter 10 open the way to adequate models for representing
the behaviour of shells with such a division.

Some shells, for example those with general cylindrical shapes, can be well represented by flat elements of rectangular or quadrilateral shape. With good stiffness matrices available for such elements the progress here has been more satisfactory. Practical problems of arch dam design, and others for cylindrical shape roofs, have been solved earlier with such sub-divisions.[7,8]

Clearly, the possibilities of analysis of shell structures by the finite element method are enormous. Problems presented by openings, variation of thickness or anisotropy are no longer of consequence once general programs are written.

A special case is presented by axi-symmetrical shells. Although it is obviously possible to deal with these in the way described in this chapter, a simpler approach can be used. This will be presented in Chapter 12.

As an alternative to the type of analysis described here, curved shell elements could be used. Here curvilinear co-ordinates are essential and general procedures of Chapter 8 can be extended to define these. The physical approximation involved in flat elements is now avoided at the expense of re-introducing an arbitrariness of various shell theories. Several approaches using a direct displacement approach as given in references 9 to 18.

A very simple and effective way of deriving curved shell elements is to use the so called 'shallow' shell theory approach.[14,16]

Here the displacement components, w, u, v, define the *normal and tangenital* components, of displacement to the curved surface and if all the elements are assumed tangent to each other, no need arises to transfer those from local to global values.

The element is assumed to be 'shallow' with respect to a local co-ordinate system representing its projection on to a plane defined by nodal points and its strain energy is defined by appropriate equations which include derivatives with respect to *co-ordinates in the plane of projection*. Thus, precisely the same shape functions can be used as in flat elements discussed in this chapter and all integrations are in fact carried out in the plane as before.

Such shallow shell elements, by coupling the effects of membrane and bending strain in the energy expressions, are slightly more efficient than flat ones where such coupling occurs on boundary only. For simple, small elements the gains are marginal but with few complex large elements advantages show up. A particularly good discussion of such a formulation is given in reference 16.

However, for many practical purposes the flat element approximation gives very adequate answers and indeed permits an easy coupling with edge beam and rib members, a facility sometimes not present in curved element formulation. Indeed in many practical problems the structure is in fact composed of flat surfaces at least in part and these can be simply reproduced. For these reasons curved general thin shell forms will not be discussed here and instead a general formulation of thick curved shells (based directly on three-dimensional behaviour and avoiding the shell equation ambiguities) will be presented in Chapter 13.

In the context of axi-symmetric shells given in the next chapter both straight and curved elements will be considered.

11.2 Stiffness of a Plane Element in Local Co-ordinates

Consider a typical polygonal flat element subject simultaneously to 'in plane' and bending actions (Fig. 11.2).

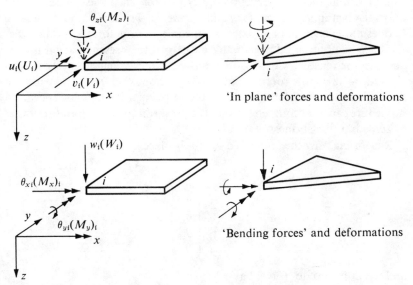

Fig. 11.2   A flat element subject to 'in plane' and bending actions

Taking first the *in plane* (plane stress) action, we know from Chapter 4 that the state of strain is uniquely described in terms of the u and v displacement of each typical node i. The minimization of the total energy potential led to the stiffness matrices described there and gives

$$\left\{ \begin{matrix} F_i^p \\ \vdots \end{matrix} \right\} = [k^p] \left\{ \begin{matrix} \delta_i^p \\ \vdots \end{matrix} \right\} \quad \text{with} \quad \begin{aligned} \{\delta_i^b\} &= \left\{ \begin{matrix} u_i \\ v_i \end{matrix} \right\} \\ \{F_i^p\} &= \left\{ \begin{matrix} U_i \\ V_i \end{matrix} \right\}. \end{aligned} \tag{11.1}$$

Similarly, when bending was considered, the state of strain was given uniquely by the nodal displacement in the z direction (w) and the two rotations θ_x and θ_y. This resulted in stiffness matrices of the type

$$
\left\{ \begin{matrix} F_i^b \\ \vdots \end{matrix} \right\} = [k^b] \left\{ \begin{matrix} \delta_i^b \\ \vdots \end{matrix} \right\} \quad \text{with} \quad
\begin{aligned}
\{\delta_i^p\} &= \left\{ \begin{matrix} w_i \\ \theta_{xi} \\ \theta_{yi} \end{matrix} \right\} \\
\{F_i^b\} &= \left\{ \begin{matrix} W_i \\ M_{xi} \\ M_{yi} \end{matrix} \right\} .
\end{aligned}
\tag{11.2}
$$

Before combining these stiffnesses it is important to note two facts. The first, that the displacements prescribed for 'in plane' forces do not affect the bending deformations and vice versa. The second, that rotation θ_z does not enter as a parameter into definition of deformations in either mode. While one could neglect this entirely at the present stage it is convenient, for reasons which will be apparent later when assembly is considered, to take this rotation into account now, and associate with it a fictitious couple M_z. The fact that it does not enter into the minimization procedure can be accounted for simply by inserting an appropriate number of zeros into the stiffness matrix.

Redefining now the combined nodal displacements as

$$
\{\delta_i\} = \left\{ \begin{matrix} u_i \\ v_i \\ w_i \\ \theta_{xi} \\ \theta_{yi} \\ \theta_{zi} \end{matrix} \right\}
\tag{11.3}
$$

and the appropriate 'forces' as

$$
\{F_i\} = \left\{ \begin{matrix} U_i \\ V_i \\ W_i \\ M_{xi} \\ M_{yi} \\ M_{zi} \end{matrix} \right\}
\tag{11.4}
$$

we can write

$$
\left\{ \begin{matrix} F_i \\ \vdots \end{matrix} \right\} = [k] \left\{ \begin{matrix} \delta_i \\ \vdots \end{matrix} \right\}
$$

or

$$
\{F\}^e = [k]\{\delta\}^e.
\tag{11.5}
$$

The stiffness matrix is now made up from the following submatrices

$$[k_{rs}] = \begin{bmatrix} [k_{rs}^p] & \begin{matrix} 0 & 0 & 0 \\ 0 & 0 & 0 \end{matrix} & \begin{matrix} 0 \\ 0 \end{matrix} \\ \begin{matrix} 0 & 0 \\ 0 & 0 \\ 0 & 0 \end{matrix} & [k_{rs}^b] & \begin{matrix} 0 \\ 0 \\ 0 \end{matrix} \\ 0 \quad 0 & 0 \quad 0 \quad 0 & 0 \end{bmatrix} \tag{11.6}$$

if we note that

$$\{\delta_i\} = \begin{Bmatrix} \delta_i^p \\ \delta_i^b \\ \theta_{zi} \end{Bmatrix}. \tag{11.7}$$

The above formulation is valid for any shape of polygonal element and, in particular, for the two important cases illustrated in Fig. 11.2.

11.3 Transformation to Global Co-ordinates and Assembly of the Elements

The stiffness matrix derived in the previous section used a system of local co-ordinates as the 'in plane', and bending components are originally derived for this system.

Transformation of co-ordinates to a common global system (which now will be denoted by xyz, and the local system by $x'y'z'$) will be necessary to assemble the elements and to write the appropriate equilibrium equations.

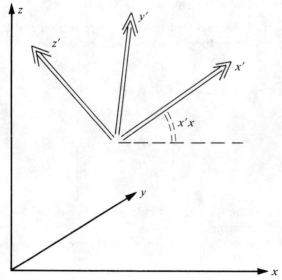

Fig. 11.3   Local and global co-ordinates

In addition it will be initially more convenient to specify the element nodes by their global co-ordinates and to establish from these the local co-ordinates, thus requiring an inverse transformation. Fortunately, all the transformations are accomplished by a simple process.

The two systems of co-ordinates are shown in Fig. 11.3. The forces and displacements of a node transform from the global to the local system by a matrix L giving

$$\{\delta_i'\} = [L]\{\delta_i\}, \qquad \{F_i'\} = [L]\{F_i\} \tag{11.8}$$

in which

$$[L] = \begin{bmatrix} \lambda & 0 \\ 0 & \lambda \end{bmatrix} \tag{11.9}$$

with $[\lambda]$ being a three by three matrix of direction cosines of angles formed between the two sets of axes, i.e.,

$$[\lambda] = \begin{bmatrix} \lambda_{x'x} & \lambda_{x'y} & \lambda_{x'z} \\ \lambda_{y'x} & \lambda_{y'y} & \lambda_{y'z} \\ \lambda_{z'x} & \lambda_{z'y} & \lambda_{z'z} \end{bmatrix} \tag{11.10}$$

in which $\lambda_{xx'}$ = cosine of angle between x and x' axes, etc.

For the whole set of forces acting on the nodes of an element we can therefore write

$$\{\delta'\}^e = [T]\{\delta\}^e, \qquad \{F'\}^e = [T]\{F\}^e. \tag{11.11}$$

By the rules of orthogonal transformation (*see* section 1.4) the stiffness matrix of an element in the global co-ordinates becomes

$$[k] = [T]^{\mathrm{T}}[k'][T]. \tag{11.12}$$

In both of the above equations $[T]$ is given by

$$[T] = \begin{bmatrix} L & 0 & 0 & \cdots \\ 0 & L & 0 & \\ 0 & 0 & L & \\ \vdots & & & \end{bmatrix} \tag{11.13}$$

a diagonal matrix built up of $[L]$ matrices in a number equal to that of the nodes in the element.

It is simple to show that the typical stiffness submatrix now becomes

$$[k_{rs}] = [L]^{\mathrm{T}}[k_{rs}'][L] \tag{11.14}$$

in which $[k_{rs}']$ is determined by Eq. (8.6) in the local co-ordinates.

The determination of local co-ordinates follows a similar pattern. If the origins of both local and global systems are identical then

$$\left\{ \begin{array}{c} x' \\ y' \\ z' \end{array} \right\} = [\lambda] \left\{ \begin{array}{c} x \\ y \\ z \end{array} \right\}. \tag{11.15}$$

As in the computation of stiffness matrices the position of the origin is immaterial, this transformation will always suffice for determination of the local co-ordinates in the plane (or a plane parallel to the element).

Once the stiffness matrices of all the elements have been determined in the common, global, co-ordinate system the assembly of the elements and the final solution follow the standard pattern. The resulting displacements calculated are referred to the global system, and before the stresses can be computed it is necessary to change these for each element of the local system. The usual stress matrices for 'in plane' bending components can then be used.

11.4 A Fictitious Rotational Stiffness

In the formulation just described a difficulty arises if all the elements meeting at a node are co-planar. This is due to the assignment of a zero stiffness in the θ_{zi} direction of Fig. 11.2.

If the set of assembled equilibrium equations *in local co-ordinates* is considered at such a point we have six equations of which the last (corresponding to θ_z direction) is simply

$$0 = 0. \tag{11.16}$$

As such, an equation of this type, presents no special difficulties (although in usual computation programs it would lead to an error message). However, if the global co-ordinate directions differ from the local ones and a transformation is accomplished, six apparently correct equations are achieved. These, being derived by a suitable addition of the above multiplied suitably by real numbers, are singular.†

Thus two alternatives are present

(*a*) to assemble the equations at points where elements are co-planar in local co-ordinates (and to delete the $0 = 0$ equation)

or

(*b*) to insert an arbitrary stiffness coefficient $k'_{\theta z}$ at such points only.

---

† The reader will recall the apparently logical practice based on multiplying such an equality and deriving 2 = 4, etc.

This leads in the local co-ordinates to replacing Eq. (11.16) by

$$k'_{\theta z}\, \theta_{zi} = 0 \qquad (11.17)$$

This, on transformation, leads to a perfectly well-behaved set of equations from which, by usual processes, all displacements, now including θ_{zi}, are obtained. As θ_{zi} does not affect the stresses and indeed is uncoupled from all equilibrium equations any arbitrary value of $k'_{\theta z}$ can be inserted as an external stiffness without affecting the result.

Both alternatives suggested above lead to certain programing difficulty (although the second one is in fact simpler) and some work has proceeded to determine the real stiffness coefficient for rotations of the type described by considering these as an additional degree of freedom in plane analysis.[15]

In a program much used by the author[6] a fictitious set of rotation stiffness coefficients was simply used in all elements whether co-planar or not. For a triangular element these were defined by a matrix such that in local co-ordinates equilibrium is not disturbed, i.e.,

$$
\begin{Bmatrix} M_{zi} \\ M_{zj} \\ M_{zk} \end{Bmatrix} = \alpha E t \Delta
\begin{bmatrix} 1, & -0{\cdot}5, & -0{\cdot}5 \\ & 1 & -0{\cdot}5 \\ \text{sym.} & & 1 \end{bmatrix}
\begin{Bmatrix} \theta_{zi} \\ \theta_{zj} \\ \theta_{zk} \end{Bmatrix} \qquad (11.18)
$$

where α is some coefficient yet to be specified.

Now this additional stiffness does in fact affect the results because it occurs also at nodes which are not co-planar and indeed the device represents an approximation. However, the effects of varying α between very wide limits are quite small. For instance in Table 11.1 given below, a set of displacements of an arch dam analysed in reference 2 is given for various values of α.

TABLE 11.1

NODAL ROTATION COEFFICIENT IN DAM ANALYSIS[2]

$\alpha =$	1·00	0·50	0·10	0·03	0·00
radial displacement (mm)	61·13	63·35	64·52	64·78	65·28

The displacements for $\alpha = 0$ are nearly exact. For practical purposes $\alpha = 0{\cdot}03$ or less is recommended.

Some authors[5] avoid this difficulty by reducing the number of degrees of freedom by the offending one and always assembling equations along the normal to the shell. Indeed this process will be used in Chapter 14. It introduces, however, a difficulty when dealing with *real* changes of direction or branches in a shell as here a 'normal' cannot be simply specified.

11.5 Local Direction Cosines

Once the direction cosine matrix $[\lambda]$ has been determined for each element the problem presents no difficulties, and the solution follows the usual lines. The determination of the direction cosine matrix gives rise to some algebraic difficulties, and indeed, is not unique since the direction of one of the axes is arbitrary, provided it lies in the plane of the element.

We shall first deal with the assembly of rectangular elements in which this problem is particularly simple.

11.5.1 *Rectangular elements.* Such elements being limited in use to representing a cylindrical or box type of surface it is convenient to take one side of the elements and the corresponding co-ordinate x' parallel to the global, x, axis. For a typical element $ijkm$, illustrated in Fig. 11.4, it is now easy to calculate all the relevant direction cosines.

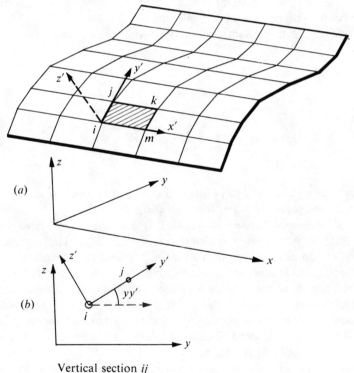

Vertical section ij

Fig. 11.4   A cylindrical shell as an assembly of rectangular elements.
Local and global co-ordinates

Direction cosines of x' are, obviously

$$\lambda_{x'x} = 1$$
$$\lambda_{x'y} = 0 \qquad (11.19)$$
$$\lambda_{x'z} = 0.$$

The direction cosines of the y' axis have to be obtained by consideration of the co-ordinates of the various nodal points. Thus

$$\lambda_{y'x} = 0$$
$$\lambda_{y'y} = +\frac{y_j - y_i}{\sqrt{\{(z_j - z_i)^2 + (y_j - y_i)^2\}}} \qquad (11.20)$$
$$\lambda_{y'z} = +\frac{z_j - z_i}{\sqrt{\{(z_j - z_i)^2 + (y_j - y_i)^2\}}}$$

simple geometrical relations which can be obtained by consideration of the sectional plane passing vertically through ij.

Similarly, from the same section we have for the z' axis

$$\lambda_{z'x} = 0$$
$$\lambda_{z'y} = -\frac{z_j - z_i}{\sqrt{\{(z_j - z_i)^2 + (y_j - y_i)^2\}}} \qquad (11.21)$$
$$\lambda_{z'z} = +\frac{y_j - y_i}{\sqrt{\{(z_j - z_i)^2 + (y_j - y_i)^2\}}}.$$

Clearly, the numbering of points in a consistent fashion is important to preserve the correct signs of the expression.

11.5.2 *Triangular elements arbitrarily oriented in space.* An arbitrary shell divided into triangular elements is shown in Fig. 11.5(*a*). Each element is in an orientation in which the angles with the co-ordinate planes are arbitrary. The problems of defining local axes and their direction cosines are therefore considerably more complex than in the previous simple example. The most convenient way of dealing with the problem is to use some features of geometrical vector algebra and for readers who may have forgotten some of this background a brief resumé of its essentials is included in Appendix 5.

One choice of local axis direction is arbitrary and a decision on this has to be made *a priori*. We shall specify this, x', axis, to be directed along the side ij of the triangle as shown in Fig. 11.5(*b*).

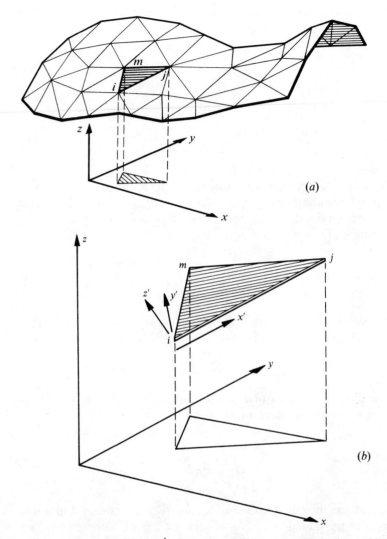

Fig. 11.5   (a) An assemblage of triangular elements representing an arbitrary
shell. (b) Local and global co-ordinates for a triangular element

The vector V_{ij} defines this side and in terms of global co-ordinates we
have

$$V_{ij} = \begin{Bmatrix} x_j - x_i \\ y_j - y_i \\ z_j - z_i \end{Bmatrix}.$$

(11.22)

The direction cosines are given by dividing the components of this vector by its length, i.e., defining a vector of unit length

$$\boldsymbol{v}_{x'} = \begin{Bmatrix} \lambda_{x'x} \\ \lambda_{x'y} \\ \lambda_{x'z} \end{Bmatrix} = \frac{1}{l_{ij}} \begin{Bmatrix} x_{ji} \\ y_{ji} \\ z_{ji} \end{Bmatrix} \tag{11.23}$$

with

$$l_{ij} = \sqrt{x_{ji}^2 + y_{ji}^2 + z_{ji}^2}$$

in which $x_{ji} = x_j - x_i$, etc., for brevity.

Now the z' direction, which must be normal to the plane of the triangle, needs to be established. By properties of the cross product of two vectors we can obtain this direction from a 'vector' (cross) product of two sides of the triangle. Thus

$$\boldsymbol{V}_{z'} = \boldsymbol{V}_{ij} \times \boldsymbol{V}_{im} = \begin{Bmatrix} y_{ji}z_{mi} - z_{ji}y_{mi} \\ \cdot \quad \cdot \quad \cdot \quad \cdot \\ \cdot \quad \cdot \quad \cdot \quad \cdot \end{Bmatrix} \tag{11.24}$$

represents a vector normal to the plane of the triangle whose length, by definition (see Appendix), is equal to twice the area of the triangle. Thus

$$l_{z'} = \sqrt{(y_{ji}z_{mi} - z_{ji}y_{mi})^2 + (\dots)^2 + (\dots)^2} = 2\Delta.$$

The direction cosines of z' axis are available simply as the direction cosines of $\boldsymbol{V}_{z'}$ and we have a unit vector

$$\boldsymbol{v}_{z'} = \begin{Bmatrix} \lambda_{z'x} \\ \lambda_{z'y} \\ \lambda_{z'z} \end{Bmatrix} = \frac{1}{2\Delta} \begin{Bmatrix} y_{ji}z_{mi} - z_{ji}y_{mi} \\ \cdot \quad \cdot \quad \cdot \quad \cdot \\ \cdot \quad \cdot \quad \cdot \quad \cdot \end{Bmatrix}. \tag{11.25}$$

Finally the direction cosines of the y' axis are established in a similar manner as the direction cosines of a vector normal to both the x' and z' directions. If vectors of unit length are taken in each of these directions as in fact defined by Eqs. (11.23) and (11.25) we have simply

$$\boldsymbol{v}_{y'} = \begin{Bmatrix} \lambda_{y'x} \\ \lambda_{y'y} \\ \lambda_{y'z} \end{Bmatrix} = \boldsymbol{v}_{z'} \times \boldsymbol{v}_{x'} = \begin{Bmatrix} \lambda_{z'y}\lambda_{x'z} - \lambda_{z'z}\lambda_{x'y} \\ \cdot \quad \cdot \quad \cdot \quad \cdot \quad \cdot \\ \cdot \quad \cdot \quad \cdot \quad \cdot \quad \cdot \end{Bmatrix} \tag{11.26}$$

without having to divide by the length of the vector which is now simply unity.

Indeed the vector operations involved can be written as a special computer routine in which vector products, normalizing (i.e., division by length), etc. are automatically carried out[19] and there is no need to specify in detail the various operations given above.

In the preceding outline the direction of the x' axis was taken as lying along one side of the element. A useful alternative is to specify this by the section of the triangle plane with a plane parallel to one of the co-ordinate planes. Thus for instance if we should desire to erect the x' axis along a horizontal contour of the triangle (i.e., a section parallel to the xy plane) we can proceed as follows.

First the normal direction cosines $v_{z'}$ are defined as in Eq. (11.25).

Now, the matrix of direction cosines of x' has to have a zero component in the z direction. Thus we have

$$v_{x'} = \begin{Bmatrix} \lambda_{x'x} \\ \lambda_{x'y} \\ 0 \end{Bmatrix}. \tag{11.27}$$

As the length of the vector is unity

$$\lambda_{x'x}^2 + \lambda_{x'y}^2 = 1 \tag{11.28}$$

and as further the *scalar* product of the $v_{x'}$ and $v_{z'}$ must be zero, we can write

$$\lambda_{x'x} \cdot \lambda_{z'x} + \lambda_{x'y} \cdot \lambda_{z'y} = 0 \tag{11.29}$$

and from these two equations $v_{z'}$ can be uniquely determined. Lastly as before

$$v_{y'} = v_{x'} \times v_{z'}. \tag{11.30}$$

Yet another alternative of a unique specification of the x' axis is given in Chapter 14.

11.6 Some Practical Examples

The first example given here is that of the solution of an arch dam shell. A simple geometrical configuration, shown in Fig. 11.6, was taken for this particular problem as results of model experiments and alternative numerical approaches were available.

A division based on rectangular elements was used as the simple cylindrical shape permitted this, although a rather crude approximation to the fixed foundation line had to be used.

Two sizes of division into elements were used, and the results given in Figs. 11.7, 11.8, and 11.9 for both deflections and stresses on the centre-

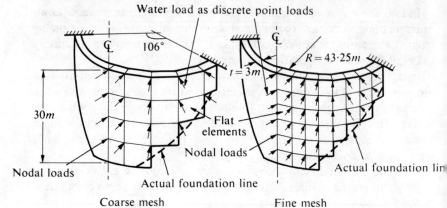

Water load as discrete point loads

106°

$R = 43 \cdot 25m$

$t = 3m$

30m

Flat elements

Nodal loads

Actual foundation line

Nodal loads

Actual foundation line

Coarse mesh   Fine mesh

Fig. 11.6   An arch dam as an assembly of rectangular elements

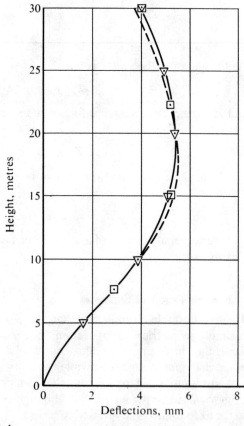

Fig. 11.7   Arch dam. Horizontal deflections on centre line

—□— Finite element solution (coarse)

—▽— Finite element solution (fine)

– – – Trial load solution (USBR)

(Poisson's ratio $\nu = 0 \cdot 15$)

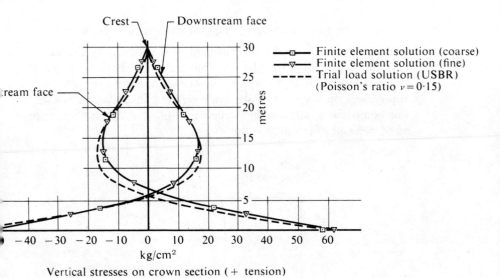

Vertical stresses on crown section (+ tension)

Fig. 11.8 Arch dam. Vertical stresses on centre line

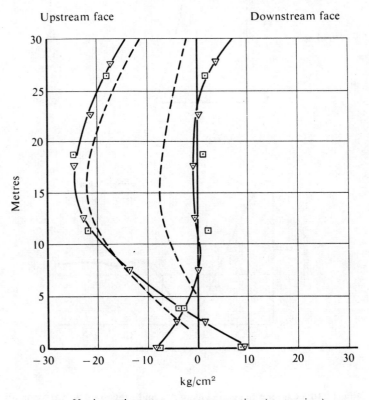

Horizontal stresses on crown section (+ tension)

Fig. 11.9 Arch dam. Horizontal (arch) stresses on centre line

line section show that little refinement was achieved by the use of the finer mesh. This indicates that the convergence of both the physical approximation to the true shape by flat elements, and of the mathematical approximation involved in the finite element formulation, is excellent. For comparison, stresses and deflection obtained by another, approximate, method of calculation are shown.

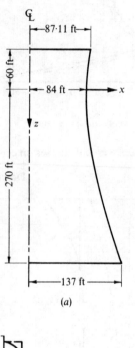

(a)

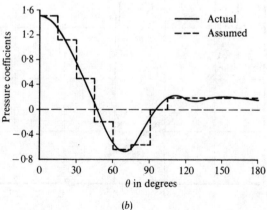

(b)

Fig. 11.10   Cooling tower.[21] Geometry and pressure load variation about circumference

A doubly curved arch dam was similarly analysed using the triangular flat element representation. The results show an even better approximation.[6]

A large number of examples have been computed by Parekh[20] using the triangular, non-conforming element and indeed show for equal division its general superiority over the conforming triangular version presented by Clough and Johnson.[5] Some examples of such analysis are shown here.

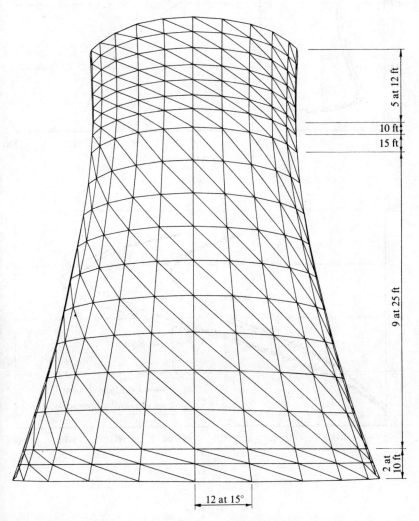

Fig. 11.11   Cooling tower. Mesh subdivisions

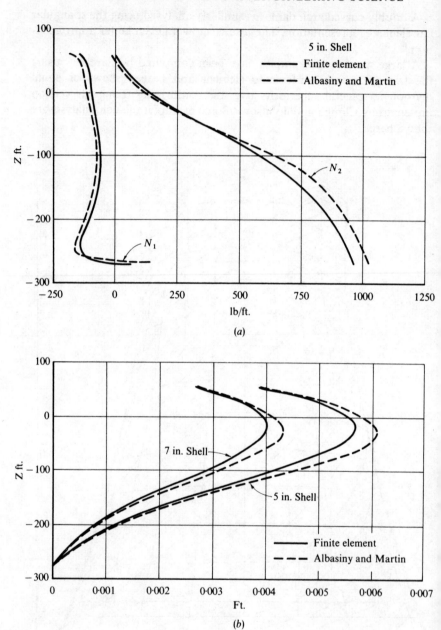

Fig. 11.12

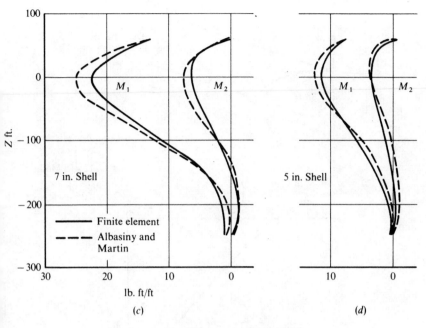

Fig. 11.12   Cooling tower of Fig. 11.11.
(a) Membrane forces of $\theta = 0°$
   N_1 = tangential forces
   N_2 = meridional force
(b) Radial displacements of $\theta = 0°$
(c) Bending moments of $\theta = 0°$
   M_1 = tangential moment
   M_2 = meridional moment

Cooling Tower. This problem of a general axi-symmetric shape could, obviously, be more efficiently dealt with by the processes of Chapters 12 or 13. However, here this example is used as a general illustration of the accuracy attainable. The answers against which the numerical solution is compared have been derived by Albasiny and Martin.[21] Figures 11.10 to 11.12 show the geometry mesh used and some results. Unsymmetric wind loading is used here.

Barrel vault. This typical shell used in civil engineering is analysed using conventional processes by Scordelis and Lo.[22] The barrel is supported on rigid diaphragms and is loaded by its own weight. Figures 11.13 and 11.14 show some comparative answers.

Folded plate structure. As no exact solution to this problem is known comparison is made with a set of experimental results obtained by Mark and Riesa.[23]

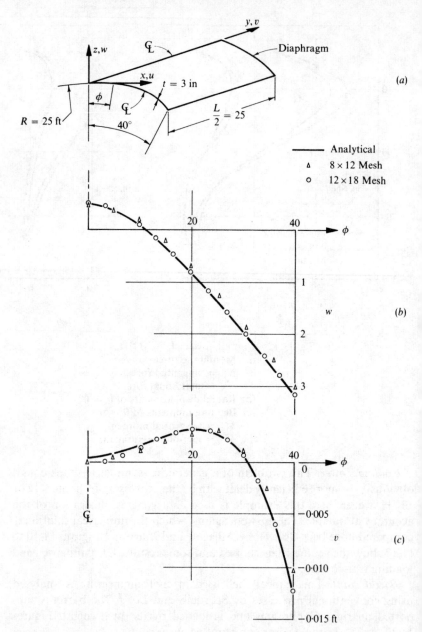

Fig. 11.13   A barrel (cylindrical) vault (*a*) finite element and exact[22] solutions under dead loads (*b*) vertical displacement of central sections (*c*) longitudinal displacement of support

$E = 3 \times 10^6$ lb/in^2 $\nu = 0$ weight of shell = 90 lb/ft^2

This example demonstrates a problem in which actual finite element representation is physically exact. Also a frame stiffness is included in analysis by suitable beam elements.

Figures 11.15 and 11.16 show the results.

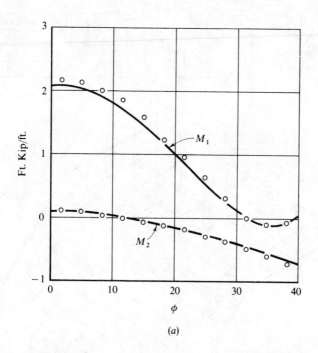

(a)

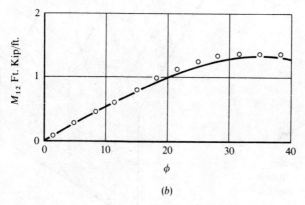

(b)

Fig. 11.14   Barrel vault of Fig. 10.23
(a) M_1 = transverse moments
     M_2 = longitudinal moments at central section
(b) M_{12} = twisting moment at support

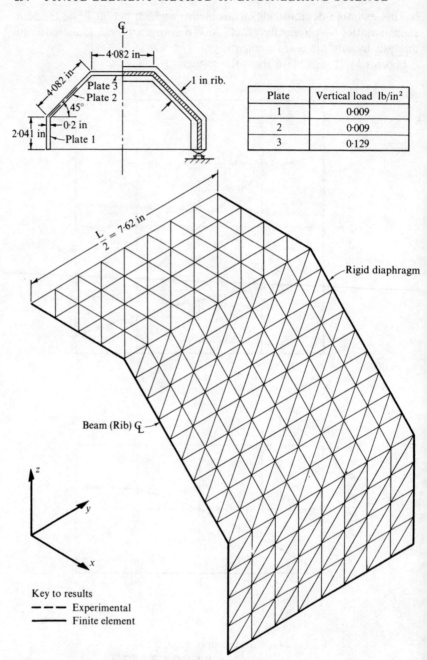

Plate	Vertical load lb/in²
1	0·009
2	0·009
3	0·129

Key to results
— — — Experimental
——— Finite element

Fig. 11.15   A folded plate structure.[23] Model geometry, loading and mesh
$E = 3560 \text{ lb/in}^2$ $v = 0.43$

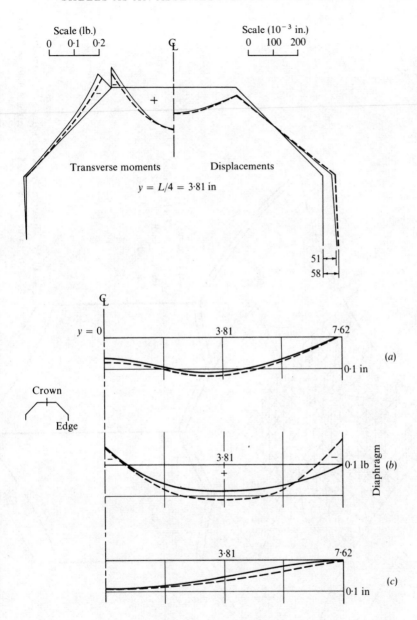

Fig. 11.16 A folded plate.[23] Moments and displacements on centre section (*a*) vertical displacements along the crown (*b*) longitudinal moments along the crown (*c*) horizontal displacements along edge

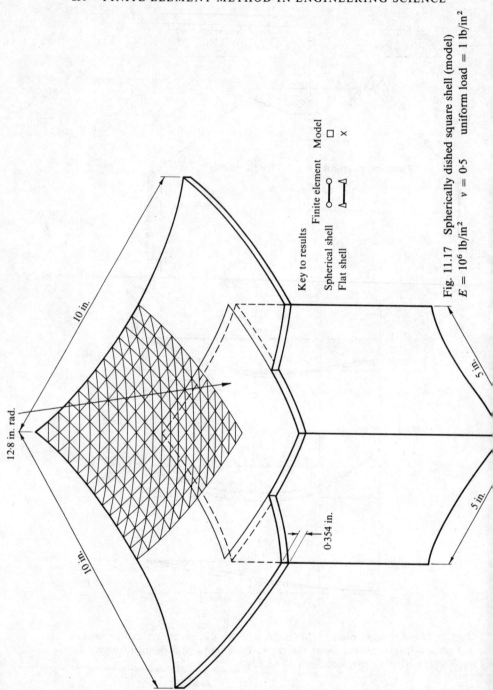

Fig. 11.17 Spherically dished square shell (model)
$E = 10^6$ lb/in^2 $v = 0.5$ uniform load $= 1$ lb/in^2

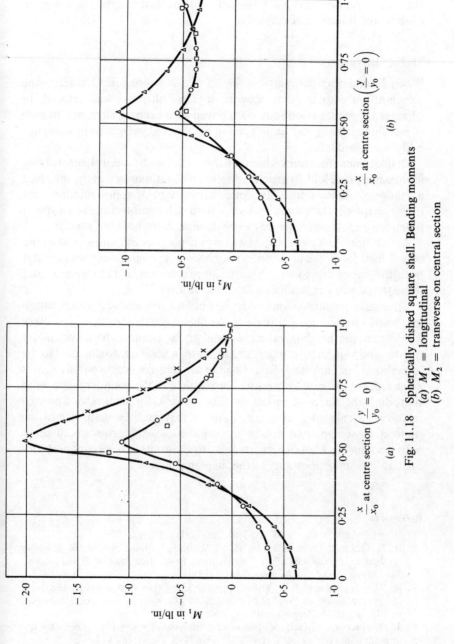

Fig. 11.18 Spherically dished square shell. Bending moments
(a) M_1 = longitudinal
(b) M_2 = transverse on central section

A general shell. The example shows a very general shape of a shell supported centrally which was recently analysed, Figs. 11.17 and 11.18. Here a comparison between results of a dished shell and flat plate is given to show the influence of curvature.

11.7 Convergence

When formulating the matrices for 'in plane' stresses in Chapter 4, the continuity of displacement between adjacent elements was ensured. In Chapter 10, similar continuity was arrived at in bending elements, though it was shown that good results could be achieved even if slope compatibility were violated.

Displacement functions which satisfy continuity between elements lying in the same plane will, in general, develop discontinuities if at the interface a change of plane occurs. The finite element type of approximation used in this chapter is therefore always based on non-conforming displacement functions and its convergence can be demonstrated only by 'experiment'.

As the size of element decreases then, if no discontinuities exist in the actual shell form, the non-conformity becomes progressively smaller and both the errors due to the physical approximation by flat elements and those to the non-conforming will tend to vanish.

The size of subdivision necessary to obtain a reasonable approximation in a shell problem is not obvious. As shells get thinner then it is often found that the bending moments tend to be confined to a 'boundary region' and vary there rapidly. In such cases a good approximation to the 'membrane' or 'in plane' forces by the use of quite coarse subdivision is achieved, but extreme fineness will be required in the boundary regions to reproduce the moment variations. Fortunately, for such cases approximate analytical procedures are relatively easy and the main use of the finite element approach can be envisaged in solving problems of shells with medium thickness where irregularities, cutouts, etc., occur and bending has the same importance as the 'in plane' action.

References

1. W. FLÜGGE, *Stresses in Shells*, Springer-Verlag, Berlin, 1960.
2. B. E. GREENE, D. R. STROME, R. C. WEIKEL, 'Application of the stiffness method to the analysis of shell structures', *Proc. Aviation Conference, Amer. Soc. Mech. Eng.*, Los Angeles, March 1961.
3. R. W. CLOUGH and J. L. TOCHER, 'Analysis of thin arch dams by the finite element method', in *Proc. of Symposium on Theory of Arch Dams*, Southampton Univ., 1964 (Pergamon Press, 1965).
4. J. H. ARGYRIS, 'Matrix displacement analysis of anisotropic shells by triangular elements', *J. Roy. Aer. Soc.*, **69**, 801–5, 1965 (Nov.).

5. R. W. CLOUGH and C. P. JOHNSON, 'A finite element approximation for the analysis of thin shells', *J. Solids & Struct.*, **4**, 43–60, 1968.
6. O. C. ZIENKIEWICZ, C. J. PAREKH, and I. P. KING, 'Arch Dams analysed by a linear finite element shell solution program', *Proc. Symp. Arch Dams.*, Inst. Civ. Eng., London, 1968.
7. O. C. ZIENKIEWICZ and Y. K. CHEUNG, 'Finite element procedures in the solution of plate and shell problems', in *Stress Analysis* (chapter 8), ed.: O. C. Zienkiewicz and G. S. Holister, J. Wiley, 1965.
8. O. C. ZIENKIEWICZ and Y. K. CHEUNG, 'Finite element method of analysis for arch dam shells and comparison with finite difference procedures', *Proc. of Symposium on Theory of Arch Dams*, Southampton Univ., 1964 (Pergamon Press, 1965).
9. F. K. BOGNER, R. L. FOX, and L. A. SCHMIDT, 'A cylindrical shell element', *J.A.I.A.A.*, **5**, 745–750, 1967.
10. G. CONTIN and R. W. CLOUGH, 'A refined, curved, cylindrical shell element', *A.I.A.A. Conference*, paper 68-176, New York, 1968.
11. G. BONNES, G. DHATT, Y. M. GIROUX, and L. P. A. ROBICHAUD, 'Curved triangular elements for analysis of shells', *Proc. 2nd Conf. Matrix Meth. in Struct Mech.*, Air Force Inst. Tech., Wright Patterson A.F. Base, Ohio, 1968.
12. G. E. STRICKLAND and W. A. LODEN, 'A doubly curved triangular shell element', *Proc. 2nd Conf. Matrix Meth. in Struct. Mech.*, Air Force Inst. Tech., Wright Patterson A.F. Base, Ohio, 1968.
13. B. E. GREENE, R. E. JONES, and D. R. STROME, 'Dynamic analysis of shells using doubly curved finite elements', *Proc. 2nd Cont. Matrix Meth. in Struct. Mech.*, Air Force Inst. Tech., Wright Patterson A.F. Base, Ohio, 1968.
14. J. CONNOR and C. BREBBIA, 'Stiffness matrix for shallow rectangular shell element', *Proc. Am. Soc. Civ. Eng.*, **93**, EM 43–65, 1967.
15. A. J. CARR, *A refined finite element analysis of thin shell structures including dynamic loading*, SEL Report No. 67–9, Univ. of California, Berkeley, 1967.
16. G. R. COWPER, G. M. LINDBERG, M. D. OLSON, 'A shallow shell finite element of triangular shape', *Inst. J. Solids & Structs.*, **6**, 1133–1156, 1970.
17. S. UTKU, 'Stiffness matrices for thin triangular elements of non zero Gaussian curvature', *J.A.I.A.A.*, **5**, 1659–67, 1967.
18. S. AHMAD, *Curved finite elements in the analysis of solid shell and plate structures*, Ph.D. Thesis, Univ. of Wales, Swansea, 1969.
19. S. AHMAD, B. M. IRONS, and O. C. ZIENKIEWICZ, 'A simple matrix-vector handling scheme for three dimensional and shell analysis', *In. J. Num. Meth. Eng.*, **2**, 509–22, 1970.
20. C. J. PAREKH, *Finite Element Solution System*, Ph.D. Thesis, Univ. of Wales, Swansea, 1969.
21. E. L. ALBASINY and D. W. MARTIN, 'Bending and Membrane equilibrium in cooling towers', *Proc. Am. Soc. Civ. Eng.*, **93**, EM3, 1–17, 1967.
22. A. C. SCORDELIS and K. S. LO, 'Computer analysis of cylindrical shells', *J. Am. Concr. Inst.*, **61**, May 1964.
23. R. MARK and J. D. RIESA, 'Photoelastic analysis of folded plate structures', *Proc. Am. Soc. Civ. Eng.*, **93**, EM4, 79–83, 1967.

12. Axi-Symmetric Shells

12.1 Introduction

The problem of axi-symmetric shells is of sufficient practical importance to include in this chapter special methods of dealing with their solution.

While the general method described in the previous chapter is obviously applicable here, it will be found that considerable simplification can be achieved if account is taken of axial symmetry of the structure. In particular, if both the shell and the loading are axi-symmetric it will be found that the elements become 'one dimensional'. This is the simplest type of element to which little attention was given in earlier chapters.

The first approach to the finite element solution of axi-symmetric shells was presented by Grafton and Strome.[1] In this, the elements are simple conical frustra and a direct approach via displacement functions is used. Refinements in the derivation of element stiffnesses are presented in Popov et al.[2] and Jones and Strome,[3] and an extension to the case of unsymmetrical loads, which was suggested in Grafton and Strome,[1] is elaborated in Percy et al.,[4] Klein,[5] and Jones and Strome.[6]

More recently much work has been accomplished to extend the processes to curved elements and indeed to refine the approximations involved. The literature on the subject is growing daily, no doubt promoted by the interest in missile behaviour, and a complete bibliography is here impracticable. References 7 to 11 show how curvilinear co-ordinates of various kinds can be introduced to the analysis while 10 and 12 discuss the use of additional nodeless degrees of freedom in improving the accuracy.

In axi-symmetric shells, in common with all other shells, both bending and 'in plane' or 'membrane' forces will occur. These will be specified uniquely in terms of the generalized 'strains', which now involve extensions and curvatures of the middle surface. If the displacement of each point of the middle surface is specified, such 'strains' and the internal stress resultants or simply 'stresses' can be determined by formulae available in standard texts dealing with shell theory.

For example, in an axi-symmetric shell under axi-symmetric loading such as is shown in Fig. 12.1, the displacement of a point on the middle surface is uniquely determined by two components u and w in the tangential and normal directions respectively.

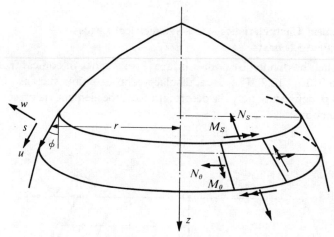

Fig. 12.1 Axi-symmetric shell and loading displacements and stress resultants. Shell represented as a series of conical frustra

The four strain components are given by the following expression, provided the angle ϕ does not vary[13]

$$\{\varepsilon\} = \begin{Bmatrix} \varepsilon_s \\ \varepsilon_\theta \\ \chi_s \\ \chi_\theta \end{Bmatrix} = \begin{Bmatrix} du/ds \\ (w\cos\phi + u\sin\phi)/r \\ -d^2w/ds^2 \\ -\dfrac{\sin\phi}{r}\dfrac{dw}{ds} \end{Bmatrix} . \tag{12.1}$$

This results in four internal stress resultants, shown in Fig. 12.1, and related to the strains by an elasticity matrix $[D]$

$$\{\sigma\} = \begin{Bmatrix} N_s \\ N_\theta \\ M_s \\ M_\theta \end{Bmatrix} = [D]\{\varepsilon\}. \tag{12.2}$$

For an isotropic shell the matrix $[D]$ becomes

$$[D] = \frac{Et}{(1-v^2)} \begin{bmatrix} 1 & v & 0 & 0 \\ v & 1 & 0 & 0 \\ 0 & 0 & t^2/12 & vt^2/12 \\ 0 & 0 & vt^2/12 & t^2/12 \end{bmatrix} \tag{12.3}$$

the upper part being a plane stress and the lower a bending stiffness matrix, the shear terms being omitted in both.

12.2 Element Characteristics—Axi-Symmetrical Loads— Straight Elements

Let the shell be divided by nodal surfaces into a series of conical frustra, as shown in Fig. 12.2. The nodal displacements at points such as i and j will have to define uniquely the deformations of the element via prescribed shape functions.

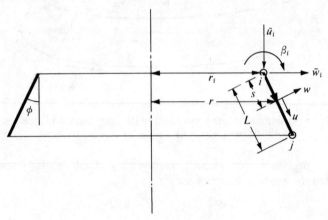

Fig. 12.2   An element of an axi-symmetric shell

At each node the axial and radial movements and a rotation will be prescribed. All three components are necessary as the shell can carry bending moments. The displacement of a node i can thus be defined by three components, the first two being in global directions,

$$\{\delta_i\} = \begin{Bmatrix} \bar{u}_i \\ \bar{w}_i \\ \beta_i \end{Bmatrix}. \tag{12.4}$$

The element with two nodes, ij, thus possesses six degrees of freedom, determined by the element displacements

$$\{\delta\}^e = \begin{Bmatrix} \delta_i \\ \delta_j \end{Bmatrix}. \tag{12.5}$$

The displacements within the element have to be uniquely determined by the nodal displacements $\{\delta\}^e$ and the position s, and maintain slope and displacement continuity.

$$\{f\} = \begin{Bmatrix} u \\ w \end{Bmatrix} = [N]\{\delta\}^e. \tag{12.6}$$

If u is taken as varying linearly with s and w as a cubic in s we shall have six undetermined constants, which can be determined from the nodal values of $\bar{u}$, $\bar{w}$, and β.

At the node i

$$\begin{Bmatrix} u_i \\ w_i \\ (dw/ds)_i \end{Bmatrix} = \begin{bmatrix} \cos\phi & +\sin\phi & 0 \\ -\sin\phi & \cos\phi & 0 \\ 0 & 0 & 1 \end{bmatrix} \begin{Bmatrix} \bar{u}_i \\ \bar{w}_i \\ \beta_i \end{Bmatrix} = [\lambda]\{\delta_i\}. \tag{12.7}$$

Writing

$$\begin{aligned} u &= \alpha_1 + \alpha_2 s \\ w &= \alpha_3 + \alpha_4 s + \alpha_5 s^2 + \alpha_6 s^3 \end{aligned} \tag{12.8}$$

it is an easy matter to state the six end conditions and arrive at†

$$\begin{Bmatrix} u \\ w \end{Bmatrix} = \begin{bmatrix} 1-s' & 0 & 0 & s' & 0 & 0 \\ 0 & 1-3s'^2+2s'^3 & L(s'-2s'^2+s'^3) & 0 & 3s'^2-2s'^3 & (-s'^2+s'^3)L \end{bmatrix} \begin{Bmatrix} u_i \\ w_i \\ (dw/ds)_i \\ u_j \\ w_j \\ (dw/ds)_j \end{Bmatrix} \tag{12.9}$$

in which

$$s' = s/L.$$

Calling the above two by six matrix $[N']$ we can now write

$$\begin{Bmatrix} u \\ w \end{Bmatrix} = [N'] \begin{bmatrix} [\lambda] & 0 \\ 0 & [\lambda] \end{bmatrix} \{\delta\}^e = \Big[[N_i'][\lambda], [N_j'][\lambda] \Big] \{\delta\}^e = [N]\{\delta\}^e. \tag{12.10}$$

From Eq. (12.10) it is a simple matter to obtain the strain matrix $[B]$ by the use of the definition Eq. (12.1). This gives

$$\{\varepsilon\} = [B]\{\delta\}^e = \Big[[B_i][\lambda], [B_j][\lambda] \Big] \{\delta\}^e \tag{12.11}$$

† The functions which occur there are, in fact, Hermitian polynomials of order 0 and 1, see section 10.11.

in which

$$[B_i] = \begin{bmatrix} -1/L & 0 & 0 \\ (1-s')\sin\phi/r & (1-3s'^2+2s'^3)\cos\phi/r & L(s'-2s'^2+s'^3)\cos\phi/r \\ 0 & (-6+12s')/L^2 & (-4+6s')/L \\ 0 & (6s'-6s'^2)\sin\phi/rL & (-1+4s'-3s'^2)\sin\phi/r \end{bmatrix}$$

$$[B_j] = \begin{bmatrix} 1/L & 0 & 0 \\ s'\sin\phi/r & (3s'^2-2s'^3)\cos\phi/r & L(-s'^2+s'^3)\cos\phi/r \\ 0 & (6-12s')/L^2 & (-2+6s')/L \\ 0 & (-6s'+6s'^2)\sin\phi/rL & (2s'-3s'^2)\sin\phi/r \end{bmatrix}$$

(12.12)

Now all the 'ingredients' required for computing the stiffness matrix (or load, stress, and initial stress matrices) by standard formulae of Chapter 2 are known. The integrations required are carried out over the area, A, of the element, i.e., with

$$dA = 2\pi r \, ds = 2\pi r L \, ds' \qquad (12.13)$$

with s' varying from 0 to 1.

Thus, the stiffness matrix k becomes by Eq. (2.10)

$$[k] = \int_0^1 [B]^T[D][B]2\pi r L \, ds'. \qquad (12.14)$$

On substitution, the element $[k_{rs}]$ of this matrix is given by

$$[k_{rs}] = [\lambda]^T\left(\int_0^1 [B_r]^T[D][B_s]r \, ds'\right)[\lambda]2\pi L. \qquad (12.15)$$

The radius r has to be expressed as a function of s before such integrations are carried.

Once again it is convenient to use numerical integration. Grafton and Strome[1] give an explicit formula for the stiffness matrix based on a single average value of the integrand and using a $[D]$ matrix corresponding to an orthotropic material. Even with this crude approximation extremely good results can be obtained, provided small elements are used.

Percy et al.[4] and Klein[5] carry out a 7-point numerical integration and a slightly improved matrix is obtained, though it is not presented in the complete form.

It should be remembered that if any external line loads or moments are present, their full circumferential value must be used in the analysis just as was the case with axi-symmetric solids discussed in Chapter 5.

12.3 Examples and Accuracy

In the treatment of axi-symmetric shells described here continuity is satisfied at all times. For a polygonal shape of shell, therefore, convergence will always occur.

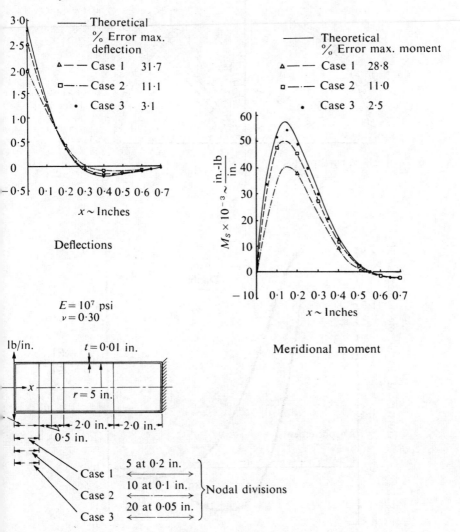

Fig. 12.3   A cylindrical shell solution by finite elements (Grafton and Strome, J. A.I.A.A., 1963)

The problem of the physical approximation to a curved shell by a polygonal shape is similar to the one discussed in Chapter 11. Intuitively,

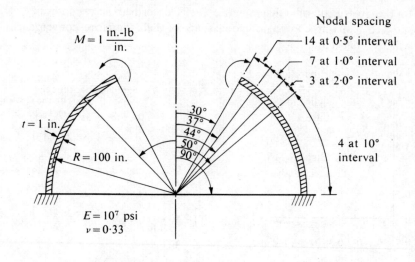

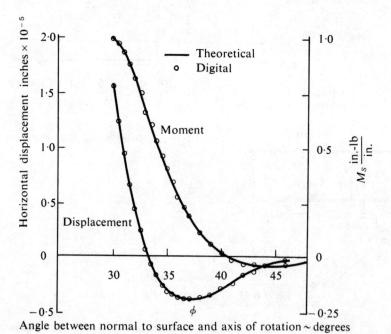

Fig. 12.4   A hemispherical shell solution by finite elements (Grafton and Strome, *J. A.I.A.A.*, 1963)

convergence can be expected, and indeed numerous examples indicate this.

When the loading is such as to cause predominantly membrane stresses, discrepancies in bending moment values have been found to exist even with reasonably fine subdivision. Again, however, these disappear as the size of the subdivision decreases particularly if moment averaging is used. This is necessary to eliminate the physical approximation involved in representing the shell as a series of conical frustra.

Figures 12.3 and 12.4 illustrate some typical examples taken from Grafton and Strome.[1]

12.4 Curved Elements and their Shape Functions

Use of curved elements has already been described in Chapter 8, in the context of analysis which involved in the definition of strain only first derivatives. Here second derivatives exist (*vide* Eq. (12.1)) and some of the theorems of Chapter 8 are no longer applicable.

It was previously mentioned that many possible definitions of curved elements have been proposed and used in the context of axisymmetric shells.[7-11] The derivation used here is one due to Irons and Delpak[10] and, to use the nomenclature of Chapter 8, is of the sub-parametric type.

The basis of curved element definition is one which gives a common tangent between adjacent elements (or alternatively a specified tangent direction). This is physically necessary to avoid 'kinks' in the description of what in practice is possibly a smooth shell.

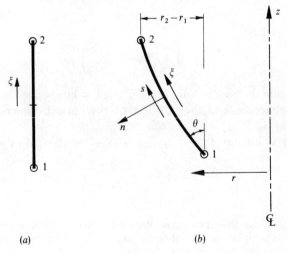

(a)   (b)

Fig. 12.5   Curved, isoparametric, shell element for axi-symmetric problems, (a) parent element, (b) curvilinear co-ordinates

Consider first a straight 'parent element' within which the unknown ϕ is described by its values and slopes at the ends 1, 2 (Fig. 12.5). The co-ordinate ξ describes the position and varies between -1 and $+1$ (as in examples of Chapter 8).

Thus using the usual definition we can write

$$\phi = \sum_{i=1}^{2} \left(N_i' \phi_i + N_i'' \left(\frac{d\phi}{d\xi}\right)_i \right) = [N]\{\bar{\phi}\}^e. \tag{12.16}$$

In this N' and N'' are scalar shape functions and if a polynomial is prescribed, will be simple cubics (similar to those used in Eq. (12.9) for the variation of w).

Explicitly we can write these cubic functions as

$$N_i' = \tfrac{1}{4}\{\xi_0 \xi^2 - 3\xi_0 + 2\}$$
$$N_i'' = \tfrac{1}{4}(1-\xi_0)^2(1+\xi_0) \quad \text{with } \xi_0 = \xi_i \xi. \tag{12.17}$$

Now we could, simultaneously, use the above functions to describe the variation of the global displacements $\bar{u}$ and $\bar{w}$† *and* of the co-ordinates r and z which define the shell (mid-surface).

Indeed if the thickness of the element is also variable the same interpolation could be applied to it.

Such an element would then be isoparametric. (See Chapter 8)

Thus we can define the geometry as

$$r = \sum_{1}^{2} \left(N_i' r_i + N_i'' \left(\frac{dr}{d\xi}\right)_i \right)$$

and   (12.18)

$$z = \sum_{1}^{2} \left(N_i' z_i + N_i'' \left(\frac{dz}{d\xi}\right)_i \right)$$

and providing the nodal values in the above can be specified, a one-to-one relation between ξ and the position on the curved element surface is defined, Fig. 12.5(b).

While specification of r_i and z_i is obvious, at the ends only the slope

$$(\tan \psi)_i = \left(\frac{dr}{dz}\right)_i \tag{12.19}$$

---

† One immediate difference will be observed from that of the previous formulation. Now both displacement components vary in at least a cubic manner along an element while previously a linear variation of the tangential displacement was permitted. This additional degree of freedom does not, however, introduce any excessive continuities in this case providing the shell is itself continuous in thickness.

is defined. What specification is to be adopted with regard to the derivatives occurring in Eq. (12.18) depends on the *scaling* of ξ along the tangent length s.

Only the ratio

$$\left(\frac{dr}{dz}\right)_i = \left(\frac{dr}{d\xi}\right)_i \bigg/ \left(\frac{dz}{d\xi}\right)_i \tag{12.20}$$

is unambiguously specified. $(dr/d\xi)_i$ (or $dz/d\xi$) can be given an arbitrary value. Here, however, practical considerations intervene as with the wrong choice of value a very uneven relationship between s and ξ will be achieved. Indeed with an unsuitable choice the shape of the curve can depart from the smooth one illustrated and loop between the end values.

To achieve a reasonably uniform spacing it suffices for well-behaved surfaces to approximate

$$\frac{dr}{d\xi} = \frac{\Delta r}{\Delta \xi} = \frac{r_2 - r_1}{2} \tag{12.21}$$

noting that the whole range of ξ is 2 between the nodal points.

12.5 Strain Expressions and Properties of Curved Elements

The variation of global displacements has been specified while, by Eq. (12.1), the strains are determinate in terms of the derivatives of locally directed displacements with respect to the tangent, s. Some transformations are therefore necessary before the strains can be determined.

If thus we take the global displacement variation to be defined by the shape function, Eq. (12.16) as

$$\bar{u} = \sum_{i=1}^{2} \left(N_i' \bar{u}_i + N_i'' \left(\frac{d\bar{u}}{d\xi}\right)_i \right)$$

$$\bar{w} = \sum_{i=1}^{2} \left(N_i' \bar{v}_i + N_i'' \left(\frac{d\bar{w}}{d\xi}\right)_i \right) \tag{12.22}$$

we can find the locally directed displacements u, v from the transformation implied in Eq. (12.7), i.e.,

$$\begin{Bmatrix} u \\ w \end{Bmatrix} = \begin{bmatrix} \cos\psi & \sin\psi \\ -\sin\psi & \cos\psi \end{bmatrix} \begin{Bmatrix} \bar{u} \\ \bar{w} \end{Bmatrix} = [L] \begin{Bmatrix} \bar{u} \\ \bar{w} \end{Bmatrix}. \tag{12.23}$$

Where ψ is the angle of the tangent to the curve and z axis (Fig. 12.5). However, before we can proceed further it is necessary to express this transformation in terms of the ξ co-ordinate. We have

$$\tan \psi = \left(\frac{dr}{d\xi}\right)\Big/ \left(\frac{dz}{d\xi}\right) \tag{12.24}$$

and hence this can now be accomplished by (12.18).

Before proceeding further we must consider whether continuity can be imposed at nodes on the parameter of Eq. (12.22). Clearly the global displacements must be continuous. However, on previous occasions we have specified a continuity of *rotation* of the tangent only. Here we shall allow usually the continuity of the s derivatives in displacements. Thus the parameters

$$\frac{d\bar{u}}{ds} \quad \text{and} \quad \frac{d\bar{w}}{ds}$$

will be given common values at nodes.

As

$$\frac{d\bar{u}}{ds} = \frac{d\bar{u}}{d\xi}\Big/\frac{ds}{d\xi}, \quad \frac{d\bar{w}}{ds} = \frac{d\bar{w}}{d\xi}\Big/\frac{ds}{d\xi} \tag{12.25}$$

$$\text{and} \quad \frac{ds}{d\xi} = \sqrt{\left(\frac{dr}{d\xi}\right)^2 + \left(\frac{dz}{d\xi}\right)^2}$$

no difficulty exists in substituting these new variables in Eqs. (12.22) and (12.23) which now take the form

$$\begin{Bmatrix} u \\ w \end{Bmatrix} = [N(\xi)]\{\delta\}^e \quad \text{with} \quad \delta_i = \begin{Bmatrix} \bar{u}_i \\ \bar{w}_i \\ (d\bar{u}/ds)_i \\ (d\bar{w}/ds)_i \end{Bmatrix}. \tag{12.26}$$

The form of the (2×4) submatrices is complicated but can be explicitly determined.

If shells which branch or in which abrupt thickness changes occur are to be treated, the nodal parameters specified in Eq. (12.26) are not satisfactory. It is better then to rewrite these as

$$\{\delta_i\} = \begin{Bmatrix} \bar{u}_i \\ \bar{w} \\ \beta_i \\ (du/ds)_i \end{Bmatrix}$$

where $\beta_i = dw/ds$ is the nodal rotation, and to connect only the first three parameters. The fourth is now an unconnected element parameter with respect to which, however, the usual minimization is still carried out.

Transformations needed in the above are implied in Eq. (12.23).

In the derivation of the $[B]$ matrix expressions which define the strains, both first and second derivatives with respect to s occur as seen in the definition of Eq. (12.1).†

If we observe that the derivatives can be obtained by the simple rules already implied in Eq. (12.25) for any function F we can write

$$\frac{dF}{ds} = \frac{dF}{d\xi} \bigg/ \frac{ds}{d\xi}$$

and (12.27)

$$\frac{d^2F}{ds^2} = \frac{d^2F}{d\xi^2} \bigg/ \left(\frac{ds}{d\xi}\right)^2 - \frac{dF}{d\xi}\left(\frac{d^2s}{d\xi^2}\right) \bigg/ \left(\frac{ds}{d\xi}\right)^3$$

and all the expressions of $[B]$ can be found.

Finally the stiffness matrix is obtained in a similar way as in Eq. (12.14) changing the variable

$$ds = \frac{ds}{d\xi}\, d\xi \tag{12.28}$$

and integrating within limits -1 and $+1$.

Once again the quantities contained in the integral expressions prohibit explicit integration and numerical integration must be used. As this is carried out in one co-ordinate only it is not very time-consuming and an adequate number of Gauss points can be used to determine the stiffness very accurately.

Stress and other matrices are similarly obtained.

The particular isoparametric formulation presented in outline here differs somewhat from the alternatives of references 7, 8, 9, and 11 and has the advantage that due to its *isoparametric* form rigid body displacement modes and indeed the states of constant first derivative are available. Proof of this is similar to that contained in section 8.5 of Chapter 8. The fact that the forms given in the alternative formulations strain under rigid body displacements may not be serious in some applications as discussed by Haisler and Stricklin.[14] However, in some modes of non-axi-symmetric loads (*vide* Chapter 13) this incompleteness may be a serious drawback and may indeed lead to very wrong results.

Constant states of curvature cannot be obtained for a *finite* element of any kind described here and indeed are not physically possible. When the size of the element decreases it will be found that such arbitrary constant curvature states are available in the limit.

† Note that here s is considered as the direction of the straight tangent and $d\psi/ds = 0$.

12.6 Additional Nodeless Variables

Addition of nodeless variables in the analysis of axi-symmetric shells is particularly valuable as large elements are then capable of reproducing with increasing accuracy the true behaviour shapes.

Thus an addition of a set

$$\sum_{j=1}^{n} N_j''' a_j \tag{12.29}$$

to the definition of the normal displacement defined in Eq. (12.6), in which a_j is a set of internal element parameters and N_j''' is a set of functions having zero values and zero first derivatives at the nodal points, allows considerable improvement in representation of the displacements to be achieved without violating any of the convergence requirements (*vide* Chapter 7).

For tangental displacements the requirements of zero first derivative of nodes can be omitted.

Webster[12] uses such additional functions in the context of straight elements.

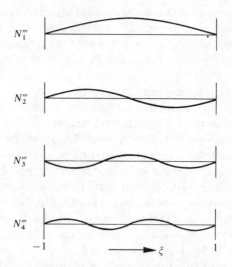

Fig. 12.6   Internal shape functions for a linear element

Whether the element is in fact straight or curved does not matter and indeed we can supplement the definitions of displacements contained in Eq. (12.22) by Eq. (12.29) for each of the components. If this is done only in the displacement definition and *not* in the co-ordinate definition (Eq.

(12.18)) the element becomes now of the category of sub-parametric.† As proved in Chapter 7 the same advantages are retained as in isoparametric forms.

The question as to the expression to be used for the additional, internal shape functions is of some importance though the choice is wide. While it is no longer necessary to use polynomial representation, Delpak[10] does so and uses a special form of Legendré polynomials suggested by Irons. The general shapes are shown in Fig. 12.6.

References

1. P. E. GRAFTON and D. R. STROME, 'Analysis of axi-symmetric shells by the direct stiffness method', *J.A.I.A.A.*, **1**, 2342–7, 1963.
2. E. P. POPOV, J. PENZIEN, and Z. A. LU, 'Finite element solution for axi-symmetric shells', *Proc. A.S.C.E.* EM, 119–45, 1964.
3. R. E. JONES and D. R. STROME, 'Direct Stiffness Method of Analysis of shells of revolution utilising curved elements', *J.A.I.A.A.*, **4**, 1519–25, 1966.
4. J. H. PERCY, T. H. H. PIAN, S. KLEIN, and D. R. NAVARATNA, 'Application of matrix displacement method to linear elastic analysis of shells of revolution', *J.A.I.A.A.*, **3**, 2138–45, Jan. 1965.
5. S. KLEIN, 'A study of the matrix displacement method as applied to shells of revolution', *Proc. Conf. on Matrix Methods in Structural Mech.*, Air Force Inst. of Tech., Wright Patterson A.F. Base, Ohio, Oct. 1965.
6. R. E. JONES and D. R. STROME, 'A survey of analysis of shells by the displacement method', *Proc. Conf. on Matrix Methods in Structural Mech.*, Air Force Inst. of Tech., Wright Patterson A.F. Base, Ohio, Oct. 1965.
7. R. E. JONES and D. R. STROME, 'Direct Stiffness method analysis of shells of revolution utilising curved elements', *A.I.A.A. Int.*, **4**, 1519–25, 1966.
8. J. A. STRICKLIN, D. R. NAVARATNA, and T. H. H. PIAN, 'Improvements in the analysis of shells of revolution by matrix displacement method (curved elements)', *A.I.A.A. Int.*, **4**, 2069–72, 1966.
9. M. KHOJASTEH-BAKHT, *Analysis of elastic-plastic shells of revolution under axi-symmetric loading by the finite element method*, Dept. Civ. Eng. Univ. of California, SE SA 67–8, 1967.
10. R. DELPAK, *Axi-symmetric vibration of shells of revolution by the finite element method*, M.Sc. Thesis, Univ. of Wales, Swansea, 1967.
11. M. GIANNINI and G. A. MILES, 'A curved element approximation in the analysis of axi-symmetric thin shells', *Int. J. Num. Meth. in Eng.*, **2**, 459–76, 1970.
12. J. J. WEBSTER, 'Free vibration of shells of revolution using ring elements', *Int. J. Mech. Sci.*, **9**, 559, 1967.
13. V. V. NOVOZHILOV, *Theory of Thin Shells* (Translation), P. Noordhoff, 1959.
14. W. E. HAISLER and J. A. STRICKLIN, 'Rigid body displacements of curved elements in the analysis of shells by the matrix displacement method', *J.A.I.A.A.*, **5**, 1525–7, 1967.

† While it would obviously be possible to include the new shape function in the element shape definition little practical advantage would be gained as a cubic represents the realistic shapes adequately.

13. Semi-Analytical Finite Element Processes— Use of Orthogonal Functions

13.1 Introduction

The standard finite element methods have been shown to be capable, in principle, of dealing with any two or three (or even four)† dimensional situations. Nevertheless the cost of solutions increases greatly with each dimension added and indeed, on occasion, overtaxes the capabilities of available machines. It is therefore always desirable to search for alternatives which may reduce the computational labour. One such class of processes of quite a wide applicability will be illustrated here.

In many physical problems the situation is such that the *geometry* and *material properties* do not vary along one co-ordinate direction. However, the 'load' terms may still exhibit a variation in that direction preventing the use of such simplifying assumptions as those which, for instance, permitted a two-dimensional, plane strain, analysis to be substituted for a full three-dimensional treatment. In such cases it is possible still to consider a 'substitute' problem, not involving the particular co-ordinate (along which the properties do not vary), and to synthesize the true answer from a series of such simplified solutions.

The method to be described is of quite general use and, obviously, is not limited to structural situations. It will be convenient, however, to use the nomenclature of structural mechanics and to use the potential energy minimization as an example.

We shall confine our attention to problems of minimizing a quadratic functional such as described in Chapters 2 and 3.

Let (x, y, z) be the co-ordinates describing the domain (in this context these do not necessarily have to be the Cartesian co-ordinates). The last one of these, z, is the co-ordinate along which the geometry and material properties do not change and which is limited to lie between two values

$$0 \leqslant z \leqslant a.$$

† *Vide*: finite elements in the time domain Chapter 16.

We shall assume that the shape functions defining the variation of displacements $\{f\}$ (Eq. (2.1)) can be written in a product form as

$$\{f\} = [N(x, y, z)]\{\delta\}^e$$

$$= \sum_{l=1}^{L} \left\{ [\bar{N}(x, y)] \cos \frac{l\pi z}{a} + [\bar{\bar{N}}(x, y)] \sin \frac{l\pi z}{a} \right\} \{\delta^e\}^e. \qquad (13.1)$$

In this type of representation completeness is preserved in view of the capability of the Fourier series to represent any continuous function within a given region (naturally assuming that the shape functions $\bar{N}$ and $\bar{\bar{N}}$ in the domain x, y satisfy the same requirements).

The loading terms will similarly be given a form

$$\{p\} = \sum_{l=1}^{L} \left(\{p_l(x, y)\} \cos \frac{l\pi z}{a} + \{\bar{\bar{p}}_l(x, y)\} \sin \frac{l\pi z}{a} \right) \qquad (13.2)$$

with similar form for concentrated loads and boundary tractions (see Chapter 2).

Indeed initial strains and stresses, if present, would be expanded again in the above form.

Applying the standard processes of Chapter 2 to the determination of the element contribution to the equation minimizing the potential energy, and limiting our attention to the contribution of $\{p\}$ only we can write

$$\frac{\partial \chi^e}{\partial \{\delta\}^e} = [k]^e \left\{ \begin{matrix} \{\delta^1\}^e \\ \vdots \\ \{\delta^L\}^e \end{matrix} \right\} + \left\{ \begin{matrix} \{F^1\}^e \\ \vdots \\ \{F^L\}^e \end{matrix} \right\}. \qquad (13.3)$$

In the above, to avoid summation signs, the vectors $\{\delta\}^e$, etc., are expanded listing the contribution of each value of l separately.

Now a typical submatrix of $[k]^e$ is

$$[k^{lm}]^e = \int \int \int_V [B^l]^T [D][B^m] \, \mathrm{d}x \, \mathrm{d}y \, \mathrm{d}z \qquad (13.4)$$

and a typical term of the 'force' vector becomes

$$\{F^l\}^e = \int \int \int_V [N^l]^T \{p\} \, \mathrm{d}x \, \mathrm{d}y \, \mathrm{d}z. \qquad (13.5)$$

Without going into details it is obvious that the matrix given by Eq. (13.4) will contain the following integrals as products of various submatrices

$$I_1 = \int_0^a \sin\frac{l\pi z}{a} \cos\frac{m\pi z}{a} \, dz$$

$$I_2 = \int_0^a \sin\frac{l\pi z}{a} \sin\frac{m\pi z}{a} \, dz. \tag{13.6}$$

$$I_3 = \int_0^a \cos\frac{l\pi z}{a} \cos\frac{m\pi z}{a} \, dz$$

These integrals arise from products of the derivatives contained in the definition of $[B]$ and, due to the well-known orthogonality property, give

$$I_2 = I_3 = 0 \quad \text{for } l \neq m \tag{13.7}$$

when $l = 1, 2, \ldots$ and $m = 1, 2, \ldots$.'

I_1 is only zero when l and m are both even or odd numbers. The term involving I_1, however, vanishes in most applications.

This means that the matrix $[k]^e$ becomes a diagonal one and that the assembled final equations of the system have the form

$$\begin{bmatrix} [K^{11}] & & & \\ & [K^{22}] & & \\ & & \ddots & \\ & & & [K^{LL}] \end{bmatrix} \begin{Bmatrix} \{\delta^1\} \\ \vdots \\ \{\delta^L\} \end{Bmatrix} + \begin{Bmatrix} \{F^1\} \\ \vdots \\ \{F^L\} \end{Bmatrix} = 0 \tag{13.8}$$

and the large system of equations splits into L separate problems

$$[K^{ll}]\{\delta^l\} + \{F^l\} = 0 \tag{13.9}$$

in which

$$[k_{ij}^{ll}] = \int\int\int_V [B_i^l][D][B_j^l] \, dx \, dy \, dz. \tag{13.10}$$

Further, from Eqs. (13.5) and (13.2) we observe that due to the orthogonal property of the integrals given by Eqs. (13.6), the typical load term becomes simply

$$[F_i^l]^l = \int\int\int_V [N^l]^T\{p^l\} \, dx \, dy \, dz. \tag{13.11}$$

This means that the force term of the lth harmonic only affects the lth system of Eqs. (13.9) and contributes nothing to the other equations. This extremely important property is of considerable practical significance for, *if the expansion of the loading factors involves only one term, only one set of equations need be solved.* The solution of this will tend to the exact one with increasing subdivision in the x–y domain only. Thus what was originally a three-dimensional problem has now been reduced to a two-dimensional one with the consequent reduction of computational effort.

The preceding derivation was illustrated on a three-dimensional, elastic situation. Clearly the arguments could be equally well applied to reduction of two-dimensional problems to one-dimensional ones, etc., and the arguments are not restricted to problems of elasticity. Any physical problem governed by a minimization of a quadratic functional (Chapter 3) is amenable to the same treatment, which under various guises has been used since time immemorial in applied mechanics.

A word of warning should be added regarding the boundary conditions imposed on $\{f\}$. For a complete decoupling to be possible these must be satisfied separately by each and every term of the expansion given by Eq. (13.1). Insertion of a zero displacement in the final reduced problem implies in fact a zero displacement fixed through the z direction by definition. Care must be taken not to treat the final matrix therefore as a simple reduced problem. Indeed this is one of the limitations of the process described.

When the loading is complex and many Fourier components need to be considered the advantages of the approach outlined here reduce and the full solution sometimes becomes superior in economy.

Other permutations of the basic definitions of the type given by Eq. (13.1) are obviously possible. For instance two independent sets of parameters $\{\delta^e\}$ may be specified with each of the trigonometric terms.

Indeed on occasion use of other orthogonal functions may be possible.

As trigonometric functions will arise frequently it is convenient to remind the reader of the following integrals

$$\int_0^a \sin\frac{l\pi z}{a}\cos\frac{l\pi z}{a}\,dz = 0 \quad \text{when } l = 0, 1, \ldots$$

$$\int_0^a \sin^2\frac{l\pi z}{a}\,dz = \int_0^a \cos^2\frac{l\pi z}{a}\,dz = \frac{a}{2} \quad \text{when } l = 1, 2, \ldots.$$

(13.12)

13.2 Prismatic Bar

Consider a prismatic bar illustrated in Fig. 13.1 which is assumed to be held at $z = 0$ and $z = a$ in a manner preventing all displacements in the x–y plane but permitting unrestricted motion in z-direction.

The problem is fully three dimensional and three components of displacement u, v, and w have to be considered.

Subdividing into finite elements in the xy plane we can prescribe the lth displacement components in x direction as

$$u^l = [N_1', N_2', \ldots] \sin\frac{l\pi z}{a} \{u^l\}$$

(13.13)

with similar expressions for the v^l and w^l but with a cosine term in the latter.

In this N', etc., are simply the (scalar) shape functions appropriate to the element used. If, as shown in Fig. 13.1, simple triangles are used then the shape functions are given by Eq. (4.8) of Chapter 4—but any of the more elaborate elements described in Chapter 7 (with or without the transformation of Chapter 8) would be equally suitable.

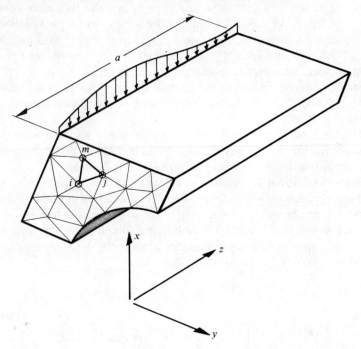

Fig. 13.1   A prismatic bar reduced to a series of two-dimensional finite element solutions

The expansion ensures zero u and w displacements and zero axial stresses at the ends.

The load terms can still be expressed in terms of a similar Fourier series, giving, for components in x–y plane

$$\{p\}^l = \{\bar{p}\} \sin \frac{l\pi z}{a}. \tag{13.14}$$

The problem being fully three dimensional, the appropriate expression for strain involving all six components needs to be considered. This expression is given in Chapter 6 by Eqs. (6.9)—(6.11). On substitution of the shape function given by Eq. (13.13) for a typical term of the $[B]$ matrix we have.

$$
[B_i^l] = \begin{bmatrix}
\dfrac{\partial N_i'}{\partial x}\sin\gamma & 0 & 0 \\[2ex]
0 & \dfrac{\partial N_i'}{\partial y}\sin\gamma & 0 \\[2ex]
0 & 0 & -N_i'\dfrac{l\pi}{a}\sin\gamma \\[2ex]
\dfrac{\partial N_i'}{\partial y}\sin\gamma & \dfrac{\partial N_i'}{\partial x}\sin\gamma & 0 \\[2ex]
0 & N_i'\dfrac{l\pi}{a}\cos\gamma & \dfrac{\partial N_i'}{\partial y}\cos\gamma \\[2ex]
N_i'\dfrac{l\pi}{a}\cos\gamma & 0 & \dfrac{\partial N_i'}{\partial x}\cos\gamma
\end{bmatrix}
\qquad (13.15)
$$

with $\gamma = l\pi z/a$. It is convenient to separate the above as

$$
[B_i^l] = [\bar{B}_i^l]\sin\frac{\pi l z}{a} + [\bar{\bar{B}}_i^l]\cos\frac{\pi l z}{a}. \qquad (13.16)
$$

In all of the above it is assumed that the parameters are listed in usual order

$$
\{\delta_i^l\} = \begin{Bmatrix} u_i^l \\ v_i^l \\ w_i^l \end{Bmatrix} \qquad (13.17)
$$

and that the axes are as shown in Fig. 13.1.

The stiffness matrix can be computed in the usual manner noting that

$$
[k_{ij}^{ll}]^e = \int\int\int_{V^e} [B_i^l]^{\mathrm{T}}[D][B_j^l]\,\mathrm{d}x\,\mathrm{d}y\,\mathrm{d}z. \qquad (13.18)
$$

On substitution of Eq. (13.16), multiplying out, and noting the value of the integrals from Eq. (13.12), this reduces to

$$
[k_{ij}^{ll}]^e = \frac{a}{2}\int\int_{A^e} \{[\bar{B}_i^l]^{\mathrm{T}}[D][\bar{B}_j^l] + [\bar{\bar{B}}_i^l]^{\mathrm{T}}[D][\bar{\bar{B}}_j^l]\}\,\mathrm{d}x\,\mathrm{d}y \qquad (13.19)
$$

when $l = 1, 2 \ldots$.

The integration is now simply carried out over the element *area*.†

---

† It should be noted that now, even for a simple triangle, the integration is not trivial as some linear terms will remain in $[\bar{B}]$.

Similarly the contributions due to distributed loads, initial stresses, etc., are found as the loading terms. Concentrated line loads would be expressed directly as nodal forces

$$\{F_i^l\} = \int_0^a \sin\frac{\pi lz}{a} \begin{Bmatrix} \bar{\bar{F}}_{xi}^l \\ \bar{\bar{F}}_{yi}^l \\ \bar{\bar{F}}_{zi}^l \end{Bmatrix} \sin\frac{\pi lz}{a}\, dz = \{\bar{\bar{F}}^l\}\frac{a}{2} \qquad (13.20)$$

in which $\{\bar{F}\}$ are intensities per unit length.

The boundary conditions used here have been of a type ensuring *simply supported* conditions for the prism. Other conditions can be inserted by suitable expansions.

The method of analysis outlined here can be applied to a range of practical problems—one of these being a popular type of concrete bridge illustrated in Fig. 13.2. Here a particularly convenient type of element is the distorted, 'serendipity', quadratic or cubic of Chapters 7 and 8.

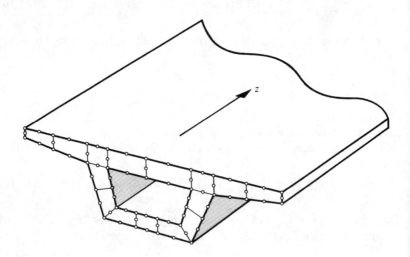

Fig. 13.2   A thick box bridge reduced to a two-dimensional problem with isoparametric, quadratic, elements

Finally it should be mentioned that some restrictions placed on the general shapes defined by Eqs. (13.1) or (13.13) can be raised by doubling the number of parameters and writing expansions in the form of two sums

$$\{f\} = \sum_{l=1}^{L} \bar{N}(x, y) \cos \frac{l\pi z}{a} \{\delta^{Al}\} + \sum_{l-1}^{L} \bar{N}(x, y) \sin \frac{l\pi z}{a} \{\delta^{Bl}\}. \quad (13.21)$$

Parameters $\{\delta^{Al}\}$ and $\{\delta^{Bl}\}$ are independent and for every component of displacement two values have to be found and two equations formed.

An alternative to the above process is to write the function as

$$\{f\} = \sum [N(x, y) \, e^{i(l\pi z/a)}] \{\delta^l\}^l$$

and to observe that both $[N]$ and $\{\delta\}$ are complex quantities.

Complex algebra is now available on standard computers and the identity of the above expression with Eq. (13.21) will be observed noting that

$$e^{i\theta} = \cos \theta + i \sin \theta.$$

13.3 Thin Membrane Box Structures

In the previous section a three-dimensional problem was reduced to that of two dimensions. Here we shall see how a somewhat similar problem can be reduced to one-dimensional elements. (Fig. 13.3.)

A box-type structure is made up of thin sheet components capable of sustaining stresses only in its own plane.

Now, just as in the previous case, three displacements have to be considered at every point and indeed similar variation can be prescribed for these. However, a typical element ij is 'one dimensional' in the sense that integrations have to be carried out only along the line ij and stresses in that

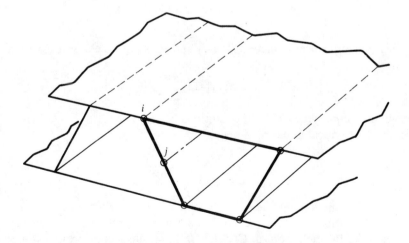

Fig. 13.3   A 'membrane' box with one-dimensional elements

direction only considered. Indeed it will be found that the situation and the solution are similar to that of a pin-jointed framework.

13.4 Plates and Boxes with Flexure

Consider now a rectangular plate simply supported at the ends and in which all strain energy is contained in flexure. Now, only one displacement, w, is needed to specify fully the state of strain (see Chapter 10).

For consistency of notation, the direction in which geometry and material properties do not change has been taken as y (see Fig. 13.4). To preserve slope continuity the functions need to include now the 'rotation' parameter θ_i.

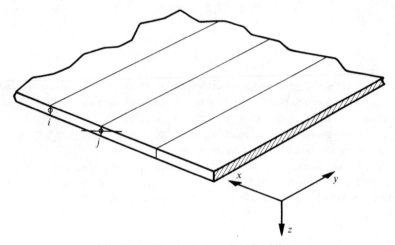

Fig. 13.4   The 'strip' method in slabs

Use of simple beam functions is easy and for a typical element ij we can write

$$w^l = [\bar{N}(x)] \sin \frac{l\pi y}{a} \{\delta^l\}^a \qquad (13.22)$$

ensuring *simply supported* end conditions.
In this, the typical nodal parameters are

$$\{\delta_i^l\} = \begin{Bmatrix} w_i \\ \theta_i \end{Bmatrix}. \qquad (13.23)$$

The shape functions of the cubic type are easy to write and are in fact identical to those used for the axi-symmetric shell problem (Chapter 12).

Using all the definitions of Chapter 10 the strains (curvature) are found and the $[B]$ matrices determined.

The problem of a two-dimensional kind has here been reduced to that of one dimension.

This application has been developed by Cheung,[1, 2, 3] named by him the 'finite strip' method, and used to solve several rectangular plate problems, box girders, shells and various folded plates.

It is illuminating to quote an example from the above papers here. This refers to a square, uniformly loaded plate with three sides simply supported and one free. Ten strips or elements in the x-direction were used in the solution and Table 1 gives the results corresponding to the first three harmonics.

TABLE 13.1

SQUARE PLATE, UNIFORM LOAD q
THREE SIDES SIMPLY SUPPORTED, ONE CLAMPED

$v = 0.3$	Central deflection	Central M_x	Max. negative $-M$
$l = 1$	0.002832	0.0409	−0.0858
$= 2$	−0.000050	−0.0016	0.0041
$= 3$	0.000004	0.0003	−0.0007
$\sum$	0.002786	0.0396	−0.0824
Exact	0.0028	0.039	−0.084
Multiplier qa^4/D		qa^2	

Not only is an accurate solution of each l term a simple one involving only some nine unknowns but the importance of higher terms in the series is seen to decrease rapidly.

Extension of the process to box structures in which both *membrane and bending effects* are present is almost obvious when this example is considered together with the ones of the previous section.

In another paper Cheung[4] shows how functions other than trigonometric ones can be used to advantage although only partial decoupling then occurs.

13.5 Axi-symmetric Solids with Non-symmetrical Load

One of the most natural and indeed earliest applications of the one-way Fourier expansion occurs in axi-symmetric bodies subject to non axi-symmetric loads.

Now, not only the radial (u) and axial (v) displacements (as in Chapter 5) will have to be considered but also a tangential component (w) associated with angular direction θ (Fig. 13.5). It is in this direction that the geometric and material properties do not vary and hence here the elimination will be applied.

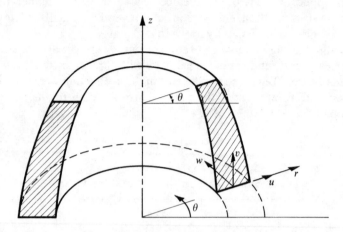

Fig. 13.5   An axi-symmetric solid. Co-ordinates and displacements

To simplify matters we shall consider first components of load which are symmetric about the $\theta = 0$ axis and separately those which are anti-symmetric. Describing now only the nodal loads (with similar expansions holding for body forces, boundary conditions, initial strains, etc.) we specify forces per unit length of circumference as

$$R = \sum_1^L \bar{R}^l \cos l\theta$$

$$Z = \sum_1^L \bar{Z}^l \cos l\theta \qquad (13.24)$$

$$T = \sum_1^L \bar{T}^l \sin l\theta$$

in direction of the various co-ordinates for symmetric loads, Fig. 13.6(a). The apparently non-symmetric sine expansion is used for T, as to achieve symmetry the direction of T has to change for $\theta > \pi$.

The displacement components are described again in terms of the two-dimensional (v, z) shape functions appropriate to the element subdivision and observing symmetry we write as in Eq. (13.13)

$$u^l = [N'_1, N'_2, \dots] \cos l\theta \{u^l\}^e$$
$$v^l = [N'_1, N'_2, \dots] \cos l\theta \{v^l\}^e \qquad (13.25)$$
$$w^l = [N'_1, N'_2, \dots] \sin l\theta \{w^l\}^e.$$

To proceed further it is necessary to specify the general, three-dimensional expression for strains in cylindrical co-ordinates. This is (*vide* Love[5])

$$
\{\varepsilon\} = \left\{ \begin{array}{c} \varepsilon_r \\ \varepsilon_z \\ \varepsilon_\theta \\ \gamma_{rz} \\ \gamma_{r\theta} \\ \gamma_{z\theta} \end{array} \right\} = \left\{ \begin{array}{c} \dfrac{\partial u}{\partial r} \\[6pt] \dfrac{\partial v}{\partial z} \\[6pt] \dfrac{u}{r} + \dfrac{1}{r}\dfrac{\partial w}{\partial \theta} \\[6pt] \dfrac{\partial u}{\partial z} + \dfrac{\partial v}{\partial r} \\[6pt] \dfrac{1}{r}\dfrac{\partial u}{\partial \theta} + \dfrac{\partial w}{\partial r} - \dfrac{w}{r} \\[6pt] \dfrac{1}{r}\dfrac{\partial v}{\partial \theta} + \dfrac{\partial w}{\partial z} \end{array} \right\}
\tag{13.26}
$$

As before, uncoupling will occur between the modes and we can proceed to evaluation of the stiffness matrices, etc., in each harmonic. Typically, we have on substitution of Eq. (13.25) into Eq. (13.26), and grouping the variables as in Eq. (13.17):

$$
[B_i^l] = \begin{bmatrix} \dfrac{\partial N_i'}{\partial r}\cos l\theta & 0 & 0 \\[8pt] 0 & \dfrac{\partial N_i'}{\partial z}\cos l\theta & 0 \\[8pt] \dfrac{N_i'}{r}\cos l\theta & 0 & -\dfrac{l N_i'}{r}\cos l\theta \\[8pt] \dfrac{\partial N_i'}{\partial z}\cos l\theta & \dfrac{\partial N_i'}{\partial r}\cos l\theta & 0 \\[8pt] -\dfrac{l N_i'}{r}\sin l\theta & 0 & \left(\dfrac{\partial N_i'}{\partial r} - \dfrac{N_i'}{r}\right)\sin l\theta \\[8pt] 0 & -\dfrac{l N_i'}{r}\sin l\theta & \dfrac{\partial N_i'}{\partial z}\sin l\theta \end{bmatrix}
\tag{13.27}
$$

The remaining steps of the formulation follow precisely the previous derivations and could be repeated by the reader as an exercise.

For the antisymmetric loading of Fig. 13.6(b) we shall simply replace the sine by cosine and vice versa in Eqs. (13.24) and (13.25).

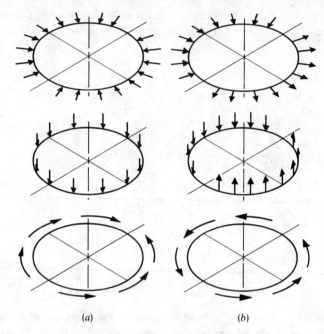

(a)   *(b)*

Fig. 13.6   Symmetric (*a*) and anti-symmetric (*b*) load and displacement components in an axisymmetric body

The load terms in each harmonic will be obtained by virtual work as

$$\{F_i^l\} = \int_0^{2\pi} \begin{Bmatrix} \bar{R}^l \cos^2 l\theta \\ \bar{Z}^l \cos^2 l\theta \\ \bar{T}^l \sin^2 l\theta \end{Bmatrix} \, d\theta = \pi \begin{Bmatrix} \bar{R}^l \\ \bar{Z}^l \\ \bar{T}^l \end{Bmatrix} \quad \text{when } l = 1, 2, \ldots$$

$$= 2\pi \begin{Bmatrix} \bar{R}^l \\ \bar{Z}^l \\ 0 \end{Bmatrix} \quad \text{when } l = 0 \qquad (13.28)$$

for the symmetric case. Similarly for the antisymmetric case

$$\{F_i^l\} = \pi \begin{Bmatrix} \bar{R}^l \\ \bar{Z}^l \\ \bar{T}^l \end{Bmatrix} \quad \text{when } l = 1, 2, \ldots = \begin{Bmatrix} 0 \\ 0 \\ \bar{T}^0 \end{Bmatrix} \quad \text{when } l = 0. \quad (13.29)$$

We see from this and from the expansion of $[k]^e$ that, as expected, for $l = 0$ the problem reduces to only two variables and the axi-symmetric case is retrieved when the loads are symmetric.

Similarly, when $l = 0$ only one set of equations remains in the variable w for the antisymmetric case. This corresponds to constant tangential traction and solves simply the torsion problems of shafts subject to known

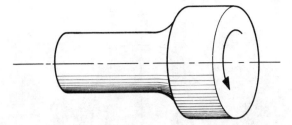

Fig. 13.7 Torsion of a variable section bar

torques, Fig. 13.7. This problem is classically treated by the use of a stress function[6] and indeed has been solved using a finite element formulation.[7] Here an alternative, more physical approach is available.

The first application of the above concepts to the analysis of axi-symmetric solids was made by Wilson.[8]

A simple example illustrating the effects of various harmonics is shown in Fig. 13.8(a) and (b).

13.6 Axi-symmetric Shells with Non-symmetric Loading

The extension of analysis of axi-symmetric shells as described in Chapter 12 to the case of non-axi-symmetric loads is simple and will again follow the standard pattern.

It is, however, necessary to extend the definition of strains and to include now all three displacements and force components, Fig. 13.9. Three membrane and three bending effects are now present and extending Eq. (12.1) we now define strains as[9]†

$$\{\varepsilon\} = \left\{ \begin{array}{c} \varepsilon_s \\ \varepsilon_\theta \\ \gamma_{s\theta} \\ \chi_s \\ \chi_\theta \\ \chi_{s\theta} \end{array} \right\} = \left\{ \begin{array}{c} \dfrac{\partial u}{\partial s} \\[2mm] \dfrac{1}{r}\dfrac{\partial v}{\partial \theta}+(w\,\cos\,\phi+u\,\sin\,\phi)\,\dfrac{1}{r} \\[2mm] \dfrac{1}{r}\dfrac{\partial u}{\partial \theta}+\dfrac{\partial v}{\partial s}-v\,\sin\,\phi\,\dfrac{1}{r} \\[2mm] -\dfrac{\partial^2 w}{\partial s^2} \\[2mm] -\dfrac{1}{r^2}\dfrac{\partial^2 w}{\partial \theta}+\dfrac{\partial v}{\partial \theta}\dfrac{\cos\,\phi}{r^2}-\dfrac{\sin\,\phi}{r}\dfrac{\partial w}{\partial s} \\[2mm] 2\left(-\dfrac{1}{r}\dfrac{\partial^2 w}{\partial s\,\partial \theta}+\dfrac{\sin\,\phi}{r^2}\dfrac{\partial w}{\partial \theta}+\dfrac{\cos\,\phi}{r}\dfrac{\partial v}{\partial s}-\dfrac{\sin\,\phi\,\cos\,\phi}{r^2}\,v\right) \end{array} \right\} \quad (13.30)$$

† Various alternatives are here present due to the multiplicity of shell theories. This one is fairly generally accepted.

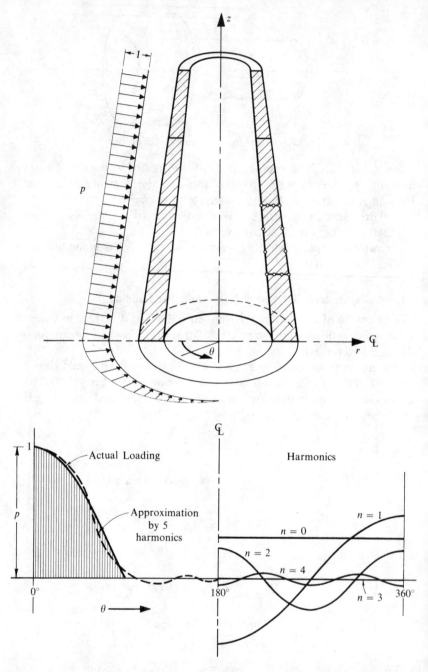

Fig. 13.8(a)   An axi-symmetric tower under non-symmetric load. Four cubic elements used in solution. Harmonics of load expansion used in analysis are shown

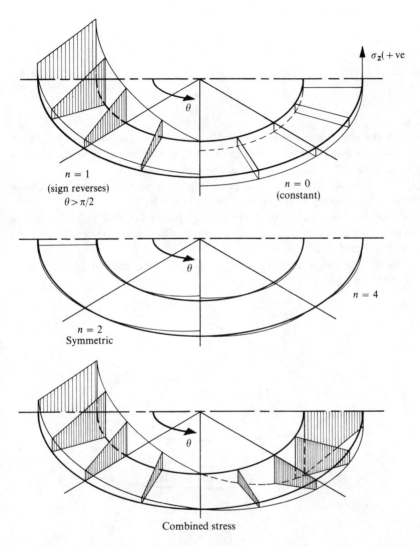

Fig. 13.8(*b*)   Distribution of σ_z—the vertical stress on base due to various harmonics and their combination (third harmonic identically zero). First two harmonics give practically complete answer

The corresponding stress matrix is

$$\{\sigma\} = \begin{Bmatrix} N_s \\ N_\theta \\ N_{s\theta} \\ M_s \\ M_\theta \\ M_{s\theta} \end{Bmatrix} \tag{13.31}$$

with the three membrane and bending 'stresses' defined as in Fig. 13.9.

Once again symmetric and antisymmetric variation of loads and displacements can be assumed as in the previous section.

As the processes involved in executing this extension of the application are now obvious no further elaboration is needed here.

The reader is referred to the original paper by Grafton and Strome[10] in which this problem is first treated and to the many later papers on the subject listed in Chapter 12.

Some examples illustrating the process in the context of thick shell analysis are given in Chapter 14.

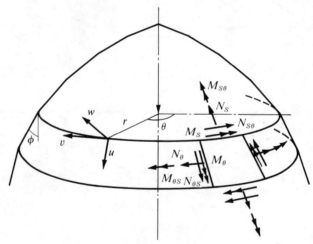

Fig. 13.9   Axi-symmetric shell with non-symmetric load. Displacements and stress resultants

13.7 Concluding Remarks

A fairly general process combining some of the advantages of finite element analysis with the economy of expansion in terms of orthogonal functions has been illustrated in several applications. Certainly these only touch on the possibilities offered but it should be borne in mind that the economy is only achieved in certain geometrically constrained situations and those to which the number of terms requiring solution is limited.

Similarly other 'prismatic' situations can be dealt with in which only a segment of a body of revolution is developed. (Fig. 13.10.) Clearly, the expansion must now be taken in terms of the angle $l\pi\theta/\alpha$ but otherwise the approach is identical to that described previously.

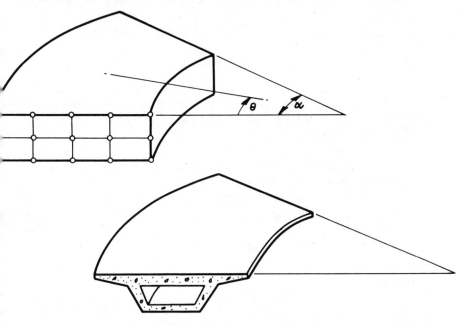

Fig. 13.10   Other segmental, prismatic situations

Other possibilities of combining the advantages of analytical solutions with those of a generality achievable in a numerically discretized formulation exist. For instance, if singularities of solution due, say, to concentrated loads exist, it is possible to eliminate these by an exact solution and to solve a subsidiary problem numerically in which, say, a removal of smoothly distributed boundary forces is carried out. The numerical solution then needs to be performed with a smaller accuracy and can therefore be attempted more economically. A description of such processes is given by Zienkiewicz et al.[11, 12]

A slightly different use of such combined approaches is given in outline by Morley[13] where singularities due to re-entrant corners are eliminated. The space limitation prohibits further discussion of these in this text; however, again a loss of generality is a penalty which has to be paid for economy.

In the methods of this chapter it was assumed that material properties remain invariant with one co-ordinate direction. This restriction can on occasion be lifted with the same general process maintained. An interesting example of this type is outlined by Stricklin and De Andrade.[14]

In yet another class of methods a 'dimension' of the problem can be reduced by using a set of exact singularity solutions and representing, say, a full three-dimensional problem by an *integral equation* applicable to a surface.

Typically we may then have to solve a problem of a type

$$f(p) + \int_S K(p, q) f(q) \, \mathrm{d}S = F(p) \tag{13.32}$$

where p and q specify the co-ordinates of separate points in the surface S and $f(p)$ is an unknown function which solves the problem. K and F are known functions of position.

Such an integral equation may very naturally be solved by a finite element process by splitting the integral into its element portions and using an approximate representation of f.

A typical formulation of this kind was suggested by Massonnet[15] in the context of elasticity. Fried[16] shows how a problem involving an unlimited flow about an object can be reduced in this way to one in which finite elements are confined to the surface alone.

References

1. Y. K. CHEUNG, 'The finite strip method in the analysis of elastic plates with two opposite simply supported ends', *Proc. Inst. Civ. Eng.*, **40**, 1–7, 1968.
2. Y. K. CHEUNG, 'Finite strip method of analysis of elastic slabs', *Proc. Am. Soc. Civ. Eng.*, **94**, EM6, 1365–78, 1968.
3. Y. K. CHEUNG, 'Folded plate structures by the finite strip method', *Proc. Am. Soc. Civ. Eng.*, **95** ST, 2963–79, 1969.
4. Y. K. CHEUNG, 'The analysis of cylindrical orthotropic curved bridge decks', *Publ. Int. Ass. Struct. Eng.*, **29**-II, 41–52, 1969.
5. A. E. H. LOVE, *The mathematical theory of elasticity*, 4th ed., Cambridge Univ. Press, 1927, p. 56.
6. S. TIMOSHENKO and J. N. GOODIER, *Theory of Elasticity*, 2nd ed., McGraw-Hill, 1951.
7. O. C. ZIENKIEWICZ and Y. K. CHEUNG, 'Stresses in Shafts', *The Engineer*, 24 Nov. 1967.
8. E. L. WILSON, 'Structural analysis of axi-symmetric solids', *J.A.I.A.A.*, **3**, 2269–74, 1965.
9. V. V. NOVOZHILOV, *Theory of thin shells* (Translation), P. Noordhoff, 1959.
10. P. E. GRAFTON and D. R. STROME, 'Analysis of axi-symmetric shells by the direct stiffness method', *J.A.I.A.A.*, **1**, 2342–7, 1963.
11. O. C. ZIENKIEWICZ and R. W. GERSTNER, 'The method of interface stress adjustment and its uses in some plane elasticity problems', *Int. J. Mech. Sci.*, **2**, 267–76, 1961.

12. O. C. ZIENKIEWICZ and R. W. GERSTNER, 'Stress analysis and special problems of prestressed dams', *Proc. Am. Soc. Civ. Eng.*, **87**, POI, 7–43, 1961.
13. L. S. D. MORLEY, 'A finite element application of modified Rayleigh–Ritz method', *Int. J. Num. Meth. in Eng.*, **2**, 85–98, 1970.
14. J. A. STRICKLIN and J. C. DE ANDRADE, 'Linear and non linear analysis of shells of revolution with asymmetrical stiffness properties', *Proc. 2nd Conf. Matrix Methods Struct Mech.*, Air Force Inst. of Techn., Wright Patterson A.F. Base, Ohio, 1968.
15. C. E. MASSONNET, 'Numerical use of integral procedures', Chapter 10 of *Stress Analysis*, ed. O. C. Zienkiewicz and G. S. Holister, J. Wiley & Son, 1965.
16. I. FRIED, 'Finite element analysis of problems formulated by an integral equation; Application to potential flow', *Inst. für Statik und Dynamik, Luft- und Raumfahrtsanstalt*, Stuttgart, 1968.

14. Thick Shells as a Special Case of Three-dimensional Analysis

14.1 Introduction

In Chapters 8 and 9 the formulation and use of complex, curved, two- and three-dimensional elements was illustrated. It seems obvious that use of such elements could be made directly in the analysis of curved shells simply by reducing their dimension in the shell thickness direction as shown in Fig. 14.1. Indeed in an axi-symmetric situation such an application has been illustrated in the example of Fig. 9.6 in Chapter 9.

With a straightforward use of the three-dimensional concept, however, certain difficulties will be encountered.

In the first place the retention of three degrees of freedom at each node leads to large stiffness coefficients for relative displacements along an edge corresponding to the shell thickness. This presents numerical problems and may lead to ill-conditioned equations when shell thicknesses become small compared with the other dimensions in the element.

The second factor is that of economy. The use of several nodes across the shell thickness ignores the well-known fact that even for thick shells the 'normals' to the middle surface remain practically straight after deformation. Thus an unnecessarily high number of degrees of freedom has to be carried, involving penalties of computer time.

Here, specialized formulation is presented overcoming both these difficulties.[1,2,3] The constraint of straight 'normals' is introduced to improve economy and the strain energy corresponding to stresses perpendicular to the middle surface is ignored to improve numerical conditioning. With these modifications an efficient tool for analysing curved thick shells becomes available. Its accuracy and wide range of applicability is demonstrated in several examples.

The reader will note that the two constraints introduced correspond only to a part of the usual assumptions in shell theory. Thus, the statement that after deformation the normals remain normal to the deformed middle

274

surface has been deliberately omitted. This omission permits the shell to experience shear deformations—an important feature in thick shell situations.

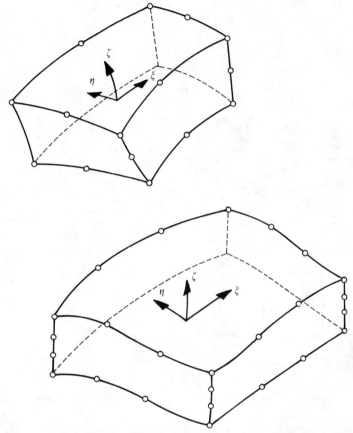

Fig. 14.1   Curved, isoparametric hexahedra in a direct approximation to a curved shell

14.2 Geometric Definition of the Element

Consider a typical thick shell element of Fig. 14.2. The external faces of the element are curved, while the sections across the thickness are genera-ted by straight lines. Pairs of points, i_{top} and i_{bottom}, each with given Cartesian co-ordinates, prescribe the shape of the element.

Let ξ, η be the two curvilinear co-ordinates in the middle plane of the shell and ζ a linear co-ordinate in the thickness direction. If further we assume that ξ, η, ζ vary between -1 and 1 on the respective faces of the element we can write a relationship between the Cartesian co-ordinates of any point of the shell and the curvilinear co-ordinates in the form

$$
\left\{ \begin{matrix} x \\ y \\ z \end{matrix} \right\} = \sum N_i'(\xi, \eta) \frac{(1+\zeta)}{2} \left\{ \begin{matrix} x_i \\ y_i \\ z_i \end{matrix} \right\}_{\text{top}} + \sum N_i'(\xi, \eta) \frac{(1-\zeta)}{2} \left\{ \begin{matrix} x_i \\ y_i \\ z_i \end{matrix} \right\}_{\text{bottom}} .
$$

(14.1)

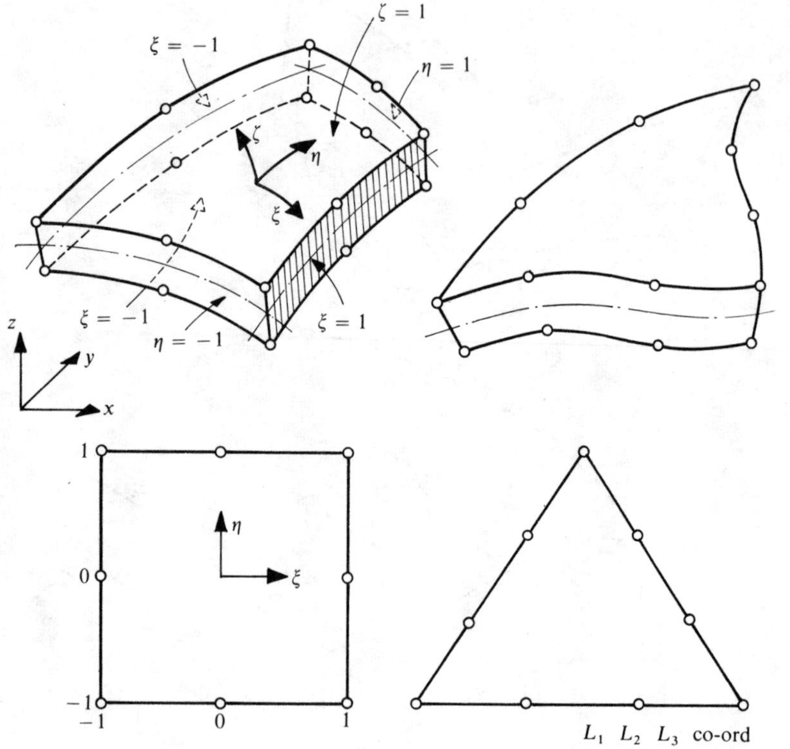

Fig. 14.2 Curved thick shell elements of various types

Here $N_i'(\xi, \eta)$ is a shape function taking a value of unity at the nodes i and zero of all other nodes (Chapter 8). If the basic functions N_i are derived as 'shape functions' of a 'parent', two-dimensional element, square or even triangular† in plan and are so 'designed' that compatibility is achieved at interfaces, then the curved space elements will fit into each other. Arbitrary curved shapes of the element can be achieved by using shape functions of different orders. Only parabolic and cubic types are shown in Fig. 14.2. By placing a larger number of nodes on the surfaces of the element more elaborate shapes can be achieved if so desired. Any of the two-dimensional shape functions of Chapter 7 can be used here.

† Area co-ordinates would be used in this case in place of ξ and η as in Chapter 7.

The relation between the Cartesian and curvilinear co-ordinates is now established and it will be found desirable to operate with the curvilinear co-ordinates as the basis.

It should be noted that the co-ordinate direction ζ is *only approximately normal* to the middle surface.

It is convenient to rewrite the relationship, Eq. (14.1) in a form specified by the 'vector' connecting the upper and lower points (i.e., a vector of length equal to the shell thickness t) and the mid-surface co-ordinates. Thus† we can rewrite Eq. 14.1 as (Fig. 14.3)

$$\left\{ \begin{matrix} x \\ y \\ z \end{matrix} \right\} = \sum N_i' \left\{ \begin{matrix} x_i \\ y_i \\ z_i \end{matrix} \right\}_{mid.} + \sum N_i' \frac{\zeta}{2} V_{3i}$$

with   (14.2)

$$V_{3i} = \left\{ \begin{matrix} x_i \\ y_i \\ z_i \end{matrix} \right\}_{top} - \left\{ \begin{matrix} x_i \\ y_i \\ z_i \end{matrix} \right\}_{bottom}.$$

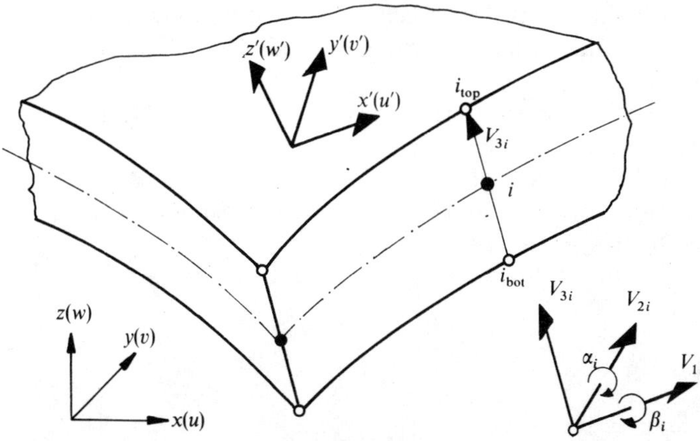

Fig. 14.3   Local and global co-ordinates

14.3 Displacement Field

The displacement field has now to be specified for the element. As the strains in the direction normal to the mid-surface will be assumed to be negligible, the displacement throughout the element will be taken to be uniquely defined by the *three Cartesian components* of the mid-surface node displacement and two rotations of the nodal vector V_{3i} about

† For details of vector algebra see Appendix 5.

orthogonal directions normal to it. If two such orthogonal directions are given by vectors v_{2i} and v_{1i} of unit magnitude) with corresponding (scalar) rotations α_i and β_i we can write, similarly to Eq. (14.2) but now dropping the suffix 'mid' for simplicity

$$\begin{Bmatrix} u \\ v \\ w \end{Bmatrix} = \sum N_i \begin{Bmatrix} u_i \\ v_i \\ w_i \end{Bmatrix} + \sum N_i \zeta \frac{t_i}{2} \, [v_{1i}, -v_{2i}] \begin{Bmatrix} \alpha_i \\ \beta_i \end{Bmatrix} \qquad (14.3)$$

from which the usual form is readily obtained as

$$\begin{Bmatrix} u \\ v \\ w \end{Bmatrix} = [N] \begin{Bmatrix} \{\delta_i\}^e \\ \vdots \\ \{\delta_j\}^e \end{Bmatrix} \quad \text{with} \quad \{\delta_i\} = \begin{Bmatrix} u_i \\ v_i \\ w_i \\ \alpha_i \\ \beta_i \end{Bmatrix}$$

where u, v, and w are displacements in the directions of the global, x, y, and z axes.

As an infinity of vector directions normal to a given direction can be generated, a particular scheme has been devised to ensure a *unique* definition.

Some such schemes were discussed in Chapter 11. Here a simpler unique alternative will be given.

Thus if V_{3i} is the vector to which a normal direction is to be constructed we form the first normal axis in a direction perpendicular to the plane defined by this vector and the x axis.†

A vector V_{1i} of this description is given by the cross product

$$V_{1i} = i \times V_{3i}. \qquad (14.4)$$

In this

$$i = \begin{Bmatrix} 1 \\ 0 \\ 0 \end{Bmatrix}$$

is a unit vector in direction of the x axis. Dividing this by its length we can write the unit vector v_{1i}.

The last vector normal to the other two is simply

$$V_{2i} = V_{1i} \times V_{3i} \qquad (14.5)$$

and all the direction cosines of the local axes can be determined by nor-

† This process fails if V_{3i} corresponds in direction with the x axis. A program checking this possibility is easily written and in such a case the local directions are obtained using the y axis.

malizing this to v_{2i}. We have thus three local, orthogonal axes defined by unit vectors

$$v_{1i}, \quad v_{2i}, \quad \text{and} \quad v_{3i}. \qquad (14.6)$$

Once again if N_i' are compatible functions then displacement compatibility is maintained between adjacent elements.

The element co-ordinate definition is now given by the relation, Eq. (14.1), which has more degrees of freedom than the definition of the displacements. The element is therefore of the super-parametric kind (*vide* Chapter 8, section 8.3) and the constant strain criteria are not automatically satisfied.

Nevertheless, it will be seen from the definition of strain components involved that both rigid body motions and constant strain conditions are available.

Physically, it has been assumed in the definition of Eq. (14.3) that no strains occur in the 'thickness' direction ζ. While this direction is not exactly normal to the middle surface it still represents to a good approximation one of the usual shell assumptions.

At each mid-surface node i of Fig. 14.3 we have now the five basic degrees of freedom (*vide* consideration of shells in Chapter 11).

14.4 Definition of Strains and Stresses

To derive the properties of a finite element the essential strains and stresses have to be defined. The components in directions of *orthogonal axes* related to the surface $\zeta = $ constant are essential if account is to be taken of the basic shell assumptions. Thus if at any point in this surface we erect a normal z' with two other orthogonal axes x' and y' tangent to it (Fig. 14.3) the strain components of interest are given simply by the three-dimensional relationships of Chapter 6.

$$\{\varepsilon'\} = \left\{ \begin{array}{c} \varepsilon_{x'} \\ \varepsilon_{y'} \\ \gamma_{x'y'} \\ \gamma_{x'z'} \\ \gamma_{y'z'} \end{array} \right\} = \left\{ \begin{array}{c} \dfrac{\partial u'}{\partial x'} \\ \dfrac{\partial v'}{\partial y'} \\ \dfrac{\partial u'}{\partial y'} + \dfrac{\partial v'}{\partial x'} \\ \dfrac{\partial w'}{\partial x'} + \dfrac{\partial u'}{\partial z'} \\ \dfrac{\partial w'}{\partial y'} + \dfrac{\partial v'}{\partial z'} \end{array} \right\} \qquad (14.7)$$

with the strain in direction z' neglected so as to be consistent with the usual shell assumptions. It must be noted that in general none of these directions coincide with those of the curvilinear co-ordinates ξ, η, ζ, although x', y' are in the ξ–η plane (ζ = constant).†

The stresses corresponding to these strains are defined by a matrix $\{\sigma'\}$ and are related by the usual elasticity matrix $[D']$. Thus

$$\{\sigma'\} = \begin{Bmatrix} \sigma_{x'} \\ \sigma_{y'} \\ \tau_{x'y'} \\ \tau_{x'z'} \\ \tau_{y'z'} \end{Bmatrix} = [D'](\{\varepsilon'\} - \{\varepsilon_0'\}) + \{\sigma_0'\} \tag{14.8}$$

where $\{\varepsilon_0'\}$ in $\{\sigma_0'\}$ may represent any 'initial' strains or stresses.

The 5×5 matrix $[D']$ can now include any anisotropic properties and indeed may be prescribed as a function of ζ if sandwich (layered) construction is used. For the present moment we shall define it only for an isotropic material. Here

$$[D'] = \frac{E}{1-v^2} \begin{bmatrix} 1 & v & 0 & 0 & 0 \\ & 1 & 0 & 0 & 0 \\ & & \frac{1-v}{2} & 0 & 0 \\ & & & \frac{1-v}{2k} & 0 \\ \text{sym.} & & & & \frac{1-v}{2k} \end{bmatrix} \tag{14.9}$$

in which E and v are Young's modulus and Poisson's ratio respectively. The factor k included in the last two shear terms is taken as $1{\cdot}2$ and its purpose is to improve the shear displacement approximation. From the displacement definition it will be seen that the shear distribution is approximately constant through the thickness, whereas in reality the shear distribution is approximately parabolic. The value $k = 1{\cdot}2$ is the ratio of relevant strain energies.

It is important to note that this matrix is *not* derived simply by deleting appropriate terms from the equivalent three-dimensional stress matrix of Chapter 6 (Eq. (6.14)). It must be derived by substituting $\sigma_z' = 0$ into Eq. (6.13) and a suitable elimination so that the important shell assumption is satisfied.

† Indeed these directions will only approximately agree with the nodal direction v_{1i}, etc., previously derived as in general the vector v_{3i} is only approximately normal to the mid-surfaces.

14.5 Element Properties and Necessary Transformations

The stiffness matrix—and indeed all other 'element' property matrices—involve integrals over the volume of the element, which are quite generally of the form

$$\int_{V^c} [S]\, dx\, dy\, dz \qquad (14.10)$$

where the matrix $[S]$ is a function of the co-ordinates.

In the stiffness matrix

$$[S] = [B]^T[D][B] \qquad (14.11)$$

for instance, with the usual definition of Chapter 2

$$\{\varepsilon\} = [B]\{\delta\}^c \qquad (14.12)$$

we have $[B]$ defined in terms of the displacement derivatives with respect to the local Cartesian co-ordinates $x'y'z'$ by Eq. (14.7).

Now, therefore, *two sets of transformations* are necessary before the element can be integrated with respect to the curvilinear co-ordinates ξ, η, ζ.

First, by identically the same process as we used in Chapter 8, the derivatives with respect to the x, y, z directions are obtained.

As Eq. (14.3) relates the global displacements u, v, w to the curvilinear co-ordinates, the derivatives of these displacements with respect to the global x, y, z co-ordinates are given by a matrix relation.

$$\begin{bmatrix} \dfrac{\partial u}{\partial x} & \dfrac{\partial v}{\partial x} & \dfrac{\partial w}{\partial x} \\[2mm] \dfrac{\partial u}{\partial y} & \dfrac{\partial v}{\partial y} & \dfrac{\partial w}{\partial y} \\[2mm] \dfrac{\partial u}{\partial z} & \dfrac{\partial v}{\partial z} & \dfrac{\partial w}{\partial z} \end{bmatrix} = [J]^{-1} \begin{bmatrix} \dfrac{\partial u}{\partial \xi} & \dfrac{\partial v}{\partial \xi} & \dfrac{\partial w}{\partial \xi} \\[2mm] \dfrac{\partial u}{\partial \eta} & \dfrac{\partial v}{\partial \eta} & \dfrac{\partial w}{\partial \eta} \\[2mm] \dfrac{\partial u}{\partial \zeta} & \dfrac{\partial v}{\partial \zeta} & \dfrac{\partial w}{\partial \zeta} \end{bmatrix}. \qquad (14.13)$$

In this, the Jacobian matrix is defined as before

$$[J] = \begin{bmatrix} \dfrac{\partial x}{\partial \xi} & \dfrac{\partial y}{\partial \xi} & \dfrac{\partial z}{\partial \xi} \\[2mm] \dfrac{\partial x}{\partial \eta} & \dfrac{\partial y}{\partial \eta} & \dfrac{\partial z}{\partial \eta} \\[2mm] \dfrac{\partial x}{\partial \zeta} & \dfrac{\partial y}{\partial \zeta} & \dfrac{\partial z}{\partial \zeta} \end{bmatrix} \qquad (14.14)$$

and is calculated from the co-ordinate definitions of Eq. (14.2).

Now, for every set of curvilinear co-ordinates the global displacement derivatives can be obtained numerically. A further transformation to local displacement directions x', y', z' will allow the strains, and hence the $[B]$ matrix, to be evaluated.

First the directions of the local axes have to be established. A vector normal to the surface ζ-constant can be found as a vector product of any two vectors tangent to the surface. Thus

$$V_3 = \left\{ \begin{array}{c} \dfrac{\partial x}{\partial \xi} \\[2mm] \dfrac{\partial y}{\partial \xi} \\[2mm] \dfrac{\partial z}{\partial \xi} \end{array} \right\} \times \left\{ \begin{array}{c} \dfrac{\partial x}{\partial \eta} \\[2mm] \dfrac{\partial y}{\partial \eta} \\[2mm] \dfrac{\partial z}{\partial \eta} \end{array} \right\} = \left\{ \begin{array}{c} \dfrac{\partial y}{\partial \xi}\dfrac{\partial z}{\partial \eta} - \dfrac{\partial y}{\partial \eta}\dfrac{\partial z}{\partial \xi} \\[2mm] \dfrac{\partial x}{\partial \eta}\dfrac{\partial z}{\partial \xi} - \dfrac{\partial x}{\partial \xi}\dfrac{\partial z}{\partial \eta} \\[2mm] \dfrac{\partial x}{\partial \xi}\dfrac{\partial y}{\partial \eta} - \dfrac{\partial x}{\partial \eta}\dfrac{\partial y}{\partial \xi} \end{array} \right\}. \tag{14.15}$$

Following the process which defines uniquely two perpendicular vectors, given previously, and reducing to unit magnitudes, we construct a matrix of unit vectors in x', y', z' directions (which is in fact the direction cosine matrix)

$$[\theta] = [v_1, v_2, v_3]. \tag{14.16}$$

The global derivatives of displacements u, v, and w are now transformed to the local derivatives of the local orthogonal displacements by a standard operation

$$\begin{bmatrix} \dfrac{\partial u'}{\partial x'} & \dfrac{\partial v'}{\partial x'} & \dfrac{\partial w'}{\partial x'} \\[2mm] \dfrac{\partial u'}{\partial y'} & \dfrac{\partial v'}{\partial y'} & \dfrac{\partial w'}{\partial y'} \\[2mm] \dfrac{\partial u'}{\partial z'} & \dfrac{\partial v'}{\partial z'} & \dfrac{\partial w'}{\partial z'} \end{bmatrix} = [\theta]^{\mathrm{T}} \begin{bmatrix} \dfrac{\partial u}{\partial x} & \dfrac{\partial v}{\partial x} & \dfrac{\partial w}{\partial x} \\[2mm] \dfrac{\partial u}{\partial y} & \dfrac{\partial v}{\partial y} & \dfrac{\partial w}{\partial y} \\[2mm] \dfrac{\partial u}{\partial z} & \dfrac{\partial v}{\partial z} & \dfrac{\partial w}{\partial z} \end{bmatrix} [\theta]. \tag{14.17}$$

From this the components of the $[B']$ matrix can now be found explicitly, noting that five degrees of freedom exist at each node

$$\{\varepsilon'\} = [B'] \left\{ \begin{array}{c} \{\delta_1\}^e \\ \vdots \\ \{\delta_j\}^e \end{array} \right\}; \quad \{\delta_i\}^e = \left\{ \begin{array}{c} u_i \\ v_i \\ w_i \\ \alpha_i \\ \beta_i \end{array} \right\}. \tag{14.18}$$

The infinitesimal volume is given in terms of the curvilinear co-ordinates as

$$dx \, dy \, dz = \det |J| \, d\xi \, d\eta \, d\zeta \qquad (14.19)$$

and this standard expression completes the basic formulation.

Numerical integration within the appropriate -1, $+1$ limits is carried out in exactly the same way as for three-dimensional elements discussed in Chapter 8.

Identical processes serve to define all the other relevant element matrices.

As the variation of the strain quantities in the thickness, ζ direction, is linear, only two Gauss points in that direction are required while three or four in the ξ, η directions are used for parabolic and cubic shape functions respectively.

It should be remarked here that, in fact, the integration with respect to ζ can be performed exactly if desired, thus saving computation time. Also a reduced order of integration in the ξ, η direction is not only economical but results in a dramatic improvement of element properties which will be discussed in sections 14.7 and 14.10.

14.6 Some Remarks on Stress Representation

The element properties are now defined, and the assembly and solution are standard processes.

It remains to discuss the presentation of the stresses, and this problem is of some consequence. The strains being defined in local directions, $\{\sigma'\}$ is readily available. Such components are indeed directly of interest but as the directions of local axes are not easily visualized it is sometimes convenient to transfer the components to the global system using the following expression

$$\begin{bmatrix} \sigma_x & \tau_{xy} & \tau_{xz} \\ \tau_{xy} & \sigma_y & \tau_{yz} \\ \tau_{xz} & \tau_{yz} & \sigma_z \end{bmatrix} = [\theta] \begin{bmatrix} \sigma_{x'} & \tau_{x'y'} & \tau_{x'z'} \\ \tau_{x'y'} & \sigma_{y'} & \tau_{y'z'} \\ \tau_{x'z'} & \tau_{y'z'} & 0 \end{bmatrix} [\theta]^{\mathrm{T}}. \qquad (14.20)$$

If the stresses are calculated at a nodal point where several elements meet then they are averaged.

In a general shell structure, the stresses in a global system do not, however, give a clear picture of shell surface stresses. It is thus convenient always to compute the principal stresses by a suitable transformation.

However, regarding the shell surface stresses more rationally, one may note that the shear components $\tau_{x'z'}$ and $\tau_{y'z'}$ are in fact zero there, and can indeed be made zero at the stage before converting to global components. The values directly obtained for these shear components are the average values across the section. The maximum transverse shear value occurs on the neutral axis and is equal to 1·5 times the average value.

14.7 Special Case of Axi-symmetric, Curved, Thick Shells

For axi-symmetric shells the formulation is, obviously, simplified.[1] Now the element mid-surface is defined by only two co-ordinates ξ, η and a considerable saving in computer effort is obtained.

The element now is derived in a similar manner but starting from a two-dimensional definition of Fig. 14.4.

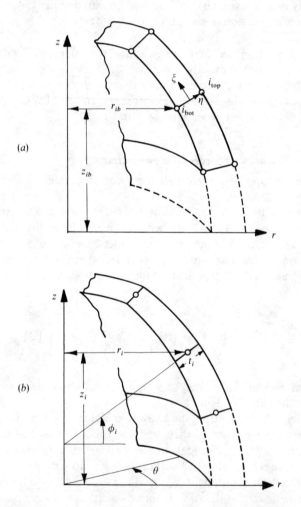

Fig. 14.4   Co-ordinates for an axi-symmetric shell problem

Equations (14.1) and (14.2) are now replaced by their two-dimensional equivalents defining the relation between the co-ordinates as

$$\begin{Bmatrix} r \\ z \end{Bmatrix} = \sum N_i(\xi)\frac{(1+\eta)}{2}\begin{Bmatrix} r_i \\ z_i \end{Bmatrix}_{\text{top}} + \sum N_i(\xi)\frac{(1-\eta)}{2}\begin{Bmatrix} r_i \\ z_i \end{Bmatrix}_{\text{bottom}}$$

$$= \sum N_i(\xi)\begin{Bmatrix} r_i \\ z_i \end{Bmatrix}_{\text{mid}} + \sum N_i(\xi)\frac{\eta}{2}V_{3i} \qquad (14.21)$$

with

$$V_{3i} = t_i \begin{Bmatrix} \cos\phi_i \\ \sin\phi_i \end{Bmatrix}$$

in which ϕ_i is the angle defined in Fig. 14.4(b) and t_i the shell thickness.

Similarly the displacement definition is specified by following the lines of Eq. (14.3).

For generality we shall consider the case of non-symmetric loading only noting the terms which can be eliminated *a priori* for the simple case of symmetry. Indeed the decomposition into trigonometric components will be tacitly assumed as it follows precisely the lines described in Chapter 13.

Thus generally we specify the three displacement components of the nth harmonic as

$$\begin{Bmatrix} u^n \\ v^n \\ w^n \end{Bmatrix} = \begin{bmatrix} \cos n\theta & 0 & 0 \\ 0 & \cos n\theta & 0 \\ 0 & 0 & \sin n\theta \end{bmatrix}\left(\sum N_i \begin{Bmatrix} u_i^n \\ v_i^n \\ w_i^n \end{Bmatrix}\right.$$

$$\left. + \sum N_i\eta\frac{t_i}{2}\begin{bmatrix} -\sin\phi_i & 0 \\ \cos\phi_i & 0 \\ 0 & 1 \end{bmatrix}\begin{Bmatrix} \alpha_i^n \\ \beta_i^n \end{Bmatrix}\right) \quad (14.22)$$

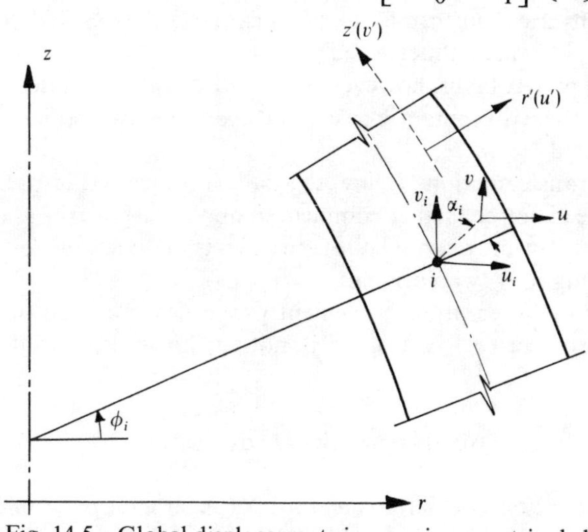

Fig. 14.5   Global displacements in an axi-symmetric shell

In this α_i stands for the rotation illustrated in Fig. 14.5, u_i, etc., for the displacement of the middle surface node and β_i is the rotation about the vector tangential (approximately) to the middle surface.

For the purely axi-symmetric case a further simplification arises by omitting the w terms, the first matrix of trigonometric constants and the rotation β_i.

Local strains are now more conveniently defined by the relationship Eq. (14.7) written in global cylindrical co-ordinates.

$$\{\varepsilon\} = \begin{Bmatrix} \varepsilon_r \\ \varepsilon_z \\ \varepsilon_\theta \\ \gamma_{rz} \\ \gamma_{r\theta} \\ \gamma_{z\theta} \end{Bmatrix} = \begin{Bmatrix} \dfrac{\partial u}{\partial r} \\ \dfrac{\partial v}{\partial z} \\ \dfrac{u}{r} + \dfrac{1}{r}\dfrac{\partial w}{\partial \theta} \\ \dfrac{\partial u}{\partial z} + \dfrac{\partial v}{\partial r} \\ \dfrac{1}{r}\dfrac{\partial u}{\partial \theta} + \dfrac{\partial w}{\partial r} - \dfrac{w}{r} \\ \dfrac{1}{r}\dfrac{\partial v}{\partial \theta} + \dfrac{\partial w}{\partial z} \end{Bmatrix}. \tag{14.23}$$

These strains are transformed to the local co-ordinates and component normal to $\eta = $ constant neglected.

The $[D']$ matrix takes, however, a form identical to that defined by Eq. (14.9). For the axi-symmetric case once again the appropriate terms are simply deleted.

All the transformations follow the pattern described in previous sections and need not be further commented upon except perhaps to remark that they are now only carried out between sets of directions $\xi, \eta; r, z;$ and r', z' involving only two variables.

Similarly the integration of element properties is carried out numerically with respect to ξ and η only, noting, however, that the volume element is

$$\mathrm{d}x\,\mathrm{d}y\,\mathrm{d}z = \det |J|\,\mathrm{d}\xi\,\mathrm{d}\eta\,r\,\mathrm{d}\theta. \tag{14.24}$$

By suitable choice of shape functions $N_i(\xi)$, straight parabolic or cubic shapes of variable thickness elements can be used as shown in Fig. 14.6.

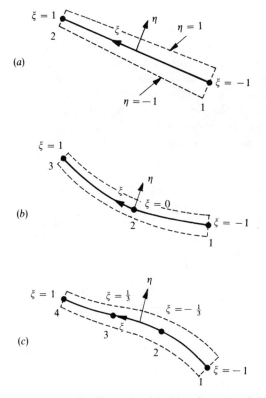

Fig. 14.6   Linear (a), parabolic (b), and cubic (c) axi-symmetric shell elements

14.8   Special Case of Thick Plates

The transformations necessary in this chapter are somewhat involved and indeed the programming needed is sophisticated. However, the application of the principle involved is available for thick plates and the reader is advised to test his comprehension on such a simple problem.

Here the following obvious simplifications arise

(1) $\zeta = z$ and unit vectors v_{1i}, v_{2i}, v_{3i} can be taken in directions of x, y, and z axes respectively.

(2) α_i and β_i are simply the rotations θ_y and θ_x (*vide* Chapter 10).

(3) it is no longer necessary to transform stress and strain components to a local system of axis x' y' z' and global definitions can be used throughout. Indeed, for elements of a simple form, numerical integration can be avoided and as an exercise the reader is encouraged to derive stiffnesses, etc., for say linear, rectangular, elements.

14.9 Convergence

While in three-dimensional analysis it is possible to talk about absolute convergence to the true exact solution of the elasticity problem, in equivalent plate and shell problems such a convergence cannot happen. The so-called convergent solution of a plate bending problem converges, as the element size decreases, only to the exact solution of the approximate model implied in the formulation. Thus, here again convergence of the above formulation will only occur to the exact solution constrained by the requirement that plane sections remain plane during deformation.

In elements of finite size it will be found that pure bending deformation modes are accompanied always by some shear stresses which in fact do not exist in the conventional plate or shell bending theory. Thus large elements deforming mainly under bending action (as would be the case of the shell element degenerated to a flat plate) tend to be appreciably too stiff. In such cases certain limits of the ratio of side of element to its thickness have to be imposed.

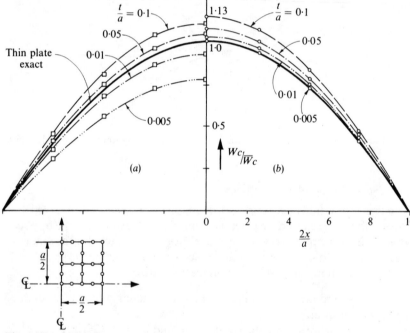

Fig. 14.7 A simply supported square plate under uniform load q_0. Plot of central deflection for elements of Ref. 1(a) and with reduced transverse shear integration (b)

$\bar{w}_c$ central deflection for thin plate theory
$= 0.004062 \, q_0 a^4 /_D$
t = plate thickness
D = plate rigidity

However, it will be found that such restrictions can be relaxed by a simple expedient of *reducing the integration order.*[4]

Figure 14.7 shows, for instance, the application of the parabolic element to a square plate situation. Here results for integration with 3×3 and 2×2 Gauss points are given and results plotted for different thickness to span ratios. For reasonably thick situations, the results are similar and both give the additional shear deformation not available in thin plate theory, but for thin plates the results with the more exact integration tend to diverge rapidly from the now correct thin plate results whereas the cruder integration (by eliminating spurious shear effects) still gives excellent results.

The limitation of elements derived on the basis of this chapter is well known in practice and various attempts have been made to overcome the difficulties.[5, 6, 7] The simplest expedient of reducing the integration order is seen to be effective in the example given and indeed is quite general.

14.10 Some Examples

A limited number of examples which show the accuracy and range of application of the thick shell formulation just described will be given. For a fuller selection the reader is referred to references 1 to 3.

Spherical dome under uniform pressure. The 'exact' solution of shell theory is known for this axi-symmetrical problem illustrated in Fig. 14.8. Twenty-four cubic-type elements were used here. These were of graded size more closely spaced towards the abutments.

The solution appears to be more accurate than the 'exact' one distinguishing between the application of pressure on the inner and outer surfaces.

Edge loaded cylinder. A further axi-symmetric example is shown in Fig. 14.9 to study the effect of subdivision. Two, six, or fourteen elements of unequal length are used and the results for both the latter subdivisions are almost coincident with the exact solution. Even the two-element solution gives reasonable results and departs only in the vicinity of the loaded edge.

Cylindrical vault. This is a test example of application of the full process to a shell in which bending action is severe, due to supports restraining deflection at the ends (see also page 231).

In Fig. 14.10 the geometry, physical details of the problem, and subdivision are given while in Fig. 14.11 the comparison of the effects of 3×3 and 2×2 integration using parabolic elements is shown on the displacements calculated. Both integrations result as expected in convergence. For the more exact integration, this is rather slow while, with reduced integration order, very accurate results are obtained even with one element. This example illustrates most dramatically the advantages of this simple

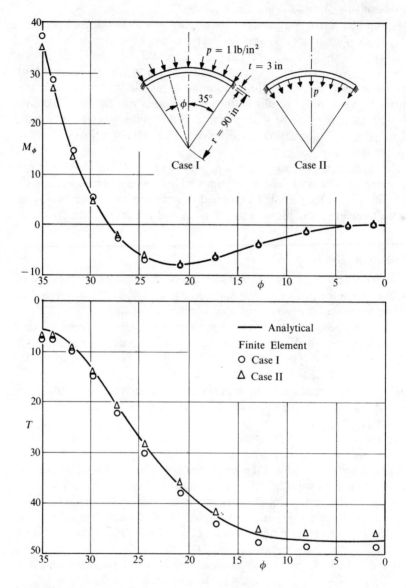

Fig. 14.8   Spherical dome under uniform pressure analysed with 24 cubic elements (first elements subtends an angle of 0·1° from fixed end, others in arithmetic progression

$$M_\phi = \text{meridional bending moment in lb/in}$$
$$T = \text{hoop force lb/in}$$
$$v = \tfrac{1}{6}$$

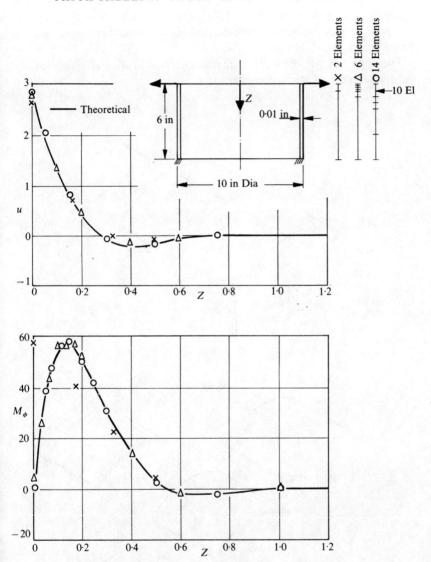

Fig. 14.9   Thin cylinder under a unit radial edge load
  u = radial displacement in 10^{-3}
  M_ϕ = meridional moment in lb/in
  E = 10^7 lb/in^2
  v = 0·3

expedient and is described more fully in references 4 and 8. The 'exact' solution for this problem is one derived on more conventional lines by Scordelis and Lo.[9]

The improved convergence of displacements is incidentally matched by the convergence of stress components.

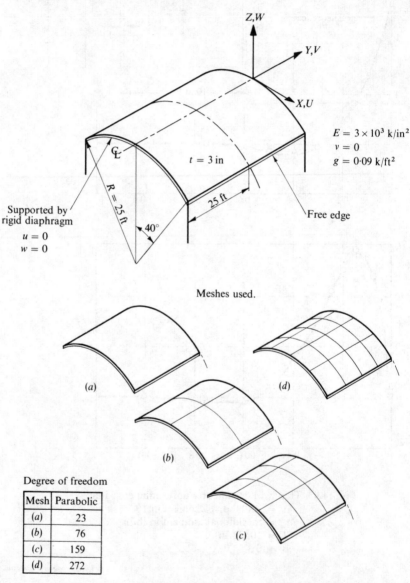

Meshes used.

Degree of freedom

Mesh	Parabolic
(a)	23
(b)	76
(c)	159
(d)	272

Fig. 14.10 Cylindrical shell example, self weight behaviour

Cooling tower. The cooling tower already referred to in Chapter 11 (section 1.6, Fig. 11.10) has been again analysed dividing the axi-symmetric shell into fifteen elements of cubic type. Using ten harmonics the unsymmetric (wind) loading is adequately represented and the results coincide with those of the test analysis against which the results of Chapter 11 are compared so that additional plots are not necessary.

Indeed in this case this type of solution is much more economical than the alternative of Chapter 11.

Curved dams. All the previous examples were rather thin shells and indeed demonstrated the applicability of the process to these situations. At the other end of the scale this formulation has been applied to the doubly curved dams illustrated in Chapter 9 (Fig. 9.8). Indeed exactly the same subdivision was again used and *results reproduced almost exactly those of the three-dimensional solution*.[3] This remarkable result was achieved at a very considerable saving in both degrees of freedom of solution and computer time.

Clearly the range of application of this type of element is very wide.

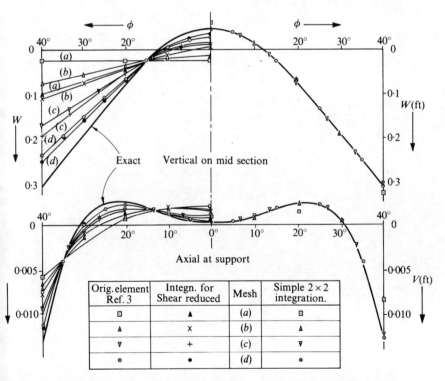

Fig. 14.11   Displacement (parabolic element), cylindrical shell roof

References

1. S. AHMAD, B. M. IRONS, and O. C. ZIENKIEWICZ, 'Curved thick shell and membrane elements with particular reference to axi-symmetric problems', *Proc. 2nd Conf. Matrix Meth. Struct. Mech.*, Wright-Patterson A.F. Base, Ohio, 1968.
2. S. AHMAD, *Curved finite elements in the analysis of solid, shell and plate structures*, Ph.D. thesis, University of Wales, Swansea, 1969.
3. S. AHMAD, B. M. IRONS, and O. C. ZIENKIEWICZ, 'Analysis of thick and thin shell structures by curved elements', *Int. J. Num. Meth. Eng.*, **2**, 419–51, 1970.
4. O. C. ZIENKIEWICZ, J. TOO and R. L. TAYLOR, 'Reduced integration technique in general analysis of plates and shells', *Int. J. Num. Meth. Eng.*, **3**, 275–90, 1971.
5. S. W. KEY and Z. E. BEISINGER, 'The analysis of thin shells with transverse shear strain by the finite element method', *Proc. 2nd Conf. Matrix Meth. Struct. Mech.*, Air Force Inst. Tech. Wright Patterson Base, Ohio, 1968.
6. G. A. WEMPNER, J. T. ODEN and D. A. KROSS, 'Finite element analysis of thin shells', *Proc. Am. Soc. Civ. Eng.*, **94**, EM6, 1273–94, 1968.
7. J. A. STRICKLIN, W. E. HAISLER, P. R. TISDALE, and R. GANDERSTON, 'A rapidly converging triangular plate element', *J.A.I.A.A.*, **7**, 180–1, 1969.
8. PAWSLEY, Dept. of Structural Mechanics, Ph.D. Thesis, Univ. of California, Berkeley, 1970.
9. A. C. SCORDELIS and K. S. LO, 'Computer analysis of cylindrical shells', *J. Am. Concr. Inst.*, **61**, 539–61, 1969.

15. Steady State Field Problems—Heat Conduction, Electric Potential, Fluid Flow, etc.

15.1 Introduction

While, in detail, most of the previous chapters dealt with problems of an elastic continuum the general procedures can be applied to a variety of physical problems. Indeed some such possibilities have been indicated in Chapter 3 and here more detailed attention will be given to a wide class of such situations.

Primarily we shall deal with situations governed by the general 'quasi-harmonic' equation, the particular cases of which are the well known Laplace and Poissons equations.[1-6] The range of physical problems falling into this category is large. To list but a few frequently encountered in engineering practice we have:

Heat conduction
Seepage through porous media
Irrotational flow of ideal fluids
Distribution of electrical (or magnetic) potential
Torsion of prismatic shafts
Bending of prismatic beams, etc.
Lubrication of pad bearings.

The formulation developed in this chapter is applicable equally to all, and hence little reference will be made to the actual physical quantities. Isotropic or anisotropic regions can be treated with equal ease.

Two-dimensional problems are discussed in the first part of the chapter. A generalization to three dimensions follows. It will be observed that the same 'shape functions' as those used previously in two- or three-dimensional formulation of elasticity problems will again be encountered. The main difference will be that now only one unknown scalar quantity (the unknown function) is associated with each point in space. Previously, several unknown quantities, represented by the displacement vector, were sought.

The discretization in finite element manner will be achieved by variational means, as indicated in Chapter 3, with the functional equivalent to the differential form given purely mathematically. This functional in specific applications can be shown to have a physical interpretation, associated generally with energy dissipation concepts. However, identical formulation could have been achieved alternatively by use of the weighted residual, Galerkin, process—and the reader is encouraged to apply this process in the way indicated in Chapter 3.

In addition to the simpler problems governed by the quasi-harmonic equation some viscous flow problems governed by higher order equations will be discussed.[7] Alternative re-formulation of some elasticity problems will also be mentioned in this context.[8]

15.2 The Extremum Problem

The general 'quasi-harmonic' equation governing the behaviour of some unknown physical quantity, ϕ, can be written as

$$\frac{\partial}{\partial x}\left(k_x \frac{\partial \phi}{\partial x}\right) + \frac{\partial}{\partial y}\left(k_y \frac{\partial \phi}{\partial y}\right) + \frac{\partial}{\partial z}\left(k_z \frac{\partial \phi}{\partial z}\right) + Q = 0 \qquad (15.1)$$

in which ϕ is the unknown function, assumed to be single valued within the region, and k_x, k_y, k_z, and Q are known, specified, functions of x, y, and z.

The reader familiar with, for instance, steady-state heat conduction will immediately identify the functions k_x, k_y, and k_z as anisotropic conductivity coefficients, the function Q as the rate of heat generation, and the unknown function ϕ as the temperature (provided the co-ordinates coincide with the principal axes of the material). In an electrical context the appropriate quantities would be associated with specific conductivities, current influx, and potential respectively. No matter what the physical interpretation, the mathematical problem remains the same.

The physical conditions of the particular problem will impose certain boundary conditions. The two most commonly encountered cases are those in which

(a) The value of ϕ is specified on the boundary

$$\phi = \phi_\beta \qquad (15.2)$$

or

(b) $$k_x \frac{\partial \phi}{\partial x} l_x + k_y \frac{\partial \phi}{\partial y} l_y + k_z \frac{\partial \phi}{\partial z} l_z + q + \alpha\phi = 0 \qquad (15.3)$$

on the boundary, in which l_x, l_y, and l_z are the direction cosines of the outward normal to the boundary surface.

If k_x, k_y, and k_z are all equal and both q and α are zero, then this reduces to a well-known condition applicable to non-conducting boundaries

$$\frac{\partial \phi}{\partial n} = 0. \tag{15.4}$$

In a conduction problem q represents the (heat) flux per unit of surface and $\alpha\phi$ the convection loss.

Equation (15.1) together with the boundary conditions specifies the problem in a unique manner. However, an alternative formulation is possible with the aid of the calculus of variations. The well-known Euler theorem[9] states that if the integral

$$\chi(u) = \int \int \int_V f\left(x, y, z, \phi, \frac{\partial \phi}{\partial x}, \frac{\partial \phi}{\partial y}, \frac{\partial \phi}{\partial z}\right) dx \, dy \, dz \tag{15.5}$$

is to be minimized over a bounded region V, then the necessary and sufficient condition for this minimum to be reached is that the unknown function $\phi(x, y, z)$ should satisfy the following differential equation

$$\frac{\partial}{\partial x}\left\{\frac{\partial f}{\partial(\partial\phi/\partial x)}\right\} + \frac{\partial}{\partial y}\left\{\frac{\partial f}{\partial(\partial\phi/\partial y)}\right\} + \frac{\partial}{\partial z}\left\{\frac{\partial f}{\partial(\partial\phi/\partial z)}\right\} - \frac{\partial f}{\partial\phi} = 0 \tag{15.6}$$

within the same region, provided ϕ satisfies the same boundary conditions in both cases.

The reader can verify immediately that the equivalent formulation to that of Eq. (15.1) is the requirement that the volume integral given below and taken over the whole region, should be minimized

$$\chi = \int \int \int \left[\frac{1}{2}\left\{k_x\left(\frac{\partial\phi}{\partial x}\right)^2 + k_y\left(\frac{\partial\phi}{\partial y}\right)^2 + k_z\left(\frac{\partial\phi}{\partial z}\right)^2\right\} - Q\phi\right] dx \, dy \, dz \tag{15.7}$$

subject to ϕ obeying the same boundary conditions.

The simultaneous imposition of the boundary conditions (a) and (b) on the assumed function form is, however, impractical in this manner. While condition (a) of prescribed values on the boundaries is easily implemented, the condition (b) would present intractable difficulties.

To overcome this it is best not to constrain the boundary values on the parts where condition (b) is to be satisfied but to add to the functional of Eq. (15.5) another integral pertaining to the boundary surface which, on minimization, automatically yields the boundary condition. In the general context by the Euler equation this integral is simply

$$\int_S (q\phi + \tfrac{1}{2}\alpha\phi^2)\, \mathrm{d}S \tag{15.8}$$

in which S is the surface where condition (b) applies. This integral is simply added to the definition of χ in Eq. (15.5) or Eq. (15.7) and on minimization it will be found that the boundary condition, Eq. (15.3) is automatically achieved. The reader interested in the details of derivation of this fairly general form of Euler equation will find the necessary facts in Appendix 6.

15.3 Finite Element Discretization

15.3.1 *General three-dimensional case.* If the unknown function ϕ is defined, element by element, in the usual manner as

$$\phi = [N_i, N_j, \ldots] \begin{Bmatrix} \phi_i \\ \phi_j \\ \vdots \end{Bmatrix} = [N]\{\phi\}^e \tag{15.9}$$

where ϕ_i, etc., are the nodal parameters, approximate minimization can be carried out.

Proceeding generally, we evaluate the element contribution using the definitions of Eqs. (15.7) to (15.9).

For any node we can write, by differentiating Eqs. (15.7) and (15.8)

$$\frac{\partial \chi^e}{\partial \phi_i} = \int_{V^e} \left\{ k_x \frac{\partial \phi}{\partial x}\frac{\partial}{\partial \phi_i}\left(\frac{\partial \phi}{\partial x}\right) + k_y \frac{\partial \phi}{\partial y}\frac{\partial}{\partial \phi_i}\left(\frac{\partial \phi}{\partial y}\right)\right.$$
$$\left. + k_z \frac{\partial \phi}{\partial z}\frac{\partial}{\partial \phi_i}\left(\frac{\partial \phi}{\partial z}\right) - Q\frac{\partial \phi}{\partial \phi_i}\right\}\, \mathrm{d}x\, \mathrm{d}y\, \mathrm{d}z \tag{15.10}$$
$$+ \int_{S^e} \left(q\frac{\partial \phi}{\partial \phi_i} + \alpha\phi\frac{\partial \phi}{\partial \phi_i}\right)\, \mathrm{d}S$$

where the second integral only applies if the element has an external boundary on which conditions of type (b) are specified.

Noting that

$$\frac{\partial \phi}{\partial x} = \left[\frac{\partial N_i}{\partial x}, \frac{\partial N_j}{\partial x}, \ldots\right]\{\phi\}^e, \text{ etc.}$$

and that

$$\frac{\partial}{\partial \phi_i}\left(\frac{\partial \phi}{\partial x}\right) = \frac{\partial N_i}{\partial x}$$
$$\frac{\partial \phi}{\partial \phi_i} = N_i, \text{ etc.}$$

we have immediately for the whole element (*vide* Chapter 3)

$$\frac{\partial \chi^e}{\partial \{\phi\}^e} = [h]^e \{\phi\}^e + \{F\}^e \tag{15.11}$$

in which the 'stiffness matrix', $[h]^e$, is obtained from Eqs. 15.9–10

$$h_{ij}^e = \int_{V^e} \left\{ k_x \frac{\partial N_i}{\partial x} \frac{\partial N_j}{\partial x} + k_y \frac{\partial N_i}{\partial y} \frac{\partial N_j}{\partial y} + k_z \frac{\partial N_i}{\partial z} \frac{\partial N_j}{\partial z} \right\} dx \, dy \, dz \tag{15.12}$$

and, with $dV = dx \, dy \, dz$

$$F_i^e = -\int_{V^e} Q N_i \, dV + \int_{S^e} q N_i \, dS + \left(\int_{S^e} [N] \alpha N_i \, dS \right) \{\phi\}^e. \tag{15.13}$$

Assembly of the whole set of minimizing equations follows the usual rules. Thus for the whole region we have

$$\frac{\partial \chi}{\partial \{\phi\}} = 0 = [H]\{\phi\} + \{F\} \tag{15.14}$$

with

$$H_{ij} = \sum h_{ij}^e \qquad F_i = \sum F_i^e$$

and summation, as usual, over all elements.

As only one variable is considered, scalar quantities only arise in the above.

Indeed the structural elastic analogy still can be applied and the appropriate coefficients considered as stiffness or forces.

Examining in detail the composition of element 'forces' given by Eq. (15.13) one can observe the similarity of the first one with those of 'body forces' in elasticity.

The second element force is contributed only from boundaries on which the 'outflow', q, is specified. It corresponds thus to a 'force' due to boundary loading in elasticity. Indeed in the case where non-conducting boundaries exist (i.e., Eq. (15.4) governs the boundary condition) the correspondence is exactly one to an unloaded and unrestrained boundary.

The last term of Eq. (15.13) presents, however, a novel feature.

Here the 'boundary force' contributed is proportional itself to boundary 'displacements' and hence to $\{\phi\}^e$. Indeed it behaves therefore as an external 'stiffness' attached to the element

$$[\bar{h}]^e = \int_{S^e} [N]^T \alpha [N] \, dS \tag{15.15}$$

and contributed only by the boundary integral.

The boundary condition which causes such an additional stiffness is one where radiation or convection losses occur. (Specifically in heat conduction problems.)

With the complete analogy to structural problems achieved, standard operations can be followed. Indeed, as a final stage of calculation we may evaluate not only the values of ϕ (corresponding to displacements) but values of its derivatives (corresponding to the stresses). Thus if we write

$$
\left\{ \begin{array}{c} \dfrac{\partial \phi}{\partial x} \\[2mm] \dfrac{\partial \phi}{\partial y} \\[2mm] \dfrac{\partial \phi}{\partial z} \end{array} \right\} = [S]^e \{\phi\}^e \tag{15.16}
$$

we have in complete analogy with the 'stress' matrix of Eq. (2.17), Chapter 2, a '*slope' matrix*.

Clearly

$$
\{S_i\} = \left\{ \begin{array}{c} \dfrac{\partial N_i}{\partial x} \\[2mm] \dfrac{\partial N_i}{\partial y} \\[2mm] \dfrac{\partial N_i}{\partial z} \end{array} \right\}. \tag{15.17}
$$

An evaluation of such gradients is often physically important as they represent 'velocities' or 'rates of flow' in appropriate situations.

15.3.2 *Convergence requirements.* As the functional is one defined by the first derivatives of ϕ, continuity of ϕ is only necessary when choosing suitable shape functions. These have to be also such that constant values of any of the first derivatives are available throughout the element when suitable nodal values $\{\phi\}^e$ are assigned. Thus in practical problems any of the shape functions discussed in Chapter 7 can be adopted with corresponding element forms.

Indeed all the distortions achievable by curvilinear co-ordinates in Chapter 8 can once again be used.

15.3.3 *Non-homogeneity and anisotropy.* It is interesting to observe that in the functional which is being minimized no derivatives of the 'conductivity' coefficient (k_x, k_y, k_z) occur. Thus the complete formulation is equally valid for constant or for variable values of this. The conductivities can change abruptly from element to element or even be allowed to vary within it providing account of such a variation is taken in the integrals evaluating the element matrices.

If anisotropy of the material occurs, however, the differential equation (15.1) is only valid if the axes x, y, and z coincide with principal axes of anisotropy. A situation may arise in a stratified material as shown in Fig. 15.1, where this is no longer true. In such cases it will be necessary to formulate the element properties with reference to the local co-ordinate system x', y', and z' and the relevant computer program must have facilities for such a transformation.

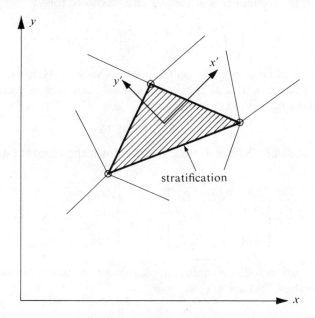

Fig. 15.1 Anisotropic material. Local co-ordinates coincide with the principal directions of stratification

An important difference arises here for the structural situation. As element matrices such as $[h]^e$ of Eq. (15.12) define relationships between scalar quantities, they are equally valid whatever the orientation of local axes. Thus for every element a different set of local axes can be used, if desired, without any matrix transformation or differences in the standard assembly technique.

15.3.4 *Two-dimensional problem*. The general governing equation (15.8) can be simply specialized to two-dimensional problems if no variation of ϕ with z is implied. Now the governing equation is simply

$$\frac{\partial}{\partial x}\left(k_x \frac{\partial \phi}{\partial x}\right) + \frac{\partial}{\partial y}\left(k_y \frac{\partial \phi}{\partial y}\right) + Q = 0 \qquad (15.18)$$

and the functional to be minimized becomes

$$\chi = \int\int \left[\frac{1}{2}\left\{k_x\left(\frac{\partial\phi}{\partial x}\right)^2 + k_y\left(\frac{\partial\phi}{\partial y}\right)^2\right\} - Q\phi\right] dx\,dy + \int_{S^c} (q\phi + \tfrac{1}{2}\alpha\phi^2)\,dS$$

(15.19)

All the previous element matrices will again be found. For example from Eq. (15.12) the components of the $[h]^e$ matrix can be found

$$h_{ij}^e = \int_{V^e} \left(k_x \frac{\partial N_i}{\partial x}\frac{\partial N_i}{\partial x} + k_y \frac{\partial N_i}{\partial y}\frac{\partial N_i}{\partial y}\right) dx\,dy.$$

(15.20)

No further discussion at this point appears necessary. However, it may be worth while to particularize here to the most simple yet very useful triangular element, Fig. 15.2. With

$$N_i = (a_i + b_i x + c_i y)/2\Delta$$

as in Eq. (4.8) of Chapter 4, we can write down the element 'stiffness' matrix as

$$[h]^e = \frac{k_x}{4\Delta}\begin{bmatrix} b_i b_i & b_i b_j & b_i b_m \\ & b_j b_j & b_j b_m \\ \text{sym.} & & b_m b_m \end{bmatrix} + \frac{k_y}{4\Delta}\begin{bmatrix} c_i c_i & c_i c_j & c_i c_m \\ & c_j c_j & c_j c_m \\ \text{sym.} & & c_m c_m \end{bmatrix}\cdot$$

(15.21)

The load matrices follow a similar simple pattern and thus for instance the reader can show that due to Q we have

$$\{F\}_Q^e = -\frac{Q\Delta}{3}\begin{Bmatrix} 1 \\ 1 \\ 1 \end{Bmatrix}$$

(15.22)

a very simple (almost 'obvious') result.

Alternatively the equation may be specialized to cylindrical co-ordinates and used for solution of axi-symmetric situations. Now the differential equation is

$$\frac{\partial}{\partial r}\left(k_r r \frac{\partial\phi}{\partial r}\right) + \frac{\partial}{\partial z}\left(k_z r \frac{\partial\phi}{\partial z}\right) + Q = 0.$$

(15.23)

The variational principle could now be again suitably transformed but it is simpler to substitute the values $(k_r r)$ and $(k_z r)$ as modified 'conductivities' and use the previous expressions directly. Integration now will be best carried out numerically as in equivalent problems of Chapter 5.

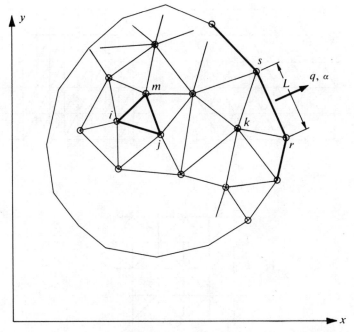

Fig. 15.2   Division of a two-dimensional region into triangular elements

15.4 Examples—An Assessment of Accuracy

It is very easy to show that by assembling explicitly worked out 'stiff-nesses' of triangular element for 'regular' meshes shown in Fig. 15.3(*a*), the equations are *identical* with those which can be derived by well-known finite difference methods.[10]

Obviously the solutions obtained by the two methods will be identical, and so will also be the orders of approximation.†

If an 'irregular' mesh based on a square arrangement of nodes is used a difference between the two approaches will be evident (Fig. 15.3(*b*)). This is confined to the 'load' vector $\{F\}^e$. The assembled equations will show 'loads' which differ by small amounts from node to node, but the sum of which is still the same as that due to the finite difference expressions. The solutions therefore differ only locally and will represent the same averages.

In Fig. 15.4 a test comparing the results obtained on an 'irregular' mesh with a relaxation solution of the lowest order finite difference approximation is shown. Both give results of the same order of accuracy, as indeed would be anticipated.

† In the case where the boundary values are prescribed.

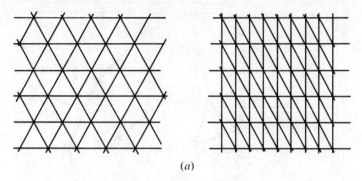

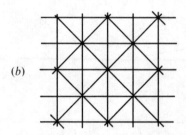

Fig. 15.3 'Regular' and 'irregular' subdivision patterns

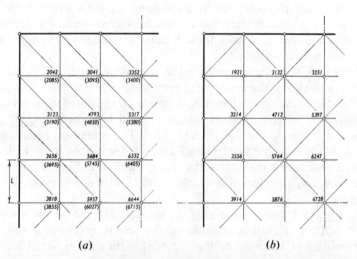

(a)   (b)

Fig. 15.4 Torsion of a rectangular shaft. Numbers in parenthesis show a more accurate solution due to Southwell using a 12×16 mesh (values of $\phi/G\theta L^2$)

At this stage the reader perhaps may be puzzled by the reasons prompting the presentation of an alternative method which appears to repeat results of a well-tried and known technique. The reason is simply that the new method possesses several outstanding advantages. These are:

(a) The simplicity of dealing with non-homogeneous and anisotropic situations (particularly when the direction of anisotropy is variable).

(b) The elements can be graded in shape and size to follow arbitrary boundaries and to allow for regions of rapid variation of the function sought.

(c) Specified gradient or 'radiation' boundary conditions are introduced naturally and with a better accuracy than in standard finite difference procedures.

(d) Higher order elements can be readily used to improve accuracy without complicating boundary conditions—a difficulty always arising with finite difference approximations of a higher order.

(e) Finally, but of considerable importance in the computer age: standard (structural) programs may be used for assembly and solution.

Two more sophisticated examples are given at this stage to illustrate the accuracy attainable in practice. The first is the problem of pure torsion of a non-homogeneous shaft illustrated in Fig. 15.5. The basic differential equation here is

$$\frac{\partial}{\partial x}\left(\frac{1}{G}\frac{\partial \phi}{\partial x}\right) + \frac{\partial}{\partial y}\left(\frac{1}{G}\frac{\partial \phi}{\partial y}\right) + 2\theta = 0 \qquad (15.24)$$

in which ϕ is the stress function, G is the shear modulus, and θ the angle of twist per unit length of the shaft.

In the finite element solution presented, the hollow section was represented by a material for which G has a value of the order of 10^{-3} compared with the other materials.† The results compare well with the contours derived from an accurate finite difference solution.[11]

An example concerning flow through an anisotropic porous foundation is shown in Fig. 15.6.

Here the governing equation is

$$\frac{\partial}{\partial x}\left(k_x\frac{\partial H}{\partial x}\right) + \frac{\partial}{\partial y}\left(k_y\frac{\partial H}{\partial y}\right) = 0 \qquad (15.25)$$

in which k_x and k_y represent the permeability coefficients in direction of the (inclined) principal axes. The answers are here compared against

† This was done to avoid difficulties due to the 'multiple connection' of the region and to permit the use of a standard program.

contours derived by an exact solution. The possibilities of the use of a graded size of subdivision are evident in this example.

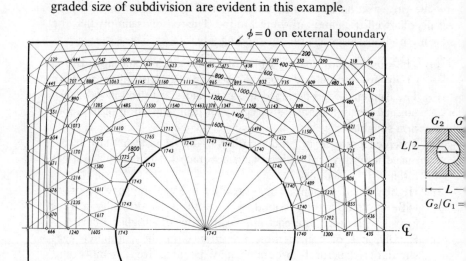

Fig. 15.5   Torsion of a hollow bi-metallic shaft. $\phi/G\theta L^2 \times 10^4$

15.5 Some Practical Problems

Anisotropic seepage. The first of the problems is concerned with the flow through highly non-homogeneous, anisotropic and contorted strata. The basic governing equation is still Eq. (15.25). However, a special feature has to be incorporated in the computer program to allow for changes of x' and y' principal directions from element to element.

No difficulties are encountered in computation, and the problem together with its solution is given in Fig. 15.7.[3]

Axi-symmetric heat flow. The axi-symmetric heat flow equation can be written in the standard form as

$$\frac{\partial}{\partial r}\left(rk\,\frac{\partial T}{\partial r}\right) + \frac{\partial}{\partial z}\left(rk\,\frac{\partial T}{\partial z}\right) = 0 \qquad (15.26)$$

if no heat generation occurs. In the above, T is the temperature and k conductivity. The co-ordinates x and y are now replaced by r and z, the radial and axial distances.

In Fig. 15.8 the temperature distribution in a nuclear reactor pressure vessel[1] is shown for a steady-state heat conduction when a uniform temperature increase is applied on the inside.

Hydrodynamic pressures on moving surfaces. If a submerged surface moves in a fluid with prescribed accelerations and a small amplitude

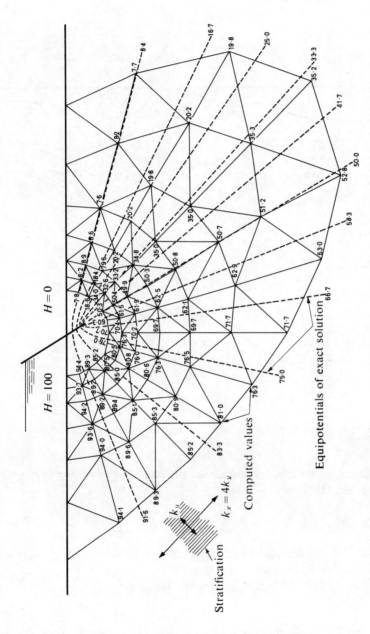

Fig. 15.6   Flow under inclined pile wall in a stratified foundation. A fine mesh near tip of pile is not shown. Comparison with exact solution given by contours

of movement, then it can be shown[12] that the excess pressures developed obey the Laplace equation

$$\nabla^2 p = 0.$$

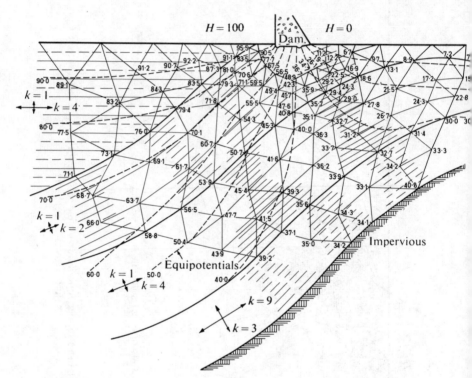

Fig. 15.7 Flow under a dam through a highly non-homogeneous and contorted foundation

On moving (or stationary) boundaries the boundary condition is of type (b) (*vide* Eq. (15.3)) and is given by

$$\frac{\partial p}{\partial n} = -\rho a_n \qquad (15.27)$$

in which ρ is the density of the fluid and a_n is the normal component of acceleration of the boundary.

On free surfaces the boundary condition is simply

$$p = 0. \qquad (15.28)$$

The problems clearly therefore come into the category of those discussed in this chapter.

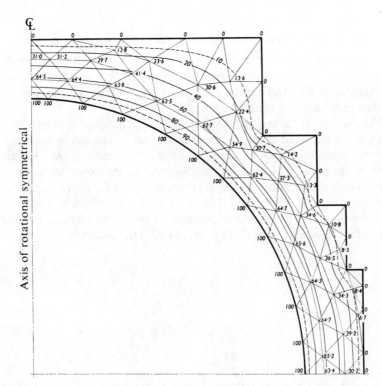

Fig. 15.8   Temperature distribution in a steady-state conduction for an axi-symmetrical pressure vessel

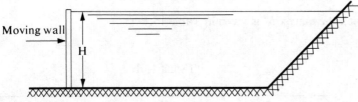

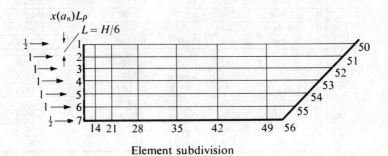

Element subdivision

Fig. 15.9   Problem of a wall moving horizontally in a reservoir

As an example, let us consider the case of a vertical wall in a reservoir, shown in Fig. 15.9, and determine the pressure distribution at points along the surface of the wall and at the bottom of the reservoir for any prescribed motion of the boundary points 1 to 7.

The division of the region into elements (42 in number) is shown. Now elements of quadrilateral shape are used. So that results can be made valid for *any* acceleration system, seven separate problems are solved. In each, in turn, the portion of the boundary adjacent to the point in question is given a unit acceleration, resulting in 'loads' $\rho\frac{1}{2}L, \rho L, \ldots, \rho L, \rho\frac{1}{2}L$ being applied, in turn, to points 1 to 7. For any arbitrary distribution of acceleration the pressures developed at points 1 to 56 can be listed as a matrix dependent on acceleration of the points 1 to 7. This becomes

$$\begin{Bmatrix} p_1 \\ \vdots \\ p_7 \\ p_{14} \\ p_{21} \\ p_{28} \\ p_{35} \\ p_{42} \\ p_{49} \\ p_{56} \end{Bmatrix} = [M] \begin{Bmatrix} a_1 \\ \vdots \\ a_7 \end{Bmatrix} \qquad (15.29)$$

in which the matrix M is given in Table 15.1.

TABLE 15.1

$$[M] = \rho\,\frac{H}{6}$$

	1						
1	0	0	0	0	0	0	0
2	0	0·7249	0·3685	0·2466	0·1963	0·1743	0·0840
3	0	0·3685	0·9715	0·5648	0·4210	0·3644	0·1744
4	0	0·2466	0·5648	1·1459	0·7329	0·5954	0·2804
5	0	0·1963	0·4210	0·7329	1·3203	0·9292	0·4210
6	0	0·1744	0·3644	0·5954	0·9292	1·5669	0·6489
7	0	0·1680	0·3488	0·5607	0·8420	1·2977	1·1459
14	0	0·1617	0·3332	0·5260	0·7548	1·0285	0·6429
21	0	0·1365	0·2754	0·4171	0·5573	0·6793	0·3710—
28	0	0·0879	0·1731	0·2519	0·3187	0·3657	0·1918
35	0	0·0431	0·0838	0·1195	0·1478	0·1661	0·0863
42	0	0·0186	0·0359	0·0150	0·0626	0·0699	0·0362
49	0	0·0078	0·0150	0·0213	0·0261	0·0291	0·0151
56	0	0·0069	0·0134	0·0190	0·0232	0·0259	0·0134

$$(L = H/6)$$

Now for any distribution of accelerations the pressures can be found. For example, if acceleration a is uniform the pressures can be computed taking

$$\begin{Bmatrix} a_1 \\ \vdots \\ a_7 \end{Bmatrix} = \bar{a} \begin{Bmatrix} 1 \\ \vdots \\ 1 \end{Bmatrix}. \tag{15.30}$$

The resulting pressure distribution on the wall and the bottom of the reservoir is shown in Fig. 15.10. The results for the pressures on the wall agree to within 1 per cent with the well-known, exact solution derived by Westergaard.

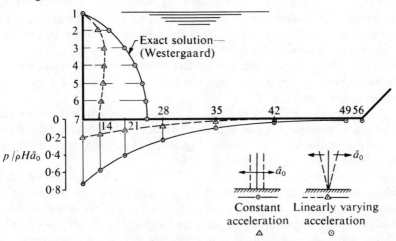

Fig. 15.10   Pressure distributions on moving wall and reservoir bottom

For any other motion the pressures can be similarly derived. If, for instance, the wall is hinged at the base and oscillates around this point with the top (point no. 1) accelerating by $\bar{a}$, then

$$\begin{Bmatrix} a_1 \\ \vdots \\ a_7 \end{Bmatrix} = \bar{a} \begin{Bmatrix} 1 \\ \frac{5}{6} \\ \frac{4}{6} \\ \vdots \\ 0 \end{Bmatrix}. \tag{15.31}$$

Again, the pressure distribution obtained is given by expression, and the results are plotted in Fig. 15.10.

The importance of deriving such an 'influence matrix' is relevant to vibration problems. If the 'wall' oscillates, then in general its acceleration is unknown. From Eq. (15.29) we can write for pressures at points 1 to 7, taking the upper part of matrix $[M]$, say $[M_0]$,

$$\left\{ \begin{array}{c} p_1 \\ \vdots \\ p_7 \end{array} \right\} = [M_0] \left\{ \begin{array}{c} a_1 \\ \vdots \\ a_7 \end{array} \right\} = [M_0]\{\ddot{\delta}\}. \tag{15.32}$$

These pressures result in nodal forces

$$\{R_p\} = \left\{ \begin{array}{c} R_1 \\ \vdots \\ R_7 \end{array} \right\} = [A][M_0] \left\{ \begin{array}{c} a_1 \\ \vdots \\ a_7 \end{array} \right\} = -[M_p]\{\ddot{\delta}\} \tag{15.33}$$

in which $[A]$ is a suitable load assignment matrix and $\{\ddot{\delta}\}$ represents the acceleration of nodal points on the wall. This can be coupled to the dynamic equations of the wall. This and related problems will be discussed in more detail in Chapter 16.

In Fig. 15.11 the solution of a similar problem in three dimensions is shown.[4] Here simple tetrahedral elements were used and very good accuracy obtained.

Electrostatic problems. Figure 15.12 shows, again, a three-dimensional solution of a simple Laplace equation.[4] Here the electrostatic field in the vicinity of an insulator is modelled. Figure. 15.13 shows a more elaborate, two-dimensional magnetic field distribution.[6]

Irrotational and free surface flows.[13–19] The basic Laplace equation which governs the flow of viscous fluid in seepage problems also is applicable in the problem of irrotational fluid flow outside the boundary layer created by viscous effects. The examples already given are adequate to illustrate the general applicability in this context. Further examples are quoted by Martin.[13] A particular class of liquid flow deserves mention. This is the case when free surface limits the extent of the flow and this surface is not known *a priori*.

The class of problem is typified by two examples—that of a freely overflowing jet, Fig. 15.14(*a*) and that of a flow through an earth dam, Fig. 15.14(*b*). In both, the free surface represents a streamline and in both the position of the free surface is unknown *a priori* but has to be determined so that an *additional condition* on this surface is satisfied. For instance in the second problem, if formulated in terms of potential H, Eq. (15.25) governs the problem.

The free surface, being a streamline, imposes the condition

$$\frac{\partial H}{\partial n} = 0 \tag{15.34}$$

to be satisfied there.

In addition, however, the pressure must be zero on the surface as this is

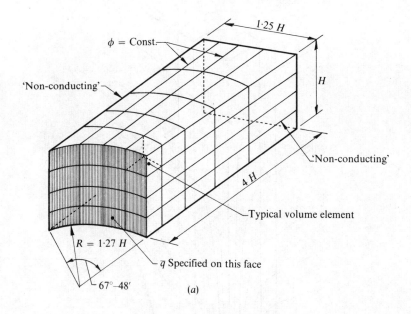

$\phi = $ Const.

'Non-conducting'

1·25 H

H

4 H

'Non-conducting'

Typical volume element

$R = 1·27\,H$

q Specified on this face

67°–48'

(a)

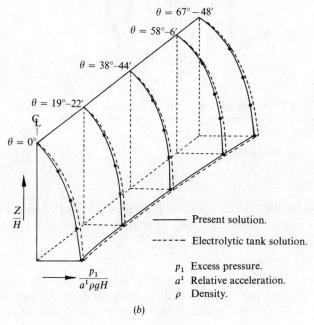

$\theta = 67° - 48'$

$\theta = 58°–6'$

$\theta = 38°–44'$

$\theta = 19°–22'$

$\theta = 0°$

℄

$\dfrac{Z}{H}$

$\dfrac{p_1}{a^1 \rho g H}$

———— Present solution.

------- Electrolytic tank solution.

p_1 Excess pressure.

a^1 Relative acceleration.

ρ Density.

(b)

Fig. 15.11 Pressures on an accelerating surface of dam in an incompressible fluid

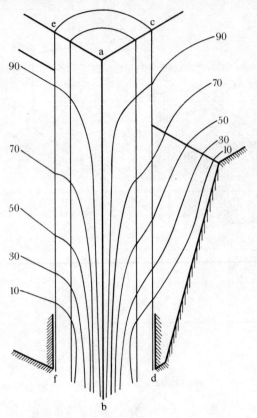

Fig. 15.12   A three-dimensional distribution of electrostatic potential around a porcelain insulator in an earthed trough

exposed to atmosphere. As

$$H = p/\gamma + y \tag{15.35}$$

where γ is the fluid density, p is the fluid pressure, and y elevation above some (horizontal) datum, we must have on the surface

$$H = y. \tag{15.36}$$

The solution may be approached iteratively. Starting with a prescribed free surface streamline the standard problem is solved. A check is carried out to see if Eq. (15.36) is satisfied and if not, an adjustment of the surface is carried out to make new y equal to H just found. A few iterations of this kind show that convergence is reasonably rapid. Taylor and Brown[19] show such a process. In Chapter 16 an alternative method is described.

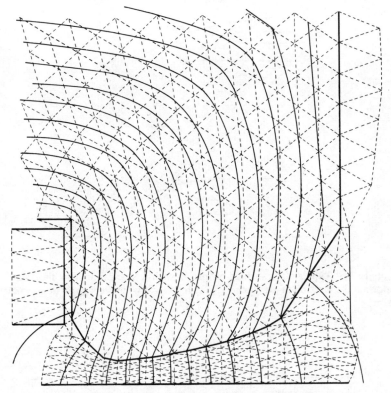

Fig. 15.13   Field near a magnet (after Winslow[6])

Lubrication problems. There once again a standard Poisson type of equation is encountered in the two dimensional domain of a bearing pad. In the simplest case of constant lubricant density and viscosity the equation to be solved is (Reynolds equation)[20]

$$\frac{\partial}{\partial x}\left(h^3\,\frac{\partial p}{\partial x}\right)+\frac{\partial}{\partial y}\left(h^3\,\frac{\partial p}{\partial y}\right) = 6\mu V\,\frac{\partial h}{\partial x} \qquad (15.37)$$

where h is the film thickness, p pressure developed, μ viscosity and V the velocity of the pad in the x direction.

Figure 15.15 shows the pressure distribution in a typical case of a stepped pad.[21] The boundary condition is simply that of zero pressure and it is of interest to note that the step causes an equivalent of a 'line load' on integration of the right hand side of Eq. (15.37).

More general cases of lubrication problems including vertical pad movements (squeeze films) and compressibility can obviously be dealt with, and much work has recently been done here.[22–24]

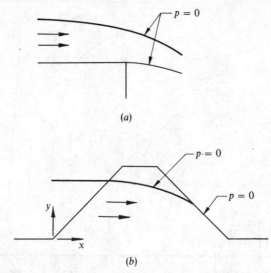

Fig. 15.14   Typical free surface problems with a streamline also satisfying an additional condition of pressure = 0. (*a*) Jet overflow (*b*) seepage through an earth dam

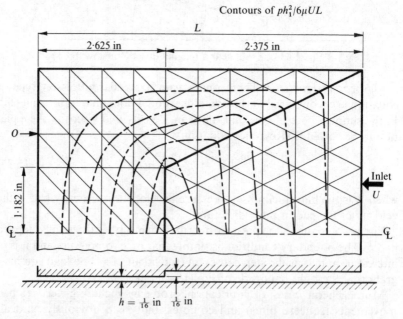

Fig. 15.15   A stepped pad bearing. Pressure distribution

The variety of problems falling into the class discussed above is so large that it is impracticable to touch upon more than a few.

15.6 Problems Governed by Biharmonic Equation; Viscous Flow

In the treatment of the quasi-harmonic problems outlined so far the 'functional' which was to be minimized was derived as a purely mathematical expression and no attempt was made to identify its physical meaning due to the variety of situations discussed. In the particular case of viscous flow through porous media its physical significance can be readily visualized as it represents *the rate of energy dissipation*. Indeed the distribution of velocities achieved by a solution is one which minimizes this dissipation—as one could well expect from the usual 'laziness of nature'. In this context of seepage flow this interpretation was proved by Zienkiewicz et al.[3] However, the principle of minimum energy dissipation has been known in fluid mechanics since the end of the last century and it is interesting to investigate its applicability in the context of viscous flow generally.

In Chapter 3, as an example of application of weighted residual processes, we have considered the Navier–Stokes equation with inertia terms omitted; a situation valid for slow (creeping) motion of fluid.

Equation (3.4) was derived as the governing differential equation for two-dimensional flow situations.

However, this differential equation could be derived directly by the Euler process by minimization of a functional representing the rate of energy dissipation.

If the velocity components in x and y directions are u and v and if these are expressed in terms of a stream function ϕ as

$$u = -\frac{\partial \phi}{\partial y}, \qquad v = \frac{\partial \phi}{\partial x} \qquad (15.38)$$

it is easy to show that the functional is[7]

$$\chi = \mu \int_V \left\{ 4\left(\frac{\partial^2 \phi}{\partial x\, \partial y}\right)^2 + \left(\frac{\partial^2 \phi}{\partial x^2}\right)^2 + \left(\frac{\partial^2 \phi}{\partial y^2}\right)^2 - 2\frac{\partial^2 \phi}{\partial x^2} \cdot \frac{\partial^2 \phi}{\partial y^2} \right\} \mathrm{d}V \qquad (15.39)$$

for a constant viscosity μ.

Such a functional can be minimized in precisely the same manner as we have established in this and previous chapters after specifying the values of ϕ in terms of element nodal parameters. Once again the standard 'stiffness' type relations will be obtained as the functional is a '*quadratic*' one.

As second derivatives occur in the definition of the functional continuity of ϕ and its inter-element, normal slopes must be imposed. The nodal parameters are now conveniently

$$\{\delta_i\} = \begin{Bmatrix} \phi_i \\ \left(\dfrac{\partial\phi}{\partial x}\right)_i \\ \left(\dfrac{\partial\phi}{\partial y}\right)_i \end{Bmatrix} \tag{15.40}$$

and the same shape functions as used for the plate bending problems of Chapter 10 can again be introduced.

Atkinson et al.[7] have used this formulation to study the velocity distribution in the entry region of flow between parallel plates. The boundary conditions and the simple rectangular region studied are shown in Fig. 15.16(a), and Fig. 15.16(b) shows the velocity profiles obtained which are in extremely good agreement with experiment. Clearly any other shapes of boundary could be tackled by the same program.

It is interesting to note that in this problem the simple, 'incompatible' triangular element of Chapter 10 was used, violating once again the full slope continuity criteria.

The same authors also give the form of functional applicable to axisymmetric situations and study similar problems in context of flow in cylindrical conduits. Atkinson et al.[25] further discuss this formulation.

15.7 Analogies

It is interesting to remark that the complete formulation of the viscous flow problem could have been bypassed and any plate bending program used directly on noting that the differential equation governing the stream function distribution (Chapter 3, Eq. (3.4)) is identical with that governing plate deflection (Chapter 10, reference 1).

Use of such analogies is of extreme importance in engineering and frequently allows a useful extension to be made with minimum effort.

As another example of such an analogy it is interesting to consider the case of simple plane elasticity. Here if the well-known Airy stress function, ψ, is used[26] to define stresses as

$$\sigma_x = \frac{\partial^2\psi}{\partial y^2}, \qquad \sigma_y = \frac{\partial^2\psi}{\partial x^2}, \qquad \tau_{xy} = -\frac{\partial^2\psi}{\partial x\,\partial y} \tag{15.41}$$

it will be found once again that the viscuous flow/plate bending biharmonic equation is obeyed. Thus a plate bending program can be used directly to solve also plane elasticity problems.

If the variational principle involved is identified we find that this solution automatically satisfying equilibrium conditions gives an *upper bound* on strain energy as against the *lower bound* achieved in a direct displacement formulation.

Reversing the process, the direct displacement formulation of plane elasticity can be used to obtain plate bending, upper bound, solutions. This possibility has been discovered by Veubeke and Zienkiewicz[8] and is fully described by them.

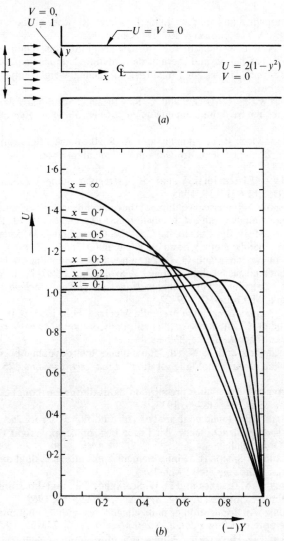

Fig. 15.16 Velocity development in viscous, laminar, flow between parallel plates. Finite element solution[7]; (a) geometry, (b) velocity profiles at different sections

15.8 Concluding Remarks

In this chapter we have but touched on the wide possibilities offered in the field of engineering and physical sciences by extension of the general formulation of the finite element process. Many more such applications will doubtless be forthcoming.

References

1. O. C. ZIENKIEWICZ and Y. K. CHEUNG, 'Finite elements in the solution of field problems', *The Engineer*, 507–10, Sept. 1965.
2. W. VISSER, 'A finite element method for the determination of non-stationary temperature distribution and thermal deformations', *Proc. Conf. on Matrix Methods in Struct. Mech.*, Air Force Inst. of Techn., Wright Patterson A.F. Base, Ohio, 1965.
3. O. C. ZIENKIEWICZ, P. MAYER, and Y. K. CHEUNG, 'Solution of Anisotropic seepage problems by finite elements', *Proc. Amer. Soc. Civ. Eng.*, **92**, EM1, 111–20, 1966.
4. O. C. ZIENKIEWICZ, P. L. ARLETT, and A. K. BAHRANI, 'Solution of three dimensional field problems by the finite element method', *The Engineer*, 27 Oct. 1967.
5. L. HERRMANN, 'Elastic torsion analysis of irregular shapes', *Proc. Am. Soc. Civ. Eng.*, **91**, EM 6, 11–19, 1965.
6. A. M. WINSLOW, 'Numerical solution of the quasi-linear Poisson equation in a non-uniform triangle mesh', *J. Computational Physics*, **1**, 149–72, 1966.
7. B. ATKINSON, M. P. BROCKLEBANK, C. C. M. CARD, and J. M. SMITH, 'Low Reynolds number developing flows', *A.I. Ch. E.J.*, **15**, 548–53, 1969.
8. B. FRAEIJS DE VEUBEKE and O. C. ZIENKIEWICZ, 'Strain Energy bounds in finite element analysis by slab analogy', *J. Strain An.*, **2**, 267–71, 1967.
9. P. N. BERG, 'Calculus of variations' in *Handbook of Eng. Mechanics*, Ch. 16, ed. N. Flügge, McGraw-Hill, 1962.
10. D. N. DE G. ALLEN, *Relaxation Methods*, McGraw-Hill, 1955, p. 199.
11. J. F. ELY and O. C. ZIENKIEWICZ, 'Torsion of Compound bars—a relaxation solution', *Int. I. Mech. Sci.*, **1**, 356–65, 1960.
12. O. C. ZIENKIEWICZ and B. NATH, 'Earthquake hydrodynamic pressures on arch dams—an electric analogue solution', *Proc. Inst. Civ. Eng.*, **25**, 165–76, 1963.
13. H. M. WESTERGAARD, 'Water pressure on dams during earthquakes', *Trans. Am. Soc. Civ. Eng.*, **98**, 418–33, 1933.
14. H. C. MARTIN, 'Finite element analysis of fluid flows', *Proc. 2nd Conf. on Matrix methods in Struct. Mech.* Air Force Inst. of Tech., Wright Patterson A.F. Base, Ohio, 1968.
15. J. T. ODEN and D. SAMOGYI, 'Finite element applications in fluid dynamics', *Proc. Am. Soc. Civ. Eng.*, **95**, EM3, 1969.
16. J. H. ARGYRIS, C. MARECZEK and D. W. SCHARPF, 'Two and three dimensional flow using finite elements', *J. Roy. Aero Soc.*, **73**, 961–64, 1969.
17. L. J. DOCTORS, 'An application of finite element technique to boundary value problems of potential flow', *Int. J. Num. Meth. Eng.*, **2**, 243–52, 1970.
18. G. DE VRIES and D. H. NORRIE, 'Application of the finite element technique to potential flow problems', *Rep. 7 & 8.*, Dept. Mech. Eng. University of Calgary, Alberta, Canada, 1969.

19. R. L. TAYLOR and C. B. BROWN, 'Darcy flow solutions with a free surface', *Proc. Am. Soc. Civ. Eng.*, **93**, HY2, 25–33, 1967.
20. W. A. GROSS, *Gas film lubrication*, J. Wiley & Sons, 1962.
21. D. V. TANESA and I. C. RAO, *Student project report on Lubrication*, Royal Naval College, Dartmouth, 1966.
22. M. M. REDDI, 'Finite element solution of the incompressible lubrication problem', *Trans. Am. Soc. Mech. Eng.*, **91**, Series F, 524, 1969.
23. M. M. REDDI and T. Y. CHU, 'Finite element solution of the steady state compressible lubrication problem', *Trans. Am. Soc. Mech. Eng.*, **92**, Series F, 495, 1970.
24. J. H. ARGYRIS and D. W. SCHARPF, 'The incompressible lubrication problem', *J. Roy. Aero Soc.*, **73**, 1044–6, 1969.
25. B. ATKINSON, C. C. M. CARD, and B. M. IRONS, 'Application of the finite element method to creeping flow problems, *Trans. Instn. Chem. Engrs.*, **48**, T276–T284, 1970.
26. S. TIMOSHENKO and J. N. GOODIER, *Theory of Elasticity*, 2nd ed., Mc-Graw Hill, 1951.

16. The Time Dimension. Basic Formulation of Transient Field and Dynamic Problems

16.1 Introduction

In all the problems considered so far in this text conditions which do not vary with time were assumed. There is little difficulty in extending the finite element idealization to situations which are time dependent.

The range of practical problems in which the time dimension has to be considered is great. Transient heat conduction, wave transmission in fluids, and dynamic behaviour of structure are typical examples. While it is usual to consider these various problems separately—sometimes classifying them according to the mathematical structure of governing equations as 'parabolic' or 'hyperbolic'[1]—we shall group them in one category to show that the formulation is identical.

In the first part of this chapter we shall formulate, by a simple extension of the methods used so far, matrix differential equations governing such problems for a variety of physical situations. Here a finite element discretization only in the space dimension will be used. In the remainder of this chapter various procedures of solution will be dealt with indicating the possibility of including the time dimension itself in a finite element discretization.

16.2 Direct Formulation of Time Dependent Problems with Spatial Finite Element Subdivision

16.2.1 The 'quasi-harmonic' equation with time differentials. In many physical problems the quasi-harmonic equation, which was discussed at length in the previous chapter, takes up a form in which time derivatives of the unknown function ϕ occur. In the three-dimensional case typically we might have

322

$$\frac{\partial}{\partial x}\left(k_x \frac{\partial \phi}{\partial x}\right) + \frac{\partial}{\partial y}\left(k_y \frac{\partial \phi}{\partial y}\right) + \frac{\partial}{\partial z}\left(k_z \frac{\partial \phi}{\partial z}\right)$$

$$+ \left(\bar{Q} - \mu \frac{\partial \phi}{\partial t} - \rho \frac{\partial^2 \phi}{\partial t^2}\right) = 0. \quad (16.1)$$

In the above, quite generally, all the parameters may be prescribed functions of time.

$$k_x = k_x(t), \qquad \bar{Q} = \bar{Q}(t), \text{ etc.}$$

If a situation at a particular instant of time is considered, the time derivatives of ϕ and all the parameters can be treated as *prescribed functions of space co-ordinates*. Thus, at that instant the problem is precisely identified with those treated in the previous chapter (section 15.2) if the whole of the quantity in the last parentheses of Eq. (16.1) is treated as the term Q of Eq. (15.1).

The finite element discretization of this in terms of *space* elements has already been fully discussed and we found that with the prescription

$$\phi = [N(x, y, z,)]\{\phi\}^e \quad (16.2)$$

for each element, a standard form of assembled equation

$$[H]\{\phi\} + \{F\} = 0 \quad (16.3)$$

was obtained. Element contributions to the above matrices are defined by Eqs. (15.12) or (15.13) which need not be repeated here except for that representing the 'load' term due to Q. This gives by Eq. (15.13)

$$F_i^e = -\int_{V^e} Q N_i \, dV \quad \text{or} \quad \{F\}^e = -\int Q[N]^T \, dV.$$

Replacing now Q by the last bracketed term of Eq. (16.1) we have

$$\{F\}^e = -\int_{V^e} [N]^T \left(\bar{Q} - \mu \frac{\partial \phi}{\partial t} - \rho \frac{\partial^2 \phi}{\partial t^2}\right) dV. \quad (16.4)$$

However, from Eq. (16.2) it is noted that ϕ is approximated in terms of its nodal parameters $\{\phi\}^e$. On substitution of this approximation we have

$$\{F\}^e = -\int_{V^e} [N]^T \bar{Q} \, dV + \left(\int_{V^e} [N]^T \mu [N] \, dV\right) \frac{\partial}{\partial t}\{\phi\}^e$$

$$+ \left(\int_{V^e} [N]^T \rho [N] \, dV\right) \frac{\partial^2}{\partial t^2}\{\phi\}^e \quad (16.5)$$

and on expanding Eq. (16.3) in its final assembled form we get the following *matrix differential equation*

$$[H]\{\phi\}+[C]\frac{\partial}{\partial t}\{\phi\}+[G]\frac{\partial^2}{\partial t^2}\{\phi\}+\{\bar{F}\} = 0 \qquad (16.6)$$

in which all the matrices are assembled from element submatrices in the standard manner with submatrices $[h]^e$ and $\{\bar{F}\}^e$ still given by relations (15.12) and (15.13), and

$$c_{ij}^e = \int_{V^e} N_i \mu N_j \, dV, \qquad (16.7)$$

$$g_{ij}^e = \int_{V^e} N_i \rho N_j \, dV. \qquad (16.8)$$

Once again these matrices are symmetric as seen from the above relations.

Boundary conditions imposed at any time instant are treated once again as in the previous chapter.

The variety of physical problems governed by Eq. (16.1) is so large that a comprehensive discussion of them is beyond the scope of this book. A few typical examples will, however, be quoted.

Equation (16.1) with $\rho = 0$. This is the standard *transient heat conduction equation*[1,2] which has been discussed in the finite element context by several authors.[3-6] This same equation is applicable in other physical situations—one of these being the *soil consolidation equations*[7] associated with *transient seepage forms.*[8]

Equation (16.1) with $\mu = 0$. Now the relationship becomes the famous *wave equation* governing a wide range of physical phenomena. Electromagnetic waves[9] fluid surface waves,[10] and compression waves[11] are but a few phenomena to which the finite element process has been applied.

Equation (16.1) with $\mu \neq \rho \neq 0$. This damped wave equation is yet of more general applicability and has particular significance in fluid mechanics (wave) phenomena.

16.2.2 *Dynamic behaviour of elastic structures with linear damping.*†
While in the previous section we have been concerned with, apparently, a purely mathematical problem, identical reasoning can be applied directly to the wide class of dynamic behaviour of elastic structures following precisely the general lines of Chapter 2.

When displacements of an elastic body vary with time two sets of additional forces are called into play. The first is the inertia force, which for an acceleration characterized by $\partial^2/\partial t^2 \{f\}$ can be replaced by its

---

† For simplicity we shall only consider *distributed* inertia and damping effects— concentrated mass and damping forces being simply a limiting case.

static equivalent

$$-\rho \frac{\partial^2}{\partial t^2} \{f\} \qquad (16.9)$$

using the well-known d'Alembert principle. ($\{f\}$ is here the generalized displacement defined in Chapter 2.)

This is a force with components in directions identical to those of the displacement $\{f\}$ and (generally) given per unit volume.

In this context ρ is simply the mass per unit volume.

The second force is that due to (frictional) resistances opposing the motion. These may be due to microstructure movements, air resistance, etc., and generally are related in a non linear way to the displacement velocity $\partial/\partial t \{f\}$,

For simplicity of treatment, however, only a linear, viscous type, resistance will be permitted resulting again in unit volume forces in an equivalent static problem of magnitude

$$-\mu \frac{\partial}{\partial t} \{f\}. \qquad (16.10)$$

In the above μ is some property which (presumably) can be given numerical values.

The equivalent static problem, at any instant of time, is now discretized precisely in the manner of Chapter 2 but replacing the distributed force $\{p\}$ by its equivalent

$$\{\bar{p}\} - \rho \frac{\partial^2}{\partial t^2} \{f\} - \mu \frac{\partial}{\partial t} \{f\}. \qquad (16.11)$$

The element (nodal) forces given by Eq. (2.11) now become

$$\{F\}_p^e = -\int_{V^e} [N]^T \{p\} \, dV = \{\bar{F}\}_{\bar{p}}^e + \int_{V^e} [N]^T \rho \frac{\partial^2}{\partial t^2} \{f\} \, dV +$$

$$\int_{V^e} [N]^T \mu \frac{\partial}{\partial t} \{f\} \, dV \quad (16.12)$$

in which the first force is precisely that due to external distributed load of Chapter 2 and need not be further considered.

As the approximation to the displacements is given by Eq. (2.1)

$$\{f\} = [N]\{\delta\}^e \qquad (2.1)$$

we can substitute Eq. (16.12) into the general equilibrium equations and obtain finally, on assembly, the following matrix differential equation

$$[K]\{\delta\} + [C] \frac{\partial}{\partial t} \{\delta\} + [M] \frac{\partial^2}{\partial t^2} \{\delta\} + \{\bar{F}\} = 0 \qquad (16.13)$$

in which $[K]$ and $\{\bar{F}\}$ are assembled stiffness and force matrices obtained by usual addition of stiffness coefficients of elements and of element forces due to external, specified loads, initial stresses, etc., in the manner fully described before. The new matrices $[C]$ and $[M]$ are assembled by the usual rule from element submatrices given by

$$[c_{ij}]^e = \int_{V^e} [N_i]^T \mu [N_j] \, dV \qquad (16.14)$$

and

$$[m_{ij}]^e = \int_{V^e} [N_i]^T \rho [N_j] \, dV. \qquad (16.15)$$

The matrix $[m_{ij}]$ is known as the *element mass matrix* and the assembled matrix $[M]$ as the system mass matrix.

It is of interest to note that in early attempts to deal with dynamic problems of this nature the mass of the elements was usually arbitrarily 'lumped' at nodes, resulting always in a diagonal matrix even if no actual concentrated masses existed. The fact that such a procedure was, in fact, unnecessary and leads to poor approximation was simultaneously recognized by Archer[12] and independently by Leckie and Lindberg[13] in 1963. The general presentation of the results given in Eq. (16.15) is due to Zienkiewicz and Cheung.[14] The name of 'consistent mass matrix' has been coined for the distributed mass element matrix, a term thought to be unnecessary since it is the only admissible matrix that can be used properly in the analysis.

By analogy the matrices $[c_{ij}]$ and $[C]$ could be called *consistent damping matrices*.

It is perhaps worth recognizing that on occasion different shape functions need to be used to describe the inertia forces from those specifying the displacements $\{f\}$. For instance in plates and beams (Chapter 10) the full strain state was prescribed simply by defining w, the lateral displacement, as the additional plate bending assumptions were introduced. When considering, however, the inertia forces it may be desirable not only to include the simple lateral inertia force given by

$$-\rho \frac{\partial^2 w}{\partial t^2}$$

(in which ρ is now the weight per unit area of the plate) but also to consider *rotary inertia couples* of the type

$$\frac{\rho t^2}{12} \frac{\partial^2}{\partial t^2} \left(\frac{\partial w}{\partial x} \right), \text{ etc.}$$

Now it will be simply necessary to describe a more generalized displacement $\{\bar{f}\}$

$$\{\bar{f}\} = \left\{ \begin{array}{c} w \\ \dfrac{\partial w}{\partial x} \\ \dfrac{\partial w}{\partial y} \end{array} \right\} = [\bar{N}]\{\delta\}^e$$

in which $[\bar{N}]$ will follow directly from the definition of $[N]$ which specifies only the w component. Relations such as Eqs. (16.14) and (16.15) still are valid providing we replace $[N]$ by $[\bar{N}]$ and put in place of ρ a matrix

$$\begin{bmatrix} \rho & 0 & 0 \\ 0 & \dfrac{\rho t^2}{12} & 0 \\ 0 & 0 & \dfrac{\rho t^2}{12} \end{bmatrix}$$

Such specialized usage is, however, rare.

16.2.3 *'Mass'* or *'damping'* matrices for some typical elements. It is impracticable to present in an explicit form all the mass matrices for the various elements discussed in previous chapters. Some selected examples only will be discussed here.

Plane stress and strain. Using triangular elements discussed in Chapter 4, the matrix $[N]$ is defined as

$$[N] = [IN'_i, IN'_j, IN'_n]$$

in which

$$I = \begin{bmatrix} 1 & 0 \\ 0 & 1 \end{bmatrix}$$

with Eq. (4.8) giving

$$N'_i = (a_i + b_i x + c_i y)/2\Delta, \text{ etc.,}$$

where Δ is the area of triangle.

If the thickness of the element is t and this is assumed to be constant within the element, we have for the mass matrix Eq. (16.15)

$$[m]^e = \rho t \int \int [N]^\mathrm{T}[N] \, \mathrm{d}x \, \mathrm{d}y \qquad (16.16)$$

or

$$[m_{rs}]^e = \rho t[I] \int \int N'_r N'_s \, \mathrm{d}x \, \mathrm{d}y. \qquad (16.17)$$

If the relationships Eq. (4.8) are substituted, it is possible to show that

$$\int N_r' N_s' \, dx \, dy \; \begin{array}{l} = \frac{1}{12}\Delta \quad \text{when } r \neq s \\ = \frac{1}{6}\Delta \quad \text{when } r = s. \end{array} \tag{16.18}$$

Thus, taking the mass of the element as

$$\rho t \Delta = W$$

the mass matrix becomes

$$[m]^e = \frac{W}{3} \left| \begin{array}{ccc:ccc} \frac{1}{2} & 0 & \frac{1}{4} & 0 & \frac{1}{4} & 0 \\ 0 & \frac{1}{2} & 0 & \frac{1}{4} & 0 & \frac{1}{4} \\ \hdashline \frac{1}{4} & 0 & \frac{1}{2} & 0 & \frac{1}{4} & 0 \\ 0 & \frac{1}{4} & 0 & \frac{1}{2} & 0 & \frac{1}{4} \\ \hdashline \frac{1}{4} & 0 & \frac{1}{4} & 0 & \frac{1}{2} & 0 \\ 0 & \frac{1}{4} & 0 & \frac{1}{4} & 0 & \frac{1}{2} \end{array} \right| \tag{16.19}$$

If the mass had been lumped at the nodes in three equal parts the mass matrix contributed by the element would have been

$$[m]^e = \frac{W}{3} \left| \begin{array}{cc:cc:cc} 1 & 0 & 0 & 0 & 0 & 0 \\ 0 & 1 & 0 & 0 & 0 & 0 \\ \hdashline 0 & 0 & 1 & 0 & 0 & 0 \\ 0 & 0 & 0 & 1 & 0 & 0 \\ \hdashline 0 & 0 & 0 & 0 & 1 & 0 \\ 0 & 0 & 0 & 0 & 0 & 1 \end{array} \right| \tag{16.20}$$

Certainly both results differ considerably.

Plate bending. Vibration of plates presents problems of considerable engineering importance. Such practical situations as bridge-deck oscillations, vibration of turbine blades, etc., result in analytically intractable formulations.

The importance of use of a proper mass matrix instead of mass 'lumping' is illustrated in several references.[15–19]

If the rectangular plate element of section 10.4 is considered, for instance, the displacement function is defined by Eq. (10.16) as

$$[N] = [P][C]^{-1} \tag{16.21}$$

with notation as defined in Chapter 10.

It will be observed that $[C]$ is not dependent on the co-ordinates and that $[P]$ is determined as

$$[P] = [1, x, y, x^2, xy, y^2, x^3, x^2y, xy^2, y^3, x^3y, xy^3].$$

Thus, the mass matrix for a plate element of constant thickness t becomes from Eq. (16.15)

$$[m]^e = \rho t [C]^{-1^\text{T}} \left(\int \int [P]^\text{T}[P] \, dx \, dy \right) [C]^{-1}. \qquad (16.22)$$

Once again only the central integral needs to be evaluated, thus presenting no difficulty, and the full matrix can be obtained by matrix multiplication. However, an explicit expression has been presented in Dawe[16] and is quoted in Table 16.1.

TABLE 16.1

MASS MATRIX OF A RECTANGULAR PLATE ELEMENT

$[m]^e = [L][M][L]$

$[M] = \lambda$

3454											
−461	80										
−461	−63	80									
1226	−274	199	3454								
274	−60	42	461	80							
199	−42	40	461	63	80						
1226	−199	274	394	116	116	3454					
−199	40	−42	−116	−30	−28	−461	80				
−274	42	−60	−116	−28	−30	−461	63	80			
394	−116	116	1226	199	274	1226	−274	−199	3454		
116	−30	28	199	40	42	274	−60	−42	461	80	
−116	28	−30	−274	−42	−60	−199	42	40	−461	−63	80

$[L]$ is defined in Table 10.1 and $\lambda = \dfrac{\rho tab}{6300}$

Similar mass matrices can be obtained for triangular elements discussed in sections 10.6 *et seq.* Explicit formulation is here avoided and the algebraic details are left to the reader.†

Numerical integration procedures are recommended for use with such elements.

Shells. If the mass matrices for the 'in plane' and 'bending' motions of an element are found, then once again the mass matrices referred to a general co-ordinate system can be found. The rules of transformation are, obviously, precisely the same as for forces. The derivation of the mass matrices for each element in general co-ordinates and the final assembly of the mass matrix associated with a node follow the steps for similar operations with stiffness matrices (*see* Chapter 11).

† Explicit integrals are available in reference 20.

In principle, therefore, shell vibration problems present no special difficulties.

Damping and other matrices. The above examples perhaps helped the reader to consolidate some of the general ideas. He will observe that damping matrices as given in Eq. (16.14) have precisely the same structure as the mass matrices. Indeed the various matrices developed in section 16.2.1 and given in Eqs. (16.7) and (16.8) again show a similar form. Thus with slight modification the results for a plane triangular element just quoted are equally applicable in all these situations and need not be evaluated again.

16.3 'Coupled' Problems

Both sets of problems discussed in the previous section led to the basic identical form of matrix differential equations, characterized by Eq. (16.6) or Eq. (16.13). Other higher order problems of governing equations may be similarly derived. On occasion two separate systems of such equations arise in problems of a coupled kind. To complete the present discussion we shall discuss two such typical cases of some considerable engineering interest.

16.3.1 *Coupled motion of an elastic structure in a fluid.*[21, 22] The differential equation governing the pressure distribution, (p), during the small amplitude motions of a compressible fluid is

$$\frac{\partial^2 p}{\partial x^2} + \frac{\partial^2 p}{\partial y^2} + \frac{\partial^2 p}{\partial z^2} + \frac{1}{\bar{c}^2}\frac{\partial^2 p}{\partial t^2} = 0 \qquad (16.23)$$

in which $\bar{c}$ stands for the velocity of the acoustic wave, and 'damping' (viscous) terms have been omitted.

On the boundaries either p is specified, or if these are solid and subject to motion

$$\frac{\partial p}{\partial n} = -\rho \frac{\partial^2}{\partial t^2}(U_n) \qquad (16.24)$$

where U_n is the normal component of the displacement. This problem, on finite element subdivision of the fluid region, leads to a discretized equation similar to the form of Eq. (16.6)

$$[H]\{p\} + [G]\frac{\partial^2}{\partial t^2}\{p\} + \{\bar{F}\}_f = 0 \qquad (16.25)$$

in which the matrices $[H]$ and $[G]$ are obtained in the usual manner. The matrix $\{\bar{F}\}$ does not contain any contribution from volume integrals, but is entirely due to boundary integrals corresponding to the prescribed motions there (see Eq. (15.27)).†

Now, the boundary (interface) motion is prescribed by the movement of the structure. If the structure itself is discretized we can write

$$U_n = [\bar{N}]\{\delta\} \qquad (16.26)$$

where $[\bar{N}]$ is determined from the appropriate shape functions and $\{\delta\}$ are the displacement (nodal) parameters. By Eq. (15.13) we have

$$\{\bar{F}\}_f = [S]\frac{\partial^2}{\partial t^2}\{\delta\} \qquad (16.27)$$

in which

$$[S] = \int_S [N]^T\rho[\bar{N}]\,\mathrm{d}S \qquad (16.28)$$

with $[N]$ being the shape functions defining the pressure distribution and S the fluid structure interface.

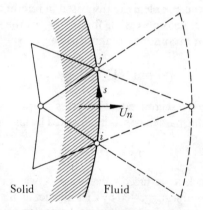

Fig. 16.1   A solid–fluid interface

For the structural problem we have similarly on discretization

$$[K]\{\delta\}+[C]\frac{\partial}{\partial t}\{\delta\}+[M]\frac{\partial^2}{\partial t^2}\{\delta\}+\{\bar{F}\}_s+\{R\}=0 \qquad (16.29)$$

in which the usual terms of Eq. (16.13) are recognized but the forcing terms have been separated into the external part $\{R\}$ assumed indepen-

† In a more general case Eq. (16.18) can be augmented by a term containing the first time derivatives of p. This will arise if viscous terms are included in the equation of fluid motion or if fluid boundaries exist which do not reflect incident pressure waves. Such boundaries are important if the fluid is extending to infinity and for analysis purposes its region is truncated.[22]

dently specified and $\{\bar{F}\}_s$ due to the fluid interface pressures. By virtual work we shall find those to be given by

$$\{\bar{F}\}_s = \int_S [\bar{N}]^T p \, dS = \frac{1}{\rho} [S]^T \{p\}. \tag{16.30}$$

as

$$p = [N]\{p\}$$

Combining Eqs. (16.25), (16.27), (16.29), and (16.30) we have finally a coupled system of matrix differential equations

$$[H]\{p\} + [G] \frac{\partial^2}{\partial t^2} \{p\} - [S] \frac{\partial^2}{\partial t^2} \{\delta\} = 0$$

and   (16.31)

$$[K]\{\delta\} + [C] \frac{\partial}{\partial t} \{\delta\} + [M] \frac{\partial^2}{\partial t^2} \{\delta\}$$

$$+ \frac{1}{\rho} [S]^T \{p\} + \{R\} = 0$$

which governs the problem.

Some aspects of this problem are discussed in references 21 and 22. For the special case of an incompressible fluid ($\bar{c} = \infty$) the second term, $[G]$, of the first equation becomes zero and this can be solved directly giving

$$\{p\} = [H]^{-1}[S] \frac{\partial^2}{\partial t^2} \{\delta\}. \tag{16.32}$$

Substitution into the second equation gives simply a standard dynamic equation in which the mass matrix is augmented by an '*added mass matrix*'

$$\frac{1}{\rho} [S]^T [H]^{-1} [S]. \tag{16.33}$$

Derivation of such a (reduced) mass matrix was in fact discussed in section 15.5 and was first suggested by Zienkiewicz *et al.* [4, 15] More recently the same process was used in deriving natural frequencies of arch dams.[23]

16.3.2 *Elastic behaviour of a porous, saturated material.*[24] This second problem is of considerable interest in soil mechanics and a variety of geotechnical situations.

In the porous, elastic medium the fluid pressures existing in pores cause body forces acting in the elastic matrix of magnitude

$$\left\{ \begin{array}{c} X \\ Y \\ Z \end{array} \right\} = - \left\{ \begin{array}{c} \dfrac{\partial p}{\partial x} \\ \dfrac{\partial p}{\partial y} \\ \dfrac{\partial p}{\partial z} \end{array} \right\}. \tag{16.34}$$

These have been discussed already in Chapter 4 (p. 63) but the interested reader may find further discussion of this phenomenon in reference 25.

If now the elastic structure is discretized in the finite element manner these body forces will contribute nodal 'forces' of magnitude

$$\{F\}_p = \left(\int_V [\bar{N}]^T \begin{Bmatrix} \partial/\partial x \\ \partial/\partial y \\ \partial/\partial z \end{Bmatrix} [N] \, dV \right) \{p\} = [L]\{p\} \qquad (16.35)$$

in which $[\bar{N}]$ stands for the shape functions defining the displacements of the elastic body while $[N]$ are shape functions defining the pressure distribution.†

Finally for the elastic continuum we have thus

$$[K]\{\delta\} + [L]\{p\} + \{R\} = 0 \qquad (16.36)$$

the standard discretized equation in which $[K]$ is the stiffness matrix and $\{R\}$ represents all specified forces except those due to pore pressure.

Turning our attention to the fluid contained in the pores we shall write the appropriate differential continuity equation. This has already been encountered in Chapter 15 as the typical Eq. (15.1) in which k_x, k_y, k_z are now the permeability coefficients and Q represents the rate at which the fluid is generated (or discharged into) a unit volume of space.

Now, with the solid matrix deforming elastically with the displacement components u, v, and w

$$Q = -\frac{\partial}{\partial t}\left(\frac{\partial u}{\partial x} + \frac{\partial v}{\partial y} + \frac{\partial w}{\partial z}\right) = -\frac{\partial}{\partial t} \begin{Bmatrix} \partial/\partial x \\ \partial/\partial y \\ \partial/\partial z \end{Bmatrix}^T [\bar{N}]\{\delta\}. \qquad (16.37)$$

On discretizing Eq. (15.1) with Eq. (16.37) substituted we have

$$[H]\{p\} + [S]\frac{\partial}{\partial t}\{\delta\} = 0 \qquad (16.38)$$

as the contribution of Q is, by Eq. (15.13),

$$\int_V [N]^T Q \, dV = \left(\int [N]^T \begin{Bmatrix} \partial/\partial x \\ \partial/\partial y \\ \partial/\partial z \end{Bmatrix} [\bar{N}] \, dV \right) \frac{\partial}{\partial t}\{\delta\}. \qquad (16.39)$$

Now Eqs. (16.36) and (16.38) form a coupled system of simultaneous matrix differential equations. These are similar to the system derived for the coupled fluid-structure dynamic interaction (Eq. (16.31)). When fluid compressibility was eliminated in the latter the form is in fact identical.

† Integrals for whole regions are written to simplify notation as in Chapter 2.

It should be noted that, formally, only from Eqs. (16.35) and (16.39)

$$[S] = [L]^T. \tag{16.40}$$

This problem was first discretized with finite elements by Sandhu and Wilson[24] using a somewhat different approach. The physical aspects of the problem are discussed by Crochet and Naghdi[26] and also by Biot.[27]

The conventional consolidation equation which is of the form of Eq. (16.1) (without the second-order time differential) is but a special case of this more general formulation.

In the above the fluid was assumed to be incompressible. However, if fluid compressibility is also added to the problem an additional term of the form

$$[A]\frac{\partial}{\partial t}\{p\} \tag{16.41}$$

arises simply in Eq. (16.38). With this extension partially saturated soil problems can be dealt with.

16.4 Alternative Formulation of Time Response

In the preceding section a variety of problems was reduced to matrix differential equations with respect to time. The procedure was exceedingly simple and involved no new principles. Alternative formulations are, however, possible.

In the first the Galerkin (or other weighted residual) process could be applied directly to the differential equations governing the problem in the manner discussed in section 3.4 of Chapter 3. With the unknown described by shape functions depending not only on geometric position but also on time, i.e.,

$$\phi = [N(x, y, z, t)]\{\Phi\}$$

the whole problem would be discretized into *finite elements of space and time*.[6,28]

Now the problem could become 'four-dimensional' but in principle at least the full numerical solution could be directly formulated in any time interval, $t_1 < t < t_2$, and solution obtained in the standard manner.

In the second approach a variational principle is established, again in terms of both the space and time variables.

Such variational processes using convolution integrals have been described by Gurtin[29] and have been used with success in references 5 and 24. Again, in principle, finite elements of time and space could be established.

In simple dynamic problems such a variational principle is provided directly from the well-known Lagrange equations. In these the stationary value is sought for

$$\chi = \int_{t_1}^{t_2} L \, dt \tag{16.42}$$

in which

$$L = U + W + T \tag{16.43}$$

where $U + W$ is the sum of strain energy and potential energy which has already been introduced in Chapter 2 and T is the kinetic energy of the system. L is known as *the Lagrangian function.*[30]

While such formulations have certain generality they can be avoided for simplicity and will not be further considered explicitly.

A simplified version of the Galerkin process will, however, be introduced directly to the discretized equations in the next section.

16.5 Recurrence Relations for Solution of Initial Value Problems. Finite Element in Time.

The matrix differential equations obtained in the previous sections are of a type in which specified values of the functions and, when necessary, of its first time derivatives at the start, uniquely define this function throughout the time interval.

Such a category of problems known as 'initial value' or 'marching' can be solved by writing suitable recurrence relations.[1] From these a step-by-step process allows a full solution of the problems. Full discussion of various recurrence relations is available in texts on numerical analysis. Only one form will be discussed here.

In certain simple circumstances such recurrence relations can be superseded by exact solutions as shown by Visser.[3] Such processes will not be considered further here.

The recurrence relation can be established in different ways. For instance, a finite difference scheme may be used directly or the Galerkin weighted residual process applied within each interval. The second process allows a more comprehensive treatment and indeed possesses all the (possible) merits of the different variational processes suggested by Wilson et al.[5,24]

The recurrence relation can be written for several intervals simultaneously thus necessitating more simultaneous equations to be solved at each step but resulting in an improved accuracy and stability.

It is convenient here to consider separately the matrix equations containing only first time derivatives and those having second time derivatives.

16.5.1 *Problems with first order time derivatives.* Typical in this category would be a problem defined by Eq. (16.6) with $[G] = 0$, i.e.,

$$[H]\{\phi\} + [C]\frac{\partial}{\partial t}\{\phi\} + \{\bar{F}\} = 0. \tag{16.44}$$

We shall consider an interval from 0 to t_n with $\{\phi\}_0$ being the specified initial values set at $t = 0$.

Generally, within the interval we shall assume an interpolated form of $\{\phi\}$ defined by its values at several time intervals

$$\{\phi\} = \sum_{i=0}^{n} N_i(t)\{\phi\}_i \tag{16.45}$$

in which $N_i(t)$ are appropriate shape functions defined continuously within the interval. (There is little virtue in specifying these discontinuously in the finite element manner here due to the 'marching' nature of the problem.)

For instance if a linear interpolation is assumed, only the initial, 0, value and that of $n = 1$, $t_n = \Delta t$ need be considered. That is, in matrix form,

$$\{\phi\} = [N_0, N_1]\begin{Bmatrix} \{\phi\}_0 \\ \{\phi\}_1 \end{Bmatrix} \tag{16.46}$$

with

$$N_0 = (\Delta t - t)/\Delta t$$
$$N_1 = t/\Delta t.$$

The time derivative is

$$\frac{\partial\{\phi\}}{\partial t} = \left[\frac{\partial N_0}{\partial t}, \frac{\partial N_1}{\partial t}\right]\begin{Bmatrix} \{\phi\}_0 \\ \{\phi\}_1 \end{Bmatrix} = \frac{1}{\Delta t}[-1, 1]\begin{Bmatrix} \{\phi\}_0 \\ \{\phi\}_1 \end{Bmatrix}. \tag{16.47}$$

As the initial value $\{\phi\}_0$ is known, only one weighted residual substitution need to be obtained by integrating Eq. (16.44) multiplied by N_1. Thus we have

$$\int_0^{\Delta t} \frac{t}{\Delta t}\left([H][N_0, N_1]\begin{Bmatrix} \{\phi\}_0 \\ \{\phi\}_1 \end{Bmatrix} + [C]\left[\frac{\partial N_0}{\partial t}, \frac{\partial N_1}{\partial t}\right]\begin{Bmatrix} \{\phi\}_0 \\ \{\phi\}_1 \end{Bmatrix} + \{\bar{F}\}\right) dt = 0 \tag{16.48}$$

or on substituting Eqs. (16.46) and (16.47) and final integration we have

$$[H]\left(\frac{1}{3}\{\phi\}_0 + \frac{2}{3}\{\phi\}_1\right) + \frac{1}{\Delta t}[C](-\{\phi\}_0 + \{\phi\}_1) + \frac{2}{\Delta t^2}\int_0^{\Delta t}\{\bar{F}\}t\, dt \tag{16.49}$$

This result is similar to that obtained by taking a simple, *central finite difference* in the increment and indeed has been used frequently in that form.[1,4,8] Its derivation is, however, different and interesting possibilities arise in use with other interpolating functions.

From Eq. (16.49), $\{\phi\}_1$ can be found, formally, as

$$\{\phi\}_1 = -\left(\frac{2}{3}[H] + [C]/\Delta t\right)^{-1}\left[\left(\frac{1}{3}[H] - [C]/\Delta t\right)\{\phi\}_0 + \frac{2}{\Delta t^2}\int_0^{\Delta t}\{\bar{F}\}t\, dt\right] \tag{16.50}$$

and this recurrence relation used for all subsequent time intervals (starting at $t = 0$ is a purely nominal exercise here).

As an alternative recurrence scheme we could consider an interval containing three time stations $(0, \Delta t, 2\Delta t)$ as shown in Fig. 16.2. Now, once again the same process could be applied and in place of Eq. (16.39) we would have

$$\{\phi\} = [N_0(t), N_1(t), N_2(t)] \begin{Bmatrix} \{\phi\}_0 \\ \{\phi\}_1 \\ \{\phi\}_2 \end{Bmatrix} \qquad (16.51)$$

with, say, parabolic (Lagrange) interpolation functions.

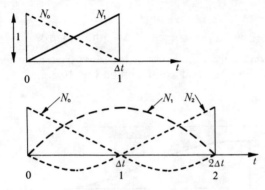

Fig. 16.2 Time 'shape functions' with discontinuous first derivative

Continuation of the same exercise as before would yield now two weighted residual equations similar to Eq. (16.47) and, once again, $\{\phi\}_1$ and $\{\phi\}_2$ could be determined from the knowledge of the initial conditions $\{\phi\}_0$.

This procedure could be continued indefinitely and progressively more refined solutions obtained by doubling, trebling, etc., the total number of simultaneous equations involved in solving a single increment. It appears that with more elaborate 'elements' in time a greater stability of solution is obtained and larger time increments can be used.

16.5.2 *Problems with second-order time derivatives.* The dynamic motion of structures and other similar problems are governed by equations of type (16.13)

$$[K]\{\delta\} + [C]\frac{\partial}{\partial t}\{\delta\} + [M]\frac{\partial^2}{\partial t^2}\{\delta\} + \{\bar{F}\} = 0. \qquad (16.13)$$

Now, from the nature of the equation, it is evident that two initial conditions are necessary. In general both $\{\delta\}_0$ and $\partial/\partial t\,\{\delta\}_0$ will be known at a start of an increment. Proceeding precisely as before, the shape functions defining the time variation will be taken as defined by the values of $\{\delta\}$ and $\partial/\partial t \{\delta\}$ at the various time stations i. The simplest interpolation will again only consider the times 0 and Δt, and in that interval we shall now have Hermitian cubics. Thus

$$\{\delta\} = [H_{00}, H_{10}, H_{01}, H_{11}] \begin{Bmatrix} \{\delta\}_0 \\ \partial/\partial t \{\delta\}_0 \\ \{\delta\}_1 \\ \partial/\partial t \{\delta\}_1 \end{Bmatrix} \qquad (16.52)$$

with

$$H_{01} = 1 - 3s^2 + 2s^3$$
$$H_{10} = (s - 2s^2 + s^3)\Delta t$$
$$H_{01} = 3s^2 - 2s^3$$
$$H_{11} = (-s^2 + s^3)\Delta t \quad \text{and } s = t/\Delta t.$$

These Hermitian polynomials are of the same type as given in Chapters 10 and 12, pp. 206–243, and are shown on Fig. 16.3.

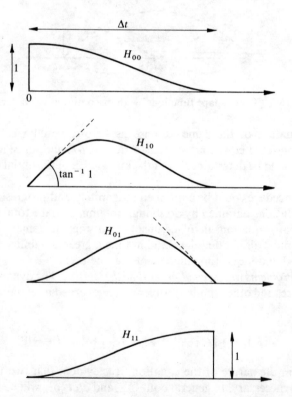

Fig. 16.3   Time 'shape functions' with discontinuous second derivative

Now, the equation needed for recurrence will again be obtained by writing a weighted residual equation for $t = \Delta t$

$$\int_0^t \begin{Bmatrix} H_{01} \\ H_{11} \end{Bmatrix} \left[\left([K]+[C]\frac{\partial}{\partial t}+[M]\frac{\partial^2}{\partial t^2} \right) [H_{00}, H_{10}, H_{01}, H_{11}] \begin{Bmatrix} \{\delta\}_0 \\ \partial/\partial t\,\{\delta\}_0 \\ \{\delta\}_1 \\ \partial/\partial t\,\{\delta\}_1 \end{Bmatrix} \right.$$

$$\left. + \{\bar{F}\} \right] dt = 0 \quad (16.53)$$

From this, on substitution of the shape function and integration equations for determining $\{\delta\}_1$ and $\partial/\partial t\,\{\delta\}_1$ in terms of initial values will be obtained. The final form of the recurrence relation is

$$\begin{bmatrix} A_{11} & A_{12} \\ A_{21} & A_{22} \end{bmatrix} \begin{Bmatrix} \{\delta\}_1 \\ \partial/\partial t\,\{\delta\}_1 \end{Bmatrix} = -\begin{bmatrix} B_{11} & B_{12} \\ B_{21} & B_{22} \end{bmatrix} \begin{Bmatrix} \{\delta\}_0 \\ \partial/\partial t\,\{\delta\}_0 \end{Bmatrix} - \begin{Bmatrix} C_1 \\ C_2 \end{Bmatrix} \quad (16.54)$$

and the reader is left to derive the appropriate expressions as a simple exercise.

The recurrence relation just derived is not the same as that obtained in a finite difference form by Wilson and Clough[31] or its alternatives used by Chan et al.[32] It has been used with success by Fried[28] though derived by him in a different manner.

Clearly, once again it is possible to use yet more comprehensive time finite elements with additional, intermediate degrees of freedom.

16.5.3 *Coupled problems.* These can be discussed once again in precisely the same way with time variations of the various functions assumed in appropriate form. Details are left out at this stage.

16.5.4 *Some examples.* A few simple examples of the use of recurrence relationships of the type discussed in section 16.5.1 are taken from reference 6 to illustrate the stability and use of the process.

Transient heat distribution in rotor blade. This example, illustrated in Fig. 16.4, shows a two-dimensional problem governed by a heat conduction equation

$$\nabla^2 T + \frac{\rho c}{k}\frac{\partial T}{\partial t} = 0. \quad (16.55)$$

On the boundaries the 'radiation' heat condition (Chapter 15.1, Eq. (15.3)) is used with various heat transfer coefficients α implying

$$\frac{\partial T}{\partial n} = -\alpha(T-T_a)/k \quad (16.56)$$

where T_a is the ambient temperature of surrounding gas, ρ, the density, c, specific heat and, k, the thermal conductivity.

Contours of temperature distribution at various times are shown. Isoparametric cubic elements were used for finite element representation of space.

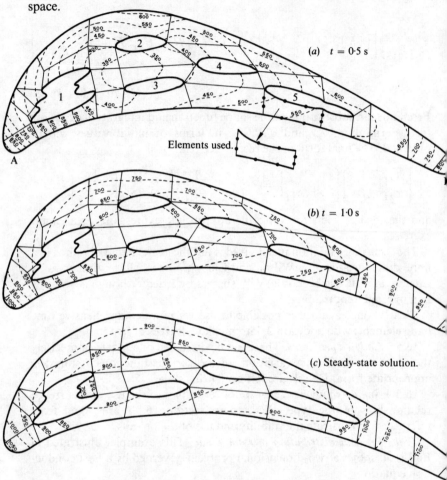

Fig. 16.4 Temperature distribution in a cooled rotor blade, initially at zero temperature ($\Delta t = 0.01$ sec)

specific heat $c = 0.11$ cal/gm °C
density $\rho = 7.99$ gm/cm^3
conductivity $k = 0.05$ cal/sec cm °C
gas temperature around blade $= 1145$°C

Heat transfer coefficient α varies from 0.390 to 0.056 on the outside surfaces of the blade (A–B)

Hole Number	Cooling Hole Temperature	α around perimeter of each hole
1	545°C	0.0980
2	587°C	0.0871

A three-dimensional heat conduction problem. A rather crude three-dimensional subdivision by three quadratic isoparametric elements only is used to represent an eighth of a spheroid. In Fig. 16.5 this subdivision is shown together with comparisons of central temperature variation with that analytically obtained.[33] Good agreement is shown by results.

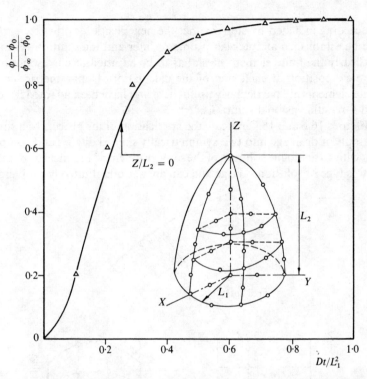

Fig. 16.5   Temperature variation with time at $x = y = z = 0$ in a prolate spheroidal solid ($\Delta t = 0.025$)

$$\frac{L_2}{L_1} = 2 \qquad \frac{\alpha L_1}{k} = \infty$$

— analytical solution
Δ finite element solution

16.6 A Different Transient Problem. Free Surface Seepage

A special class of transient problems is involved in ground water flow with no compressibility but where progressive changes of the free surface occur.

The governing equation here is that given in Chapter 15 (Eq. (15.25)) and no time dependence occurs.

The free surface is a line of zero pressure (see Chapter 15, p. 312) but is *not a streamline* during unsteady conditions. If a solution is carried out at any instant of time with the position of the free surface known, the normal seepage velocity, v_n, for the free surface can be found. As the fluid is leaving the pores, the normal velocity *of the free surface* $\bar{v}_n$ can be found as

$$\bar{v}_n = \frac{1}{\mu} v_n. \qquad (16.57)$$

Proceeding in a step-by-step manner the new position of the free surface can be established an interval of time Δt later and the solution repeated.

Clearly the finite element mesh has to be adjusted to correspond with the new position at each step of the calculation. Isoparametric, curved finite elements are particularly useful here and have been adapted for two- and three-dimensional solutions.[34, 35]

Figures 16.6 and 16.7 indicate the application of the process to a simple example of drainage into two symmetrically shaped ditches and comparison with an analogue solution of the same problem.[36] Practical application of this type of solution is large and can answer quantitatively problems of

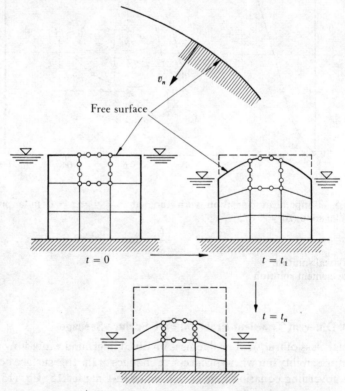

Fig. 16.6   Seepage flow with free surface. Velocity of free surface found for every time instant and mesh automatically adjusted

rapid drawdown, etc. Other attempts to deal with this type of transient problem are listed in references 37–39.

16.7 Concluding Remarks

The outline of several transient type problems was given here together with the basic formulation. In this field very wide application can be made

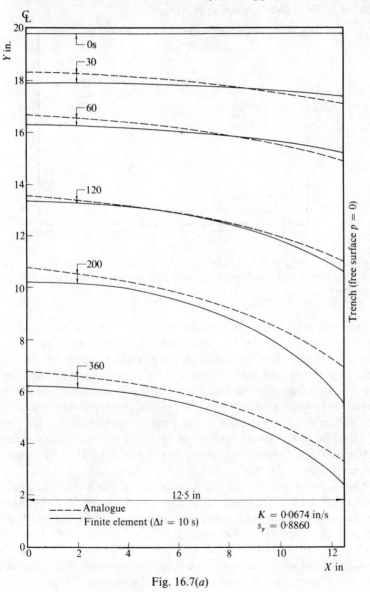

Fig. 16.7(a)

and many different problems of real physical significance can now be formulated and solved.

Such solutions, while previously possible by use of finite difference processes, can now use the advantages inherent in finite element formulations. However, the difficulties involved in stability of such solutions still remain although the 'implicit' type of recurrence relations derived in section 16.3 are usually good in this respect.

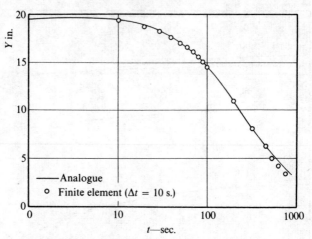

Fig. 16.7   (a) Free surface configuration at various times—for problem of Fig. 16.6.   (b) Variation of the free surface with time on centre line section during rapid drawdown

In the solution of the problems by the recurrence relation—typically of the form given in Eq. (16.50)—a solution of a large matrix occurs in each time step. If equal time increments are used and the properties do not vary with time the same matrix occurs at each step of the computation and using a *partial inverse* the time taken for such subsequent solutions can be reduced to a small fraction of that required for the first solution.[6]

A further economy in solution can be achieved by reducing the number of variables in the space dimensions by using an economizer technique similar to that described in Chapter 17 (17.4.3) or by Hurty's component mode synthesis[40, 41]

This is unfortunately not the case in essentially non-linear problems such as involved in the free surface problem of section 16.6 and others of similar nature. Some such non-linear situations will be discussed later in Chapter 18. A special problem which falls into this category has recently been dealt with.[42] In that paper a transient heat conduction equation is considered but with a phase change (*freezing*) involved. Full discussion of this and other related situations is beyond the scope of this book.

References

1. S. CRANDALL, *Engineering Analysis*, McGraw-Hill, 1956.
2. H. S. CARSLAW and J. C. JAEGER, *Conduction of Heat in Solids*, 2nd ed., Clarendon Press, 1959.
3. W. VISSER, 'A finite element method for the determination of non stationary temperature distribution and thermal deformation', *Proc. Conf. on Matrix Meth. in Struct. Mech.*, Air Force Inst. of Technology, Wright Patterson A.F. Base, Ohio, 1965.
4. O. C. ZIENKIEWICZ and Y. K. CHEUNG, *The Finite element method in structural and continuum mechanics*, 1st ed., McGraw-Hill, 1967.
5. E. L. WILSON and R. E. NICKELL, 'Application of finite element method to heat conduction analysis', *Nuclear Eng. and Design*, **4**, 1–11, 1966.
6. O. C. ZIENKIEWICZ and C. J. PAREKH, 'Transient field problems—two and three dimensional analysis by isoparametric finite elements', *Int. J. Num. Meth. in Eng.*, **2**, 61–71, 1970.
7. K. TERZHAGI and R. B. PECK, *Soil Mechanics in Engineering Practice*, J. Wiley & Son, 1948.
8. D. K. TODD, *Ground water hydrology*, J. Wiley & Son, 1959.
9. P. L. ARLETT, A. K. BAHRANI, and O. C. ZIENKIEWICZ, 'Application of finite elements to the solution of Helmholz's equation', *Proc. I.E.E.*, **115**, 1762–6, 1968.
10. C. TAYLOR, B. S. PATIL, and O. C. ZIENKIEWICZ, 'Harbour oscillation: a numerical treatment for undamped natural modes', *Proc. Inst. Civ. Eng.*, **43**, 141–56, 1969.
11. O. C. ZIENKIEWICZ and R. E. NEWTON, 'Coupled vibrations in a structure submerged in a compressible fluid', *Int. Symp. on finite element techniques*, Stuttgart, 1969.
12. J. S. ARCHER, 'Consistent mass matrix for distributed systems', *Proc. Amer. Soc. Civ. Eng.*, **89**, ST4, 161, 1963.
13. F. A. LECKIE and G. M. LINDBERG, 'The effect of lumped parameters on beam frequencies', *The Aero. Quarterly*, **14**, 234, 1963.
14. O. C. ZIENKIEWICZ and Y. K. CHEUNG, 'The finite element method for analysis of elastic isotropic and orthotropic slabs', *Proc. Inst. Civ. Eng.*, **28**, 471, 1964.
15. O. C. ZIENKIEWICZ, B. IRONS, and B. NATH, 'Natural frequencies of complex, free or submerged, structures by the finite element method' in *Symposium on Vibration in Civil Engineering*, London, April 1965. (Butterworth, 1966)
16. D. J. DAWE, 'A finite element approach to plate vibration problems', *J. Mech. Eng. Sci.*, **7**, 28, 1965.
17. R. J. GUYAN, 'Distributed mass matrix for plate elements in bending', *J.A.I.A.A.*, **3**, 567, 1965.
18. G. P. BAZELEY, Y. K. CHEUNG, B. M. IRONS, and O. C. ZIENKIEWICZ, 'Triangular elements in plate bending—conforming and non-conforming solutions', *Proc. Conf. on Matrix Meth. in Struct. Mech.*, Air Force Inst. of Technology, Wright Patterson A.F. Base, Ohio, 1965.
19. R. G. ANDERSON, B. M. IRONS, and O. C. ZIENKIEWICZ, 'Vibration and Stability of plates using finite elements', *Int. J. Solids Struct.*, **4**, 1031–55, 1968.
20. R. G. ANDERSON, *The application of the non-conforming triangular plate bending element to plate vibration problems*, M.Sc. thesis, University of Wales, Swansea, 1966.
21. O. C. ZIENKIEWICZ, Discussion of 'Earthquake Behaviour of reservoir-dam systems', by A. K. Chopra, *Proc. Am. Soc. Civ. Eng.*, **95**, EM3, 801–3, 1969.

22. O. C. ZIENKIEWICZ and R. E. NEWTON, 'Coupled vibrations of a structure submerged in a compressible fluid', *Proc. Int. Symp. on Finite Element Techniques*, Stuttgart, 1969.

23. P. A. A. BACK, A. C. CASSELL, R. DUNGAR, and R. T. SEVERN, 'The seismic study of a double curvature dam', *Proc. Inst. Civ. Eng.*, **43**, 217–48, 1969.

24. R. S. SANDHU and E. L. WILSON, 'Finite element analysis of seepage in elastic media', *Proc. Am. Soc. Civ. Eng.*, **95**, EM3, 641–51, 1969.

25. J. L. SERAFIM, Ch. 3, *Rock Mechanics and Eng. practice*, ed., K. G. Stagg and O. C. Zienkiewicz, J. Wiley & Son, 1968.

26. J. CROCHET and P. M. NAGHDI, 'On constitutive equations for flow of fluid through an elastic solid', *Int. J. Eng. Sci.*, **4**, 383–401, 1966.

27. M. A. BIOT, 'General theory of three dimensional consolidation', *J. Appl. Phys.*, **12**, 155–64, 1941.

28. I. FRIED, 'Finite element analysis of time dependent phenomena', *Int. Report. Stuttgart Univ.*, 1969.

29. M. GURTIN, 'Variational principles for linear elastodynamics', *Arch. for National Mech. and Analysis*, **16**, 34–50, 1969.

30. K. WASHIZU, *Variational methods in elasticity and plasticity*, pp. 2–3, Pergamon Press, 1968.

31. E. L. WILSON and R. W. CLOUGH, 'Dynamic response by step by step matrix analysis', *Symp. on Use of Computers in Civil Eng.*, Lisbon, October 1962.

32. S. P. CHAN, H. L. COX, and W. A. BENFIELD, 'Transient analysis of forced vibrations of complex structural-mechanical systems', *J. Roy. Aero. Soc.* **66**, 457–60, 1962.

33. A. HAJI-SHEIKH and E. M. SPARROW, Transient heat conduction in a prolate spheroidal solid, *Trans. ASME HT*, **88**, 331–3, 1966.

34. C. J. PAREKH, *Finite Element Solution System*, Ph.D thesis, Univ. of Wales, Swansea, 1969.

35. C. TAYLOR, C. J. PAREKH, J. C. PETERS, and P. FRANCE, 'Numerical analysis of linear free surface seepage problems', *Proc. Am. Soc. Civ. Eng.* (to be published).

36. R. HERBERT and K. R. RUSHTON, 'Groundwater flow studies by resistance networks', *Geotechnique*, **16**, 53–75, 1966.

37. S. P. NEUMAN and P. A. WITHERSPOON, 'Finite element method of analyzing steady seepage with a free surface', *Water Resources Res.*, **6**, no. 3, 889, 1970a.

38. S. P. NEUMAN and P. A. WITHERSPOON, 'Variational principles for confined and unconfined flow of groundwater', *Water Resources Res.*, **6**, no. 5, 1970b.

39. I. JAVANDEL and P. A. WITHERSPOON, 'Application of the finite element method to transient flow in porous media', *Soc. Pet. Eng. J.*, 241–252, Sept. 1968.

40. W. HURTY, 'Dynamic analysis of structural systems using component modes', *J.A.I.A.A.*, **6**, July 1968.

41. R. H. GALLAGHER and R. H. MALLETT, *Efficient solution processes for finite element analysis of transient heat conduction*, Bell Aerosystems, Buffalo, 1969.

42. O. C. ZIENKIEWICZ, C. J. PAREKH, and H. J. WILLS, 'The application of finite elements to heat conduction problems involving latent heat' (to be published).

17. The Time Dimension.
Semi-analytical Treatment
[VIBRATIONS AND EIGENVALUES]

17.1 Introduction

In Chapter 13 we have shown how certain problems involving one 'dimension' in the direction of which the properties did not change could be simplified and that dimension eliminated by use of orthogonal functions. This type of solution has long been practised in problems including the *time dimension* and indeed forms the foundation of the linear vibration theory. In this chapter we shall start with the discretized equations obtained in the previous chapter in the form of Eq. (16.13):

$$[K]\{\delta\}+[C]\,\frac{\partial}{\partial t}\,\{\delta\}+[M]\,\frac{\partial^2}{\partial t^2}\,\{\delta\}+\{F(t)\} = 0. \qquad (17.1)$$

This equation is applicable to all the classes of problems mentioned by making one or more of the matrices zero. Indeed the coupled problem can, on elimination, also be reduced to the above form.

17.2 Response of the Basic Dynamic Equation to 'Periodic' Input

Let the forcing term $\{F\}$ be of a form

$$\{F(t)\} = \{F_0\}\,e^{at} \qquad (17.2)$$

with $\{F_0\}$ not dependent on time. Further, if we assume that the solution for $\{\delta\}$ can be taken to exist in a similar form

$$\{\delta(t)\} = \{\delta_a\}\,e^{at} \qquad (17.3)$$

then on substitution into Eq. (17.1) we have

$$([K]+a[C]+a^2[M])\{\delta_0\}+\{F_0\} = 0. \qquad (17.4)$$

Solution of Eq. (17.4) for $\{\delta_0\}$ gives a possible form of response *providing the initial conditions* on $\{\delta\}$ are satisfied.

347

If we take a as an 'imaginary' quantity i.e.

$$a = i\omega \qquad (17.5)$$

then

$$e^{at} = e^{iwt} = \cos \omega t + i \sin \omega t$$

and the real part of expression (17.2) corresponds to a periodic input.

Now in general both $\{F_0\}$ and $\{\delta_0\}$ will be complex and Eq. (17.4) has to be treated as a set of two equations by equating the real and imaginary parts.

Thus if

$$\{F_0\} = \{\bar{F}_0\} + i\{\bar{\bar{F}}_0\}$$
$$\{\delta_0\} = \{\bar{\delta}_0\} + i\{\bar{\bar{\delta}}_0\} \qquad (17.6)$$

in which the quantities with bars are real, we have, on equating the real and imaginary parts of Eq. (17.4), two simultaneous equations written as one in matrix form:

$$\begin{bmatrix} [K] - \omega^2[M] \;, & -\omega[C] \\ -\omega[C] \;, & [K] - \omega^2[M] \end{bmatrix} \begin{Bmatrix} \bar{\delta}_0 \\ \bar{\bar{\delta}}_0 \end{Bmatrix} = - \begin{Bmatrix} \bar{F}_0 \\ \bar{\bar{F}}_0 \end{Bmatrix} \qquad \begin{matrix} (17.7a) \\ (17.7b) \end{matrix}$$

Equations (17.7) form a system in which all quantities are real and from which the response to any periodic input can be determined by direct solution.

The system is no longer positive definite although it is still symmetric.

With periodic input the solution after an initial transient is not sensitive to the initial conditions and therefore this, guessed, solution represents the finally established response. It is valid for problems of dynamic structural response as well as for the problems typical of heat conduction in which simply we put

$$[M] = 0.$$

17.3 Natural Frequencies

If the matrix $[C]$ is zero, i.e., in a dynamic problem no damping exists, and if no forcing $\{F\}$ is present, the general equation (17.1) reduces to

$$[K]\{\delta\} + [M] \frac{\partial^2}{\partial t^2} \{\delta\} = 0. \qquad (17.8)$$

Now a solution in the simple, real, periodic form

$$\{\delta\} = \{\delta_0\} \cos \omega t$$

exists if

$$([K] - \omega^2[M])\{\delta_0\} = 0. \tag{17.9}$$

This is only possible for certain values of ω for which the determinant of the matrix in parentheses is zero. As such a determinant is of the nth order (with matrices of size $n \times n$), in general n real roots ω^2 exist. These give the *natural angular frequencies* of the system and the problem is recognized as a typical *eigenvalue* one.[1]

$$\det |[K] - \omega^2[M]| = 0. \tag{17.10}$$

In the type of problems characteristic of dynamic vibration, the n roots of the above are real.

Each frequency at which Eq. (17.9) is satisfied determines a vector $\{\delta_0\}_n$ in which the components bear specified ratios to each other but the magnitude of each can be arbitrary. Such vectors are called *modes* of the system.

In practice it is convenient to scale such vectors so that

$$\{\delta_0\}_i^T[M]\{\delta_0\}_i = I, \quad \text{(an identity matrix)}. \tag{17.11}$$

With this scaling the vectors are known as *normalized modes* of the system.

Another important property of the modes is that for any two different frequencies $i \neq j$

$$\{\delta_0\}_i^T[M]\{\delta_0\}_j = 0. \tag{17.12}$$

This property is known as *orthogonality* of modes.[1]

It is of interest to observe that the matrix $([K] - \omega^2[M])$ occurs in the solution of the response of the general system to a forced vibration (Eq. (17.7)). As is well known, when ω approaches the natural frequency the response increases and the phenomenon of *resonance* occurs.

17.4 Solution of the Eigenvalue Problem

17.4.1 *General remarks.* To find the actual eigenvalues it is seldom practicable to write the polynomial expanding the determinant given in Eq. (17.10) and alternative techniques have to be developed. The discussion of such techniques is best left to specialist texts[1,2] and indeed many specialist computer programs exist today as library routines.

In most processes the starting point is the *special eigenvalue* problem given by

$$[H]\{X\} = \lambda\{X\} \tag{17.13}$$

in which $[H]$ is a symmetric, positive definite, matrix. Equation (17.9) can be written as

$$[K]^{-1}[M]\{\delta_0\} = \lambda\{\delta_0\} \tag{17.14}$$

on inverting $[K]$ with $\lambda = 1/\omega^2$ but symmetry is in general lost.

If, however, we write in a triangular form

$$[K] = [L][L]^{\mathrm{T}} \quad \text{and} \quad [K]^{-1} = [L]^{\mathrm{T}-1}[L]^{-1}$$

in which $[L]$ is a matrix having only zero coefficients above the diagonal we have, on multiplying Eq. (17.14) by $[L]^{\mathrm{T}}$

$$[L]^{-1}[M]\{\delta_0\} = \lambda[L]^{\mathrm{T}}\{\delta_0\}.$$

Calling

$$[L]^{\mathrm{T}}\{\delta_0\} = \{X\} \tag{17.15}$$

we have finally

$$[H]\{X\} = \lambda\{X\} \tag{17.16}$$

in which

$$[H] = [L]^{-1}[M][L]^{-1^{\mathrm{T}}} \tag{17.17}$$

which is of the form of Eq. (17.13), as $[H]$ is now symmetric.

Having determined λ (all, or only few selected largest values corresponding to fundamental periods) the modes of $\{X\}$ are found, and hence by use of Eq. (17.15) the modes of $\{\delta_0\}$.

17.4.2 *'Free' vibration.* In static problems we have always introduced a suitable number of *support* conditions to allow $[K]^{-1}$ to be inverted, or which is equivalent, to solve the static equations uniquely (*vide* Chapter 1). If such 'support' conditions are in fact not specified, as may well be the case with a rocket travelling in space, an arbitrary fixing of a minimum number of support conditions allows a static solution to be obtained without affecting the stresses. In dynamic problems such a fixing is not permissible and frequently one is faced with a problem of a free oscillation for which $[K]$ is singular and therefore does not possess an inverse.

To preserve the applicability of the general methods described in the previous section a simple artifice is possible. Equation (17.9) is modified to

$$[([K]+\alpha[M])-(\omega^2+\alpha)[M]]\{\delta_0\} = 0 \tag{17.18}$$

in which α is an arbitrary constant of the same order as the typical ω^2 sought.

The new matrix $([K]+\alpha[M])$ can be inverted and the standard process maintained to find $(\omega^2+\alpha)$.

This simple but effective sidestepping of otherwise serious difficulties was first suggested by Cox.[3]

17.4.3 *Eigenvalue economizer methods*. Whatever technique is used in the process of determining the eigenvalues and eigenmodes of the system, for a given size of problem the computer effort is larger by an order of magnitude than the solution of an equivalent static situation. Fortunately, reasonably good eigenvalues can be determined with fewer degrees of freedom than needed for a normal static solution.

If a rather fine subdivision is used in the static analysis we can eliminate a number of degrees of freedom and 'lump' the 'mass' and 'damping' effects at a reduced number of nodal parameters. A *consistent* way of doing this has been suggested by Irons[4,5] and later by Guyan.[6] The similarity with substructure analysis described in Chapter 7, section 7.6, will not escape the notice of the reader.

Let the total degree of freedom $\{\delta\}$ be divided into two parts

$$\{\delta\} = \left\{ \begin{matrix} \bar{\delta} \\ \bar{\bar{\delta}} \end{matrix} \right\} \tag{17.19}$$

and assume that the displacements $\bar{\delta}$ depend in some unique way on the displacements $\bar{\bar{\delta}}$. The latter we shall call therefore, 'master' and the former 'slave' variables. Thus,

$$\{\bar{\delta}\} = [L]\{\bar{\bar{\delta}}\} \tag{17.20}$$

we have

$$\{\delta\} = \begin{bmatrix} I \\ L \end{bmatrix} \{\bar{\bar{\delta}}\} \tag{17.21}$$

in which $[L]$ is the matrix specifying the dependence.

Now the dynamic equation of the whole system

$$[K]\{\delta\} + [M] \frac{\partial^2}{\partial t^2} \{\delta\} = 0 \tag{17.22}$$

has to be further reduced by applying the constraint of the deformation freedom implied in Eq. (17.21). This reduction is best achieved by once again minimizing the total potential energy of the system with respect to the reduced parameters.

From Chapter 2 we have seen that this potential energy can be written as

$$\chi = \{\delta\}^{\mathrm{T}}[K]\{\delta\} + \left([M] \frac{\partial^2}{\partial t^2} \{\delta\} \right)^{\mathrm{T}} \{\delta\} \tag{17.23}$$

using the d'Alembert principle for dynamic 'loads'. After some transformation we can write

$$\frac{\partial \chi}{\partial \{\bar{\bar{\delta}}\}} = [K^*]\{\bar{\bar{\delta}}\} + [M^*]\{\bar{\bar{\delta}}\} = 0 \tag{17.24}$$

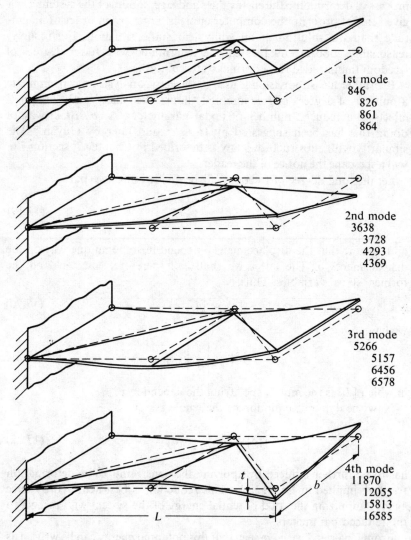

Fig. 17.1   Vibration of a cantilever plate divided into four triangular elements Modal shapes. Data: $E = 30 \times 10^6$ lb/in^2; $t = 0.1$ in; $L = 2$ in; $b = 1$ in; $v = 0.3$; density $\rho = 0.283$ lb/in^3. The numbers listed show frequencies in cycles/sec for (1) Exact solution (ref. 9); (2) 'Non conforming' triangle; (3) Conforming triangle. Corrective function Eq. (10.28); (4) Conforming triangle. Corrective function Eq. (10.29)

in which

$$[K^*] = \begin{bmatrix} I \\ L \end{bmatrix}^\mathrm{T} [K] \begin{bmatrix} I \\ L \end{bmatrix}$$

and $\hspace{10cm}$ (17.25)

$$[M^*] = \begin{bmatrix} I \\ L \end{bmatrix}^\mathrm{T} [M] \begin{bmatrix} I \\ L \end{bmatrix}$$

which now correspond with the lesser degrees of freedom associated with $\{\delta_i\}$.

The expression (17.25) can be derived directly from the principles of contragradient transformation discussed in Chapter 1, if Eq. (17.2) is considered as specifying the transformation matrix.

The important question is how to determine reasonably the relation between 'slave' and 'master' deflections. A suitable assumption which can be reasonably justified by engineering intuition is to assume that the general pattern of deformation will follow that which would be obtained by imposing displacements $\{\delta\}$ on an otherwise unloaded structure. Thus writing similarly to Eq. (7.18)

$$[K]\{\delta\} = \begin{bmatrix} \bar{K} & \hat{K} \\ \hat{K}^\mathrm{T} & \bar{\bar{K}} \end{bmatrix} \begin{Bmatrix} \delta \\ \bar{\delta} \end{Bmatrix}$$ $\hspace{3cm}$ (17.26)

we have

$$[\hat{K}]^\mathrm{T}\{\delta\} + [\bar{\bar{K}}]\{\bar{\delta}\} = 0$$

as the 'slave' nodes are unloaded, and

$$\{\bar{\delta}\} = -[\bar{\bar{K}}]^{-1}[\hat{K}]^\mathrm{T}\{\delta\}$$

or $\hspace{10cm}$ (17.27)

$$[L] = -[\bar{\bar{K}}]^{-1}[\hat{K}]^\mathrm{T}.$$

Application of such techniques is illustrated well in the literature[7,8] and some examples will be cited later.

17.5 Some Eigenvalue Examples

There are a variety of problems for which practical solutions exist, so only a few simple examples will be shown.

17.5.1 *Vibration of plates.* Figure 17.1 shows the vibration of a rectangular cantilever plate solved using only four triangular elements. The results are compared against an elaborate calculation carried out by Barton.[9] It is seen that the results using the simple non-conforming triangle are here superior to those using the more elaborate formulation

and the accuracy is quite remarkable both in frequency and mode shape.
A fuller list of results obtained by using the non-conforming triangle and various mesh subdivisions is given in Table 17.1.[7]

TABLE 17.1

COMPARISON BETWEEN THEORETICAL AND TEST FREQUENCIES FOR A
UNIFORM THICKNESS RECTANGULAR CANTILEVER PLATE[7]
(LENGTH a; WIDTH $a/2$)

Mode	$\omega/\sqrt{D/\rho h a^4}$					
	Results from Barton			Finite Element (triangular non-conforming)		
	Conventional Ritz method	Test	Test Results of Plunkett	2×1 mesh 4 elements	4×2 mesh 16 elements	2×8 mesh on half plate with use of symmetry equivalent to 64 elements
1	3·47	3·42†	3·50	3·39	3·44	3·44 (s)
2	14·93	14·52†	14·50	15·30	14·76	14·77 (a)
3	21·26	20·86	21·70	21·16	21·60	21·50 (s)
4	48·71	46·90	48·10	49·47	48·28	48·19 (a)
5			60·50	67·46	60·56	60·54 (s)
6			92·30		88·84	91·79 (s)
7	94·49	93·99	92·80		92·24	92·78 (a)
8			118·70		117·72	119·34 (s)
9			125·10		118·96	124·23 (s)
10			154·00			153·15 (a)
11			176·00			174·46 (s)
12			196·00			199·61 (s)

† Results have been modified by Barton to correct for the means of testing used by him.
(s) denotes symmetrical mode; (a) antisymmetrical mode.

A similar problem is presented in Fig. 17.2 where the effect of using the *eigenvalue economizer* method is examined. It will be seen how very small the changes in the first four frequencies are on restricting the degree of freedom from 90 through various stages to six.

So many further examples of plate vibration analysis are included in current literature that a list of references is here impracticable.

17.5.2 *Plane vibration.* A vibration problem of a plane section of an earth dam solved by Clough and Chopra[10] is shown in Fig. 17.3. Simple triangular elements are used here.

17.5.3 *Shell vibration.* Application of the process to any elastic two- or three-dimensional continuum can obviously be made and shell vibrations are a typical problem of much interest. In Fig. 17.4, by contrast to the previous simple example, the elaborate thick shell elements described in Chapter 14 are used to solve a problem of turbine blade vibration.[11, 12]

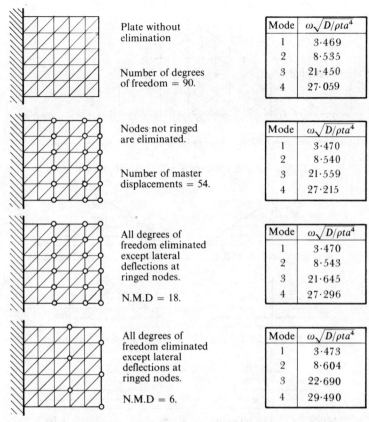

	Plate without elimination	Mode	$\omega\sqrt{D/\rho ta^4}$
		1	3·469
		2	8·535
	Number of degrees of freedom = 90.	3	21·450
		4	27·059

	Nodes not ringed are eliminated.	Mode	$\omega\sqrt{D/\rho ta^4}$
		1	3·470
		2	8·540
	Number of master displacements = 54.	3	21·559
		4	27·215

	All degrees of freedom eliminated except lateral deflections at ringed nodes.	Mode	$\omega\sqrt{D/\rho ta^4}$
		1	3·470
		2	8·543
		3	21·645
	N.M.D = 18.	4	27·296

	All degrees of freedom eliminated except lateral deflections at ringed nodes.	Mode	$\omega\sqrt{D/\rho ta^4}$
		1	3·473
		2	8·604
		3	22·690
	N.M.D = 6.	4	29·490

Fig. 17.2   Use of eigenvalue elimination in vibration of a square cantilever plate

Figure 17.5 shows the same type of element applied to dynamic analysis of an arch dam.

Some other dynamic analyses of shells are given in references 13–16. Reference 7 also shows some application utilizing this full three-dimensional isoparametric elements.

17.5.4 *The 'wave' equation. Electromagnetic and fluid problems.* Clearly the basic dynamic Eq. (17.1) can be derived from a variety of non-structure problems as indeed was shown in the previous chapter. The eigenvalue problem once again occurs with 'stiffness' and 'mass' matrices now having alternate physical meaning.

A particular form of the more general equations discussed earlier is the well-known wave equation which, in two dimensional form is

$$\frac{\partial^2\phi}{\partial x^2}+\frac{\partial^2\phi}{\partial y^2}+\frac{1}{\bar{c}^2}\frac{\partial^2\phi}{\partial t^2} = 0. \tag{17.28}$$

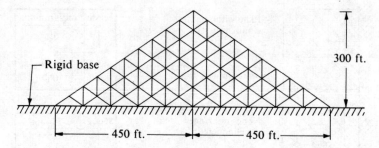

Fig. 17.3(a)   Finite element idealization of an earth dam

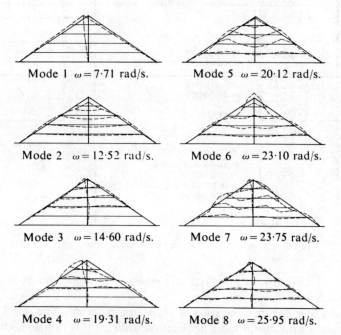

Fig. 17.3(b)   Free vibration mode shapes and frequencies of an earth dam (modes 1–8) (Clough and Chopra, ref. 10)

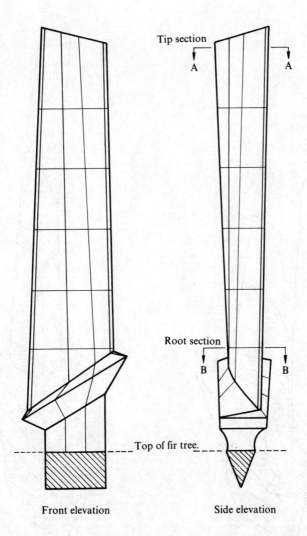

Tip section

A   A

Root section

B   B

Top of fir tree

Front elevation   Side elevation

Fig. 17.4   Vibration of a turbine blade treated as a thick shell (*a*) element sub-division (parabolic type), (*b*) modal shapes and frequencies compared with experiment

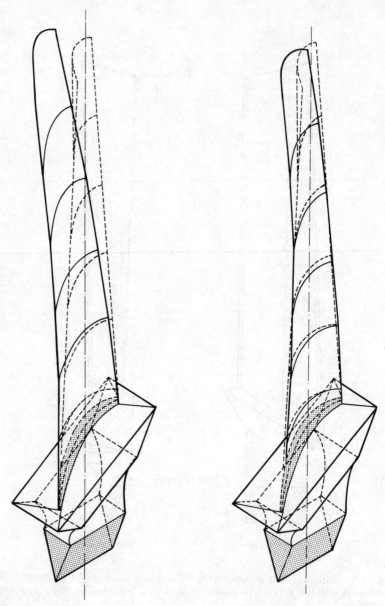

Fig. 7.4(*b*) (*cont.*)

Mode 1—1st flap.   Measured frequency =   517 c/s
                      Calculated frequency =   518 c/s
Mode 2—1st edgewise. Measured frequency = 1326 c/s
                      Calculated frequency = 1692 c/s

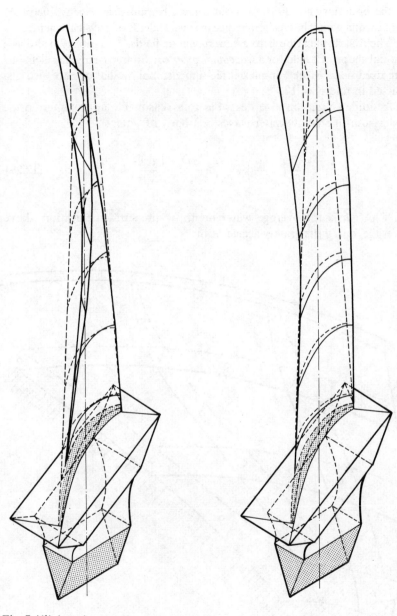

Fig. 7.4(*b*) (*cont.*)

Mode 3—1st torsion. Measured frequency = 2885 c/s
                     Calculated frequency = 2686 c/s
Mode 4—2nd flap.   Measured frequency = 2510 c/s
                     Calculated frequency = 2794 c/s

If the boundary conditions do not force a response, an eigenvalue problem results which has a significance in several fields of physical science.

The first application is to *electromagnetic* fields.[17] Figure 17.6 shows a modal shape of a field for a *waveguide problem*. Simple triangular elements are used here. More complex three-dimensional oscillations are also discussed in reference 17.

A similar equation also describes to a reasonable approximation the behaviour of shallow water waves in a body of water:

$$\frac{\partial}{\partial x}\left(h\,\frac{\partial \psi}{\partial x}\right) + \frac{\partial}{\partial y}\left(h\,\frac{\partial \psi}{\partial y}\right) + \frac{1}{g}\,\frac{\partial^2 \psi}{\partial t^2} = 0 \qquad (17.29)$$

in which h is the average water depth, ψ the surface elevation above average, and g the gravity acceleration.

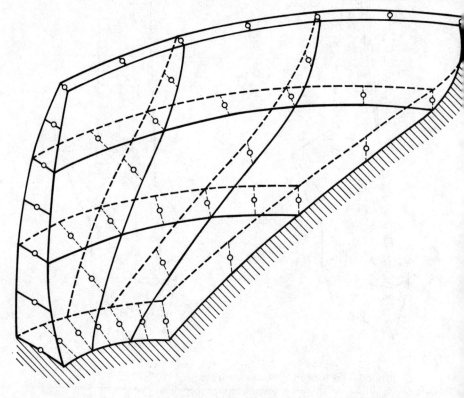

Fig. 17.5 (*a*) A 3×3 mesh of parabolic thick shell elements used to solve vibration of an arch dam

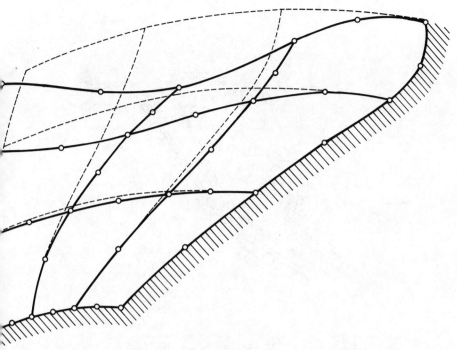

Fig. 17.5(*b*)   First mode-shape and frequency = 2·20 c/sec

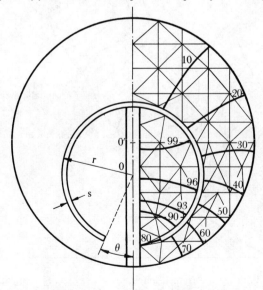

Fig. 17.6   A 'lunar' waveguide; mode of vibration for electro-magnetic field. Outer diameter = *d*, 00′ = 1·3*d*, *r* = 0·29*d*, *S* = 0·055*d*, *θ* = 22°

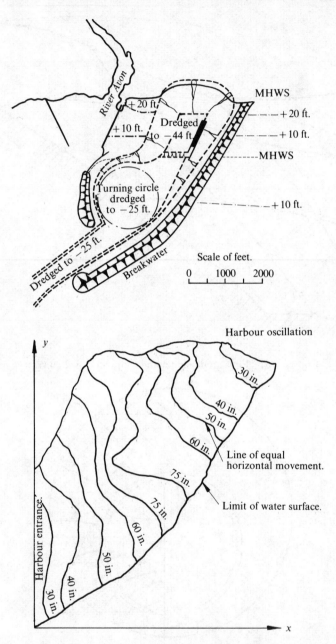

Fig. 17.7   Oscillations of a natural harbour: (*a*) layout, (*b*) contours of velocity amplitudes

Thus natural frequencies of bodies of water contained in harbours of varying depths may easily be found.[18] Figure 17.7 shows the modal shape for a particular harbour.

17.5.5 *Coupled Structures—fluid motion.* The theory of the problem was outlined in the previous chapter and once again, if damping or forcing is not present the problem leads to an eigenvalue solution.

When fluid is incompressible its inclusion results simply in an 'added mass matrix' which augments the structural problem. In Chapter 15 we have in fact derived just such a matrix in detail so that it could be assembled with a suitable structure. This type of formulation was first given by Zienkiewicz *et al.*[19] and later applied by Back *et al.*[20]

If compressibility is taken into account the problem is a little more complex as both fluid and structure oscillations interact.[21]

A simple two-dimensional example showing interaction of an idealized dam and a body of fluid is shown in Fig. 17.8 and indicates the effects of different element subdivisions.[22]

In the actual reduction of the coupled problem to a standard eigenvalue form certain special transformations are helpful. Some of these are outlined in reference 21 and another computation process is presented by Irons.[23]

17.6 Transient Solutions via Eigenvalues. Normalized Mode Procedure

In the previous chapter we have discussed the solution of transient problems by various recurrence relations. However, once natural frequencies and modes of the undamped system are known one can obtain fairly simply the response to transient forces of the full damped system characterized by Eq. (17.1).

The process is described in many texts and, with certain approximations, leads simply to the calculation of responses to such complex inputs as earthquake shocks, etc.[20, 24, 25]

Considering again the basic equation

$$[K]\{\delta\} + [C]\frac{\partial}{\partial t}\{\delta\} + [M]\frac{\partial^2}{\partial t^2}\{\delta\} + \{F(t)\} = 0 \qquad (17.1)$$

we first observe that we can represent any type of motion as a linear combination of the modes $\{\delta_0\}_i$ obtained as solution of the eigenvalue problem

$$([K] - \omega^2[M])\{\delta_0\} = 0. \qquad (17.9)$$

Thus

$$\{\delta\} = [\{\delta_0\}_1, \{\delta_0\}_2, \ldots, \{\delta_0\}_n]\{z\} = [\Delta_0]\{z\} \qquad (17.30)$$

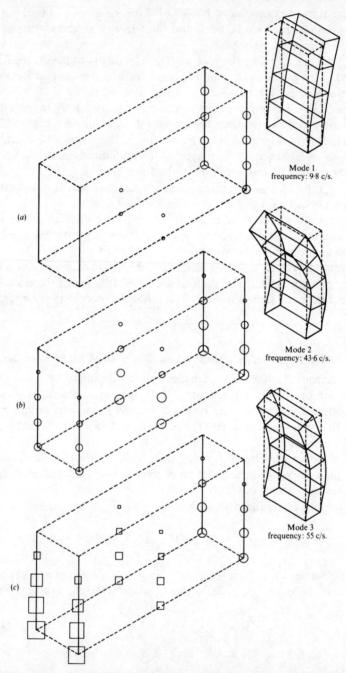

Fig. 17.8 Body of fluid with a free surface oscillating with a wall. Circles show pressure amplitudes and squares indicate opposite signs. A three-dimensional approach using parabolic elements

in which the matrix $[\Delta_0]$ lists all the modes (assumed to be normalized) and $\{z(t)\}$ represents the proportions of motion in each mode.

Now if Eq. (17.30) is substituted into Eq. (17.1) and the whole pre-multiplied by $[\Delta_0]^T$ we have

$$[\Delta_0]^T[K][\Delta_0]\{z\} + [\Delta_0]_0^T[C][\Delta_0] \frac{\partial}{\partial t}\{z\}$$

$$+ [\Delta_0]^T[M][\Delta_0] \frac{\partial^2}{\partial t^2}\{z\} + [\Delta_0]^T\{F\} = 0. \quad (17.31)$$

By the orthogonality property, Eq. (17.12), we know that when $i \neq j$

$$\{\delta_0\}_i[M]\{\delta_0\}_j = 0, \quad \text{and when } i = j, = 1.$$

Also, as by definition

$$[K]\{\delta_0\}_i = \omega_i^2[M]\{\delta_0\}_i$$

then when $i \neq j$

$$\{\delta_0\}_i[K]\{\delta_0\}_j = 0, \quad \text{and when } i = j, = \omega_i^2.$$

If we also *assume†* that $[C]$ is of such a form that again when $i \neq j$

$$\{\delta_0\}_i^T[C]\{\delta_0\}_j = 0, \quad \text{and when } i = j, = 2\omega_i c_i$$

then the system of Eq. (17.31) contains only *diagonal terms* and we have simply a set of ordinary differential equations which, as the modes are normalized, are

$$\omega_1^2 z_1 + 2\omega_1 c_1 \frac{d}{dt} z_1 + \frac{d^2}{dt^2} z_1 = -\{\delta_0\}_1^T\{F\}$$

$$\cdot \quad \cdot \quad \cdot \quad \cdot \quad \cdot \quad \cdot \quad \cdot \quad \cdot \quad \cdot \quad \cdot \quad \cdot \quad \cdot$$

$$\omega_n^2 z_n + 2\omega_n c_n \frac{d}{dt} z_n + \frac{d^2}{dt^2} z_n = -\{\delta_0\}_n^T\{F\}. \quad (17.32)$$

Each one of the ordinary differential equations (17.32) can now be solved in an elementary manner and complete solution obtained by Eq. (17.30).

This type of solution is particularly useful if all the forces $\{F(t)\}$ vary in the same manner with time. For instance, if the foundation of a structure is subject to a certain acceleration $\ddot{U}(t)$, then, by superposing an equal and opposite motion on the whole structure we can consider it as one with a fixed foundation and forces

$$-[M]\{A\}\ddot{U} \quad (17.33)$$

† This assumption is a reasonable one as we have seen in the previous chapter that this form of $[C]$ is similar to that of $[M]$.

acting on the nodes (Fig. 17.9). In this $\{A\}$ is a matrix geometrically connecting accelerations at nodes and $\ddot{U}$. (It consists of ones and zeroes only, is U corresponds with one at the co-ordinate direction.)

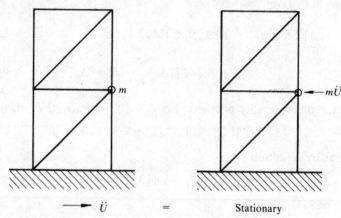

━━━▶ $\ddot{U}$ =   Stationary

Fig. 17.9   Foundation motion as equivalent force

A typical differential equation can now be written as

$$\omega_i^2 z_i' + 2\omega_i c_i \frac{d}{dt} z_i' + \frac{d^2}{dt^2} z_i' = \ddot{U}(t) \tag{17.34}$$

with

$$z_i = R_i z_i'$$

and

$$R_i = \{\delta_0\}_i^T [M]\{A\}. \tag{17.35}$$

Solution to Eq. (17.34) can be written simply as

$$z_i' = \int_0^t \ddot{U}(t) \, e^{-c\omega_i(t-\tau)} \sin \omega_i(t-\tau) \, d\tau \tag{17.36}$$

and can be evaluated for various types of motion once and for all.

For any particular structure the knowledge of the weighting factors R_i is important and any eigenvalue program should be so designed that these can be obtained in output.

For various earthquake motions these responses of a single degree of freedom system typical of Eq. (17.34) have been evaluated. Often one can observe that the response is only serious in a few modes and the maximum responses in these modes added to estimate the maximum possible response.

References

1. S. H. CRANDALL, *Engineering Analysis*, McGraw-Hill, 1956.
2. J. H. WILKINSON, *The Algebraic Eigenvalue Problem*, Oxford Univ. Press, 1965.
3a. H. L. COX, 'Vibration of missiles', *Aircraft Eng.*, **33**, 2–7 and 48–55, 1961.
3b. A. JENNING, 'Natural vibration of a free structure', *Aircraft Eng.*, **34**, 81–3, 1962.
4. B. IRONS, 'Eigenvalue Economisers in Vibration Problems', *J. Roy. Aero. Soc.*, **67**, 526, 1963.
5. B. IRONS, 'Structural Eigenvalue Problems: Elimination of Unwanted Variables', *J.A.I.A.A.* **3**, 961, 1965.
6. R. J. GUYAN, 'Reduction of Stiffness and Mass Matrices', *J.A.I.A.A.*, **3**, 380, 1965.
7. R. G. ANDERSON, B. M. IRONS, and O. C. ZIENKIEWICZ, 'Vibration and stability of plates using finite elements', *Int. J. Solids and Struct.*, **4**, 1031–55, 1968.
8. J. N. RAMSDEN and J. R. STOKER, 'Mass condensation; a semi automatic method for reducing the size of vibration problems', *Int. J. Num. Meth. Eng.*, **1**, 333–49, 1969.
9. M. V. BARTON, 'Vibration of rectangular and skew cantilever plates', *J. Appl. Mech.*, **18**, 129–34, 1951.
10. R. W. CLOUGH and A. K. CHOPRA, *Earthquake Stress Analysis in Earth Dams*, Structures and Materials Research Report No. 65-8, Univ. of California, Berkeley, California, 1965.
11. S. AHMAD, R. G. ANDERSON, and O. C. ZIENKIEWICZ, 'Vibration of thick, curved, shells with particular reference to turbine blades', *J. Strain Analysis*, **5**, 200–6, 1970.
12. R. G. ANDERSON, *A finite element eigenvalue system*, Ph.D. Thesis, University of Wales, Swansea, 1968.
13. J. S. ARCHER and C. P. RUBIN, 'Improved linear axi-symmetric shell-fluid model for launch vehicle longitudinal response analysis', *Proc. Conf. on Matrix Methods in Struct. Mech.*, Air Force Inst. of Tech., Wright Patterson A.F. Base, Ohio, Oct. 1965.
14. J. H. ARGYRIS, 'Continua and Discontinua', *Proc. Conf. on Matrix Methods in Struct. Mech.*, Air Force Inst. of Tech., Wright Patterson A.F. Base, Ohio, Oct. 1965.
15. S. KLEIN and R. J. SYLVESTER, 'The linear elastic dynamic analysis of shells of revolution by the matrix displacement method', *Proc. Conf. on Matrix Methods in Struct. Mech.*, Air Force Inst. of Tech., Wright Patterson A.F. Base, Ohio, Oct. 1965.
16. R. DUNGAR, R. T. SEVERN, and P. R. TAYLOR, 'Vibration of plate and shell structures using triangular finite elements', *J. of Strain Analysis*, **2**, 73–83, 1967.
17. P. L. ARLETT, A. K. BAHRANI, and O. C. ZIENKIEWICZ, 'Application of finite elements to the solution of Helmholtz's equation', *Proc. I.E.E.*, **115**, 1762–964, 1968.
18. C. TAYLOR, B. S. PATIL, and O. C. ZIENKIEWICZ, 'Harbour oscillation: a numerical treatment for undamped natural modes', *Proc. Inst. Civ. Eng.*, **43**, 141–55, 1969.
19. O. C. ZIENKIEWICZ, B. IRONS, and B. NATH, 'Natural frequencies of complex, free or submerged structures, by the finite element method', *Symp. on Vibrations in Civil Eng.*, Inst. Civ. Eng., London (Butterworth), 1965.

20. P. A. A. BACK, A. C. CASSELL, R. DUNGAR, D. R. GAUKROGER, and R. T. SEVERN, 'The seismic design study of a double curvature arch dam', *Proc. Inst. Civ. Eng.*, **43**, 217–48, 1969.
21. O. C. ZIENKIEWICZ and R. E. NEWTON, 'Coupled Vibrations of a Structure submerged in a compressible fluid', *Int. Symposium on finite element techniques*, Stuttgart, 1969.
22. J. HOLBECHE, Ph.D. Thesis, Univ. of Wales, Swansea, 1971.
23. B. M. IRONS, 'Role of part-inversion in fluid structure problems with mixed variables', *J.A.I.A.A.*, **7**, 568, 1970.
24. G. W. HOUSNER, 'Behaviour of structures during earthquakes', *Proc. Am. Soc. Civ. Eng.*, **85**, EM4, 110–29, 1959.
25. O. C. ZIENKIEWICZ, R. G. ANDERSON, and B. IRONS, 'Buttress dam analysis for earthquake loads', *Water Power*, **19**, 359–63, 1967.

18. Non-Linear Material Problems. Plasticity, Creep, Non-Linear Field Problems, etc.

18.1 Introduction

In all the problems discussed so far the differential equations governing the situations were linear—leading to the standard quadratic form of the functional. In elastic solid mechanics this was implied in

(a) a linear form of strain-displacement relationships (*vide* Eq. (2.2), Chapter 2)

and

(b) a linear form of stress-strain relationships (*vide* Eq. (2.3), Chapter 2).

In various field problems similar linearity was implied by such constants as the permeability k remaining independent of the variation of the unknown potential ϕ (*vide* Eq. (15.1), Chapter 15).

Many problems of practical consequence exist in which such linearity is not preserved and it is of interest to extend the numerical processes described to cover these. In this context we have a whole range of *solid mechanics* situations in which such phenomena as plasticity, creep, or other *complex constitutive relations* supersede the simple linear elasticity assumptions.

Similarly in flow-type situations the dependence of viscosity on velocity distribution, the inapplicability of Darcy's seepage laws in a porous medium due to onset of turbulence, or dependence of magnetic permeability on flux densities tends to non-linearity with respect to material properties.

These classes of problems can be simply dealt with without reformulation of the complete problem (i.e., without recourse to rewriting of the basic variational postulates). If a solution to the linear problem can be

369

arrived at by some iterative process in which, at the final stage, the material constants are so adjusted that the appropriate new constitutive law is satisfied, then a solution is achieved.

However, if the strain-displacement relationship is non-linear, then a more fundamental reorganization of the formulation is necessary. For this reason alone such problems have been removed from this chapter and will be dealt with separately in Chapter 19. It will nevertheless be found that the basic iteration processes remain unchanged and indeed combination of both types of non-linearities may easily be achieved.

One important point needs, however, to be mentioned. While in linear problems the solution was always unique this no longer is the case in many non-linear situations. Thus, if *a solution* is achieved it may not necessarily be *the solution* sought. Physical insight into the nature of the problem and, on occasion, small-step, incremental approaches are essential to obtain the significant answers.

The iterative approaches used can, on occasion, be interpreted as purely 'numerical analysis' processes such as Newton-Raphson methods, etc. Again, however, the physical insight into the nature of the problem is essential and the successful methods invariably are derived by the engineer (or physicist) rather than the formal mathematician.

NON-LINEAR CONSTITUTIVE PROBLEMS IN SOLID MECHANICS

18.2 General Physical Approach

18.2.1 *Fundamentals.* In small strain linear elastic problems formulated by the displacement approach we have always arrived at the final answer by solving the assembled (stiffness) equations (*vide* Chapters 1 and 2).

$$[K]\{\delta\} - \{R\} = 0 \tag{18.1}$$

in which the vector $\{R\}$ lists all the 'forces' due to external loads, initial stresses and strains, etc.

In the above the validity of a linear elastic constitutive law

$$\{\sigma\} = [D](\{\varepsilon\} - \{\varepsilon_0\}) + \{\sigma_0\} \tag{18.2}$$

was assumed in addition to a linear strain-displacement relation (Eq. (2.2), Chapter 2), continuity of displacements, and an approximate satisfaction of equilibrium.

In small displacements analysis of problems in which a different, possibly non-linear, constitutive relationship applies, displacement continuity and equilibrium still have to be satisfied. Thus the only relationship which has to be replaced is Eq. (18.2).

This new relation, in general, will be given by some relation

$$F(\{\sigma\}, \{\varepsilon\}) = 0. \tag{18.3}$$

If a solution of Eq. (18.1) can be achieved in which, by adjustment of one or more of the parameters $[D]$, $\{\varepsilon_0\}$ or $\{\sigma_0\}$ in Eq. (18.2), this and Eq. (18.3) are made to yield the same stress and strain values, then a solution is found.

An iterative approach is obviously essential.

Which of the three quantities mentioned above is to be adjusted in the iteration process depends on:

(a) the solution method used in the equivalent linear elastic problem,

(b) the nature of the physical law defining the stress-strain relation.

If the iteration is conducted by adjustment of the $[D]$ matrix the process will be known as one of *variable stiffness*.

If $\{\varepsilon_0\}$ or $\{\sigma_0\}$ are adjusted, so-called *initial strain* or *initial stress* approaches will be obtained.

In many real situations relations of the type of Eq. (18.3) cannot be written in terms of total strains and stresses, but nevertheless can be established for increments $\Delta\{\sigma\}$ and $\Delta\{\varepsilon\}$ of these. In such cases the same processes can be applied for an increment of load (or time in creep situation). Such *incremental processes* can be combined with any of the previous methods.

As we have seen, the specification of $[D]$, $\{\varepsilon_0\}$ and $\{\sigma_0\}$ forms the essential data through which any linear elastic analysis program is entered. Thus such programs will form the essential core of any non-linear analysis solution. Indeed at this stage it is immaterial whether such programs are derived on the basis of a finite element discretization—and what follows could be used in conjunction with any other process of discretization (such as for example finite difference schemes) providing the same data were used in formulating the solution.

18.2.2 *Variable stiffness methods.* If the stress-strain relation Eq. (18.3) for the behaviour of a particular material can be written in the form of Eq. (18.2) but with the elasticity matrix being now a function of the strain level reached, i.e.,

$$[D] = [D(\{\varepsilon\})] = [D(\{\delta\})] \tag{18.4}$$

then the process of *variable stiffness* can be applied.

As the elasticity matrix influences the final stiffness matrix of the assembly we are left with the solution of a problem

$$\{\psi\} = [K(\{\delta\})]\{\delta\} - \{R\} = 0 \tag{18.5}$$

which can be accomplished iteratively in different ways.

A simple iterative process, in which we first take $\{\delta\}_0 = 0$ to evaluate $[K(\{\delta\}_0)] = [K_0]$ and solve $\{\delta\}_1 = [K_0]^{-1}\{R\}$ repeating the process with

$$\{\delta\}_n = [K]_{n-1}^{-1}\{R\} \tag{18.6}$$

until no further displacement changes occur, is an obvious one.

If the constitutive law is such that a relation of type (18.4) can only be written for increments of stress and strain, then the process has to be adopted for small load increments starting from previously arrived conditions.

In either case the standard linear elasticity program can be used, providing the form of $[D]$ arrived at is symmetric. This is essential as such programs in general make use of the symmetry properties.

One serious disadvantage of the variable elasticity approaches is the fact that at each step the stiffness matrices have to be reformulated and a new solution of equations obtained. If direct solution methods are used in the elastic program, this is extremely uneconomical and, therefore, the alternative processes described in the next section are generally favoured.

18.2.3 *Initial stress methods.* If the constitutive law is such that for a given strain the stress levels can be determined, i.e., Eq. (18.3) takes the form

$$\{\sigma\} = f(\{\varepsilon\}), \tag{18.7}$$

then the elastic constitutive law, Eq. (18.2), can be made to coincide with the above by adjusting the value of $\{\sigma_0\}$. As $\{\sigma_0\}$ affects the forces $\{R\}$ we are left with an iterative process of solving

$$\{\psi\} = [K_0]\{\delta\} - R(\{\delta\}) = 0 \tag{18.8}$$

in which we proceed as follows. Solve first

$$\{\delta_0\} = [K_0]^{-1}\{R_0\}$$

in which $\{R_0\}$ corresponds to the actual loads applied. Determine level of $\{\sigma_0\}_1$ *required to bring the elastic solution into coincidence with the true stresses corresponding to the strains reached* and find $\{R\}_1$ taking the new 'initial stress' and using Eq. (2.13) of Chapter 2. Obtain

$$\{\delta_1\} = [K_0]^{-1}\{R_1\}, \text{ etc.}$$

with

$$\{\delta_n\} = [K_0]^{-1}\{R_n\} \tag{18.9}$$

until no further changes occur.

A convenient alternative is to determine only the changes of $\{R\}$ due to the changes of initial stress required. Pursuing this, $\{\delta_0\}$ is found as before but

$$\Delta\{\delta_1\} = [K_0]^{-1}\Delta\{R_1\}, \text{ etc.}$$

and the iteration continues until $\Delta\{\delta\}_n$ is sufficiently close to zero.

Numerically the latter alternative is desirable and indeed it has a distinct physical significance. At every stage we determine at all points of the structure the difference between the *true stress level corresponding to appropriate strains and that corresponding to an elastic solution*. This stress difference is then redistributed elastically to restore equilibrium and indeed the process has been named originally as one of 'stress transfer'.[1]

The force quantity $\Delta\{R\}_n$ calculated at the n-th stage of iteration can be interpreted physically as an *unbalanced residual force* left on the structure and hence is an extremely convenient measure of error which can be assessed against the active forces.

The reader will note that now at every stage of iteration the same stiffness matrix is used and if this is once partially inverted, each step can be accomplished in a small fraction of time needed for the first solution.

The question may be posed at this stage as to what value of elastic constants should be used to determine the matrix $[K_0]$. If the material behaves essentially in a linear elastic manner with departures from linearity being localized then clearly the original elastic constants are the obvious choice. However, if the non-linearity is evident at all stress levels it may be worth while to adjust the elastic constants after the first iteration to accelerate the convergence.

18.2.4 *Initial strain methods.* In some problems, notably those of creep, the stress level cannot be explicitly determined in terms of strain. On the other hand it is then possible to determine strains (or increments of strain) in terms of stresses. Thus symbolically

$$\{\varepsilon\} = f(\{\sigma\}). \tag{18.10}$$

Now, the equality between Eq. (18.10) and the elastic relation Eq. (18.2) can be obtained by adjusting $\{\varepsilon_0\}$. Once again Eq. (18.8) is solved iteratively but the elastic strains obtained at every stage are compared with those corresponding to the constitutive relation, Eq. (18.10), and the difference used in evaluating the *residual forces*, $\Delta\{R\}_n$. Otherwise the process is identical to the one previously described and possesses the same merits of the constant stiffness matrix being maintained at all stages.

With some creep laws (*vide* section 18.7) the additional (creep) strains are explicitly separated from the elastic strains and hence the corrective initial strain at each stage of iteration is given directly. The difference between the initial stress and initial strain approaches is perhaps best illustrated diagramatically. In Fig. 18.1 the stress-strain level reached by the first solution is shown as point 1. In the initial stress process the stresses are brought down to the correct level by introducing an initial stress $\Delta\{\sigma_0\}_1$ while with the initial strain process the strains are adjusted by a correction $\Delta\{\varepsilon_0\}_1$. The first process is clearly advantageous when strains increase rapidly with increasing stress while the latter when the reverse is true (locking materials).

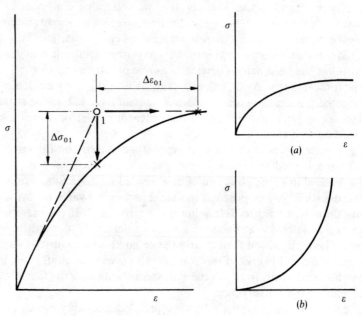

Fig. 18.1   Initial strain and initial stress processes (*a*) softening, (*b*) locking materials

18.2.5 *Acceleration*. In both the initial stress and initial strain approaches the final solution could be achieved if correct values of $\{\sigma_0\}$ or $\{\varepsilon_0\}$ could be suitably guessed in the first place. The systematic adjustment processes outlined may not always be rapidly convergent. By studying the convergence during the calculation process it is possible to accelerate the convergence by overcorrecting at each step. A suitable process is outlined in references 2a and 2b but the ingenuity of the engineer designing his program may be used here to the full. No process is 'illegal' providing the final solution is found to satisfy all the requirements.

18.3 **A more Mathematical Approach**

At this stage it is worth while to re-examine the whole problem mathematically.[3] The reader is undoubtedly familiar with the Newton method of solving general non-linear equations of the form

$$\psi(x) = 0.$$

with a single variable x.

If a trial value of x_n is found sufficiently close to the correct one but at which $\psi(x_n) \neq 0$, the improved, trial solution can be obtained by finding

$$x_{n+1} = x_n + \Delta x_{n+1}$$

with

$$\Delta x_{n+1} = -\psi(x_n) \bigg/ \frac{d}{dx}(\psi)_n.$$

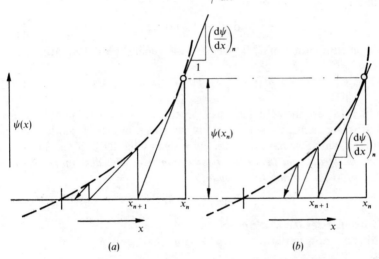

Fig. 18.2   Newton (a) and constant slope (b) iteration process

Graphically, the convergence of the Newton process is illustrated in Fig. 18.2(a). An alternative approach would be to use at all stages a constant value of

$$\frac{d}{dx}(\psi)_0$$

and obtain correction as

$$\Delta x_{n+1} = -\psi(x_n) \bigg/ \frac{d}{dx}(\psi)_0.$$

Convergence of such a process would be slower and is illustrated in Fig. 18.2(b). The same ideas can fairly obviously be extended to non-linear equations of many variables. Here, the process is known as the Newton–Raphson method which once again could be modified as shown above. It seems that the processes of variable or constant stiffness used in the general consideration of section 18.2 fall into these two categories.

To proceed further it is convenient to return to the basic formulation of the finite element equations from the virtual work principle as in Chapter 2. In Eq. (2.28) of that chapter we derive equilibrium conditions by studying internal and external work changes. Thus if $\{\psi\}$ represents the vector of the sum of the internal and external forces we can write

$$d\{\delta\}^T\{\psi\} = \int_V d\{\varepsilon\}^T\{\sigma\}\,dV - d\{\delta\}^T\{\overline{R}\} = 0 \qquad (18.11)$$

where $\{\overline{R}\}$ represents all the external forces due to imposed loads. If we can write for the variation of strains

$$d\{\varepsilon\} = [B]\,d\{\delta\} \qquad (18.12)$$

then, on elimination of $d\{\delta\}^T$ we have the generally valid equation

$$\{\psi(\{\delta\})\} = \int_V [B]^T\{\sigma\}\,dV - \{\overline{R}\} = 0 \qquad (18.13)$$

in which $\{\sigma\}$ are the actual stresses dependent on the strain level reached.

If displacements are small, $[B]$ is the strain matrix dependent on co-ordinates which we have found previously in Chapter 2. *If the dependence of $\{\sigma\}$ on strain and hence on displacements can be determined we have therefore to solve a non-linear equation*

$$\psi(\{\delta\}) = 0.$$

This summarizes the whole problem.

Consider now variations of $\{\psi\}$ due to changes $d\{\delta\}$,

$$d\{\psi\} = \int_V [B]^T\,d\{\sigma\}\,dV \qquad (18.14)$$

as $\{\overline{R}\}$ is independent of $\{\delta\}$ and $d\{\overline{R}\} = 0$. Now if we can write

$$d\{\sigma\} = [D_T(\{\varepsilon\})]\,d\{\varepsilon\} \qquad (18.15)$$

in which $[D_T]$ is the incremental (or tangent) elasticity matrix, then using Eq. (18.15) together with Eq. (18.12) allows Eq. (18.14) to be rewritten as

$$d\{\psi\} = \left(\int_V [B]^T[D_T(\{\varepsilon\})][B]\,dV\right)d\{\delta\} = [K_T]\,d\{\delta\}. \qquad (18.16)$$

Now if the Newton-Raphson process is applied on a trial solution, $\{\delta\}_n$ which results in a non-zero value $\{\psi\}_n$ then we can write the correction to be applied in the trial process as

$$\Delta\{\delta\}_{n+1} = -[K_T]_n^{-1}\{\psi\}_n \qquad (18.17)$$

in which $[K_T]_n$ is the tangential matrix evaluated for displacements and strain given for trial $\{\delta\}_n$.

The Newton-Raphson process leads thus to yet another method of treating non-linear problems using a variable stiffness approach. This differs from the one described in section 18.2.2 as a *tangential* rather than *secant* stiffness is now used. Indeed, in practice, this is much more convenient as physical laws are usually formulated that way.

However, if the tangential matrix is substituted by a constant one corresponding to that of the initial elastic stiffness, the modified Newton-Raphson procedure (Fig. 18.2b) becomes identical with the initial stress or initial strain methods previously described.

Thus, these methods derived by a simple physical reasoning are given here their mathematical basis.† Clearly a greater number of iterative steps will in general be required though the overall economy, as mentioned earlier, is achieved as only one stiffness matrix has to be inverted. It may well be that the optimum economy can be obtained by a judicious combination of both constant and variable stiffness approaches.

It seems thus that what is essential in all non-linear processes is the means of a direct calculation of the vector $\{\psi\}$ which gives the *total force unbalance*. The elastic solution is used simply as a means of accelerating the convergence of trial solutions.

The vector $\{\psi\}_n$ can be interpreted as the *unbalanced force residual* and thus has an important role in the computation.

All processes of accelerating the convergence can be used in conjunction with all the general approaches discovered.

18.4 Plasticity

18.4.1 *General theory*. This particular departure from linear elastic behaviour is well known in metals and has been studied extensively from the theoretical viewpoint.[4-7] In essence it is characterized by an irreversible straining which is not time dependent and which can only be sustained once a certain level of stress, known as the yield limit, has been reached.

Yield surface. It is quite generally postulated, as an experimental fact, that yielding can occur only if the stresses $\{\sigma\}$ satisfy the general yield criterion

$$F(\{\sigma\}, \kappa) = 0. \tag{18.18}$$

in this κ is a 'hardening' parameter. This yield condition can be visualized as a surface in n-dimensional space of stress with the position of the surface dependent on the instantaneous value of the parameter κ (Fig. 18.3).

Flow rule (Normality principle). von Mises[4] first suggested the basic constitutive relation defining the plastic strain increments in relation to

† The initial stress process is in fact identical to this formulation with $[K_T]$ approximated by $[K_0]$.

the yield surface. Heuristic arguments for the validity of the relationship proposed have been given by various workers in the field[4,5] and at the present time the following hypothesis appears to be generally accepted: If $d\{\varepsilon\}_p$ denotes the increment of plastic strain then

$$d\{\varepsilon\}_p = \lambda \frac{\partial F}{\partial \{\sigma\}} \tag{18.19}$$

or for any component n

$$d\varepsilon_{n,p} = \lambda \frac{\partial F}{\partial \sigma_n}.$$

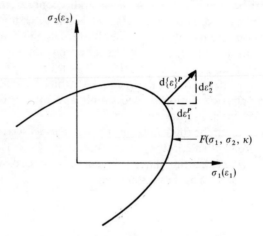

Fig. 18.3   Yield surface and normality criterion in two-dimensional stress space

In this λ is a proportionality constant, as yet undetermined. The rule is known as the *normality* principle because relation (18.19) can be interpreted as requiring the normality of the plastic strain increment 'vector' to the yield surface in the space of n stress dimensions.

Total stress-strain relations. During an infinitesimal increment of stress, changes of strain are assumed to be divisible into elastic and plastic parts. Thus

$$d\{\varepsilon\} = d\{\varepsilon\}_e + d\{\varepsilon\}_p. \tag{18.20}$$

The elastic strain increments are related to stress increments by a symmetric matrix of constants $[D]$ as usual. We can thus write Eq. (18.20) as

$$d\{\varepsilon\} = [D]^{-1} d\{\sigma\} + \frac{\partial F}{\partial \{\sigma\}} \lambda. \tag{18.21}$$

When plastic yield is occurring the stresses are on the yield surface given by Eq. (18.18). Differentiating this we can write therefore

$$\frac{\partial F}{\partial \sigma_1}\, d\sigma_1 + \frac{\partial F}{\partial \sigma_2}\, d\sigma_2 + \cdots + \frac{\partial F}{\partial \kappa}\, d\kappa = 0$$

or (18.22)

$$\left\{\frac{\partial F}{\partial \{\sigma\}}\right\}^{\mathrm{T}} d\{\sigma\} - A\lambda = 0$$

in which we make the substitution

$$A = -\frac{\partial F}{\partial \kappa}\, d\kappa \frac{1}{\lambda}. \tag{18.23}$$

Equations (18.21) and (18.22) can be written in a single symmetric matrix form as

$$
\left\{\begin{array}{c} d\varepsilon_1 \\ \\ d\varepsilon_2 \\ \vdots \\ 0 \end{array}\right\} =
\left[\begin{array}{ccc|c}
 & & & \dfrac{\partial F}{\partial \sigma_1} \\
 & [D]^{-1} & & \dfrac{\partial F}{\partial \sigma_2} \\
 & & & \vdots \\ \hline
\dfrac{\partial F}{\partial \sigma_1} & \dfrac{\partial F}{\partial \sigma_2} & \cdots & -A
\end{array}\right]
\left\{\begin{array}{c} d\sigma_1 \\ \\ d\sigma_2 \\ \vdots \\ \lambda \end{array}\right\}. \tag{18.24}
$$

The indeterminate constant λ can be eliminated (taking care not to multiply or divide by A which may be zero in general). This results in an explicit expansion which determines the *stress changes* in terms of imposed *strain changes* with

$$d\{\sigma\} = [D]_{ep}^{*}\, d\{\varepsilon\} \tag{18.25}$$

$$[D]_{ep}^{*} = [D] - [D]\left\{\frac{\partial F}{\partial \{\sigma\}}\right\}\left\{\frac{\partial F}{\partial \{\sigma\}}\right\}^{\mathrm{T}}[D]\left[A + \left\{\frac{\partial F}{\partial \{\sigma\}}\right\}^{\mathrm{T}}[D]\left\{\frac{\partial F}{\partial \{\sigma\}}\right\}\right]^{-1}. \tag{18.26}$$

The elasto-plastic matrix $[D]_{ep}^{*}$ takes the place of the elasticity matrix $[D]$ in incremental analysis. It is symmetric, and is valid whether or not 'A' takes on a zero value. Explicit formulation of plasticity in this form was first introduced by Yamada et al.[8] and Zienkiewicz et al.[9]

Significance of parameter 'A'. Clearly for ideal plasticity with no hardening 'A' is simply zero. If hardening is considered, attention must be given to the nature of the parameter (or parameters) κ on which the shifts of the yield surface depend.

With a 'work hardening' material κ is taken to be represented by the amount of plastic work done during plastic deformation. Thus

$$d\kappa = \sigma_1 \, d\varepsilon_1^p + \sigma_2 \, d\varepsilon_2^p + \cdots = \{\sigma\}^T \, d\{\varepsilon\}_p. \qquad (18.27)$$

Substituting the flow rule Eq. (18.19) we have simply

$$d\kappa = \lambda \{\sigma\}^T \frac{\partial F}{\partial \{\sigma\}}. \qquad (18.28)$$

By Eq. (18.23) we now see that λ disappears and we can write

$$A = -\frac{\partial F}{\partial \kappa} \{\sigma\}^T \frac{\partial F}{\partial \{\sigma\}} \qquad (18.29)$$

a strictly determinate form if explicit relationship between F and κ is known.

Prandtl-Reuss relations. To illustrate some of the concepts consider the particular case of the well-known von Mises yield surface. This is given by

$$F = [\tfrac{1}{2}(\sigma_1 - \sigma_2)^2 + \tfrac{1}{2}(\sigma_2 - \sigma_3)^2 + \tfrac{1}{2}(\sigma_3 - \sigma_1)^2 + 3\sigma_4^2$$
$$+ 3\sigma_5^2 + 3\sigma_6^2]^{1/2} - \bar{\sigma} \qquad (18.30)$$

in which suffixes 1, 2, 3 refer to the normal stress components and 4, 5, 6 to shear stress components in a general three-dimensional stress state.

On differentiation it will be found that

$$\frac{\partial F}{\partial \sigma_1} = \frac{3\sigma_1'}{2\bar{\sigma}}, \qquad \frac{\partial F}{\partial \sigma_2} = \frac{3\sigma_2'}{2\bar{\sigma}}, \qquad \frac{\partial F}{\partial \sigma_3} = \frac{3\sigma_3'}{2\bar{\sigma}}$$

$$\frac{\partial F}{\partial \sigma_4} = \frac{3\sigma_4}{\bar{\sigma}}, \qquad \frac{\partial F}{\partial \sigma_5} = \frac{3\sigma_5}{\bar{\sigma}}, \qquad \frac{\partial F}{\partial \sigma_6} = \frac{3\sigma_6}{\bar{\sigma}}$$

in which the dashes stand for so called deviatoric stresses, i.e.,

$$\sigma_1' = \sigma_1 - \frac{(\sigma_1 + \sigma_2 + \sigma_3)}{3} \text{ etc.}$$

The quantity $\bar{\sigma} = \bar{\sigma}(\kappa)$ is the uniaxial stress at yield. If a plot of the uniaxial test giving $\bar{\sigma}$ versus the *plastic* uniaxial strain ε_{up} is available then

$$d\kappa = \bar{\sigma} \, d\varepsilon_{up}$$

and

$$-\frac{\partial F}{\partial \kappa} = \frac{\partial \bar{\sigma}}{\partial \kappa} = \frac{\partial \bar{\sigma}}{\partial \varepsilon_{up}} \cdot \frac{1}{\bar{\sigma}} = \frac{H'}{\bar{\sigma}}$$

in which H' is the slope of the plot at the particular value of $\bar{\sigma}$.

On substituting into Eq. (18.29) we obtain after some transformation simply

$$A = H'. \tag{18.31}$$

This re-establishes the well-known Prandtl-Reuss stress-strain relations. For a generalization of the concepts to yield surface possessing 'corners' the reader is referred to the work of Koiter.[6]

18.4.2 *Historical notes*. It is evident from the theory outlined that as the plasticity relations are formulated incrementally by the laws stated in Eqs. (18.25) and (18.26), the iterative process must be *applied strictly to small load increments*. Within such increments, however, any of the three processes described in section 18.2 can be applied.

In the earliest applications of the finite element process to plasticity, *initial strain* processes were favoured. Here the work of Gallagher *et al.*[10] and Argyris[11] is significant. This process fails entirely, however, if ideal, non-strain-hardening plasticity is considered, as the strains cannot then be uniquely determined for prescribed stress levels. In subsequent work the variable stiffness approach appears to have been favoured for this reason.[12-16] A reasonable economy could still be achieved as an iterative process was used for solving the simultaneous equations involved and then the stiffness modification was incorporated into the general iteration.

The initial stress process first applied to plasticity by Zienkiewicz *et al.*[9] appears ideally suited here as any unloading automatically proceeds on the purely elastic basis—an additional and important feature if load cycling is involved. This process appears at the time of writing to be widely accepted.[17]

18.4.3 *Application of the 'initial stress' process to some plasticity problems*. Adaptation of the initial stress method in plasticity problems, though fairly straightforward, is complicated by two facts:

(*a*) The incremental, stress-strain relation, Eq. (18.25), is only valid from the instant when stresses reach the yield surface, $F(\sigma) = 0$. If $F(\sigma) < 0$ purely elastic behaviour continues.

(*b*) The incremental relation Eq. (18.25) is valid only for infinitesimal strain increases. For finite steps it is possible for stresses to depart somewhat from the yield surface. To guard against this stresses should *be reduced to the yield condition after each iteration*.

The process used with success, and on which the later examples are based, is of the following pattern.

(*a*) The load increment is applied and elastic stress and strain increments corresponding to this are calculated.

(*b*) Value of $F(\{\sigma\})$ is calculated for the total stress reached in (*a*). If $F < 0$ the process is elastic and no further iteration is needed.

If $F > 0$, the value of F at the start of the interval is computed and the proportion of the elastic stress and strain increment which has taken place in the range above the yield point is determined by interpolation.

For the above values of elastic stress the corresponding elasto-plastic strain increment is computed using the expression (18.25).† The stress at start of yield augmented by the above increment is compared with total stresses previously reached and the difference used as an initial (corrective) stress.

(c) Residual forces are now calculated and a new elastic solution obtained giving another value of total stress. If the residual forces are below a certain limit the process is stopped here. If not:

(d) Steps (b)–(c) are repeated, etc.

As is seen, at every stage the total stresses are brought down to the yield surface. The elasto-plastic matrix is either calculated from stress values at which $F = 0$ is reached or is varied as iteration proceeds.

In all the examples this straightforward iterative process without any acceleration was used, and rapid convergence achieved within 5–15 cycles. A slowness or lack of convergence is usually a symptom of collapse of the structure.

While the elasto-plastic matrix deduced previously is valid for a general three-dimensional continuum, in two-dimensional elasticity it has to be reduced to special forms. In *plane stress* for instance this reduction is obvious by a simple deletion of appropriate columns in Eq. (18.24) to which zero stress components are assigned; in a *plane strain* situation, all stresses exist but appropriate strain components have to be made zero. Appropriate elimination has now to be carried out and explicit expressions will be found in reference 9. It is of interest to note that in such cases the diagonal term corresponding to A is no longer zero even in the case of ideal plasticity.

Perforated plate with and without strain hardening. Figure 18.4 shows the configuration and the division into simple triangular elements. In this example plane stress conditions are assumed and solution is obtained for both ideal plasticity and strain hardening. The von Mises criterion is used and, in the case of strain hardening, a constant slope of the uniaxial hardening curve, H' (Eq. (18.31)) was taken. The spread of plastic zones at various load levels is shown in Fig. 18.4(b) and (c).

Although the plasticity relation is only incremental, if the loads are applied in a single large step the initial stress process will still yield an equilibrating solution and one which does not exceed the yield stresses.

---

† As the load increment is finite it is possible for the stresses calculated by 18.25 to exceed slightly the yield conditions. This is tested and if excess found stresses can be scaled down to remain on yield surface.

Such a single-step solution for a very large load increment is shown in Fig. 18.4(d). It is of interest to note that even now despite the violation of the incremental strain laws very similar results for plastic zones are achieved.

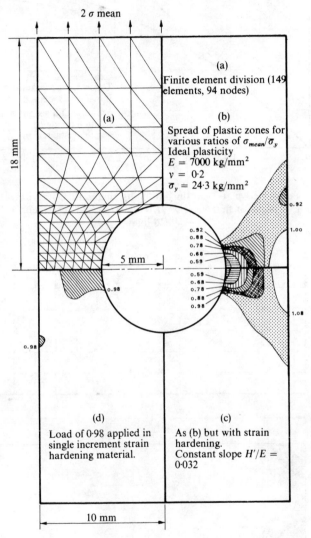

Fig. 18.4 Perforated tension strip (plane stress)

It is even more significant to note that the maximum strains reached at the point of first yield are almost identical with those achieved incrementally, Fig. 18.5.

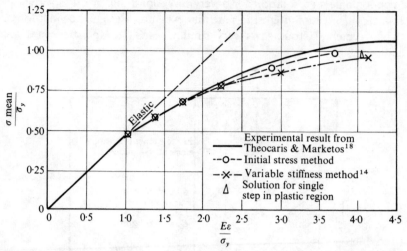

Fig. 18.5   Perforated plate—strain hardening material. Development of maximum strain at point of first yield $H'/E = 0.032$. Load increment $= 0.2 \times$ first yield load

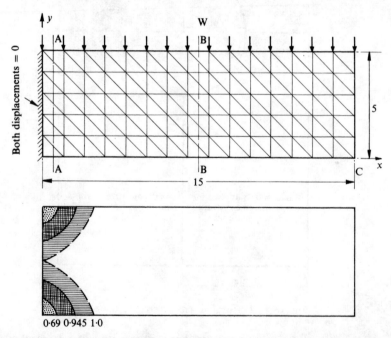

Fig. 18.6   Cantilever beam—plane stress, ideal plasticity. The spread of plastic zones for different ratios of w/w_c when w_c is calculated as from plastic beam theory (w_c = collapse load)

Indeed the same figure shows excellent comparison with experimental results[18] and those obtained using a variable stiffness process.[14]

A cantilever beam—load cycling. Figure 18.6 shows a simple, plane stress, cantilever beam for which an ideal plasticity behaviour of von Mises type is assumed. The loads are given in terms of the collapse load estimated on the basis of elementary plastic hinge theory. First a load cycle is given as shown in Fig. 18.7 to illustrate the ability of the method to

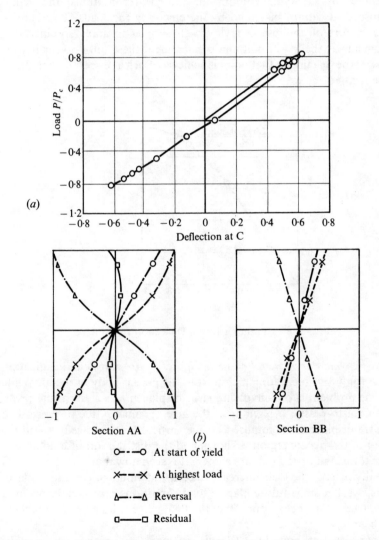

Fig. 18.7   Cantilever beam of Fig. 18.6: (*a*) deflections for load reversal; (*b*) σ_x/σ_y stress distribution at various stages of unloading

follow the elastic unloading behaviour. The 'hysteresis' of displacement shown in Fig. 18.7(*a*) and the residual stresses which exist after load removal as a result of plastic straining are worth noting.

Figure 18.8 shows the increase of displacements with load. As the collapse load is approached progressively larger numbers of iterations are required and indeed at $P/P_c = 1$ no convergence was achieved. Thus although the non-linear solution allows a *lower bound* in collapse load to be found (by satisfying equilibrium and yield conditions) the actual collapse load cannot be found by incrementing the loads. To obtain a better picture of collapse behaviour it is simpler to apply specified displacements at the load point and to increment these until no further increase of the reaction at that point is achieved. Such a process is considered in the next example.

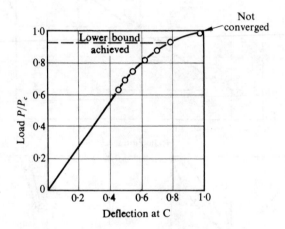

Fig. 18.8   Cantilever beam. Deflection versus w/w_c

Plastic yield during metal cutting. Figure 18.9(*a*) shows an idealization of a cutting tool separating a chip from the parent body of metal. While the true problem is one involving large displacements a substitute problem of elasto-plastic behaviour of the given geometry due to prescribed uniform displacements imposed on the vertical face is solved. Again the spread of the plastic region is shown and the distribution of load as well as the total load on the tool are shown. It is seen now that, as this material is ideally plastic, the loads increase to constant values at certain displacements. At that stage full 'collapse' load conditions exist and correspond to the true 'chip' behaviour. Only the final stage is here of any practical significance.

Mohr-Coulomb material—Tunnels. In many materials such as soils, rocks, ceramics, and concrete, phenomena similar to those of plasticity occur. Here again, irreversible deformation may proceed at almost constant stress levels. However, the 'yield surface' in such conditions depends now not only on the deviatoric (shear) stresses as in the von Mises law but also on the magnitude of the average compressive stress.

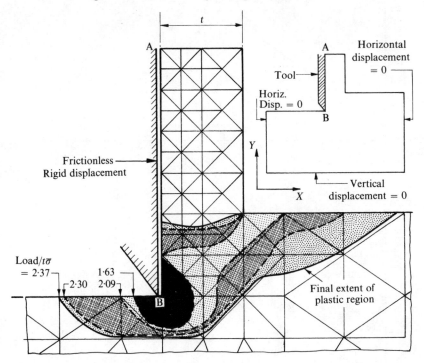

Fig. 18.9(a) An approximation to machining process by imposing equivalent displacements at cutting edge, $\bar{\sigma}$ = uniaxial yield stress. Geometry and spread of plastic zones. Ideal plasticity and plane strain assumed. $v = 0$

The well-known Mohr-Coulomb criterion specifying maximum shear stress on any plane as

$$\tau = C + \sigma_n \tan \phi \qquad (18.32)$$

in which C is the cohesion, σ_n the normal stress on the plane, and ϕ angle of internal friction, can be approximated to by a more manageable form suggested by Drucker.[19]

$$F = \alpha J_1 + \sqrt{J_2} - K = 0 \qquad (18.33)$$

where J_1 is the first invariant

$$J_1 = \sigma_x + \sigma_y + \sigma_z$$

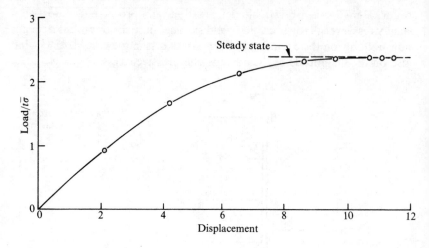

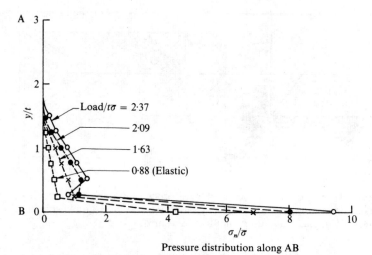

Pressure distribution along AB

Fig. 18.9(*b*)   Approximation to machining processes. Total load versus displacement and distribution of pressure in the cutting tool

and J_2 is the second invariant given as

$$J_2 = \tfrac{1}{6}[(\sigma_x - \sigma_y)^2 - (\sigma_y - \sigma_z)^2 + (\sigma_z - \sigma_x)^2] + \tau_{xy}^2 + \tau_{yz}^2 + \tau_{zx}^2$$

α and K are constants depending on cohesion and friction of the material. The constants of Eq. (18.33) are related to the standard ones of Eq. (18.32) as

$$\alpha = \frac{2 \sin \phi}{\sqrt{3}(3 - \sin \phi)}, \qquad K = \frac{6C \cos \phi}{\sqrt{3}(3 - \sin \phi)}.$$

Other possible forms are discussed in some detail by Bishop[20] but for the present purposes the formulation given by Drucker will suffice.

If in addition to this yield surface we assume the validity of the *normality principle*, the problems in which such materials are involved can be dealt with by the principles already described. Figure 18.10 shows such a solution for development of plastic zones around a lined tunnel on removal of the stresses resulting from the excavation. Other similar solutions are given in references 9, 15, 21, and 22.

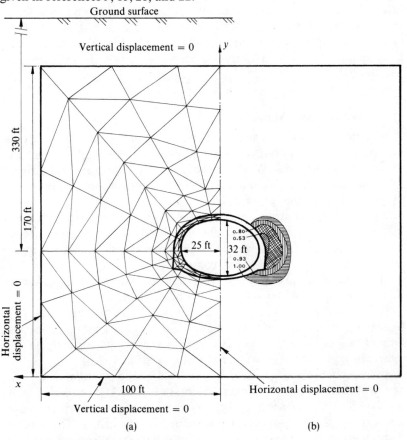

Fig. 18.10   A lined tunnel
(*a*) Mesh 153 elements 94 nodes
Lining $E = 3 \times 10^6$ lb/in^2
$v = 0.15$

Rock $Ec = 5 \times 10^5$ lb/in^2
$v = 0.20$
$c = 140$ lb/in^2
$\phi = 30°$

Initial stress $\sigma_{y0} = \gamma h$ with origin of h at 400 ft
$\sigma_{x0} = 0.2\, \gamma h$, $\gamma = 150$ lb/ft^3
(*b*) Spread of plastic zones

The main difficulty in the solution of such problems appears to be not the computation, but in the establishment of appropriate constitutive relations. In particular it appears that the normality principle is not valid generally in Mohr-Coulomb materials and that so called 'non-associated' laws of plasticity operate.[23] A simple suggestion made by Davis[24] makes the plastic strains obey

$$d\{\varepsilon\}_p = \lambda[D_0(\{\sigma\})]^{-1} \qquad (18.34)$$

in which $[D_0]$ is a matrix dependent on stress level but similar in structure to the elasticity matrix. Repeating now the steps of Eqs. (18.20) to (18.26) a new elasto-plastic matrix will be obtained which now no longer is symmetric.[25] The initial stress process can deal with this, however, without difficulty.

18.5 The No-tension Material

A hypothetical material capable of sustaining only compressive stresses and straining without resistance in tension is in many respects similar to an ideal plastic material. While in practice probably such an ideal material does not exist, it gives a close approximation to the behaviour of randomly jointed rock and other granular materials.

While an explicit stress-strain relation cannot be generally written it suffices to carry out the analysis elastically and wherever tensile stresses develop to reduce these to zero. The initial stress process is here natural and indeed was developed in this context.[1]

The steps of calculation are obvious but it is important to remember that the *principal tensile stresses* have to be eliminated.

The 'constitutive law' as stated above can at best approximate to the true situation, no account being taken of closing of fissures on re-application of compressive stresses. However, these results certainly give a clearer insight into the behaviour of real rock structures.

An underground power station. Figure 18.11(a) and (b) show an application of this model to a practical problem. In Fig. 18.11(a) an elastic solution is shown for stresses in the vicinity of an underground power station with cable prestressing applied in the vicinity of the opening. The zones in which tension exists are indicated. In Fig. 18.11(b) a *no tension* solution is given for the same problem indicating the rather small general stress redistribution and the zones where 'cracking' has occurred.

A variant on this type of material may be one in which a finite tensile strength exists but when this is once exceeded the strength drops to zero (on fissuring). Such an analysis was used by Valliappan and Nath[26] in the study of the behaviour of reinforced concrete beams. Very good correlation with experimental results for over-reinforced beams (in which

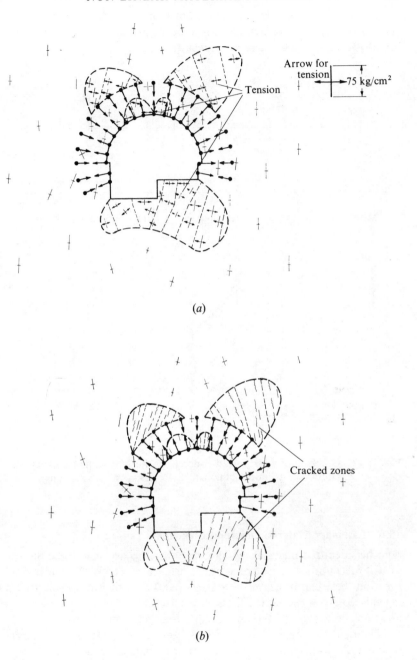

(a)

(b)

Fig. 18.11 Underground power station gravity and prestressing (a) elastic
stresses, (b) 'no-tension' stresses

development of compressive yield is not important) have been obtained. The beam is one for which tests have been carried out by Krahl *et al.*[27] Figure 18.12 shows some relevant results.

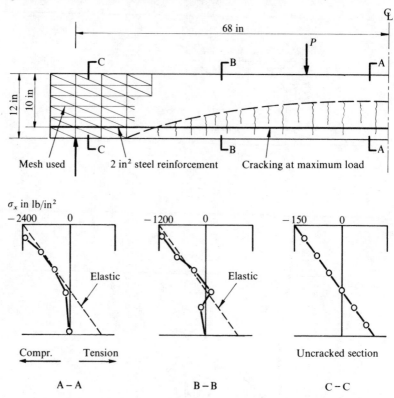

Fig. 18.12   Cracking of a reinforced concrete beam. Maximum tensile strength 200 lb/in². Distribution of concrete stresses at various sections

18.6 'Laminar' Material and Joint Elements

Another idealized material model is one which is assumed to be built up of a large number of isotropic and elastic laminae. When under compression these can transmit shear stress parallel to their direction providing this does not exceed the frictional resistance. No tensile stresses can, however, be transmitted in the normal direction to the laminae.

This idealized material has obvious uses in the study of rock masses with parallel joints but as will be seen later has a much wider applicability.

Figure 18.13 shows a two-dimensional situation involving such a material. With a local co-ordinate axis x' oriented in the direction of the laminae we can write

$$|\tau_{x'y'}| \leqslant \mu\sigma_y \qquad (18.35a)$$

and

$$\sigma_{y'} \leqslant 0 \qquad (18.35b)$$

for stresses at which purely elastic behaviour occurs. In the above, μ is the friction coefficient applicable between the laminae.

If elastic stresses exceed the limits imposed the stresses have to be reduced to the limiting values given by Eqs. (18.35).

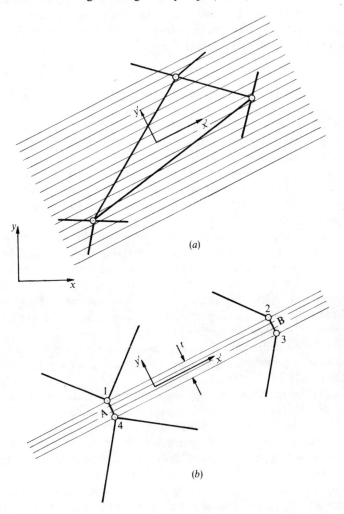

Fig. 18.13 'Laminar' material (*a*) general (*b*) in a narrow joint

The application of the initial stress process in this context is again self evident, and the problem is very similar to that implied in the *no tension* material of previous section. At each step of elastic calculation first the existence of tensile stresses $\sigma_{y'}$ is checked and if these develop, a corrective initial stress reducing these and the shearing stresses to zero is applicable. If $\sigma_{y'}$ = stresses are compressive, the absolute magnitude of the shearing stresses $\tau_{x'y'}$ are checked and again, if these exceed the value given by Eq. (18.35b) they are reduced to their proper limit.

Again, as specified above the mathematical model will not necessarily reflect the true behaviour on load reversal as the interlaminar gaps have to close before compressive stresses can be resumed. A simple way out of this difficulty is (for the case of zero Poissons ratio) to control tensile strains and write in place of Eq. (18.35a); if

$$\varepsilon_{y'} \geqslant 0, \qquad \sigma_{y'} = 0 \tag{18.36}$$

otherwise the behaviour is elastic. This in fact gives the law in the form of correct strain dependence.

Needless to say, the directions of laminae may vary element to element and it is possible to analyse with such methods very complex behaviour of rock masses with random joints.

Introduction of a cohesive strength and of a coefficient of friction which varies with the amount of shear strain (generally decreasing with it) is only a matter of some elaboration of programing. Work 'softening' situations can then be dealt with.[25]

In some instances the laminar behaviour is confined to a narrow joint between relatively homogeneous elastic masses. This may well be of a nature of a geological fault or a major crushed rock zone. In such cases it is convenient to use narrow, generally rectangular, elements whose geometry may be specified by mean co-ordinates of two ends A and B (Fig. 18.13b) and the thickness. The element still has, however, separate points of continuity (1–4) with the adjacent masses.

Such joint elements can be simple rectangles as shown here, but equally well can take up more complex shapes if isoparametrically specified (see Chapter 8).

Goodman et al.[28] describe somewhat similar joint elements used in the context of stability of joint rock masses. However, non-linear behaviour of the joint elements here described has a wider field of application. Problems of *interference fit* or *clearance* between machine parts may, for instance be investigated by use of thin joint elements. If a very narrow joint element is assumed to exist between two parts of the structure or machine, the effect of a clearance is to introduce an initial tensile strain $\varepsilon_{y'0}$ such that $t\varepsilon_{y'0}$ is equal to the clearance. As the laminar joint element cannot transmit tension, a rapid indication of whether or not clearances have closed will be obtained. Conversely an 'interference fit' is equivalent to a negative initial strain in the direction normal to the joint element.

One drawback in this approximation is that the thickness of a joint element must be made finite to avoid very large stiffness coefficients in the normal direction and hence numerical ill-conditioning of equations. Alternative procedures of a more special kind can be derived to avoid the difficulties mentioned.[29]

18.7 Creep: Time-dependent Strain

18.7.1 *General.* Creep phenomena are those in which strain depends not only on the stress level but also on time. Most generally some law is implied from which strains at a given time can be deduced from the full knowledge of the previous stressing history. Any process of computation must thus proceed in an *incremental manner* considering suitable small time intervals. In every such time interval, from the knowledge of the specified creep law, the average stress levels in that interval, and if necessary of the previous history, the *increments* of *strain* can be found. Thus the initial strain process described in section 18.2.4 is a natural one to use here.

It is, however, sometimes possible to reverse the creep law into one defining the *stresses* of any time in terms of the *strain history*. If such law can be conveniently defined in terms of suitable *relaxation* function, then the initial stress process of section 18.2.3 can be applied as an alternative.

As creep behaviour is more conveniently measured the initial strain approach is generally advocated and will be used here.

The 'initial strain' process applied to creep takes usually the following steps in detail.[30-34]

(a) Consider all load (temperature, etc.) changes to occur at the start of the interval, t, and by solving the elastic problem determine the state of stress and deformation.

(b) Determine the 'creep' change of strain which occurs during the interval, $\{\Delta\varepsilon_c\}_t$, assuming that the stress state during the interval remains constant at values found in step (a).

(c) Treating $\{\Delta\varepsilon_c\}_t$ as an *initial strain* determine, by resolving the elastic problem, the new state of stress and deformation at the end of the time interval.

If time interval Δt is relatively small this process is generally adequate and the next step can now be dealt with in a similar manner. If relatively large strain changes occur, it is clearly possible to repeat steps (b) and (c) using improved, average, stress values to estimate $\{\Delta\varepsilon_c\}_t$. Such iteration is sometimes desirable but seldom more than two cycles are necessary.

Stability of the above-described process will clearly depend on the magnitude of the time intervals chosen and in new applications it is essential to test this numerically.

At this stage a word on computational efficiency is perhaps in order. If the elastic, instantaneous, properties of the material remain unchanged with time (or temperature changes which may occur with time) it is apparent that an identical process of elastic solution will be repeated many times. In such instances, it is convenient to invert at least partially the solution matrices rather than to resort to numerical iteration solutions. Conversely, if a change of elastic properties occurs with time and essentially different elastic problems arise at each time step, iterative solution may be preferable making use of previously obtained displacement values as a starting point.

The main problem in the process described centres around the basic definition of the algorithm by which the creep increment $\{\Delta\varepsilon_c\}$ is to be evaluated and the following subsections will deal with this problem.

18.7.2 *History dependence of creep (visco-elasticity).* Visco-elastic phenomena are characterized by the fact that the rate at which creep strains develop depends not only on the current state of stress and strain but, in general, on the *full history* of their development. Thus to determine the increment of strain $\{\Delta\varepsilon_c\}_t$ at a particular time interval it is necessary to know the state of stress and strains at all *preceding time intervals*. While in the computation process these have in fact been obtained, *in principle* the problem presents little difficulty. Practical limitations, however, appear immediately. Even with the largest computers available it is not practicable to store the full history on core and the repeated use of backing storage is too slow and therefore too costly to be contemplated.

A method of overcoming this difficulty was described by Zienkiewicz et al.[31] in the context of *linear visco-elastic* analysis and presents possibilities for suitably formulated *non-linear* visco-elastic materials.

In linear visco-elasticity it is always possible to write the stress-strain relationship in a form similar to that of elasticity, as in Eq. (18.2) for example, with the terms of the $[D]$ matrix representing now in place of elastic constants, suitable differential or integral operators.[35] Thus in an isotropic continuum a pair of operators corresponding to an appropriate pair of elastic constants will appear—while for anisotropic materials up to 21 separate operators may be necessary.

Typically the creep part of the strain may thus be described by

$$\{\varepsilon_c\} = [\bar{D}]^{-1}\{\sigma\}$$

where each term of the 'visco-elastic matrix', $[\bar{D}]^{-1}$, may take up a form

$$\bar{d}_{rs} = \frac{a_0 + a_1(\mathrm{d}/\mathrm{d}t) + a_2(\mathrm{d}^2/\mathrm{d}t^2) + \cdots}{b_0 + b_1(\mathrm{d}/\mathrm{d}t) + b_2(\mathrm{d}^2/\mathrm{d}t^2) + \cdots} \tag{18.37}$$

if the operators are written in a differential form. If this expansion is finite, then separating any instantaneous elastic effects one can usually rewrite Eq. (18.37) in terms of partial fractions as

$$\bar{d}_{rs} = \frac{A_1}{d/dt + B_1} + \frac{A_2}{d/dt + B_2} + \cdots \tag{18.38}$$

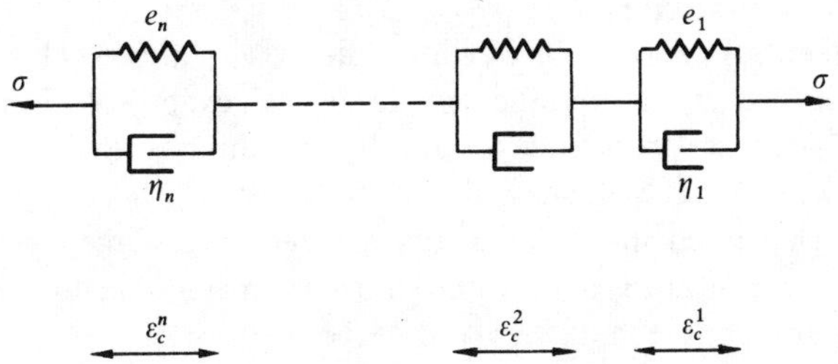

Fig. 18.14   A series of Kelvin elements

This, as is well known, can be interpreted as a response of a series of Kelvin elements illustrated in Fig. 18.14 (even though physically no significance need be attached to such models) with each term representing one Kelvin unit. A typical contribution to a strain component is thus an addition of terms of the form

$$e_n = \frac{A_n}{d/dt + B_n}\, \sigma_s \tag{18.39}$$

or

$$\frac{d}{dt}(e_n) = A_n\sigma_s - B_n e_n. \tag{18.40}$$

The increment of each such term in a time interval may now be found from the above expression from the knowledge of the *current value* of appropriate stress component σ_s and the *current value* of e_n. Thus it becomes necessary to store only a finite number of such terms as e_n at their current value to represent the full history effect.†

In practice only a limited number of Kelvin elements are needed to represent the material behaviour and, additionally, only a few 'visco-elastic' operators exist. For instance, in an isotropic incompressible material only one operator serves to define the $[\bar{D}]^{-1}$ matrix. With two elements of expansion, Eq. (18.38), defining this operator only two quantities will have to be stored during the computation process.[31]

The values of A_n and B_n for each Kelvin model can be age and temperature dependent without introduction of any complexity of calculation—thus dealing with problems of thermo-visco-elasticity, such as occur in the creep of concrete or plastics.

† In subsequent literature on the subject, such terms have been given the name of 'state variables'.

Indeed it appears possible to extend the process to non-linear visco-elastic phenomena by specifying a dependence of the 'spring and dash-pot' constants A and B as the current stress level. Much work yet remains to be done to formulate such laws in a consistent manner with suitable experimental evidence.

To illustrate the applicability of the above process an example from reference 31 will be cited.

This presents a problem of a cylinder filled with a visco-elastic material and surrounded by a metallic envelope. An exact solution of this is available[36]—as the problem is essentially one-dimensional. In the present context it was solved by a general two-dimensional analysis program and the results presented show the accuracy attainable. Time intervals of 0·1 were used necessitating a hundred steps to reach the final solution at time 10, as shown in Figs. 18.15 and 18.16.

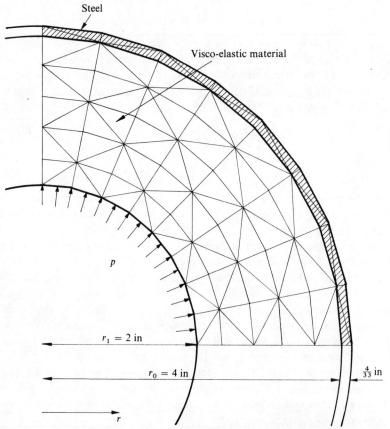

Fig. 18.15   A reinforced visco-elastic cylinder under internal pressure solved as a general two-dimensional problem

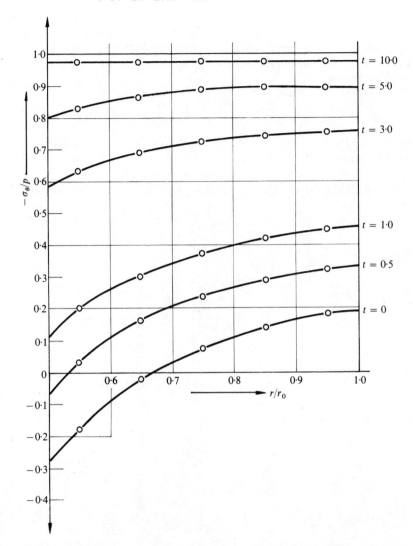

Fig. 18.16   Variation of tangential stress in example of Fig. 18.15 with time. External material is elastic while the interior is visco-elastic in shear but elastic in hydrostatic compression (refs. 31 and 36). Exact results of ref. 36 coincide

Various other more complex examples can be found in reference 31.

18.7.3 *State dependent creep laws.* While undoubtedly the full history of stress and strain development plays some part in the creep laws governing most materials, the high degree of non-linearity with respect to stress evident in most metals has led to simplified descriptive laws from which the *strain rate* can be evaluated from the knowledge of current state variables only (in particular stress, strain, time, and temperature).

A survey of such laws is given by Leckie and Martin.[37] Typically, with isotropy and incompressibility assumed these give the creep strains in the following form

$$\frac{d}{dt}\{\varepsilon\}_c = F_1(t)F_2(\bar{\varepsilon}_c)F_3(\bar{\sigma})F_4(\theta)[D_0]^{-1}\{\sigma\}/E \qquad (18.41)$$

in which $[D_0]^{-1}$ is equivalent to an appropriate elasticity matrix with Poisson's ratio equal to 0·5, $\bar{\varepsilon}_c$, $\bar{\sigma}$ denote the second invariants of creep strain and stress respectively, and θ the temperature.

For secondary creep the dependence on time and accumulated strain

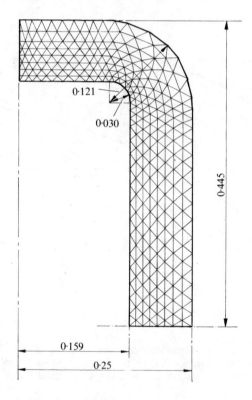

Internal pressure — 445 lb/in²
Youngs modulus — 20 × 10⁶ lb/in²
Poisson's ratio — 0·3
$\varepsilon^c = 19\cdot8 \times 10^{-16} \sigma^{3\cdot61} t^{1\cdot06}$

Fig. 18.17   Idealization of the pressure vessel with a flat end closure[33]

is small and often an exponential law given below is used[38,39]

$$\frac{d}{dt}\{\varepsilon\}_c = K\bar{\sigma}^n[D_0]^{-1}\{\sigma\}/E. \tag{18.42}$$

While the physical logic of such laws is arguable, particularly so with respect to the time function which represents the so called 'time hardening law', their practical application in numerical solution is simple. The creep strain rate

$$\frac{d}{dt}\{\varepsilon\}_c$$

is easily determined at any instant and thus the increment of creep strain can be found simply as

$$\Delta\{\varepsilon\}_c = \frac{d}{dt}\{\varepsilon\}_c \cdot \Delta t \tag{18.43}$$

and fed directly into the general process.

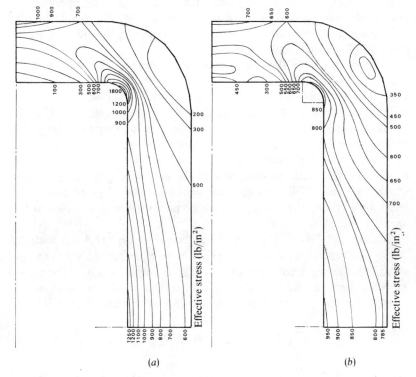

(a)   (b)

Fig. 18.18   Variation of effective (octahedral) stress with time after internal[33] pressure applied (a) $t = 0$, (b) $t = 3\cdot0$ hr.

Applications of the process can be found in references 33, 34, and 40. Figures 18.17 and 18.18 show some examples of the process.[33]

With such and indeed other creep problems it is important to achieve the best compromise between economy and stability of solution. Thus the time intervals should normally be adjusted as the computation proceeds. These can get progressively longer if, as often is the case, the stress distribution tends to settle down to steady-state values. A suitable criterion for such an adjustment may be the requirement that stress changes in an interval should not exceed a specified percentage.[34]

18.7 Special Approximations for Creep Solutions

Quite frequently generalizations and approximations are possible which permit adequately accurate solutions incorporating creep effects to be achieved without the labour and cost largely involved in the step-by-step treatment.

Linear visco-elasticity. In the case of a homogeneous structure with linear isotropic visco-elasticity and constant Poisson ratio operator, the Alfrey-McHenry analogies allow single-step elastic solutions to be used to obtain stresses and displacements at a given time by the use of *equivalent loads, displacements,* and *temperatures.*[41]

Some extensions of these analogies have been proposed by Hilton.[42]

Further, when creep deformation is of the type tending to a constant value at infinite time it is possible to determine the final stress distribution even in cases where the above analogies are not applicable. Thus for instance where the visco-elastic properties are temperature dependent and the structure is subject to a system of loads and temperatures which remain constant with time, long term 'equivalent elastic constants' can be found and the problem solved as a single, non-homogeneous elastic one of a linear kind.[43] Effect of such variations of 'elastic' properties on distribution of thermal stresses in a reactor pressure vessel is shown in Fig. 18.19.

'Steady state' creep. If creep, characterized by Eq. (18.42) is such that the total creep strains are so large that by comparison with it the elastic strains can be neglected, then a considerable simplification can be arrived at. Now the total strain rate and creep strain rate are the same and the constitutive law governing the problem can be written completely as

$$\frac{\mathrm{d}}{\mathrm{d}t}\{\varepsilon\} = \frac{\mathrm{d}}{\mathrm{d}t}\{\varepsilon\}_c = F(\bar{\sigma})[D_0]^{-1}\{\sigma\}/E \qquad (18.44)$$

for an isotropic and incompressible material.

If the displacement-strain (or compatibility) relations of the analysis are

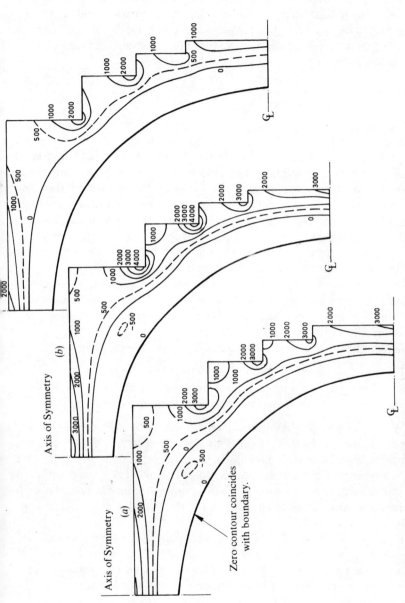

Fig. 18.19 Distribution of thermal stresses in a pressure vessel as influenced by variation of elastic modulus. Major principal stress contours. Thermal expansion coefficient $= 5 \times 10^{-6}/^{\circ}C$

    (a) Constant average value of $E = 2 \cdot 58 \times 10^{6}$ lb/in^2
    (b) Initial stress—E variable
    (c) Long term stress including creep effect—E variable

differentiated with respect to time, then it is clear that the problem becomes identical with one of non-linear elasticity, with strain and displacement rates replacing the usual strains and displacements. Solution in these terms is time independent and thus can be carried out non-incrementally by one of the general processes described before. A constant state of stress is reached in such a structure but strains increase proportionally with time.

18.8 Concluding Remarks

In the preceding sections the general processes of dealing with complex, non-linear constitutive relations have been examined and some particular applications were discussed. Clearly, the subject is so large and of so great a practical importance that presentation in a single chapter is impracticable. For different materials different forms of constitutive relations can be proposed and experimentally verified. *Once such constitutive relations are available the standard processes of this chapter can be adapted;* indeed it is now possible to build standard computing systems applicable to a wide variety of material properties in which new specifications of behaviour are simply inserted as an appropriate 'black box'.

Thus the treatment of such phenomena as *visco-plasticity* in which the plastic deformations are themselves time dependent, or the treatment of various soil or rock mechanics relations as soon as these are adequately described by experiment, can be envisaged.[44]

What must be once more re-stated is that in non-linear problems

(a) non-uniqueness of solution may arise
(b) convergence can never be, *a priori*, guaranteed
(c) cost of solution is invariably greater than in linear solutions.

While physical insight is necessary in the first two, much further work is needed to reduce the cost. In the examples shown so far only the simplest elements have been used. Obviously the same procedures are applicable with any form of element shape functions. Recent work shows that, even in two-dimensional situations, use of complex (numerically integrated) elements such as were discussed in Chapters 7 and 8 may lead to considerable economy.[45]

Figure 18.20 shows detail comparison of plastic zones in a case analysed by constant stress and isoparametric element. The smooth spread of plastic zones (identified by Gauss points) in the latter case leads to a very considerable improvement in convergence rates and accuracy.

One last point is that the processes described may also be used conveniently for solving *linear problems* formulated originally in terms of another set of *linear constants*. This does not appear on the face of it attractive until (for instance) we consider the case of elastic solutions for Poissons ratio of one-half. It was already noted that for such cases the $[D]$ matrix becomes indeterminate and special formulations are necessary (e.g. Chapter 4, section 4.5).

It is possible, however, to formulate the problem elastically in terms of an acceptable Poissons ratio and adjust the strains in the 'initial strain' method until incompressibility is achieved.[34, 46]

OTHER NON-LINEAR PROBLEMS

18.9 Non-linear quasi-harmonic field problems

Non-linearity arises in a wide variety of field problems of the type discussed in Chapter 15. For instance in a situation governed by the differential equation (*vide* Eq. (15.1)):

$$\frac{\partial}{\partial x}\left(k\frac{\partial\phi}{\partial x}\right)+\frac{\partial}{\partial y}\left(k\frac{\partial\phi}{\partial y}\right)+\frac{\partial}{\partial z}\left(k\frac{\partial\phi}{\partial z}\right)+Q = 0 \qquad (18.45)$$

the 'conductivity coefficient', k, may be dependent on ϕ or its gradients. Two typical physical situations may be given here to illustrate the problems. In the first, connected with seepage flow, velocity may not obey the laminar, (Darcy) condition which implies velocity given by

$$v_x = k\frac{\partial\phi}{\partial x}, \text{etc.} \qquad (18.46)$$

but, by becoming turbulent, requires some form of a law in which the head loss (grad ϕ) depends on a higher power of velocity. Such laws have been for instance derived by Forschheimer[47] and others[48] and can still be expressed in the form of Eq. (18.46) but with[49-51]

$$k = k(\bar{v}),$$
$$\bar{v} = \sqrt{v_x^2+v_y^2+v_z^2}.$$

A second similar situation arises in magnetostatic problems. Here, ϕ being the magnetic potential and k the inverse of magnetic permeability, it is found that the latter depends in a strong way on the gradients of the magnetic field.[52]

The situation is thus almost identical in the two problems.

While in this context the terminology of 'variable elasticity' and 'initial stress and strain' is obviously not applicable, essentially similar iterations can be adapted (*vide* section 18.3). The discretized equations still become, as shown in Chapter 15 (Eq. (15.14)) of a similar form to those of elastic problems

$$\{\psi\} = [H]\{\phi\}+\{F\} = 0. \qquad (18.47)$$

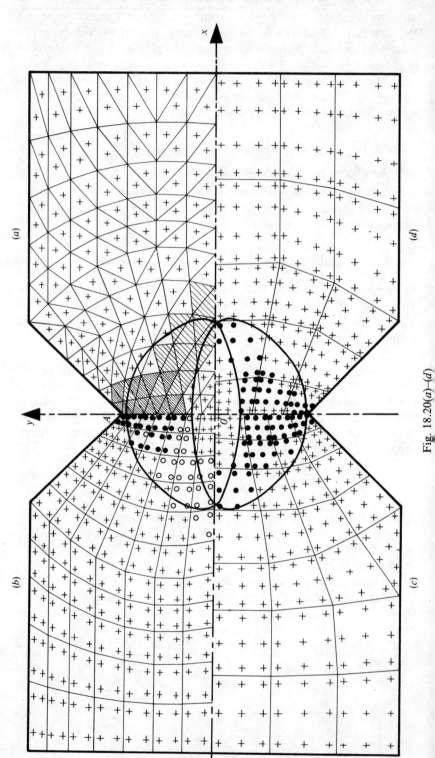

Fig. 18.20(a)–(d)

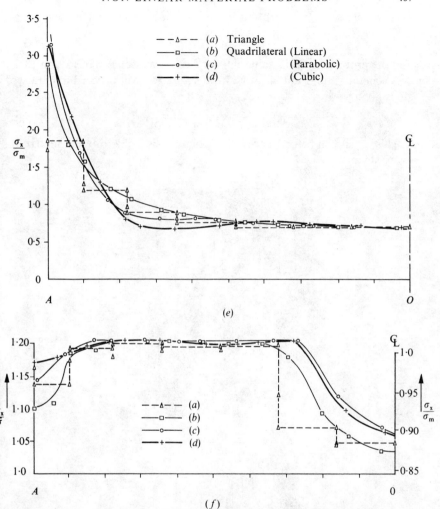

Fig. 18.20   An assessment of the performance of various elements in elasto-
plastic solution of a notched, plane stress, specimen
Spread of plastic zone
(a) Triangular element $\sigma_m/\bar{\sigma} = 1\cdot186$ and $1\cdot226$
(b) Linear quadrilateral $= 1\cdot186$ and $1\cdot226$
(c) Quadratic quadrilateral $= 1\cdot186$
(d) Cubic quadrilateral $= 1\cdot186$
      (σ_m = mean stress at notch, $\bar{\sigma}$ = uniaxial yield stress—ideal plasticity)
Distribution of stresses in notch section
(e) Elastic
(f) Elasto plastic for $\sigma_m/\bar{\sigma} = 1\cdot186$
Number of degrees of freedom approximately equal of 172–178 in all the four
solutions

As k enters the 'prescription' for calculating $[H]$ we have now

$$[H] = [H(\{\phi\})]$$

and the problem is of the same category as those discussed in section 18.3.

A scheme similar to that of Newton's iteration will proceed in iterative steps giving

$$\Delta\{\phi\}_{n+1} = -[H_n]^{-1}\{\psi(\{\phi_n\})\}. \qquad (18.48)$$

This, as shown before, necessitates an inversion of a different matrix at every stage.

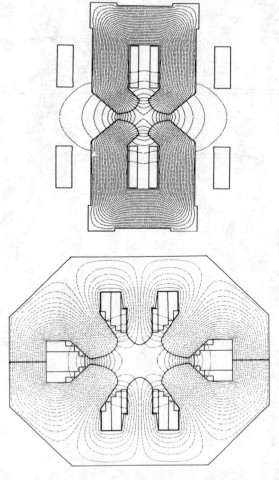

Fig. 18.21   Magnetic field in a six pole magnet with non-linearity due to saturation[52]

Alternatively a 'constant slope' process can be used with

$$\Delta\{\phi\}_{n+1} = -[H_0]^{-1}\{\psi(\{\phi\}_n)\} \qquad (18.49)$$

where $[H_0]$ is the matrix derived at using the first step coefficients.
Again various accelerators[2] can be used to speed the solution.
The analogy to constant and variable stiffness processes discussed in the context of elasticity is obvious.

Relatively few such applications have as yet been made to particular problems using the finite element process. Volker[49] solve the non-laminar flow problem through porous media using the first (variable $[H]$) process with success obtained in a few iteration cycles. Winslow[52] again uses a similar process to solve various magnetostatic situations. Figure 18.21 shows some rather spectacular field distributions in a non-linear material obtained by him.†

18.10 Some Other Possible Extensions

Clearly other direct uses of the non-linear solution described in the previous section are possible. An obvious one for instance is the heat conduction problem where at higher temperatures conductivities show a pronounced temperature dependence.

However, even wider possibilities in other properly formulated physical problems are obvious. One of these is for instance the problem of laminar flow of non-Newtonian fluids. Here the essential formulation is identical to that of viscous laminar flow described in section 15.6 of Chapter 15 but the viscosity is now highly dependent on the velocity gradients.

Such and other applications are left to the ingenuity of the reader.

† In both references an iterative solution of equations was adapted thus making the choice of method obvious.

References

1. O. C. ZIENKIEWICZ, S. VALLIAPPAN, and I. P. KING, 'Stress analysis of rock as a "no-tension" material', *Geotechnique*, **18**, 56–66, 1968.
2a. B. M. IRONS and R. C. TUCK, 'A version of the Aitken accelerator for computer iteration', *Int. J. Num. Meth. Eng.*, **1**, 275–8, 1969.
2b. O. C. ZIENKIEWICZ and B. M. IRONS, 'Matrix iteration and acceleration processes in finite element problems of structural mechanics', Chapter 9 of *Numerical Methods for non-linear algebraic equations*, ed. P. Rabinowitz, Gordon and Breach, 1970.
3. J. T. ODEN, 'Numerical formulation of non linear elasticity problems', *Proc. Am. Soc. Civ. Eng.*, **93**, ST3, 235–55, 1967.
4. R. VON MISES, 'Mechanik der plastischen Formänderung der Kristallen' *Z. angew. Math. Mech.* **8**, 161–85, 1928.
5. D. C. DRUCKER, 'A more fundamental approach to plastic stress-strain solutions', *Proc. 1st U.S. natn. Cong. appl. Mech.*, 487–91, 1951.

6. W. T. Koiter, 'Stress-strain relations, uniqueness and variational theorems for elastic plastic materials with a singular yield surface', *Q. appl. Math.*, **11**, 350–4, 1953.

7. W. Johnson and P. W. Mellor, *Plasticity for Mechanical Engineers*, Van Nostrand, Princeton, 1962.

8. Y. Yamada, N. Yoshimura, and T. Sakurai, 'Plastic Stress-Strain Matrix and its Application for the Solution of Elastic-Plastic Problems by the Finite Element Method', *Int. J. Mech. Sci.*, **10**, 343–54, 1968.

9. O. C. Zienkiewicz, S. Valliappan, and I. P. King, 'Elasto-plastic solutions of engineering problems. Initial-stress, finite element approach', *Int. J. Num. Meth. in Eng.*, **1**, 75–100, 1969.

10. R. H. Gallagher, J. Padlog, and P. P. Bijlaard, 'Stress analysis of heated complex shapes', *J. Am. Rocket Soc.*, **32**, 700–7, 1962.

11. J. H. Argyris, 'Elasto-plastic matrix displacement analysis of three-dimensional continua', *J. Roy. Aero. Soc.*, **69**, 633–5, 1965.

12. G. G. Pope, *A discrete element method for analysis of plane elasto-plastic strain problems*, R.A.E. Farnborough, T.R. 65028, 1965.

13a. J. L. Swedlow, M. L. Williams, and W. M. Yang, 'Elasto-plastic stresses in cracked plates', *Calcit*, Report SM, 65–19, California Institute of Technology, 1965.

13b. J. L. Swedlow, 'Elastic plastic cracked plates in plane strain', *Int. J. Fracture Mech.*, **5**, 33–44, 1969.

14. P. V. Marcal and I. P. King, 'Elastic-plastic analysis of two dimensional stress systems by the finite element method', *Int. J. mech. Sci.*, **9**, 143–55, 1967.

15. S. F. Reyes and D. U. Deere, 'Elasto-plastic analysis of underground openings by the finite element method', *Proc. 1st Int. Congr. Rock Mechanics*, **11**, 477–86, Lisbon, 1966.

16. E. P. Popov, M. Khojasteh-Bakht, and S. Yaghmai, 'Bending of circular plates of hardening material', *Intern. J. Sol. Struct.*, **3**, 975–88, 1967.

17. J. H. Argyris and D. W. Scharpf, 'Methods of elasto-plastic analysis', *Symp. on Finite Element techniques*, Stuttgart, June 1969.

18. P. S. Theokaris and E. Marketos, 'Elastic-plastic analysis of perforated thin strips of strain-hardening material', *J. Mech. Phys. Sol.*, **12**, 377–90, 1964.

19. D. C. Drucker and W. Prager, 'Soil mechanics and plastic analysis or limit design', *Q. appl. Math.*, **10**, 157–65, 1952.

20. A. W. Bishop, 'The strength of soils as engineering materials', *Geotechnique*, **16**, 91–128, 1966.

21. O. C. Zienkiewicz, 'Continuum mechanics as an approach to rock mass problems', Ch. 8 of *Rock Mechanics in Engineering Practice*, ed. K. G. Stagg and O. C. Zienkiewicz, J. Wiley & Son, 1969.

22. S. Valliappan, *Non-linear Stress Analysis of two-dimensional Problems with Special Reference to Rock and Soil Mechanics*, Ph.D. Thesis, University of Wales, 1968.

23. Z. Mroz, 'Non associated laws in plasticity', *J. Mec. & Phys. Appli.*, **2**, 21–41, 1963.

24. E. M. Davis, 'Theories of plasticity and the failure of soil masses', Ch. 6 of *Soil Mechanics*, ed. I. K. Lee, Butterworth, 1969.

25a. O. C. Zienkiewicz and B. Best, 'Some non-linear problems in soil and rock mechanics—finite element solution', *Conf. on Rock Mechanics*, Univ. of Queensland, Townsville, June 1969.

25b. O. C. ZIENKIEWICZ, B. BEST, C. DULLAGE, and K. G. STAGG, 'Analysis of non-linear problems in rock mechanics with particular reference to jointed rock systems', *Proc. 2nd Int. Congress on Rock Mechanics*, Belgrade, 1970.

26. S. VALLIAPPAN and P. NATH, 'Tensile crack propagation in reinforced concrete beams by finite element techniques', *Int. Conf. on Shear Torsion and Bond in reinforced concrete*, Coimbatore, India, January 1969.

27. N. W. KRAHL, W. KHACHATURIAN, and C. P. SEISS, 'Stability of tensile cracks in concrete beams', *Proc. Am. Soc. Civ. Eng.*, **93**, ST1, 235–54, 1967.

28. R. E. GOODMAN, R. L. TAYLOR, and T. BREKKE, 'A model for the mechanics of jointed rock', *Proc. Am. Soc. Civ. Eng.*, **94**, SM3, 637–59, 1968.

29. A. SCHOLES and E. M. STROVER, 'The piecewise linear analysis of two connected structures including the effect of clearance at the connections', *Int. J. Num. Meth. in Eng.*, **3**, 45–52, 1971.

30. A. MENDELSON, M. H. HISCHBERG, and S. S. MANSON, 'A general approach to the practical solution of creep problems', *J. of Basic Engineering, Trans. ASME*, Series D, **81**, 585–98, 1959.

31. O. C. ZIENKIEWICZ, M. WATSON, and I. P. KING, 'A numerical method of visco-elastic stress analysis', *Int. J. of Mech. Sci.*, **10**, 807–27, 1968.

32. O. C. ZIENKIEWICZ, *The finite element method in structural and continuum mechanics*, 1st edn., McGraw-Hill, 1967.

33. G. A. GREENBAUM and M. F. RUBINSTEIN, 'Creep analysis of axi-symmetric bodies using finite elements', *Nucl. Eng. and Design*, **7**, 379–97, 1968.

34. G. TREHARNE, *Applications of the finite element method to the stress analysis of materials subject to creep*, Ph.D. Thesis, University of Wales, Swansea, 1971.

35. E. H. LEE, 'Visco-elasticity' in *Handbook of Engineering Mechanics*, ed. W. Flügge, McGraw-Hill, 1962.

36. E. H. LEE, T. R. M. RADOK, and W. B. WOODWARD, 'Stress analysis for linear visco-elastic materials', *Trans. of the Soc. of Rheology*, **3**, 41–59, 1959.

37. F. A. LECKIE and J. B. MARTIN, 'Deformation bounds for bodies in a state of creep', *J. Appl. Mech., A.S.M.E.*, 411–17, June 1967.

38. I. FINNIE and W. R. HELLER, *Creep of Engineering Materials*, McGraw-Hill, 1959.

39. A. E. JOHNSON, 'Complex stress creep', *Met. Rev.*, **5**, 447, 1960.

40. C. O. FREDERICK, E. J. CHUBB, and W. P. BROMLEY, 'Cyclic loading of a tube with creep, plasticity and thermal effects', Applied Mechanics Convention, *Proc. Inst. Mech. Eng.*, **180**, 3 I, 1965.

41. O. C. ZIENKIEWICZ, 'Analysis of visco-elastic behaviour of concrete structures with particular reference to thermal stresses', *Proc. Am. Concr. Inst.*, **58**, 383–94, 1961.

42. H. H. HILTON and H. G. RUSSELL, 'An extension of Alfrey's analogy to thermal stress problems in temperature dependent linear visco-elastic media', *J. Mech. Phys. Solids*, **9**, 152–64, 1961.

43. O. C. ZIENKIEWICZ, M. WATSON, and Y. K. CHEUNG, 'Stress analysis by the finite element method—thermal effects', *Proc. Conf. on Prestressed Concrete Pressure Vessels*, Inst. Civ. Eng., London, 1967.

44. H. MALINA, 'Berechnung von Spannungsumlagerungen in Fels und Boden mit Hilfe der Elementenmethode', *Veröffentlichungen Univ. Karlsruhe*, **40**, 1–90, 1969.

45. G. C. NAYAK, *Plasticity and large deformation problems by finite element method*, Ph.D. Thesis, Univ. of Wales, Swansea, 1971.

46. O. C. ZIENKIEWICZ and S. VALLIAPPAN, 'Analysis of real structures for creep, plasticity and other complex constitutive laws', *Conf. on Materials in Civ. Eng.*, Univ. of Southampton, 1969.

47. P. H. FORCHHEIMER, 'Wasserbewegung durch Boden', *Zeit Ver. Dt. Ing.*, 1782, 1901.

48. M. MUSKAT, *The flow of homogeneous fluids through porous media*, J. W. Edwards Inc., 1946.

49. R. W. VOLKER, *Numerical solutions to problems of nonlinear flow through porous media*, Ph.D. Thesis, University of Queensland, Townsville, 1969.

50. R. W. VOLKER, 'Non-linear flow in porous media by finite elements', *Proc. Am. Soc. Civ. Eng.*, **95**, HY, 2093–114, 1969.

51. N. AHMED and D. K. SUNEDA, 'Non-linear flow in porous media', *Proc. Am. Soc. Civ. Eng.*, **95**, HY6, 1847–59, 1969.

52. A. M. WINSLOW, 'Numerical solution of the quasi-linear Poisson's equation in a non-uniform triangle mesh', *J. Comp. Physics*, **1**, 149–72, 1967.

19. Geometrically Non-Linear Problems; Large Displacement and Structural Instability

19.1 Introduction

In the previous chapter the question of non-linearities arising from material properties was discussed and methods were developed to allow the standard linear forms to be used in an iterative way to obtain solutions. In this chapter a similar path will be followed in the treatment of geometric non-linearity.

In all problems discussed so far it has been implicitly assumed that both displacements and strains developed in the structure are small. In practical terms this means that geometry of the elements remains basically unchanged during the loading process and that first-order, infinitesimal, linear strain approximations can be used.

In practice such assumptions fail frequently even though actual strains may be small and elastic limits of ordinary structural materials not exceeded. If accurate determination of the displacements is needed, geometric non-linearity may have to be considered in some structures. Here, for instance, stresses due to membrane action, usually neglected in plate flexure may cause a considerable decrease of displacements as compared with the linear solution even though displacements are still quite small. Conversely, it may be found that a load is reached where deflections increase more rapidly than predicted by a linear solution and indeed a state may be attained where load-carrying capacity *decreases* with continuing deformation. This classic problem is that of structural stability and obviously has many practical implications. The applications of such analysis are clearly of considerable importance in aerospace engineering, design of radio telescopes, cooling towers, and other relatively slender structures.

Further in many cases physically *large displacements* may occur without causing large strains. Typical in this context is the classical problem of the 'elastica' of which an example is a watch spring.

In this chapter an attempt is made to unify the treatment of all the above problems and to present generally applicable procedures.

One aspect of geometric non-linearity is, however, not discussed in detail. This is the case of large strain such as may occur, even elastically, with such materials as rubber, etc. Here specialized relations between stress and strain have to be introduced[1] and the length of this book prohibits the full discussion. Nevertheless the general processes of the next section are still applicable providing suitable stress and strain laws are introduced.

Geometric non-linearity may often be combined with material non-linearity of the type discussed in the previous chapter, such as small strain plasticity, etc. In principle this does not introduce addditional complexities and the methods of this chapter can easily be extended to deal with this situation.

19.2 General Considerations

19.2.1 *The basic problem.* Whether the displacements (or strains) are large or small, equilibrium conditions between internal and external 'forces' have to be satisfied. Thus, if the displacements are prescribed in the usual manner by a finite number of (nodal) parameters $\{\delta\}$, as in Chapter 2, then as shown there and reiterated in Eq. (18.13) of the previous chapter we must have†

$$\{\psi(\{\delta\})\} = \int_V [\bar{B}]^T\{\sigma\} \, dV - \{\bar{R}\} = 0 \qquad (19.1)$$

where $\{\psi\}$ once again represents the sum of external and internal generalized forces, and in which $[\bar{B}]$ is defined from the strain definition as

$$d\{\varepsilon\} = [\bar{B}] \, d\{\delta\}. \qquad (19.2)$$

The bar suffix has now been added as, if displacements are large, the strains depend non-linearly on displacement, and the matrix $[\bar{B}]$ is now dependent on $\{\delta\}$. We shall see later that we can always conveniently write

$$[\bar{B}] = [B_0] + [B_L(\{\delta\})] \qquad (19.3)$$

in which $[B_0]$ is the same matrix as in linear infinitesimal strain analysis and only $[B_L]$ depends on the displacement. In general $[B_L]$ will be found to be a *linear function* of such displacements.

If strains are reasonably small we can still write the general elastic

† This expression is valid for large strain if the stress is interpreted as the Kirchhoff–Piola stress.

relation

$$\{\sigma\} = [D](\{\varepsilon\} - \{\varepsilon_0\}) + \{\sigma_0\} \tag{19.4}$$

in which $[D]$ is the usual set of elastic constants.†

However, any non-linear stress-strain relationship could equally well be written, as the whole process of solution once again reduces to the solution of a non-linear set of equations (19.1).

It is perhaps too obvious to restate that in Eq. (19.1) integrals are in fact carried out element by element and contributions to 'nodal equilibrium' summed in the usual manner.

19.2.2 *Iteration processes.* Clearly the solution of Eq. (19.1) will have to be approached iteratively and the general methods described in the previous chapter (in section 18.3) are particularly clear.

If the Newton process is to be adopted we have to find the relation between $d\{\delta\}$ and $d\{\psi\}$, as explained there. Thus taking appropriate variations of Eq. (19.1) with respect to $d\{\delta\}$ we have‡

$$d\{\psi\} = \int_V d[\bar{B}]^{\mathrm{T}}\{\sigma\}\,dV + \int_V [\bar{B}]^{\mathrm{T}}\,d\{\sigma\}\,dV \tag{19.5}$$

and using Eqs. (19.4) and (19.2) we have ‡

$$d\{\sigma\} = [D]\,d\{\varepsilon\} = [D][\bar{B}]\,d\{\delta\}$$

and from Eq. (19.3)

$$d[\bar{B}] = d[B_L].$$

Therefore

$$d\{\psi\} = \int_V d[B_L]^{\mathrm{T}}\{\sigma\}\,dV + [\bar{K}]\,d\{\delta\} \tag{19.6}$$

where

$$[\bar{K}] = \int_V [\bar{B}]^{\mathrm{T}}[D][\bar{B}]\,dV = [K_0] + [K_L] \tag{19.7}$$

in which $[K_0]$ represents the usual, small displacements stiffness matrix,

---

† It is important to remember here that the stress components defined in Eq. (19.4) are those *corresponding* to the strain component used. In some gross displacement problems such strain components are subject to considerable change of direction from original, fixed axes.

‡ Once again if non-linear stress-strain relations are used $[D] = [D(\{\sigma\})]$ is the incremented elasticity matrix as given by Eq. (18.15).

i.e.,

$$[K_0] = \int_V [B_0]^T [D] [B_0] \, dV. \tag{19.7a}$$

The matrix $[K_L]$ is due to the large displacement and is given by

$$[K_L] = \int_V ([B_0]^T [D] [B_L] + [B_L]^T [D] [B_L] + [B_L]^T [D] [B_0]) \, dV. \tag{19.7b}$$

$[\bar{K}]$ is variously known as the *initial displacement* matrix,[2] *large displacement matrix*, etc. It will be found that this is a matrix which would alternatively be obtained by using an infinitesimal strain approach but adjusting element co-ordinates in the computation of the stiffness.

The first term of Eq. (19.6) can generally be written (perhaps less obviously until particular cases are examined) as

$$\int_V d[B_L]^T \{\sigma\} \, dV = [K_\sigma] \, d\{\delta\} \tag{19.8}$$

where $[K_\sigma]$ is a symmetric matrix dependent on the stress level. This matrix is known as *initial stress* matrix[2,12] or *geometric* matrix.[3,4] Thus

$$d\{\psi\} = ([K_0] + [K_\sigma] + [K_L]) \, d\{\delta\} = [K_T] \, d\{\delta\} \tag{19.9}$$

with $[K_T]$ being the total, *tangential stiffness*, matrix. Newton-type iteration can once more be applied precisely in the manner of section 18.3.

To summarize:

(a) Elastic linear solution is obtained as a first approximation $\{\delta\}$;
(b) $\{\psi\}_1$ is found using Eq. (19.1) with appropriate definition of $[\bar{B}]$ and stresses as given by Eq. (19.4) (or any other linear or non-linear law);
(c) Matrix $[K_T]$ is established; and
(d) Correction is established as

$$\Delta\{\delta\}_1 = -[K_T]^{-1} \{\psi\}_1$$

and process repeated until $\{\psi\}_n$ becomes sufficiently small.

Again a constant matrix could be used, increasing the number of iterating steps but making use of a semi-inverted, resolve process at smaller computer cost, providing that at each step $\{\psi\}_n$ is calculated by the correct expressions[5] but convergence is sometimes slow by this procedure.

While all solutions can be accomplished in a one-step operation for a full load on occasion, as in all non-linear problems, the possibility of a non-unique solution arises and the physically unimportant one may be obtained. In such cases it is wise to proceed by incrementing the load and obtaining the non-linear solution for each increment. This indeed is sometimes computationally cheaper as effects of non-linearity in each step are reduced. Indeed, if load increments of sufficiently small magnitude are taken each incremental solution may be accomplished sufficiently accurately in one step.[3,4,6]† It is important, however, to check periodically the total equilibrium by using the full Eq. (19.1).

19.2.3 *Initial Stability problem.* It is of interest to note at this stage that $[K_\sigma]$ does not explicitly contain the displacements and is proportional to the stress level $\{\sigma\}$. Thus, if at the first step of computation we evaluate $\{\sigma\}$ by a linear solution we have from Eq. (19.6)

$$d\{\psi\} = ([K_\sigma] + [K_0]) \, d\{\delta\} \qquad (19.10)$$

if $[K_L] = 0$ at this stage.

If the loads are increased by a factor λ we may find that neutral stability exists, i.e.,

$$d\{\psi\} = ([K_0] + \lambda[K_\sigma]) \, d\{\delta\} \equiv 0 \qquad (19.11)$$

From this λ can be obtained by solving the typical *eigenvalue problem* defined above (*vide* Chapter 17).

This is the classical, 'initial' stability problem such as occurs in the buckling of struts, plates, shells, etc.

Quite frequently in the literature this type of approach is used beyond its limits of applicability. The 'initial stability' expressed can only give physically significant answers if the elastic ($[K_0]$) solution gives such deformations that the *large deformation matrix* $[K_L]$ *is identically zero.* This only happens in a very limited number of practical situations (e.g., a perfectly straight strut under axial load, complete sphere under uniform pressure, etc.) The preoccupation of such investigators with the subject of 'initial imperfections' is strictly limited to such situations where a true bifurcation can occur. In real engineering situations such problems should be investigated using the full tangential stiffness matrix.[6] When $[K_T] \, d\{\delta\}$ is identically zero, neutral equilibrium is obtained. A step-by-step approach is clearly necessary here.

19.2.4 *Energy interpretation of the stability criteria.* It was shown in Chapter 2 that the virtual work done during a displacement variable $d\{\delta\}$ is in fact equal to the variation of total potential energy χ. Thus for equilibrium

$$d\chi = d\{\delta\}^T\{\psi\} = 0, \qquad (19.12)$$

† This in fact makes the process identical with a forward integration procedure of Euler. Clearly, elaboration could be applied to this using Runge-Kutta methods or 'predictor-corrector' processes.[28]

i.e., *the total potential energy is stationary* (which is equivalent to Eq. (19.1)).

The second variation of χ is (by Eq. (19.9))

$$d^2\chi = d(d\chi) = d\{\delta\}^T d\{\psi\} = d\{\delta\}^T[K_T] d\{\delta\}. \qquad (19.13)$$

Stability criterion is given by a positive value of this second variation and conversely instability by a negative value (as in first case energy has to be added to the structure while in second it contains surplus energy). In other words *if $[K_T]$ is positive-definite, stability exists.* This criterion is well known and of considerable use when investigating stability during large deformation.†[7-9]

19.2.5 *Forces dependent on deformation.* In the derivation of Eq. (19.5) it was implicitly assumed that the forces $\{\bar{R}\}$ are not themselves dependent on the deformation. In some instances this is not true. For instance pressure loads on a grossly deforming structure are in general in this category as indeed are some aerodynamic forces depending on the deformation (flutter).

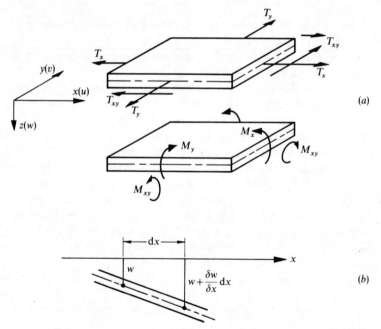

Fig. 19.1   (*a*) 'In plane' and bending stress resultants for a flat plate. (*b*) Increase of middle surface length due to lateral displacement

---

† An alternative if less practicable test is to investigate the sign of the determinant of $[K_T]$.[9]

If forces vary with displacement then in relation to Eq. (19.5) the variation $d\{\bar{R}\}$ has to be considered with respect to $d\{\delta\}$. Stability and large deformation problems under such (non-conservative) loads can be once again studied if proper consideration is given to the above term.

19.3 Large Deflection and 'Initial' Stability of Plates

19.3.1 *Definitions*. As a first example we shall consider the problems associated with the deformation of plates subject to 'in-plane' and 'lateral' forces, when displacements are not infinitesimal but also not excessively large. It is well known that in such situations the lateral displacements will be responsible for development of 'membrane' type strains and now the two problems of 'in-plane' and 'lateral' deformation can no longer be dealt with separately but are *coupled*.

We shall, as before, describe the plate 'strains' in terms of middle surface displacements, i.e., if the x–y plane coincides with the middle surface as in Fig. 19.1(a) we shall have (see Chapters 10 and 11)

$$\{\varepsilon\} = \left\{\begin{array}{c} \varepsilon_x \\ \varepsilon_y \\ \gamma_{xy} \\ -\dfrac{\partial^2 w}{\partial x^2} \\ -\dfrac{\partial^2 w}{\partial y^2} \\ 2\dfrac{\partial^2 w}{\partial x\,\partial y} \end{array}\right\} = \left\{\begin{array}{c} \varepsilon_{pl} \\ \varepsilon_b \end{array}\right\}; \qquad \{\sigma\} = \left\{\begin{array}{c} T_x \\ T_y \\ T_{xy} \\ M_x \\ M_y \\ M_{xy} \end{array}\right\} = \left\{\begin{array}{c} \sigma_{pl} \\ \sigma_b \end{array}\right\}. \qquad (19.14)$$

The 'stresses' are defined in terms of the usual resultants.†

$T_x = \bar{\sigma}_x t$, where $\bar{\sigma}_x$ is the average membrane stress, etc. Now, if the deformed shape is considered as in Fig. 19.1(b), we see that displacement w produces some additional extension in the x and y directions of the middle surface and the length dx stretches to

$$dx' = \sqrt{1+\left(\frac{\partial w}{\partial x}\right)^2} = dx\left\{1+\frac{1}{2}\left(\frac{\partial w}{\partial x}\right)^2 + \ldots\right\},$$

i.e., in defining the x elongation we can write (to second approximation)

$$\varepsilon_x = \frac{\partial u}{\partial x} + \frac{1}{2}\left(\frac{\partial w}{\partial x}\right)^2.$$

† In-plane and bending components have here been separated by appropriate subscripts.

Considering in a similar way the other components[10] we can write as the definition of strain

$$\{\varepsilon\} = \left\{ \begin{array}{c} \dfrac{\partial u}{\partial x} \\[2mm] \dfrac{\partial v}{\partial y} \\[2mm] \dfrac{\partial u}{\partial y}+\dfrac{\partial v}{\partial x} \\[2mm] -\dfrac{\partial^2 w}{\partial x^2} \\[2mm] -\dfrac{\partial^2 w}{\partial y^2} \\[2mm] 2\dfrac{\partial^2 w}{\partial x\,\partial y} \end{array} \right\} + \left\{ \begin{array}{c} \dfrac{1}{2}\left(\dfrac{\partial w}{\partial x}\right)^2 \\[2mm] \dfrac{1}{2}\left(\dfrac{\partial w}{\partial y}\right)^2 \\[2mm] \left(\dfrac{\partial w}{\partial x}\right)\left(\dfrac{\partial w}{\partial y}\right) \\[2mm] 0 \\[2mm] 0 \\[2mm] 0 \end{array} \right\} = \left\{ \begin{array}{c} \varepsilon_{pl}^0 \\[1mm] \varepsilon_b^0 \end{array} \right\} + \left\{ \begin{array}{c} \varepsilon_{pl}^L \\[1mm] 0 \end{array} \right\} \qquad (19.15)$$

in which the first term is the linear expression already encountered many times and the second gives the non-linear terms. In above u, v, w stand for appropriate displacements of middle surface.

If only linear elastic behaviour is considered, the $[D]$ matrix is composed of plane stress and a bending component (*vide* Chapters 4 and 10).

$$[D] = \begin{bmatrix} [D^{p'}] & 0 \\ 0 & [D^b] \end{bmatrix}. \qquad (19.16)$$

Finally the displacements are defined in terms of nodal parameters using the appropriate shape functions.

Thus for instance

$$\left\{ \begin{array}{c} u \\ v \\ w \end{array} \right\} = [N]\{\delta\}^e \qquad (19.17)$$

where a typical set of nodal parameters will be for convenience divided into those which influence in-plane and bending deformation respectively.

$$\{\delta_i\} = \left\{ \begin{array}{c} \delta_i^{pl} \\ \delta_i^b \end{array} \right\} \quad \text{with} \quad \{\delta_i^{pl}\} = \left\{ \begin{array}{c} u_i \\ v_i \end{array} \right\} \quad \text{(as in Chapter 4)} \qquad (19.18)$$

$$\{\delta_i^b\} = \left\{ \begin{array}{c} w_i \\[2mm] \dfrac{\partial w}{\partial x_i} \\[2mm] \dfrac{\partial w}{\partial y_i} \end{array} \right\} \quad \text{(as in Chapter 10).}$$

Thus the shape function can also be subdivided as

$$[N_i] = \begin{bmatrix} [N_i]^{p^l} & 0 \\ 0 & [N_i]^b \end{bmatrix} \tag{19.19}$$

and indeed we shall assume in what follows that the final assembled displacement vector is also subdivided in the manner of Eq. (19.18).

This is convenient as with the exception of the non-linear strain $\{\varepsilon_{pl}^L\}$ all the definitions of standard linear analysis apply and therefore do not have to be repeated here.

19.3.2 *Evaluation of* $[\bar{B}]$. For further formulation it will be necessary to establish expressions for $[\bar{B}]$ and $[K_T]$ matrices. First we shall note that

$$[\bar{B}] = [B_0] + [B_L] \tag{19.20}$$

where

$$[B_0] = \begin{bmatrix} [B_0^{pl}] & 0 \\ 0 & [B_0^b] \end{bmatrix} \quad ; \quad [B_L] = \begin{bmatrix} 0 & [B_L^b] \\ 0 & 0 \end{bmatrix}$$

where $[B_0^{pl}]$, $[B_0^b]$ are the well-defined, standard matrices of appropriate linear in-plane and bending elements and $[B_L^b]$ is found by taking a variation of $\{\varepsilon_{pl}^L\}$ with respect to the parameters $\{\delta^b\}$.

This, non-linear, strain component of Eq. (19.15) can be written conveniently as

$$\{\varepsilon_{pl}^L\} = \frac{1}{2} \begin{bmatrix} \dfrac{\partial w}{\partial x} & 0 \\ 0 & \dfrac{\partial w}{\partial y} \\ \dfrac{\partial w}{\partial y} & \dfrac{\partial w}{\partial x} \end{bmatrix} \begin{Bmatrix} \dfrac{\partial w}{\partial x} \\ \dfrac{\partial w}{\partial y} \end{Bmatrix} = \frac{1}{2}[A]\{\theta\}. \tag{19.21}$$

The derivatives (slopes) of w can be related to the nodal parameters $\{\delta^b\}$ as

$$\{\theta\} = \begin{Bmatrix} \dfrac{\partial w}{\partial x} \\ \dfrac{\partial w}{\partial y} \end{Bmatrix} = [G]\{\delta^b\} \tag{19.22}$$

in which we have

$$[G] = \begin{bmatrix} \dfrac{\partial N_1^b}{\partial x}, & \dfrac{\partial N_2^b}{\partial x} & \cdots \\ \dfrac{\partial N_1^b}{\partial y}, & \dfrac{\partial N_2^b}{\partial y} & \cdots \end{bmatrix}. \tag{19.23}$$

Thus $[G]$ is a matrix defined purely in terms of the co-ordinates.

Taking the variation of Eq. (19.21) we have†

$$\mathrm{d}\{\varepsilon_{pl}^L\} = \tfrac{1}{2}\,\mathrm{d}[A]\{\theta\} + \tfrac{1}{2}[A]\,\mathrm{d}\{\theta\} = [A]\,\mathrm{d}\{\theta\} = [A][G]\,\mathrm{d}\{\delta^b\} \quad (19.24)$$

and hence immediately, by definition

$$[B_L^b] = [A][G]. \quad (19.25)$$

19.3.3 *Evaluation of* $[K_T]$. The linear, small deformation, matrices are written as

$$[K_0] = \begin{bmatrix} K_0^{pl} & 0 \\ 0 & K_0^b \end{bmatrix} \quad (19.26)$$

with appropriate definitions given in Chapters 3 and 10. Using Eq. (19.7b) the large displacement matrices can be defined on substituting Eq. (19.20). Thus after some manipulation

$$[K_L] = \int_V \begin{bmatrix} 0, & [B_0^{pl}]^{\mathrm{T}}\,[D^{pl}] & [B_L^b] \\ \mathrm{Sym.,}[B_L^b]^{\mathrm{T}} & [D^{pl}] & [B_L^b] \end{bmatrix} \mathrm{d}V. \quad (19.27)$$

† The manipulation of Eq. (19.24) is due to an interesting property of the matrices $[A]$ and $\{\theta\}$. It is easy to verify that if

$$\{x\} = \begin{Bmatrix} x_1 \\ x_2 \end{Bmatrix}$$

is an arbitrary vector then

$$\mathrm{d}[A]\{x\} = \begin{bmatrix} \mathrm{d}\left(\dfrac{\partial w}{\partial x}\right) & 0 \\ 0 & \mathrm{d}\left(\dfrac{\partial w}{\partial y}\right) \\ \mathrm{d}\left(\dfrac{\partial w}{\partial y}\right) & \mathrm{d}\left(\dfrac{\partial w}{\partial x}\right) \end{bmatrix} \begin{Bmatrix} x_1 \\ x_2 \end{Bmatrix} \equiv \begin{bmatrix} x_1 & 0 \\ 0 & x_2 \\ x_2 & x_1 \end{bmatrix} \mathrm{d}\{\theta\}$$

thus

$$\mathrm{d}[A]\{\theta\} = [A]\,\mathrm{d}\{\theta\}.$$

Similarly if

$$\{y\} = \begin{Bmatrix} y_1 \\ y_2 \\ y_3 \end{Bmatrix}$$

$$\mathrm{d}[A]^{\mathrm{T}}\{y\} = \begin{bmatrix} \mathrm{d}\left(\dfrac{\partial w}{\partial x}\right) & 0 & \mathrm{d}\left(\dfrac{\partial w}{\partial y}\right) \\ 0 & \mathrm{d}\left(\dfrac{\partial w}{\partial y}\right) & \mathrm{d}\left(\dfrac{\partial w}{\partial x}\right) \end{bmatrix} \begin{Bmatrix} y_1 \\ y_2 \\ y_3 \end{Bmatrix} = \begin{bmatrix} y_1 & y_3 \\ y_3 & y_2 \end{bmatrix} \mathrm{d}\{\theta\}.$$

Use of this second property will be made later.

Finally $[K_\sigma]$ has to be found using the definition of Eq. (19.8). From Eq. (19.20) we have on taking a variation

$$\mathrm{d}[B_L]^{\mathrm{T}} = \begin{bmatrix} 0 & 0 \\ \mathrm{d}[B_L^b]^{\mathrm{T}} & 0 \end{bmatrix} \tag{19.28}$$

which on substitution into Eqs. (19.8) and (19.25) gives

$$[K_\sigma]\,\mathrm{d}\{\delta\} = \int_V \begin{bmatrix} 0 & , & 0 \\ [G]^{\mathrm{T}}\,\mathrm{d}[A]^{\mathrm{T}} & , & 0 \end{bmatrix} \begin{Bmatrix} T_x \\ T_y \\ T_{xy} \\ M_x \\ M_y \\ M_{xy} \end{Bmatrix} \mathrm{d}V. \tag{19.29}$$

But by the special property described in the footnote of page 422, we can write

$$\mathrm{d}[A]^{\mathrm{T}} \begin{Bmatrix} T_x \\ T_y \\ T_{xy} \end{Bmatrix} = \begin{bmatrix} T_x & T_{xy} \\ T_{xy} & T_y \end{bmatrix} \mathrm{d}\{\theta\} = \begin{bmatrix} T_x & T_{xy} \\ T_{xy} & T_y \end{bmatrix} [G]\,\mathrm{d}\{\delta^b\}$$

and finally we obtain

$$[K_\sigma] = \begin{bmatrix} 0 & 0 \\ 0 & [K_\sigma^b] \end{bmatrix} \tag{19.30}$$

with

$$[K_\sigma^b] = \int_V [G]^{\mathrm{T}} \begin{bmatrix} T_x & T_{xy} \\ T_{xy} & T_y \end{bmatrix} [G]\,\mathrm{d}V \tag{19.31}$$

a well known *symmetric form of the initial stress*, plate matrix.

19.3.4 *Large deflection problem.* All the ingredients necessary for computing the large deflection plate problem are now available.

As a first step displacements $\{\delta\}$ are found according to the small displacement, uncoupled solution. This determines the actual strains by considering the non-linear contribution defined by Eq. (19.21) together with the appropriate linear contributions. Corresponding stresses can be found by the elastic expressions and $\{\psi\}_0$ determined according to Eq. (19.1). For successive approximations $[K_T]$ is found from Eqs. (19.26), (19.27), and (19.30).

A typical solution thus obtained[9], Fig. 19.2, shows the stiffening of the plate with increasing deformation due to development of 'membrane' stresses. At the edges of the plate all in-plane and lateral deformations are restrained. The results show an excellent agreement with an alternative analytical solution.

The element properties were derived using for the in-plane deformation the simplest rectangle function of Chapter 7 and for bending deformation the non-conforming shape function for a rectangle (section 10.4, Chapter 10).

Several other examples of large plate deformation obtained by finite element methods are available in literature.[11-15]

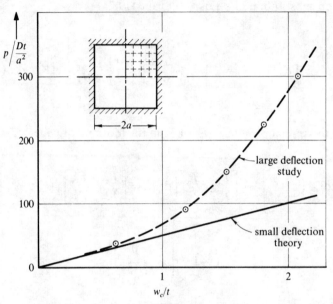

Fig. 19.2   Central deflection, w_c, of a clamped square plate under uniform load p (from ref. 9), $u = v = 0$ at edge

19.3.5 *Bifurcation instability.* In a few practical cases as in the classical Euler problem a bifurcation instability is possible. Consider the situation of a plate loaded purely in its own plane. As lateral deflections, w, are not produced the small deflection theory gives an exact solution. However, even with zero lateral displacements, the initial stress matrix $[K_\sigma^b]$ can be found while $[K_L] = 0$. If the in-plane stresses are compressive this matrix will generally be such that real eigenvalues of the bending deformation equation can be found

$$([K_0^b] + \lambda[K_\sigma^b])\{\delta^b\} = 0 \qquad (19.32)$$

in which λ denotes the increase factor on in-plane stresses necessary to achieve neutral equilibrium (instability).

At such an increased load incipient buckling occurs and lateral deflections can occur without any lateral load.

The problem is simply formulated by writing only the bending equation with $[K_0^b]$ determined as in Chapter 10 and $[K_\sigma^b]$ found from Eq. (19.31).

Points of such incipient stability (buckling) for a variety of plate problems have been determined using various element formulations.[16–21] Some comparative results for a simple problem of a square, simply supported plate under a uniform compression T_x in one direction, are given in Table 19.1. In this the buckling parameter is defined as

$$C = T_x a^2 / \pi^2 D$$

where a is the side of the plate and D the bending rigidity.

TABLE 19.1

VALUES OF C FOR A SQUARE PLATE SIMPLY SUPPORTED
AND COMPRESSED UNIAXIALLY

	Non-compatible		Compatible	
	Rectangle[17] 12 D.O.F.	Triangle[19] 9 D.O.F.	Rectangle[20] 16 D.O.F.	Quadrilateral[21] 16 D.O.F.
2×2		3·22		
4×4	3·77	3·72	4·015	4·029
8×8	3·93	3·90	4·001	4·002

Exact $C = 4·00$[10]
D.O.F. = degrees of freedom.

The elements are all of the type described in Chapter 10 and it is of interest to note that all those which are slope compatible always overestimate the buckling factor. The non-conforming elements in this case under-estimate it although no such bound could be, at present, determined.

Figure 19.3 shows a buckling mode for a geometrically more complex case.[19] Here again the non-conforming triangle was used.

Such incipient stability problems in plates are of limited practical importance. As soon as lateral deflection occurs a stiffening of the plate follows and additional loads can be carried. This stiffening was noted in the example of Fig. 19.2. Post-buckling behaviour thus should be studied by the large deformation process generally described in previous sections.[22–24] To avoid the bifurcation difficulty a slight perturbation (or lateral load) should then be imposed.

19.4 Shells

In shells stability problems are much more relevant than in plates. Here, in general, the problem is one in which the tangential stiffness matrix $[K]_T$ should always be determined taking the actual displacements into

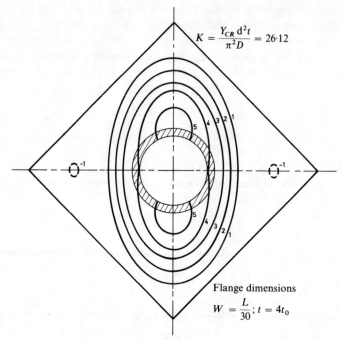

$$K = \frac{Y_{CR}\, d^2 t}{\pi^2 D} = 26 \cdot 12$$

Flange dimensions

$$W = \frac{L}{30};\ t = 4t_0$$

Fig. 19.3   Buckling mode of a square plate under shear—clamped edges, central hole stiffened by flange[19]

account, as now the special case of uncoupled membrane and bending effects does not occur under load except in most trivial cases. If the *initial stability* matrix $[K_\sigma]$ is determined for the elastic stresses it is, however, sometimes possible to obtain useful results concerning the stability factor λ, and indeed in the classical work on the subject of shell buckling this initial stability has been almost exclusively considered. The true collapse load may, however, be well *below* the initial stability load and it is important to determine at least approximately the deformation effects.

If shells are assumed to be built up of flat plate elements the same transformations as given in Chapter 11 can be followed with the plate tangential stiffness matrix.[25, 26] If curved shell elements are used it is essential to revert to the equation of shell theory and to include in these the non-linear terms.[9, 27] For the complete formulation required the reader is referred to these references.

It is extremely important to emphasize again, that initial instability calculations are meaningful only in special cases, and that they often overestimate the collapse loads considerably. For correct answers a full non-linear process has to be invoked. The progressive 'softening' of a shell under a load well below the one given by linearized buckling is shown in

Fig. 19.4 taken from reference 9. Figure 19.5 shows the progressive collapse of an arch at a load much below that given by the linear stability value.[6]

The determination of the actual collapse load of a shell or other slender structure presents obvious difficulties (of a kind already encountered in Chapter 18) as convergence of displacements cannot be obtained when load is increased near the 'peak' carrying capacity.

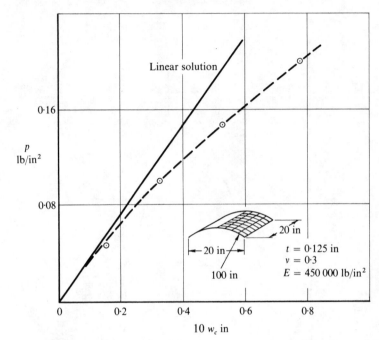

Fig. 19.4   Deflections of a cylindrical shell at centre. All edges clamped (from ref. 9)

It is convenient, then, to proceed immediately prescribing displacement increments and computing the corresponding reactions if one concentrated load is considered. By such processes, Argyris[4] succeeds in following a complete snap through behaviour of an arch.

Pian and Ping Tong[28] show how the process can be simply generalized when a system of proportional loads is considered.

Alternative processes—if approaching the collapse problem—have been described and much work is in progress in this important field.[29–33]

19.5 General, Large Strain and Displacement Formulation

The non-linear strain displacement relationship for plates, used in section 19.3 (Eq. (19.15)) was derived on *ad hoc* basis. For shells alternative

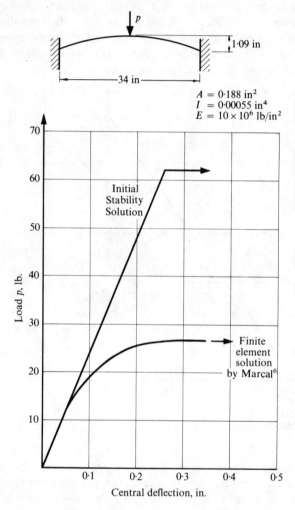

Fig. 19.5   'Initial stability' and incremental solutions for large deformation of an arch under central load p (ref. 6)

relationships may be similarly derived but possibility of diverse approximations arises at all stages. It is, however, possible to use a general definition of strains which is *valid whether displacements or strains are large or small*. Such a definition was introduced by Green and St. Venant and is known as the Green's strain tensor. Referred to a fixed Cartesian system of co-ordinates, x, y, z, the displacements u, v, w define strains as[34]

$$\varepsilon_x = \frac{\partial u}{\partial x} + \frac{1}{2}\left[\left(\frac{\partial u}{\partial x}\right)^2 + \left(\frac{\partial v}{\partial x}\right)^2 + \left(\frac{\partial w}{\partial x}\right)^2\right]$$

$$\gamma_{xy} = \frac{\partial u}{\partial y} + \frac{\partial v}{\partial x} + \left[\frac{\partial u}{\partial x}\cdot\frac{\partial u}{\partial y} + \frac{\partial v}{\partial x}\cdot\frac{\partial v}{\partial y} + \frac{\partial w}{\partial x}\cdot\frac{\partial w}{\partial y}\right]$$

(19.33)

with other components obtained by suitable permutation.

If displacements are small the general first-order linear strain approximation is obtained by neglecting the quadratic terms.

Geometric interpretation of the above strain definitions is not obvious in the general case but it should be noted that they give a measure of elongation and angular distortion of an originally orthogonal element and for small strain result in usual definitions even if the displacements are large.

If the actual strain quantities are small then it is simple to show that ε_x defines the change of length of a unit length *originally oriented parallel to the x axes* while γ_{xy} gives similarly the angle change between two lines *originally* parallel to x and y axes. This is true in the above definition even if large movements have occurred which have rotated or displaced the original axes by gross amounts.

We shall now establish the general non-linear expressions $[\bar{B}]$ and $[K_T]$ for a complete three-dimensional state of stress. It is a simple matter to specialize from here to one- or two-dimensional forms and such exercises will be left to the reader. Indeed plate and shell problems are conveniently approached via such a general formulation and some terms neglected in the specialized approach to the plate problem of the previous section are now easily included.

19.5.1 *Derivation of the* $[B_L]$ *matrix.* The general strain vector in three dimensions can be defined in terms of the infinitesimal and large displacement components

$$\{\varepsilon\} = \{\varepsilon^0\} + \{\varepsilon^L\}$$

(19.34)

where

$$\{\varepsilon^0\} = \left\{\begin{array}{c} \varepsilon_x \\ \varepsilon_y \\ \varepsilon_z \\ \gamma_{yz} \\ \gamma_{zx} \\ \gamma_{xy} \end{array}\right\} = \left\{\begin{array}{c} \dfrac{\partial u}{\partial x} \\ \dfrac{\partial v}{\partial y} \\ \dfrac{\partial w}{\partial z} \\ \dfrac{\partial v}{\partial z}+\dfrac{\partial w}{\partial y} \\ \dfrac{\partial w}{\partial x}+\dfrac{\partial u}{\partial z} \\ \dfrac{\partial u}{\partial y}+\dfrac{\partial v}{\partial z} \end{array}\right\}$$

(19.35)

is the same as defined in Chapter 6. The non-linear terms of Eq. (19.33) can be conveniently rewritten as

$$\{\varepsilon^L\} = \tfrac{1}{2} \begin{bmatrix} \{\theta_x\}^{\mathrm{T}} & 0 & 0 \\ 0 & \{\theta_y\}^{\mathrm{T}} & 0 \\ 0 & 0 & \{\theta_z\}^{T} \\ 0 & \{\theta_z\}^{\mathrm{T}} & \{\theta_y\}^{T} \\ \{\theta_z\}^{\mathrm{T}} & 0 & \{\theta_x\}^{T} \\ \{\theta_y\}^{\mathrm{T}} & \{\theta_x\}^{\mathrm{T}} & 0 \end{bmatrix} \begin{Bmatrix} \{\theta_x\} \\ \{\theta_y\} \\ \{\theta_z\} \end{Bmatrix} = \tfrac{1}{2}[A]\{\theta\} \quad (19.36)$$

in which

$$\{\theta_x\}^{\mathrm{T}} = \left[\frac{\partial u}{\partial x}, \frac{\partial v}{\partial x}, \frac{\partial w}{\partial x}\right], \text{ etc.}$$

and $[A]$ is a 6×9 matrix.

The reader can readily verify the validity of the above definition and re-establish the properties of the matrices $[A]$ and $\{\theta\}$ defined in section 19.3.2 (footnote to p. 422). Once again

$$\mathrm{d}\{\varepsilon^L\} = \tfrac{1}{2}\,d[A]\{\theta\} + \tfrac{1}{2}[A]\,\mathrm{d}\{\theta\} = [A]\,\mathrm{d}\{\theta\} \quad (19.37)$$

and as we can determine $\{\theta\}$ in terms of the shape function $[N]$ and nodal parameters $\{\delta\}$ we can write

$$\{\theta\} = [G]\{\delta\} \quad (19.38)$$

or

$$\mathrm{d}\{\varepsilon^L\} = [A][G]\,\mathrm{d}\{\delta\}$$

and

$$[B_L] = [A][G] \quad (19.39)$$

19.5.2 *Derivation of* $[K_T]$ *matrix.* Noting that

$$[\bar{B}] = [B_0] + [B_L]$$

we can readily form the matrix of Eq. (19.7)

$$[\bar{K}] = [K_0] + [K_L] = \int_V [\bar{B}]^{\mathrm{T}}[D][\bar{B}]\,\mathrm{d}V. \quad (19.40)$$

To complete the total tangential stiffness matrix it is necessary only to determine the initial stress matrix $[K_\sigma]$. Again by Eq. (19.8) we have

$$[K_\sigma]\,\mathrm{d}\{\delta\} = \int_V \mathrm{d}[B_L]^{\mathrm{T}}\{\sigma\}\,\mathrm{d}V = \int_V [G]^{\mathrm{T}}\,\mathrm{d}[A]^{\mathrm{T}}\{\sigma\}\,\mathrm{d}V. \quad (19.41)$$

Once again we can verify that we can write

$$d[A]^T\{\sigma\} = \begin{bmatrix} \sigma_x I_3 & \tau_{xy} I_3 & \tau_{xz} I_3 \\ & \sigma_y I_3 & \tau_{yz} I_3 \\ \text{sym.} & & \sigma_z I_3 \end{bmatrix} d\{\theta\} = [M][G] d\{\delta\} \quad (19.42)$$

in which I_3 is a 3×3 identity matrix.

Substituting Eq. (19.42) into Eq. (19.41) yields

$$[K_\sigma] = \int_V [G]^T [M][G] \, dV \quad (19.43)$$

in which $[M]$ is a 9×9 matrix of the six stress components arranged as shown in Eq. (19.42). The *symmetric* form of $[K_\sigma]$ is once again demonstrated.

Once again we have omitted element superscripts though in fact all of the above matrices would be obtained element by element and added in the standard manner.

The use of the general expressions is a useful starting point in the analysis of plates and shells if consistent approximations are to be made. In the case of the thick shell formulation of Chapter 14 such expressions are essential.

Further if a suitable stress-strain relation can be found they are valid for large strain analysis. Here, however, it is more usual to define directly a strain energy function in terms of the strain components and to obtain generalized forces by direct minimization. Some examples of such large strain analysis have been given by Oden[35-38] who discusses large deformation of rubber membranes and continua.

19.6 Concluding Remarks

This chapter attempted to present a unified approach to all large deformation problems. Various methods of solution on the basic non-linear equation system have been outlined and the reader may, rightly, wonder which is preferable. If a single solution of a non-linear large deformation problem is desired the Newton process appears to converge quite rapidly in most instances. For certain cases, however, the constant matrix methods are more economical.

If a full load deformation study is required it has been the common practice to proceed with small load increments and treat for each such increment the problem as a linear elastic one with the tangential stiffness matrix evaluated at the start of the increment.[2,3] Such methods may accumulate error and Brebbia and Connor[9] recommend a complete Newton-type solution to be used every few increments.

Extension of geometrically non-linear problems to dynamic situations is possible especially if initial stress stiffness matrices exist and the problem to be considered is quasi linear. Anderson et al.[19] for instance solve many problems of vibrations of initially compressed plates.†

Combination of material non-linearity together with geometric non-linearity is particularly simple if an incremental elasticity matrix may be established. Marçal[2] solves a number of such problems in which large deformation is coupled with plasticity. It is interesting to note that the operations required in solution of problems of material and geometric non-linearity are similar and computer systems capable of dealing with both can be developed.

Finally two matters should be noted. One is the apparently lengthy derivation of the initial stress matrix for plates which in previous publications[17, 19] is derived in a more direct way. This is due to an attempt at complete generality which hopefully was achieved. The second point is that somewhat involved operations were required in the section dealing with general large strain in order to preserve the convenient matrix formulation used throughout this book. Some simplification would have arisen if tensor notation were used and indeed this could have been used throughout the book as an alternative. No apology is, however, being made for the choice of the more direct and better understood notation.

† Stricklin et al.[39] discuss this problem in the context of transient response.

References

1. C. TRUESDELL (Editor), *Continuum Mechanics IV*, 'Problems of non-linear elasticity', Vol. 8, p. 4, Gordon and Beach, 1965.
2. P. V. MARÇAL, *Finite element analysis of combined problems of material and geometric behaviour*, Techn. Rep. 1, ONR, Brown University, 1969, also *Proc. Am. Soc. Mech. Eng. Conf.* on 'Computational approaches in Applied Mechanics', 133, June 1969.
3. J. H. ARGYRIS, S. KELSEY, and H. KAMEL, *Matrix Methods of Structural Analysis*, AGARD-ograph 72, Pergamon Press, 1963.
4. J. H. ARGYRIS, 'Continua and Discontinua', *Proc. Conf. Matrix methods in Structural Mechanics*, Air Force Inst. of Tech., Wright Patterson A.F. Base, Ohio, Oct. 1965.
5. G. C. NAYAK, *Plasticity and large deformation problems by finite element method*, Ph.D. Thesis, Univ. of Wales, Swansea, 1971.
6. P. V. MARÇAL, *Effect of initial displacement on problem of large deflection and stability*, Techn. Report ARPA E54, Brown University, 1967.
7. K. MARGUERRE, 'Über die Anwendung der energetischen Methode auf Stabilitätsprobleme', *Hohrb.*, D.V.L., 252–62, 1938.
8. B. FRAEIJS DE VEUBEKE, 'The second variation test with algebraic and differential contrasts', *Advanced problems and methods for space flight optimisation*, Pergamon Press, 1969.

9. C. BREBBIA and J. CONNOR, 'Geometrically non-linear finite element analysis', *Proc. Am. Soc. Civ. Eng.*, **95**, EM2, 463–83, 1969.
10. S. P. TIMOSHENKO and J. M. GERE, *Theory of elastic stability*, McGraw-Hill, 2nd edition, 1961.
11. L. A. SCHMIT, F. K. BOGNER, and R. L. FOX, 'Finite deflection structural analysis using plate and cylindrical shell discrete elements', *Proc. AIAA/ASME 8th Struct. and Stress dynamic conference*, Palm Springs, California, 197–211, March 1967. Also *J.A.I.A.A.*, **5**, 1525–7, 1968.
12. M. J. TURNER, E. H. DILL, H. C. MARTIN and R. J. MELOSH, 'Large deflection of structures subjected to heating and external loads', *J. of Aero. Sciences*, **27**, 97–106, 1960.
13. T. KAWAI and N. YOSHIMOTO, 'Analysis of large deflection of plates by finite element method', *Int. J. Num. Meth. Eng.*, **1**, 123–33, 1969.
14. R. H. MALLETT and P. V. MARÇAL, 'Finite element analysis of non-linear structures', *Proc. Am. Soc. Civ. Eng.*, **94**, S.T.9, 2081–105, 1968.
15. D. W. MURRAY and E. L. WILSON, 'Finite element large deflection analysis of plates', *Proc. Am. Soc. Civ. Eng.*, **94**, EM 1, 143–165, 1968.
16. H. C. MARTIN, 'On the derivation of stiffness matrices for the analysis of large deflection and stability problems', *Proc. Conf. Matrix Methods in Struct. Mech.*, Air Force Inst. of Tech., Wright Patterson A.F. Base, Ohio, Oct. 1965.
17. K. K. KAPUR and B. J. HARTZ, 'Stability of thin plates using the finite element method', *Proc. Am. Soc. Civ. Eng.*, EM2, 177–95, 1966.
18. R. H. GALLAGHER and J. PADLOG, 'Discrete element approach to structural instability analysis', *J.A.I.A.A.*, **1**, 1537–9, 1963.
19. R. G. ANDERSON, B. M. IRONS, and O. C. ZIENKIEWICZ, 'Vibration and stability of plates using finite elements', *Int. J. Solids Struct.*, **4**, 1031–55, 1968.
20. W. G. CARSON and R. E. NEWTON, 'Plate buckling analysis using a fully compatible finite element', *J.A.I.A.A.*, **8**, 527–9, 1969.
21. A. P. KABAILA and B. FRAEIJS DE VEUBEKE, 'A quadrilateral element for plate buckling analysis', *Int. J. Num. Meth. in Eng.*, to be published 1971.
22. D. W. MURRAY and E. L. WILSON, 'Finite element post buckling analysis of thin elastic plates', *Proc. 2nd Conf. Matrix Meth. in Struct. Mech.*, Wright Patterson Air Force Base, Ohio, 1968.
23. K. C. ROCKEY and D. K. BAGCHI, 'Buckling of plate girder webs under partial edge loadings', *Int. J. Mech. Sci.*, **12**, 61–76, 1970.
24. T. M. ROBERTS and D. G. ASHWELL, 'Post-buckling analysis of slightly curved plates by the finite element method', *Report 2*, Dept. of Civil and Struct. Engineering, University of Wales, Cardiff, 1969.
25. R. G. ANDERSON, *A finite element eigenvalue solution system*, Ph.D. thesis, Univ. of Wales, Swansea, 1968.
26. R. GALLAGHER, R. GELLATLY, R. MALLETT, and J. PADLOG, 'A discrete element procedure for thin shell instability analysis', *J.A.I.A.A.*, **5**, 138–145, 1967.
27. R. H. GALLAGHER and H. T. Y. YANG, 'Elastic Instability predictions for doubly curved shells', *Proc. 2nd Conf. Matrix Methods*, Air Force Inst. of Tech., Wright Patterson A.F. Base, Ohio, 1968.
28. T. H. H. PIAN and PING TONG, 'Variational formulation of finite displacement analysis', *Symp. Int. Un. Th. Appl. Mech. on 'High speed computing of elastic structures'*, Liége, 1970.
29. H. C. MARTIN, 'Finite Elements and the analysis of geometrically non-linear

problems', U.S.–Japan Seminar on Matrix Methods in Structural Analysis and Design, Tokyo, 1970.

30. A. C. WALKER, 'A non-linear finite element analysis of shallow circular arches', *Int. J. Solids Struct.*, 5, 97–107, 1969.

31. J. M. T. THOMPSON and A. C. WALKER, 'A non-linear perturbation analysis of discrete structural systems', *Int. J. Solids Struct.*, 4, 757–767, 1968.

32. J. S. PRZEMIENIECKI, 'Stability analysis of complex structures using discrete element techniques', Symp. on Struct. Stability and optimisation, Loughborough Univ., March 1967.

33. J. CONNOR and N. MORIN, 'Perturbation techniques in the analysis of geometrically non-linear shells', Symp. Int. Un. Th. Appl. Mech. on 'High speed computing of elastic structures', Liége, 1970.

34. Y. C. FUNG, *Foundation of solid mechanics*, Prentice Hall Int., 1965.

35. J. T. ODEN, 'Finite plane strain of incompressible elastic solids by the finite element method', *The Aeronautical Quarterly*, 19, 254–64, 1967.

36. J. T. ODEN and T. SATO, 'Finite deformation of elastic membranes by the finite element method', *Int. J. Solids & Struct.*, 3, 471–88, 1967.

37. J. T. ODEN, 'Numerical formulation of non-linear elasticity problems', *Proc. Am. Soc. Civ. Eng.*, 93, ST3, 235–55, 1967.

38. J. T. ODEN, 'Finite element applications in non-linear structural analysis', Proc. Symp. on Application of Finite Element Methods in Civil Engineering, *Am. Soc. Civ. Eng.*, Vanderbilt Univ., 1969.

39. J. A. STRICKLIN, 'Non-linear dynamic analysis of shells of revolution', Symp. Int. Un. Th. Appl. Mech. on 'High speed computing of elastic structures', Liége, 1970.

20. Computer Methods and Computer Programs

[Y. K. CHEUNG and I. P. KING]

20.1 Introduction

The finite element method is readily programmed for high-speed digital computers and in fact the procedure would be of little use if computers were not available to solve the simultaneous equations that result[1] from the discretization process.

A number of very large capacity finite element programs have been developed. The earlier ones were highly specialized application programs and were often written in machine language. The similarity of program structure which was recognized in the course of different applications led to the development of more sophisticated general systems. The ASKA† program is an early example of such a development; it too was highly machine oriented. In applications for aerospace type problems the capability to solve the problem at all levels is emphasized and efficiency of the system for smaller size analyses is considerably impaired.

The rapid development of successive generations of computers has made it essential to write programs that are easily interchangeable from machine to machine. The availability of Fortran as such a language has led to its use for most of the programing effort associated with finite elements.

The NASA ‡ program represents an attempt to create a flexible programing system for application to the large scale research and development problems of the American Aerospace industry.

The development of FESS (Finite Element Solution Swansea) and FINESSE at Swansea have been oriented more to the efficient solution of small and medium size systems typified by structural engineering problems such as bridges, dams, and reactor vessels. In these systems much attention has been paid to creating a simple concept which is readily modified for special cases.

† Developed under Prof. J. H. Argyris at Stuttgart, Germany.

‡ National Aeronautical Space Administration.

435

In all programing efforts it is important to bear in mind that program efficiency must be matched against effort to program. Thus, the less program that must be written from scratch the more justification there is for an effort to create an efficient program. When programing finite element problems it is important to recognize the limitations of the computer that is available, and to change to a larger size machine as soon as 'squeezing' or special programing becomes necessary. Special coding is seldom worth the effort as the program invariably runs more slowly and development costs are usually higher.

The program and programing techniques described in this chapter have some common features with FESS but only represent it at a rudimentary level. Many storage saving devices and refinements which exist in FESS are omitted for the sake of simplicity. This system has, however, been extended to the analysis of complex elasto-plastic problems without any basic change of structure. The analyses of stability and vibration problems using advanced eigenvalue techniques have also been incorporated in the system, although only a simple program will be presented here.

20.2 Finite Element Systems

Programs utilizing the finite element concept may have a variety of different aims. In most cases only linear elastic analysis is required but problem size may vary from less than a hundred to several thousand degrees of freedom. In dynamic analysis or stability evaluation eigenvalue solution may be sought or various incremental iterative procedures may be needed for non-linear problems.

A potential user with a particular finite element problem would be faced with impossible difficulties if forced to program from scratch for each new class of problems. It is therefore essential that the programing effort of previous workers should be utilized.

The typical finite element program is composed of a series of common modules, which may have different uses in different contexts. Typical modules are data input, element stiffness, equation solving procedures, mass matrix and eigenvalue programs, stress calculations, and output display.

In programing applications these modules appear as subroutines. It is convenient if the interfaces and data structure of these subroutines are standardized sufficiently that they may be used interchangeably. In a given application it is then possible to assemble appropriate routines with the new programing effort restricted only to the area of user innovation or special need.

In such systems the *master driving program* is a very simple routine whose only function is calling the various subroutines in appropriate order. For certain classes of problems standard master programs can be written and the subroutine selection automated. In large organizations with specific types of problems, such standard applications can be the most satisfactory solution. However, for research uses the flexibility left by using a manually assembled program is probably advantageous.

It is important that the development of such modules be accompanied by sufficient documentation that allows easy use by persons other than the original writer. The inclusion of comment statements at relevant positions can be extremely effective in giving hints to the users.

Example master program. The example program presented in this chapter is a plane strain linear analysis program with a limited size capability which is aimed at allowing its use on small computers. The whole program is written in Fortran IV, and represents a very simple application of modular concept. Even so it is workable for practical problems and may be easily expanded by a reader with experience in Fortran. An example of a plane stress problem (using modified material constants) together with the assembly of subroutines used in the program is given in section 20.7. For other elements or purposes appropriate master programs must be constructed. Typical flow chart is given on p. 438.

Note that the loop on load cases is a means of saving storage at the expense of computer time. This is sometimes mandatory when the individual effects of the many load cases have to be examined, as in bridge analysis. For problems with only a few load cases, it is often more advantageous to solve them simultaneously.

Variable definitions—common block /CONTR/

VARIABLE	DEFINITION
TITLE (12)	12 word title array
NP	Number of nodal points
NE	Number of elements
NB	Number of restrained boundary nodes
NDF	Number of degrees of freedom per node
NCN	Maximum number of nodes per element
NLD	Number of load cases
NMAT	Number of element material types
NSZF	Number of equations in the system
LI	Load case counter
NT4	Logical storage device number

(*continued p. 439*)

Flow chart—PROGRAM MAIN

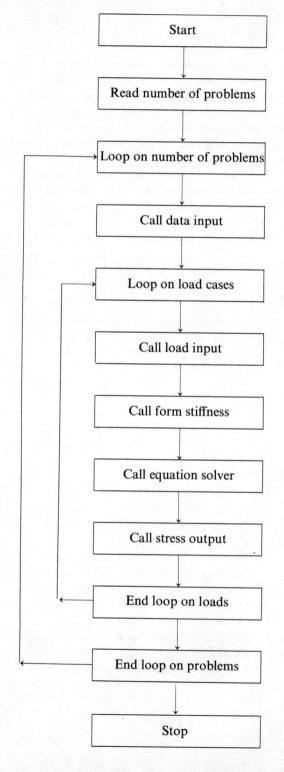

Basic blank common

VARIABLE

VARIABLE		DEFINITION
CORD	(100,2)	Nodal point co-ordinate array
NOP	(200,4)	Element connection array
IMAT	(200)	Element material type array
ORT	(25,2)	Element type material properties
NBC	(25)	Restrained boundary node numbers
NFIX	(25)	Boundary condition type
R1	(200)	Load vector
SK	(200,40)	Rectangular matrix for equations

Variable definitions—program MAIN

VARIABLE	DEFINITION
NPROB	Number of problems
NPR	Counter on number of problems

Pr. 20–1

```
CONTROL MAIN PROGRAM
COMMON/CONTR/TITLE(12),NP,NE,NB,NDF,NCN,NLD,NMAT,NSZF,LI,NT4
COMMON CORD(100,2),NOP(200,4),IMAT(200),ORT(25,2),NBC(25),NFIX(25)
1,R1(200),SK(200,40)
                                                                        10
              INITIALIZE TAPE NO.
              AND NUMBER OF CORNER NODE MAX.

NT4=11
NCN=3
READ(5,1) NPROB

              LOOP ON NO. OF PROBLEMS

DO 400 NPR=1,NPROB                                                       13
REWIND NT4                                                               16
              READ INPUT GEOMETRY AND PROP.
                                                                        14
CALL GDATA                                                               19
NSZF=NP*NDF                                                              21
DO 200LI=1,NLD                                                           22

              READ LOADS
```

```
        CALL LOAD                                                        23
C
C                               FORM THEN SOLVE SIMULTANEOUS
C                               EQUATIONS
C
        CALL FORMK
        CALL SOLVE                                                       28
C
C                               CALCULATE STRESSES
C
        CALL STRESS
  200 CONTINUE                                                           32
  400 CONTINUE                                                           33
    1 FORMAT(9I5)                                                        35
        STOP                                                             36
        END                                                             37
```

20.3 Data Input

In the internal operations of a finite element program four fundamental sets of data are required in addition to control information. They are:

(a) Junction co-ordinates and element characteristics;
(b) Material properties for each element type;
(c) Boundary conditions;
(d) Loads.

Special data input routines may be written but their basic function is to create data of the four types shown above from simplified input which describes the problem. For the main program the full set of data is necessary, however.

20.3.1 *Junction co-ordinates and element characteristics.* The junction co-ordinates refer to the co-ordinates of all the nodal points (e.g., x_i and y_i of any node i in a plane stress problem), and they are listed in sequential order. The resulting stiffness matrices for most cases are independent of the position of the origin of the axes, which is usually fixed arbitrarily by the analyst.

Element characteristics include the element connections, in which all the nodal numbers associated with each element are given, and a type number representing the material properties of that element. These characteristics are also listed sequentially.

20.3.2 *Material properties.* In most finite element applications the material properties are the same for large groups of elements. It is therefore convenient to give each element a material number and to read in separately the information that describes element properties.

20.3.3 *Loads.* For the greatest simplicity and flexibility, the loads may be read in as a single vector, which is used directly in the solution routine. In many cases, when the nodes which are loaded form only a small percentage of the total nodes in the system, it is advantageous to read in only the non-zero loads together with their nodal numbers. The load vector would of course be set to zero beforehand, to take care of the unloaded nodes.

In some applications, however, body forces must be included and a special routine must be programed to generate the load vector from the geometry of the system and the material properties. Load generation subroutines can also be used in generating nodal loads from distributed load conditions. The final output for such routines are load vectors which are identical in form to the simple vectors that may be read from cards.

20.3.4 *Boundary conditions.* Boundary conditions can be applied either at the element level (during element generation) or by modification of the simultaneous equations immediately prior to solution. The latter method is convenient for simple elements but becomes complex when applied to higher order elements or to unusual boundary conditions, such as restraint in an arbitrary direction. In the example subprogram listed in this section, nodal boundary conditions are read in as combinations of 0 and 1 for each degree of freedom with zero denoting a free degree of freedom and a 1 denoting a fixed degree of freedom. That is,

01 means free in X direction fixed in Y direction,
10 means fixed in X direction free in Y direction,
11 means fixed in both directions.

Example subroutines. Two subroutines are listed below. Subroutine GDATA reads the basic geometric data and subroutine LOAD reads the load vector. Neither of these routines contains any data generation capability. Flow charts are given on pp. 442 and 443.

Variable definition—subroutine GDATA

VARIABLE	DEFINITION
I1	Control for print of input data

Variable definition—subroutine LOAD

VARIABLE	DEFINITION
R(3)*	Temporary array of loads at node NQ

(*continued p. 443*)

* This array is in blank common.

Flow chart—subroutine GDATA

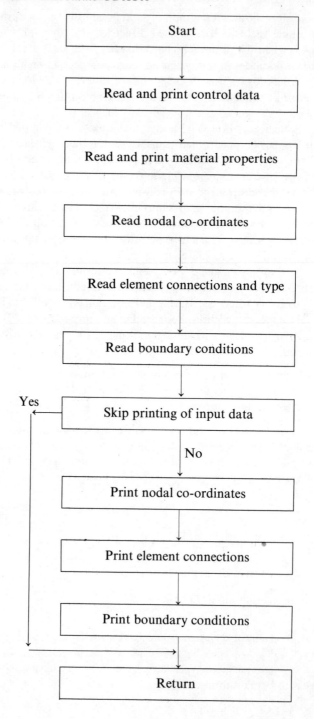

Flow chart—subroutine LOAD

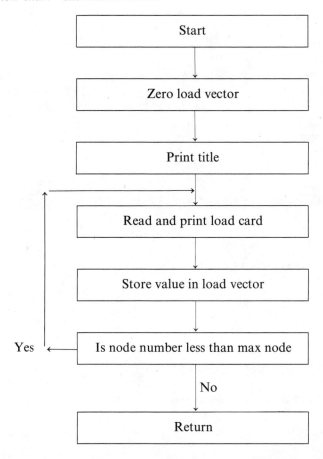

Pr. 20–2

```
SUBROUTINE GDATA                                                          1
COMMON/CONTR/TITLE(12),NP,NE,NB,NDF,NCN,NLD,NMAT,NSZF,LI,NT4
COMMON CORD(100,2),NOP(200,4),IMAT(200),ORT(25,2),NBC(25),NFIX(25)
1,R1(200),SK(200,40)
2,R(3)
```

                                   READ AND PRINT TITLE AND CONTROL

```
READ(5,7) TITLE                                                         11
WRITE(6,100) TITLE                                                      15
READ(5,1) NP,NE,NB,NLD,NDF,NMAT,I1
WRITE(6,1) NP,NE,NB,NLD,NDF,NMAT,I1
```

```
C
C                                    READ AND PRINT MATERIAL DATA
C
      READ(5,8) (N,(ORT(N,I),I=1,2),L=1,NMAT)
      WRITE(6,108)                                                 17
      WRITE(6,8) (N,(ORT(N,I),I=1,2),N=1,NMAT)
C                                                                  35
C                                    READ NODAL POINT DATA
C                                                                  37
      READ(5,2) (N,(CORD(N,M),M=1,2),L=1,NP)
C                                                                  40
C                                    READ ELEMENT DATA
C                                                                  42
      READ(5,3) (N,(NOP(N,M),M=1,4),IMAT(N),L=1,NE)
C                                                                  44
C                                    READ BOUNDARY DATA
C                                                                  46
      READ(5,4) (NBC(I),NFIX(I),I=1,NB)
  480 IF(I1.NE.0) GO TO 500                                        50
C
C                                    PRINT INPUT DATA
C
      WRITE(6,102)                                                 51
      WRITE(6,2) (N,(CORD(N,M),M=1,2),N=1,NP)                      52
      WRITE(6,103)                                                 53
      WRITE(6,3) (N,(NOP(N,M),M=1,4),IMAT(N),N=1,NE)
      WRITE(6,104)                                                 55
      WRITE(6,4) (NBC(I),NFIX(I),I=1,NB)

  500 CONTINUE                                                     58
    1 FORMAT(9I5)                                                  71
    2 FORMAT(I10,2F10.3)                                           72
    3 FORMAT(6I5)
    4 FORMAT(2I5)
    7 FORMAT(12A6)                                                 75
    8 FORMAT(I10,2F10.2)
  100 FORMAT(1H1,12A6)                                             77
  102 FORMAT(20H0 NODAL POINTS         )
  103 FORMAT(20H0 ELEMENTS             )
  104 FORMAT(21H0 BOUNDARY CONDITIONS)                             80
  108 FORMAT(1H0,20H MATERIAL PROPERTIES)                          81
      RETURN                                                       82
      END                                                          83
```

Pr. 20–3

```
SUBROUTINE LOAD                                                    1
COMMON/CONTR/TITLE(12),NP,NE,NB,NDF,NCN,NLD,NMAT,NSZF,LI,NT4
COMMON CORD(100,2),NOP(200,4),IMAT(200),ORT(25,2),NBC(25),NFIX(25)
1,R1(200),SK(200,40)
2,R(3)


                         ZERO LOAD ARRAY


    DO 160 J = 1,NSZF                                             10
160 R1(J) = 0.                                                    11
    WRITE(6,100) TITLE,LI                                         12
    WRITE(6,109)                                                  13


               READ, PRINT AND STORE LOAD CARD


165 CONTINUE                                                      20
    READ(5,9)                                                     21
   1NQ,(R(K),K = 1,NDF)                                           22
    WRITE(6,9)                                                    23
   1NQ,(R(K),K = 1,NDF)                                           24
    DO 170 K = 1,NDF                                              25
    IC = (NQ − 1)∗NDF + K                                         26
170 R1(IC) = R(K) + R1(IC)                                        27


               IF NODE NUMBER NOT MAX. NODE PT.
               GO BACK AND READ MORE
                                                                  9
    IF(NQ.LT.NP) GO TO 165                                        28
  9 FORMAT(I10,3F10.2)                                            39
 20 FORMAT(10X,4I5)                                               40
100 FORMAT(1H1,12A6,5X, 10HLOAD CASE, I5)                         41
109 FORMAT(1H0,6H LOADS)                                          42
    RETURN                                                        43
    END                                                           44
```

20.4 Stiffness Generation

The general purpose of a stiffness generation routine is the creation of the element stiffness appropriate to the problem. It usually has all necessary data transmitted to it through common storage and passes the element stiffness matrix back to the calling program, or writes it on peripheral storage. It is highly dependent upon the basic mathematical formulation for element stiffness, and in particular it depends upon whether numerical integration is needed for the element or whether direct integration is possible.

For simple elements the basic operations are to:

(a) Reduce element to a local co-ordinate system,
(b) Construct the strain displacement matrix B (or its equivalent),
(c) Construct the stress-strain relationships D,
(d) Carry out the matrix multiplications $B^T DB$,
(e) Apply integration over the area for the terms of the product matrix. (For the plane stress case this reduces to a simple multiplication by the triangular area.),
(f) If necessary transform the resulting matrix back into the global co-ordinate system.

The local co-ordinate system usually depends upon the form of derivation used for the stiffness matrix. In simple formulations (such as the triangular plane strain element) the local co-ordinate system can be simply the global co-ordinate system or a changing set of axes using one of the nodes or the centroid of the triangle as the origin.

Area, volume, or curvilinear co-ordinates are naturally used at this stage if necessary as described in Chapters 7 and 8.

The stiffness generation routine may also be used to generate the stress matrix, which produces the element stresses when multiplied by the relevant nodal displacements. Such a matrix is frequently a by-product of the stiffness generation and little computer time is required to generate it. Two approaches are possible. Firstly the stress matrix may be generated at the same time as the stiffness matrix and then stored in a peripheral storage device for later use (i.e., first of all computing DB, and then $B^T DB$), or alternatively the stress matrix DB may be regenerated when required. The choice depends on the speed of access to peripheral storage and on the time required to duplicate certain calculations.

In complex elements such as the isoparametric types, the order of calculation outlined above is not economical generally. Special computational devices may be used such as outlined for example by Irons.[2]

Depending on the nature of the problem, various modifications may be introduced into the basic procedure. A few such cases are listed below:

(a) When higher order elements with mid-side nodes or small element groups with a pre-arranged pattern are used the nodal data may be given only for certain nodes, and generation procedures used to construct the complete geometry of the elements. Occasionally an element will contain a node unattached to any other element (e.g., an internal degree of freedom) and in such a case the corresponding degrees of freedom may be eliminated and a reduced stiffness matrix used for the assembly.

(b) A further modification may be the use of displacement co-ordinate axes (e.g., nodal reference co-ordinates in reference 3) and therefore of transformation matrices which vary from node to node. This leads to an element stiffness matrix which is not referred to a unique co-ordinate system. Such a formulation possesses advantages in the following cases:

(i) for a node in which one (or some) of its degrees of freedom are restrained in a direction inclined to the global axes and direct introduction of boundary conditions would be cumbersome;

(ii) for applying symmetry or antisymmetry conditions to reduce the total number of equations; e.g., in analysing $\frac{1}{8}$ instead of $\frac{1}{4}$ of a plate in a case of double symmetry, or in using non-axisymmetric elements for analysing axi-symmetric problems[3]; and

(iii) for analysing doubly-curved shells, in which the z axis at any node is made to coincide with the outward normal of the shell surface, so that only five degrees of freedom are needed for each node.[4]

Example program. The example subroutine constructs the 6×6 stiffness matrix for a plane strain element and stores the stress matrix on a peripheral tape for later use in deriving the element stresses. Flow chart is given on p. 448.

Variable definitions—subroutine STIFT2(N)

N in calling sequence defines element numbers

VARIABLE	DEFINITION
I, J, K	Element connections, later used as loop counters
AJ, BJ, AK, BK	Local co-ordinates of triangle
A(3, 6)*	Strain displacement matrix
ESTIFM (12, 12)*	Stress-strain matrix, later used for element stiffness matrix
B(3, 9)*	Stress back-substitution matrix

* These arrays are in blank common.

Pr. 20–4

```
SUBROUTINE STIFT2(N)                                                    1
COMMON/CONTR/TITLE(12),NP,NE,NB,NDF,NCN,NLD,NMAT,NSZF,LI,NT4
COMMON CORD(100,2),NOP(200,4),IMAT(200),ORT(25,2),NBC(25),NFIX(25)
1,R1(200),SK(200,40)
2,ESTIFM(12,12),A(3,6),B(3,9)
```

Flow chart—subroutine STIFT2

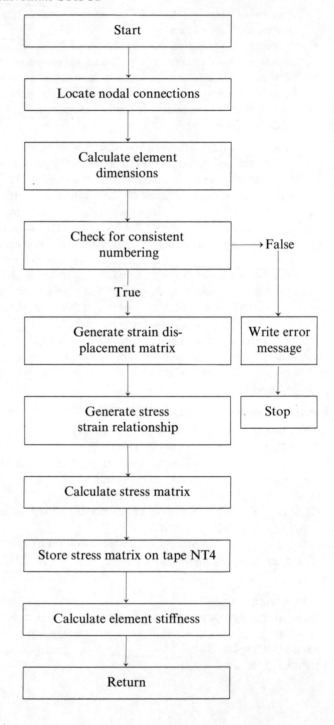

DETERMINE ELEMENT CONNECTIONS

```
I = NOP(N,1)                                                    11
J = NOP(N,2)                                                    12
K = NOP(N,3)                                                    13
L = IMAT(N)                                                     14
```

SET UP LOCAL COORDINATE SYSTEM

```
AJ = CORD(J,1) - CORD(I,1)                                      15
AK = CORD(K,1) - CORD(I,1)                                      16
BJ = CORD(J,2) - CORD(I,2)                                      17
BK = CORD(K,2) - CORD(I,2)                                      18
AREA = (AJ*BK - AK*BJ)/2.                                       19
IF(AREA.LE.0.) GO TO 220                                        20
```

FORM STRAIN DISP. MATRIX

```
A(1,1) = BJ - BK                                                23
A(1,2) = 0.                                                     24
A(1,3) = BK                                                     25
A(1,4) = 0.                                                     26
A(1,5) = - BJ                                                   27
A(1,6) = 0.                                                     28
A(2,1) = 0.                                                     29
A(2,2) = AK - AJ                                                30
A(2,3) = 0.                                                     31
A(2,4) = - AK                                                   32
A(2,5) = 0.                                                     33
A(2,6) = AJ                                                     34
A(3,1) = AK - AJ                                                35
A(3,2) = BJ - BK                                                36
A(3,3) = - AK                                                   37
A(3,4) = BK                                                     38
A(3,5) = AJ                                                     39
A(3,6) = - BJ                                                   40
```

FORM STRESS STRAIN MATRIX

```
COMM = ORT(L,1)/((1. + ORT(L,2))*(1. - ORT(L,2)*2.)*AREA)
ESTIFM(1,1) = COMM*(1. - ORT(L,2)   )
ESTIFM(1,2) = COMM*ORT(L,2)                                     42
ESTIFM(1,3) = 0.                                                43
```

```
      ESTIFM(2,1) = ESTIFM(1,2)                                      44
      ESTIFM(2,2) = ESTIFM(1,1)
      ESTIFM(2,3) = 0.                                               46
      ESTIFM(3,1) = 0.                                               47
      ESTIFM(3,2) = 0.                                               48
      ESTIFM(3,3) = ORT(L,1)/(2.*(1.+ORT(L,2))*AREA)
C
C                          B IS THE STRESS BACKSUBSTITUTION
C                          MATRIX AND IS SAVED ON TAPE
C
      DO 205 I = 1,3                                                 50
      DO 205 J = 1,6                                                 51
      B(I,J) = 0.                                                    52
      DO 205 K = 1,3                                                 53
  205 B(I,J) = B(I,J) + ESTIFM(I,K)/2.*A(K,J)                        54
      WRITE(NT4) N,((B(I,J),J=1,6),I=1,3)
C
C                          ESTIFM IS STIFFNESS MATRIX
C
      DO 210 I = 1,6                                                 55
      DO 210 J = 1,6                                                 56
      ESTIFM(I,J) = 0.                                               57
      DO   210 K = 1,3                                               58
  210 ESTIFM(I,J) = ESTIFM(I,J) + B(K,I)/2.*A(K,J)                   59
      RETURN                                                         63
C
C                          ERROR EXIT FOR BAD CONNECTIONS
C
  220 WRITE(6,100) N                                                 64
  100 FORMAT(33H1ZERO OR NEGATIVE AREA ELEMENT NO,14/21 H0EXECUTION
     1TERMINATED)                                                    66
      STOP                                                           67
      END                                                            68
```

20.5 Assembly and Solution of Equations

The key factor in any finite element program is the subroutine for the solution of simultaneous equations. The choice of technique depends upon the size of problem envisaged and upon the type of computer available.

In the simplest formulation the equations are completely formed. This approach requires storage equal to N^2 where N is the number of equations, and is possible only where the problem size is small and the computer large. For example, 100 equations require 10,000 locations of storage.

Two methods of solution have been highly developed for the solution of the simultaneous equations: (*a*) Direct solution, in which an exact (within round-off accuracy) solution is sought; (*b*) Iteration, in which a successive approximation technique is used to converge on the true solution.

The Gauss elimination procedure is frequently used for direct solution and the Gauss-Seidel procedure for iterative solution.

20.5.1 *The Gauss elimination procedure.* Let a set of N equations be represented in partitioned form as

$$\begin{bmatrix} K_{11} & K_{12} \\ K_{21} & K_{22} \end{bmatrix} \begin{bmatrix} \delta_1 \\ \delta_2 \end{bmatrix} = \begin{bmatrix} F_1 \\ F_2 \end{bmatrix} \tag{20.1}$$

where K_{11} is a 1×1 matrix
K_{12} is a $1 \times (N-1)$ matrix
K_{21} is a $(N-1) \times 1$ matrix
K_{22} is a $(N-1) \times (N-1)$ matrix.

δ is a vector of unknowns and F a vector of known values. Then the Gaussian elimination procedure allows the reduction of the K matrix to an $N-1$ matrix equation of the form

$$K^*\delta = F^* \tag{20.2}$$

where

$$K^* = K_{22} - K_{21}K_{11}^{-1}K_{12}, \tag{20.3}$$

$$F^* = F_2 - K_{21}K_{11}^{-1}F_1. \tag{20.4}$$

This procedure may be repeated by partitioning K^* in the same way. The fundamental operation is the triple product $K_{21}.K_{11}^{-1}.K_{12}$.

Since K_{11} is (1×1), the number of operations is proportional to $(N-1)^2$. When the matrix K^* is reduced to a 1×1 matrix, direct solution is possible for the last unknown δ_n.

Back-substitution may now be applied to solve for the remaining δ's from equations of the type

$$\delta_1 = K_{11}^{-1}F_1 - K_{11}^{-1}K_{12}\delta_2. \tag{20.5}$$

This procedure represents the simplest direct method in which all terms of the matrix are stored and operated upon. However, it is possible to take advantage of the symmetry that exists in structural stiffness matrices by restricting operations to the upper diagonal area, whereupon the number of operations is reduced approximately by half. The total number of operations for solution is about $\frac{1}{6}N^3$.

The typical assembled stiffness matrix contains many zero terms, and in particular there is a distance from the diagonal beyond which no terms exist. This is called banding of the matrix and the distance from the diagonal term to the last term in any row is called the semi-bandwidth. The banded nature of the matrix may be demonstrated by partitioning the matrix, as shown below, where a zero submatrix replaces that part of K_{12} which has zero values, i.e.,

$$K = \begin{bmatrix} K_{11} & K_{12} & 0 \\ K_{12}^T & K_{22} & K_{23} \\ 0 & K_{23}^T & K_{33} \end{bmatrix}. \tag{20.6}$$

Symmetry has been assumed and the matrix sizes are as follows:

$$K_{11} \, (1 \times 1), \quad K_{12} \, (1 \times m), \quad K_{22} \, (m \times m),$$

$$K_{23} \, (m \times (N-1-m)), \quad K_{33}((N-1-m) \times (N-1-m)).$$

When K_{11} is eliminated only K_{22} is modified as the zero submatrix causes no change in K_{23} and K_{33}. The number of operations in an elimination is now proportional to m^2 and total number of operations to

$$\left[\frac{1}{2} \sum_{n=1}^{N} m_n^2 \right]$$

or approximately to $\frac{1}{2} N m_{max}^2$ where m_{max} is the maximum semi-bandwidth.

In practice the semi-bandwidth is usually less than $\frac{1}{10}$ of the matrix size, and the band-matrix technique as described reduces the arithmetic to some 3 per cent of that without taking advantage of banding.

A further advantage is the compaction of storage that can result since the matrix can be stored in a rectangular $N \times m_{max}$ array as is shown in Fig. 20.1. However, the total number of equations that can be solved will be limited by the size of the rectangular array.

The banded form of Fig. 20.6 is well suited to solution of large systems of equations because at the time of elimination only K_{22} is operated upon, and so only K_{22} is required in fast core at the time of elimination. However, to be really efficient the assemblage and elimination processes should go hand in hand, so that the stiffness equations for a node are eliminated as soon as they are formed completely. This can be achieved quite easily by always having the smallest nodal number of an element as its first nodal number, and then ordering the elements so that all the first nodal numbers are in sequential order. In this way, the assemblage will stop automatically whenever the first nodal number of an element is larger than the nodal number which is currently being solved. After the elimination of K_{11} the whole remaining matrix will be shifted so that the first coefficient of the modified K_{22} matrix will now take up the (1, 1) position, while the others take up their relevant positions accordingly. The elimina-ted equations may be stored temporarily in a buffer area, and then written on peripheral storage as a block for subsequent back-substitution. For smaller problems, the buffer area might be large enough to accommodate all the eliminated equations and no data transfer will be necessary.

$$
\begin{bmatrix}
K_{11} & K_{12} & & & \\
K_{12}^T & K_{22} & K_{23} & K_{24} & \\
 & K_{23}^T & K_{33} & K_{34} & \\
 & K_{24}^T & K_{34}^T & K_{44} & K_{45} \\
 & & & K_{45}^T & K_{55}
\end{bmatrix}
\qquad
\begin{bmatrix}
K_{11} & K_{12} & 0 \\
K_{22} & K_{23} & K_{24} \\
K_{33} & K_{34} & 0 \\
K_{44} & K_{45} & 0 \\
K_{55} & 0 & 0
\end{bmatrix}
$$

(a) Original Square Matrix   (b) Rectangular Representation

Fig. 20.1   Storage of matrix for banded solution

The new matrix can then be rearranged in the form of K_{11}, K_{12}, and K_{22}, and the elimination process repeated.

The total core required at any stage of the elimination is $(m+1) \times (m+2)$, or half of this if symmetry is allowed for. This process makes it possible to solve an unlimited number of equations subject to a maximum bandwidth limitation. In most finite element applications, accuracy is not a significant problem. If necessary it is possible to convert the equation solving procedure to double precision with a resulting increase in storage and execution time. It is sometimes possible to obtain improved accuracy if the computed values are substituted into the original set of equations to obtain the residuals. If the residuals are now used as the new right-hand side and the equations solved again, the sum of the two sets of solution vectors will represent an improved solution. However, the computed residuals are more often used as a means for assessing round-off damage.

20.5.2 *An efficient storage structure for banded systems.* To reduce com-puter storage requirements, the large equation-solver of the FESS pro-gram (not listed in this chapter) uses a one-dimensional vector to store the upper triangular part of the stiffness matrix that is currently needed at the time of elimination of the uppermost equation. Figure 20.2 shows an example of the arrangement in storage.

The columnwise storage order was chosen because it is easier to implement than the row-wise order. In the FESS equation solver, the back-substitution matrices (Eq. (20.5)) are stored at the high end of the one-dimensional array. When the stiffness matrix and these matrices overlap, the high end of storage is written on tape and the process is repeated. This method is efficient because it insures that long tape records can be used. Sometimes it is possible to solve the equations without peripheral storage.

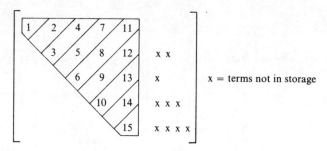

Fig. 20.2   Layout of equation storage in FESS

20.5.3 *The Gauss-Seidel iterative method.* In general the nth equation of the N equation system may be written as

$$\sum_{i=1}^{n-1} k_{ni}\delta_i + k_{nn}\delta_n + \sum_{i=n+1}^{N} k_{ni}\delta_i = F_n. \tag{20.7}$$

This may be arranged so that

$$\delta_n = k_{nn}^{-1}\left\{F_n - \sum_{i=1}^{n-1} k_{ni}\delta_i - \sum_{i=n+1}^{N} k_{ni}\delta_i\right\}. \tag{20.8}$$

If an iterative procedure is assumed in which the values of δ_i on the right-hand side are assumed to be the latest approximation, then at the mth cycle of iteration

$$\delta_n^m = k_{nn}^{-1}\left\{F_n - \sum_{i=1}^{n-1} k_{ni}\delta_i^m - \sum_{i=n+1}^{N} k_{ni}\delta_i^{m-1}\right\}. \tag{20.9}$$

This is the Gauss-Seidel iterative procedure.

One refinement commonly used is that the change in δ for any cycle is multiplied by a factor to give a modified final estimate of δ, i.e.,

$$\delta_n^m = \delta_n^{m-1} + \beta(\delta_n^{m*} - \delta_n^{m-1}) \tag{20.10}$$

where δ_n^{m*} is the value calculated using Eq. (20.9) and β is the *over-relaxation factor* which usually lies between 1·0 and 2·0. For many practical applications a value close to 1·8 has been found to be effective.

The Gauss-Seidel iterative method is readily programed for computers. The stiffness matrix is stored in a compact form with all non-zero terms skipped, and with a pointer matrix indicating the column location of a particular term. Equation (20.9) with the modification of Eq. (20.10) is then applied for each equation. The process is then repeated on the improved vector for enough cycles to give an acceptable solution, convergence generally being measured in terms of the variation from one solution to the next.

Iterative methods are attractive for non-linear problems, because they frequently require repeated solutions to very similar problems, and good initial guesses are therefore available for the solution vector. Also, in such cases arithmetic can be saved by accepting solutions with a lower level of accuracy during the intermediate steps.

One drawback of the computer application of iterative methods is the requirement of repetition of the basic cycle through all the equations, which makes the process slow if peripheral storage is needed to store the equations. However, the compact storage of the stiffness matrix enables a large number of equations to be solved within core storage; e.g., 1000 plus equations for 32K word-storage. But a major disadvantage is that only one load vector can normally be treated for each solution, because storage of the displacements is critical.

A pair of subroutines FORMK (which forms the appropriate stiffness and pointer matrices) and SOLVE (which solves the equations by Gauss-Seidel iteration) are given in Appendix 20A. These routines are simplified systems in which the number of cycles and the convergence limits are specified. They also use a one-to-one correspondence between stiffness and pointer matrices. These two routines are completely compatible with the other routines given in this chapter. Note that in this case FORMK creates terms both above and below the diagonal in the compacted stiffness matrix, and is thus different from the other FORMK (pr. 20.5) which is used for direct solution.

20.5.4 *Other direct solution procedures.* A variation of the band matrix elimination process is the so-called *sparse matrix method* which is basically a bookkeeping device. Here the submatrix is stored in a compacted form with a pointer matrix to indicate the row and column location in the full matrix. In finite element problems with the same number of degrees of freedom at every node, the pointer matrix may be compacted to represent nodal submatrices.

The sparse matrix procedure carries out the elimination in the same form as previously described but uses the pointer matrix as an index. This makes it possible to operate only on non-zero submatrices. The advantage gained from operations avoided must be weighed against the extra time required to access locations through the pointer matrix. The storage requirement is dependent upon the number of non-zero submatrices at any time during the elimination process and is independent of bandwidth. It should be noted that the elimination process creates non-zero submatrices in locations that were previously zero. For maximum efficiency of storage and solution time the equations should be ordered to maintain the minimum number of terms in the matrix at any time in the solution. To define the optimum order is a complex problem in dynamic programing and alternative approximate procedures must be used.[5] Incidentally such re-ordering procedures can be used to advantage to minimize the number of non-zero operations in banded procedures. However, the bandwidth may become excessive and destroy any gain.

Appendix 20B lists two subroutines FORMK and SOLVE which construct the stiffness matrix (in upper triangular, rectangular form) and a matching pointer matrix, and solve the equations by a sparse matrix solution method.

A more fundamental change of approach is the *front solution method.*[6] Like the sparse matrix method the stiffness is generated in a compacted form with a pointer matrix. The method is, however, geared to elimination based upon elements, and is independent of nodal numbering. The front solution derives its name from the creation of a front which proceeds through the nodal system. The method is particularly applicable when elements have mid-side nodes as it can lead to appreciable savings in storage over the banded solution process.

The advance of the FINESSE system which uses frontal elimination has indeed been especially concerned with higher order elements, and the emphasis is on element data. For example, because the preferred mode of output is per element, a greatly increased number of load cases can be accommodated in core storage. Accordingly during elimination only a subset of the load vector appears in core at any time.

The front solution method is most efficient when the large size problems of three-dimensional elements appear.

20.5.5 *Some special facilities.* In more extensive programs some special facilities may be inserted to advantage:

(a) Substructure capability. Instead of completely solving the equations it is convenient at times to produce a reduced matrix in which a limited number of equations are not eliminated and a stiffness matrix and a reduced load vector is then output. This can be used to create a stiffness matrix for an assemblage of elements in which all but the outer points have been eliminated.

(b) Insertion of additional stiffness. Complementary to the substructure capability is the facility to insert additional special stiffness terms into the total stiffness matrix. This allows direct insertion of elastic boundary conditions such as spring supports as well as substructure stiffnesses. These two capabilities are particularly useful in non-linear problems where large parts of the structure remain linearly elastic. In such cases the linearly elastic structure may be reduced to some line interface substructure close to the non-linear area of interest, and used by the non-linear program as an elastic boundary condition. The resulting non-linear problem is much reduced in size.

20.5.6 *Application of boundary conditions.* In finite element analysis, stress boundary conditions are automatically taken care of by the load vector; thus for a free boundary, the loading terms corresponding to the nodes on the boundary are zero.

For specified displacements (e.g., settlement of foundation, etc.), the stiffness matrix together with the load vector have to be modified. In general, for ease of indexing, the size of the matrix should remain unchanged, i.e., no rows or columns of the matrix should be deleted. With the aforementioned requirements in mind, there are two procedures which may be applied at solution time in the application of boundary conditions not inserted at the element level. Let us assume that we have a set of N equations,

$$
\begin{bmatrix}
k_{11} & k_{12} & \cdots & k_{1n} & \cdots & k_{1N} \\
k_{21} & k_{22} & \cdots & k_{2n} & \cdots & k_{2N} \\
\vdots & \vdots & & \vdots & & \vdots \\
k_{n1} & k_{n2} & \cdots & k_{nn} & \cdots & k_{nN} \\
\vdots & \vdots & & \vdots & & \vdots \\
k_{N1} & k_{N2} & & k_{Nn} & & k_{NN}
\end{bmatrix}
\begin{Bmatrix}
u_1 \\ u_2 \\ \vdots \\ u_n \\ \vdots \\ u_N
\end{Bmatrix}
=
\begin{Bmatrix}
F_1 \\ F_2 \\ \vdots \\ F_n \\ \vdots \\ F_N
\end{Bmatrix}
\tag{20.11}
$$

and that we have, say $u_1 = \alpha$.

The first procedure requires the modification of the loading column such that $\bar{F}_i = F_i - k_{1i}\alpha$ $(i = 2, N)$, and $\bar{F}_1 = \alpha$. Then the corresponding row and column of the matrix is made zero and the diagonal term is made unity. In the special but common case of $\alpha = 0$ (i.e., fixed support), it is only necessary to modify the matrix as described above, leaving the load matrix unchanged except for $\bar{F}_1 = 0$.

The second procedure involves the multiplication of the appropriate diagonal term by a large number, say, 10^8, and then only modifying the corresponding load coefficient. In the present case we would have

$$
\bar{k}_{11} = k_{11} \times 10^8 \quad \text{and} \quad \bar{F}_1 = k_{11} \times 10^8 \times \alpha
$$

while

$$
\bar{k}_{ij} = k_{ij} \quad \text{(except for } i = 1, j = 1)
$$
$$
\bar{F}_i = F_i \quad (i \neq 1).
$$

This will yield a solution in which x_1 is very nearly equal to α. The above procedure is suitable for all types of solution methods.

In many cases the reaction forces incurred at the boundary points are required as a matter of necessity, e.g., at bridge supports and dam abutments.

When such reactions are required then in the back-substitution process it is necessary to reformulate the equations concerned so that instead of solving for an unknown displacement due to a given load at the point of support, the procedure is reversed and the solution is for an unknown load due to a given displacement. Referring to the first equation of Eq. (20.11), we would now have for the reaction

$$R_1 = F_1 - k_{11}\alpha - \sum_{j=2}^{N} k_{1j}u_j.$$

20.5.7 *Example subroutine.* Two subroutines are flow-charted and listed below. FORMK is used to create the banded rectangular stiffness matrix and to insert the boundary conditions by using the first procedure (with $\alpha = 0$) described in the previous section. SOLVE is used to solve the simultaneous equations using the band matrix technique.† Flow charts are given on pp. 459–60.

Variable definitions—subroutine FORMK

VARIABLE	DEFINITION
NBAND	Maximum bandwidth for the program
NROWB, NCOLB, NCOL	Variables defining location of element stiffness matrix
NR, NX	Variables used in defining boundary condition
ESTIFM* (12, 12)	Element stiffness matrix

Variable definitions—subroutine SOLVE

VARIABLE	DEFINITION
NBAND	Maximum bandwidth for the program
N	Equation counter for elimination and back-substitution
C	Working variable of the elimination process
R1* (200)	Initially contains right-hand side vector, but solution vector replaces it

(*continued p. 461*)

* Array is in blank common.

† A second set of subprograms which is not compatible with the FESS system will be given in Appendix 20C.

(a) *Flow chart—subroutine FORMK*

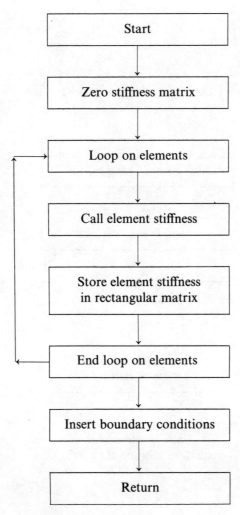

(b) *Flow chart—subroutine SOLVE*

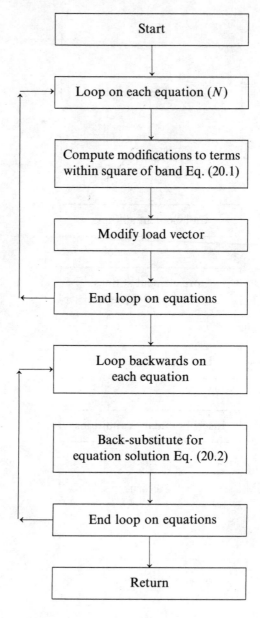

Pr 20–5

SUBROUTINE FORMK

FORMS STIFFNESS MATRIX
IN UPPER TRIANGULAR FORM

```
COMMON/CONTR/TITLE(12),NP,NE,NB,NDF,NCN,NLD,NMAT,NSZF,LI,NT4
COMMON CORD(100,2),NOP(200,4),IMAT(200),ORT(25,2),NBC(25),NFIX(25)
1,R1(200),SK(200,40)
2,ESTIFM(12,12)
```

SET BANDMAX AND NO OF EQUATIONS

```
NBAND = 40
```

ZERO STIFFNESS MATRIX

```
      DO 300 N = 1,NSZF
      DO 300 M = 1,NBAND
300  SK(N,M) = 0.
```

SCAN ELEMENTS

```
      DO 400 N = 1,NE
      CALL STIFT2(N)
```

RETURNS ESTIFM AS STIFFNESS MATRIX

STORE ESTIFM IN SK

FIRST ROWS

```
      DO 350 JJ = 1,NCN
      NROWB = (NOP(N,JJ) − 1)*NDF
      DO 350 J = 1,NDF
      NROWB = NROWB + 1
      I = (JJ − 1)*NDF + J
```

THEN COLUMNS

```
      DO 330 KK = 1,NCN
      NCOLB = (NOP(N,KK) − 1)*NDF
      DO 320 K = 1,NDF
```

```
      L=(KK-1)*NDF+K
      NCOL=NCOLB+K+1-NROWB
C
C                                              SKIP STORING IF BELOW BAND
C
      IF(NCOL) 320,320,310
  310 SK(NROWB,NCOL)=SK(NROWB,NCOL)+ESTIFM(I,L)
  320 CONTINUE
  330 CONTINUE
  350 CONTINUE
  400 CONTINUE
C
C                                              INSERT BOUNDARY CONDITIONS
C
      DO 500 N=1,NB
      NX=10**(NDF-1)
      I=NBC(N)
      NROWB=(I-1)*NDF
C
C                                              EXAMINE EACH DEGREE OF FREEDOM
C
      DO 490 M=1,NDF
      NROWB=NROWB+1
      ICON=NFIX(N)/NX
      IF(ICON) 450,450,420
  420 SK(NROWB,1)=1.
      DO 430 J=2,NBAND
      SK(NROWB,J)=0.
      NR=NROWB+1-J
      IF(NR) 430,430,425
  425 SK(NR,J)=0.
  430 CONTINUE
      NFIX(N)=NFIX(N)-NX*ICON
  450 NX=NX/10
  490 CONTINUE
  500 CONTINUE
      RETURN
      END
```

Pr. 20–6

```
      SUBROUTINE SOLVE
C
C                                              SPECIFICATION STATEMENTS
C
```

```
      COMMON/CONTR/TITLE(12),NP,NE,NB,NDF,NCN,NLD,NMAT,NSZF,LI,NT4
      COMMON CORD(100,2),NOP(200,4),IMAT(200),ORT(25,2),NBC(25),NFIX(25)
     1,R1(200),SK(200,40)
      NBAND=40
```

REDUCE MATRIX

```
      DO 300 N=1,NSZF
      I=N
      DO 290 L=2,NBAND
      I=I+1
      IF(SK(N,L)) 240,290,240
  240 C=SK(N,L)/SK(N,1)
      J=0
      DO 270 K=L,NBAND
      J=J+1
      IF(SK(N,K)) 260,270,260
  260 SK(I,J)=SK(I,J)-C*SK(N,K)
  270 CONTINUE
  280 SK(N,L)=C
```

AND LOAD VECTOR
FOR EACH EQUATION

```
      R1(I)=R1(I)-C*R1(N)
  290 CONTINUE
  300 R1(N)=R1(N)/SK(N,1)
```

BACK-SUBSTITUTION

```
      N=NSZF
  350 N=N-1
      IF(N) 500,500,360
  360 L=N
      DO 400 K=2,NBAND
      L=L+1
      IF(SK(N,K)) 370,400,370
  370 R1(N)=R1(N)-SK(N,K)*R1(L)
  400 CONTINUE
      GO TO 350
      
  500 RETURN
      END
```

20.6 Internal Force Calculation and Output of Results

The final step in solution of conventional linear finite element problems is the calculation of element internal forces.

Two steps are usually necessary for each element.

(a) The creation of a solution vector in the co-ordinate system of the element.

(b) The construction of a stress back-substitution matrix to transform the solution vector into internal forces. This matrix is the one referred to in discussion of the stiffness generation routine in section 20.3 and is created either by reading from peripheral storage or by calling the stiffness generation routine an extra time.

When the internal forces have been created it is frequently convenient to compute several other forces, for example in plane stress/strain, the values of maximum stress and minimum stress along with their directions are also calculated. Finally the desired stresses are printed.

In more complex non-linear problems the stress calculation routine is usually the starting point for the recycling process of calculating either an amended stiffness matrix (dependent upon stress level) or a load vector. Such a load vector is usually constructed by application of the initial stress or strain process (see Chapter 15).

Flow chart and example subroutine. Subroutine STRESS outputs displacements, and calculates and prints the element stresses in the plane strain problem.

Variable definition—subroutine STRESS

VARIABLE	DEFINITION
DIS (2, 100)* (see note below)	Vector of displacement
FORCE (200, 3)* (see note below)	Vector of element forces
B(3, 6)*	Back-substitution matrix
R (8)*	Vector of element displacements
SMAX	Maximum stress for element N
SMIN	Minimum stress for element N
ANG	Clockwise angle from vertical of line of action of maximum stress for element N

Note: EQUIVALENCE statement allows array DIS (2, 100) to be used for the solution vector R1 (200), and array of element forces FORCE (200, 3) to use storage of SK array.

* Array is in blank common.

Flow chart—subroutine STRESS

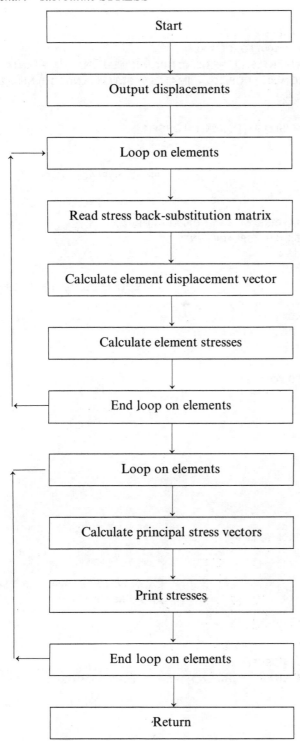

Pr. 20–7

```
      SUBROUTINE STRESS                                                      1
      DIMENSION DIS(2,100),FORCE(200,3)
      COMMON/CONTR/TITLE(12),NP,NE,NB,NDF,NCN,NLD,NMAT,NSZF,LI,NT4
      COMMON CORD(100,2),NOP(200,4),IMAT(200),ORT(25,2),NBC(25),NFIX(25)
     1,R1(200),SK(200,40)
     2,B(3,6), R(8)
      EQUIVALENCE (DIS(1),R1(1)),(SK(1),FORCE(1))
      REWIND NT4
C                                                                            9
C                                    PRINT DISPLACEMENTS
C
      WRITE(6,100)
      WRITE(6,110) (M,(DIS(J,M),J=1,NDF),M=1,NP)
  100 FORMAT(///,15X,13HDISPLACEMENTS    )
  110 FORMAT(I10,2F15.4)
C
C                                    CALCULATE ELEMENT FORCES
C
      DO 200 NC=1,NE                                                        10
      READ(NT4) N,((B(I,J),J=1,6),I=1,3)
      DO 260 I=1,NCN                                                        12
      M=NOP(N,I)
      IF(M.EQ.0) GO TO 260
      K=(I−1)*NDF                                                           16
      DO 240 J=1,NDF                                                        16
      IJ=J+K                                                                17
  240 R(IJ)=DIS(J,M)                                                        18
  260 CONTINUE                                                              19
      IA=K+NDF                                                              20
      DO 300 I=1,3                                                          21
      FORCE(N,I)=0.                                                         22
      DO 300 J=1,IA                                                         23
  300 FORCE(N,I)=FORCE(N,I)+B(I,J)*R(J)                                     24
  200 CONTINUE                                                              26
      WRITE(6,101)                                                          28
C                                    CALCULATE PRINCIPAL STRESSES
C                                    AND DIRECTIONS
C
C
      DO 600 N=1,NE                                                         29
  250 C=(FORCE(N,1)+FORCE(N,2))/2.                                          38
      A=SQRT(((FORCE(N,2)−FORCE(N,1))/2.)**2+FORCE(N,3)**2)                 39
```

```
     SMAX = C + A                                                    40
     SMIN = C − A                                                    41
     IF(FORCE(N,2).EQ.SMIN) GO TO 700                                42
     ANG = 57.29578 * ATAN(FORCE(N,3)/(FORCE(N,2) − SMIN))           43
     GO TO 210                                                       44
700  ANG = 90.                                                       45
210  CONTINUE                                                        46

                              WRITE ALL STRESS COMPONENTS

400  WRITE(6,111)                                                    47
    1N,(FORCE(N,I),I = 1,3),SMAX,SMIN, ANG
500  CONTINUE                                                        51
 01  FORMAT(107H0      ELEMENT       X-STRESS        Y-STRESS        X
    1Y-STRESS          MAX-STRESS     MIN-STRESS      ANGLE)
 11  FORMAT(I10,5F17.4,F12.3)
     RETURN                                                          54
     END                                                             55
```

20.7 Example Problem

Figure 20.3 shows a simple plane strain triangle subject to vertical load, divided into a finite element mesh of 10 points and 9 elements. The triangle is assumed fixed at points 1 and 4.

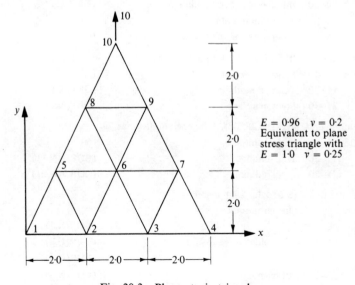

$E = 0.96 \quad v = 0.2$
Equivalent to plane stress triangle with
$E = 1.0 \quad v = 0.25$

Fig. 20.3   Plane strain triangle

The following routines are used for this case:

(a)	MAIN	program	(Pr. 20–1)
(b)	GDATA	subroutine	(Pr. 20–2)
(c)	LOAD	subroutine	(Pr. 20–3)
(d)	STIFT2	subroutine	(Pr. 20–4)
(e)	FORMK	subroutine	(Pr. 20–5)
(f)	SOLVE	subroutine	(Pr. 20–6)
(g)	STRESS	subroutine	(Pr. 20–7).

The input data instructions are listed below together with a sample data set and printed results for the problem shown in Fig. 20.3.

Data input instructions

1. Problem Card (I5)
    Col 1–5* No of Problems   (NPROB)

2. Title Card (12A6)
    Col 1–72 Title to be printed with output   (TITLE)

3. Control Card (7I5)
    Col   1–5* Number of nodal points   (NP)
    Col   6–10* Number of elements   (NE)
          11–15* Number of boundary points   (NB)
          16–20* Number of load conditions   (NLD)
          21–25* Number of degrees of freedom = 2   (NDF)
          26–30* Number of different materials   (NMAT)
          31–35* { 0 print input data
                  { 1 skip print of input data   (I1)

4. Material Cards (I10,2F10.2) 1 for each material
    Col   1–10* Material number   (N)
          11–20   Young's Modulus   (ORT(N,1))
          21–30   Poisson's Ratio   (ORT(N,2))

5. Co-ordinate Cards (I10.2F10.0) 1 for each node point
    Col   1–10* Node number   (N)
          11–20   X-co-ordinate   (CORD(N,1))
          21–30   Y-co-ordinate   (CORD(N,2))

6. Element Cards (6I5) 1 for each element
    Col   1–5* Element number   (N)
           6–10* i   (NOP(N,1))
          11–15* j   } element connections   (NOP(N,2))
          16–20* m   (NOP(N,3))
          21–25   not used   (NOP(N,4))
          26–30* Material number   (IMAT(N))

7. Boundary Cards (2I5) 1 for each boundary condition

    Col 1–5* Boundary node no.   (NBC(I))
          6–10* 01 fixed in Y direction
              10 fixed in X direction
              11 fixed in both directions   (NFIX(I))

8. Load Cards (I10, 2 F10.2) 1 for each loaded point

    Col 1–10* Node number   NQ
          11–20 X-Load   R(1)
          21–30 Y-Load   R(2)

Note: LOAD cards are terminated with a *load at the last numbered node* whether or not a load exists there.

  * Indicates that numbers should be right adjusted with no decimal point in the field, all other numbers should have decimal points inserted.

SAMPLE DATA

COLUMNS

```
        1         2         3         4         5         6         7         8
34567890123456789012345678901234567890123456789012345678901234567890123456789012345678 90
1
TEST TRIANGLE
10    9   2   1   2   1
      1   0.96    0.2
      1
      2 2.
      3 4.
      4 6.
      5 1.        2.
      6 3.        2.
      7 5.        2.
      8 2.        4.
      9 4.        4.
     10 3.        6.
1     1   2   5         1
2     2   3   6         1
3     3   4   7         1
4     3   7   6         1
5     2   6   5         1
6     5   6   8         1
7     6   7   9         1
8     6   9   8         1
9     8   9  10         1
```

```
1    11
4    11
     10            10.
```

TEST TRIANGLE

```
10    9    2    1    2    1    0
```

MATERIAL PROPERTIES

```
     1        .96        .20
```

NODAL POINTS

```
     1      .000       .000
     2     2.000       .000
     3     4.000       .000
     4     6.000       .000
     5     1.000      2.000
     6     3.000      2.000
     7     5.000      2.000
     8     2.000      4.000
     9     4.000      4.000
    10     3.000      6.000
```

ELEMENTS

```
     1    1    2    5    0    1
     2    2    3    6    0    1
     3    3    4    7    0    1
     4    3    7    6    0    1
     5    2    6    5    0    1
     6    5    6    8    0    1
     7    6    7    9    0    1
     8    6    9    8    0    1
     9    8    9   10    0    1
```

BOUNDARY CONDITIONS

```
     1    11
     4    11
```

TEST TRIANGLE   LOAD C

LOADS

```
    10         .00      10.00
```

DISPLACEMENTS

```
     1       .0000       .0000
     2      1.0941     17.7565
     3     -1.0941     17.7565
     4       .0000       .0000
```

5	−1.6412	15.6785
6	.0000	20.9599
7	1.6412	15.6785
8	.8206	25.3126
9	−.8206	25.3126
10	.0000	44.4729

_EMENT	X-STRESS	Y-STRESS	XY-STRESS	MAX-STRESS	MIN-STRESS	ANGLE
	1.4902	3.7727	3.1136	5.9477	−.6847	34.935
	−.7399	1.4167	−.0000	1.4167	−.7399	−.000
	1.4902	3.7727	−3.1136	5.9477	−.6847	−34.935
	.9503	.5189	−.6733	1.4417	.0276	−53.881
	.9503	.5189	.6733	1.4417	.0276	53.881
	1.8077	3.9487	1.3845	4.6283	1.1281	26.145
	1.8077	3.9487	−1.3845	4.6283	1.1281	−26.145
	−.2949	2.1027	.0000	2.1027	−.2949	.000
	1.6794	10.0000	.0000	10.0000	1.6794	.000

20.8 Display of Results

One of the major practical problems of the finite element method analysis is the voluminous output produced by the analysis and the time needed to interpret the printed output. The use of the automatic plotter as a means of displaying results alleviates this difficulty to a great extent.

Contours of stress level are one of the most convenient types of display. They may be drawn over the whole area of the system or over some particular area of interest. In the simplest application, element stresses are averaged to nodal values. Contours are then plotted as a series of straight lines over each element consistent with this nodal data. Figure 20.4 shows an example of such a plot.[7] The lack of smoothness of the plot gives some idea of the validity of the solution. Programs which draw smooth curves from a field of data defined at distinct points are available commercially from plotter manufacturers.

A second use of the automatic plotter is to draw the scaled principal stress vectors in appropriate directions for each element. Figure 20.5 shows such stresses being plotted.

Most elements currently in use exhibit discontinuities in stresses from one element to the next, although the stresses in two adjacent elements, often straddle the true stress curve. To facilitate the interpretation of stresses by smoothing out the stress jumps (and sometimes to obtain better accuracy), two types of stress averaging are in common use. The first type involves averaging the stresses of two adjacent elements, e.g., a quadrilateral is formed from two triangles, and the average stress of the

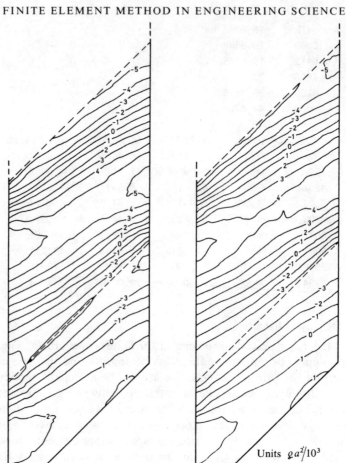

Fig. 20.4   Contours of moments on a skew bridge (from *Proc. Inst. Civ. Eng.*, 821, Aug. 1967)

two triangles is taken as the stress at some point in the quadrilateral. In the second type the stresses of all the elements connected to a node are summed and divided by the number of elements. This approach usually gives a fairly smooth and accurate stress distribution, except at the boundary points or in the region of high stress gradient.

Flow chart and example program. The stress vector program outlined below is a free standing routine that reads cards containing stresses and outputs vectors to an appropriate scale for each element specified. All subroutines are part of the Calcomp Fortran applications package. A typical flow chart is given on p. 474.

Fig. 20.5   Automatic plotting of principal stresses by vector plot routine

Pr. 20–8

```
                                    VECTOR PLOT ROUTINE FOR CALCOMP
      DIMENSION IBUF(1000)


                                    OUTPUT REEL NO.
                                    AND SET UP BUFFER AREA


      LDEV = 1
      CALL PLOTS(IBUF,1000,LDEV)


                                    READ SCALE INFORMATION

      READ (5,10) XSHIFT,XSCALE,YSHIFT,YSCALE
   10 FORMAT(4F10.2)
      WRITE(6,11) XSHIFT,XSCALE,YSHIFT,YSCALE
   11 FORMAT(13H1   X SHIFT = ,F10.2/
     1        13H    X SCALE = ,F10.2/
     2        13H    Y SHIFT = ,F10.2/
     3        13H    Y SCALE = ,F10.2)
      READ(5,15) PSCALE
   15 FORMAT(F10.2)
      WRITE(6,16) PSCALE
   16 FORMAT(13H0PLOT SCALE = ,F10.2,9H UNITS/IN)
C
```

Flow chart—PROGRAM STVECT

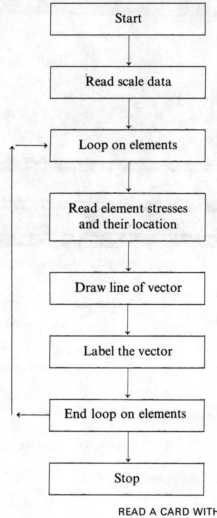

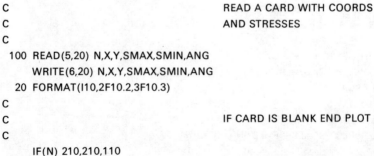

```
C                                  READ A CARD WITH COORDS
C                                  AND STRESSES
C
100  READ(5,20) N,X,Y,SMAX,SMIN,ANG
     WRITE(6,20) N,X,Y,SMAX,SMIN,ANG
 20  FORMAT(I10,2F10.2,3F10.3)
C
C                                  IF CARD IS BLANK END PLOT
C
     IF(N) 210,210,110
```

CHANGE SCALES

```
110  X = (X − XSHIFT)*XSCALE
     Y = (Y − YSHIFT)*YSCALE
     SMAX = SMAX/PSCALE
     SMIN = SMIN/PSCALE
     ANG = ANG/57.3
```

COMPUTE ENDS OF VECTORS

```
R = X + SMAX/2.*SIN(ANG)
S = Y + SMAX/2.*COS(ANG)
P = 2.*X − R
Q = 2.*Y − S
```

AND DRAW LINES

```
CALL PLOT(R,S,3)
CALL PLOT(P,Q,2)
R = X − SMIN*COS(ANG)
S = Y + SMIN*SIN(ANG)
P = 2.*X − R
Q = 2.*Y − S
CALL PLOT(R,S,3)
CALL PLOT(P,Q,2)
```

DRAW ELEMENT NO.

```
A = X + 0.2
B = Y + 0.1
FPN = N
CALL NUMBER (A,B,.14,FPN,0.,0)
```

RETURN FOR NEXT ELEMENT

```
GO TO 100
```

END PLOT

```
210  CONTINUE
     CALL PLOT (0.,0.,999)
     STOP
     END
```

20.9 Eigenvalue Solution by Iteration

In vibration and stability analysis, in the finite element formulation of wave-guide problems, etc., a set of matrix equations in the form of $HX = \lambda X$ can be derived, where H is a square matrix with known co-efficients, X is of the form $[x_1, x_2, \ldots, x_n]^T$, and λ is a scalar quantity related to the natural frequencies, critical load, cut-off frequencies, etc. The equations $HX = \lambda X$ are called eigenvalue equations and in general there are as many solutions, i.e., eigenvalues and corresponding eigen-vectors, as there are degrees of freedom x_i. An example arises in free vibra-tion problems where

$$H = K^{-1}M. \tag{20.12}$$

The highest eigenvalue can be determined by a simple iteration tech-nique as follows:

(a) Guess a set of values for the vector X and call this X_{g1}. Since the eigenvector represents some modal shape of the system we need only the relative values in the vector X. We can therefore assume that one of the unknowns (say x_1) is always unity.

(b) Compute AX_{g1}.

(c) The product AX_{g1} is a vector and can be written as $\lambda_{g2}X_{g2}$, in which λ_{g2} is a common factor, such that x_1 in X_{g2} is again unity while the other variables $x_2, x_3, \ldots, x_n$ take corresponding values.

(d) Compare X_{g2} with X_{g1}, or in general X_{gr} and $X_{g(r+1)}$. If no change (up to a certain specified accuracy requirement) is recorded then the new set of guessed values give the eigenvector and the common fac-tor is the highest eigenvalue. Otherwise repeat step (a).

Other eigenvalues and their corresponding eigenvectors are found by a 'zooing' process combined with the iteration technique. The 'zooing' process modifies H to change the highest eigenvalue in the system to zero, so that the next highest λ now becomes the highest, and the iteration process is repeated.

Let us now assume that at some stage we have completed the rth modal analysis, and that λ_r and X_r are the eigenvalue and eigenvector obtained.

The matrix used for determining λ_r and X_r can now be zooed to remove the rth root, or rather to make $\lambda_r = 0$, without altering the other eigen-values or any of the eigenvectors. Obviously, if this is achieved, then λ_{r+1} would have become the highest eigenvalue in the zooed matrix.

Let

$$Z_r = \frac{X_r X_r^T M}{X_r^T M X_r}. \tag{20.13}$$

We have

$$[H - \lambda_1 Z_1 - \lambda_2 Z_2 - \cdots - \lambda_r Z_r] X_r$$
$$= HX_r - \lambda_1 Z_1 X_r - \lambda_2 Z_2 X_r - \cdots - \lambda_r Z_r X_r$$
$$= \lambda_r X_r - \frac{\lambda_1 X_1 (X_1^T M X_r)}{X_1^T M X_1} - \frac{\lambda_2 X_2 (X_2^T M X_r)}{X_2^T M X_2} - \cdots - \frac{\lambda_r X_r (X_r^T M X_r)}{X_r^T M X_r}. \quad (20.14)$$

By virtue of the orthogonal property of modal shapes, it can be shown that for $r \neq s$, we have

$$X_r^T M X_s = 0. \quad (20.15)$$

Equation (20.12) can now be rewritten as

$$[H - \lambda_1 Z_1 - \lambda_2 Z_2 - \cdots - \lambda_r Z_r] X_r = \lambda_r X_r - \lambda_r X_r = 0 X_r \quad (20.16)$$

because $X_r^T M X_r$ is a scalar and can be cancelled.

From Eq. (22.16), X_r is still an eigenvector of the 'zooed' matrix, but the corresponding λ_r is effectively zero.

Now it remains to be proved that the other roots of the system have not been changed during the zooing process. Assuming that λ_s and X_s are the eigenvalue and eigenvector of the sth mode ($s > r$), we write

$$[H - \lambda_1 Z_1 - \lambda_2 Z_2 - \cdots - \lambda_r Z_r] X_s$$
$$= HX_s - \lambda_1 Z_1 X_s - \lambda_2 Z_2 X_s - \cdots - \lambda_r Z_r X_s$$
$$= \lambda_s X_s - \frac{\lambda_1 X_1 (X_1^T M X_s)}{X_1^T M X_1} - \frac{\lambda_2 X_2 (X_2^T M X_s)}{X_2^T M X_2} - \cdots - \frac{\lambda_r X_r (X_r^T M X_s)}{X_r^T M X_r}$$
$$= \lambda_s X_s. \quad (20.17)$$

Therefore λ_s remains a root of the 'zooed' matrix.

The orthogonal property used in Eqs. (20.14) and (20.17) is proved as follows:

$$K^{-1} M X_s = \lambda_s X_s, \quad (20.18)$$

$$K^{-1} M X_r = \lambda_r X_r. \quad (20.19)$$

Premultiplying Eq. (20.18) by $X_r^T M^T$ and Eq. (20.19) by $X_s^T M^T$ and then transposing the latter equation (bearing in mind that K^{-1} and M are symmetric), we obtain

$$X_r^T M^T K^{-1} M X_s = \lambda_s X_r^T M X_s, \quad (20.20)$$

$$X_r^T M^T K^{-1} M X_s = \lambda_r X_r^T M X_s. \quad (20.21)$$

If Eq. (20.21) is now subtracted from Eq. (20.20), the result will be

$$(\lambda_s - \lambda_r) X_r^T M X_s = 0. \quad (20.22)$$

Since in general $\lambda_s \neq \lambda_r$, we must have

$$X_r^T M X_s = 0. \quad (20.23)$$

Example program
Flow chart for EIGEN

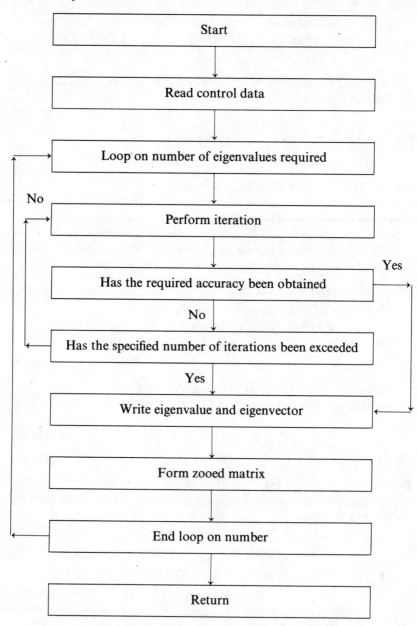

Variable definition for subroutine EIGEN

VARIABLE	DEFINITION
EGG	Eigenvalue matrix ($K^{-1}M$ or $M^{-1}K$)
W	Mass (or Stiffness) matrix
TEST	Accuracy required for eigenvector
NIT	Maximum number of iterations allowed
NEIG	Number of eigenvalues required
OM	Square root of 1/eigenvalue, used in conjunction with $K^{-1}M$ for determining lower natural frequencies.

Pr. 20–9

```
SUBROUTINE EIGEN(EGG,W,NV)
DIMENSION EGG(4,4),X(4),XAUX(4),XUX(4),EAUX(4,4),W(4,4)
                        EGG – EIGENVALUE MATRIX H
                        W – MASS MATRIX


    READ (5,10) TEST,NIT,NEIG
10  FORMAT(F10.5,2I10)
                        TEST – ACCURACY REQUIRED
                        NIT – MAXIMUM NUMBER OF ITERATIONS
                        NEIG – NUMBER OF EIGENVALUES REQUIRED


    DO 1 II=1,NEIG
    DO 66 I=1,NV
    XUX(I) =1.
66  X(I) =1.
14  CALL MPRD(EGG,X,XAUX,NV,NV,1)
    EIG =XAUX(1)
    DO 57 I=1,NV
57  X(I) =XAUX(I)/EIG
    DO 67 I=1,NV
    IF(ABS((X(I) –XUX(I))/X(I)) – TEST)67,67,82
67  CONTINUE
                        GOOD ENOUGH


    GO TO 50
                        REPEAT

82  ITS =ITS –1
    IF(ITS) 21,21,25
21  WRITE(5,22)
22  FORMAT(26H ITERATION COUNT EXCEEDED)
```

```
      GO TO 50
   25 DO 26 I=1,NV
   26 XUX(I) =X(I)
   42 FORMAT (4E16.8)
      GO TO 14
   50 OM =SQRT(1./EIG)
      WRITE(5,13) II,OM
      WRITE(5,42) (X(I),I =1,4)
   13 FORMAT (15,E16.8)
C                                    FORM ZOOED MATRIX
C
      CALL TPRD(X,W,XUX,NV,1,NV)
      CALL MPRD(XUX,X,XAUX,1,NV,1)
      AA =EIG/XAUX(1)
      DO 68 I=1,NV
   68 XAUX(I) =X(I)*AA
      CALL MPRD(XAUX,XUX,EAUX,NV,1,NV)
      DO 110 I =1,NV
      DO 110 J=1,NV
  110 EGG(I,J) =EGG(I,J) −EAUX(I,J)
    1 CONTINUE
      RETURN
      END
```

Pr. 20–10

```
SUBROUTINE MPRD(D,B,DB,L,M,N)
    DIMENSION D(4,4),B(4,4)DB(4,4)
C                                    DB(L,N) =D(L,M)*B(M,N)
    DO 110 J =1,N
    DO 110 I =1,L
    DB(I,J) =0
    DO 110 K =1,M
110 DB(I,J) =DB(I,J) +D(I,K)*B(K,J)
    RETURN
    END
```

Pr. 20–11

```
SUBROUTINE TPRD(D,B,DB,M,L,N)
DIMENSION D(4,4),B(4,4),DB(4,4)
C                              DB(L,N) =(TRANSPOSE D(M,L) )*B(M,N)
    DO 110 J =1,N
```

```
   DO 110 I=1,L
   DB(I,J)=0
   DO 110 K=1,M
10 DB(I,J)=DB(I,J)+D(K,I)*B(K,J)
   RETURN
   END
```

20.10 Concluding Remarks

In this chapter the complete process of finite element solution is discussed and sample programs presented. The material given herein does not represent a sophisticated level of development, which would obscure the subject-matter for beginners. Instead, the authors have given a reasonably simple but efficient working program, at the same time pointing out other methods and features which could be incorporated into the system.

The eigenvalue solution program given in this chapter is very simple and does not utilize the symmetry of the stiffness and mass (or geometric stiffness) matrices. Readers who are interested in more advanced techniques and in the saving of computer storage should refer to the work of Anderson[8] on vibration and stability problems.

References

1. R. W. CLOUGH, 'The Finite Element in Plane Stress Analysis', *Proc. 2nd ASCE Conf. on Electronic Computation*, Pittsburgh, Pa., Sept. 1960.
2. B. M. IRONS, 'Economical Computer Techniques for Numerically Integrated Finite Elements', *Int. J. Num. Meth. Eng.*, 1, 201–3, 1969.
3. H. C. MARTIN, *Introduction to Matrix Methods of Structural Analysis*, McGraw-Hill, 1966.
4. R. W. CLOUGH and C. P. JOHNSON, 'A Finite Element Approximation for the Analysis of Thin Shells', *Int. J. Solids Struct.*, 4, 43–60, 1968.
5. I. P. KING, 'An Automatic Recording Scheme for Simultaneous Equations Derived from Network Systems', to be published. *Int. J. Num. Meth. Eng.*, 1970.
6. B. M. IRONS, 'A Frontal Solution Program for Finite Element Analysis', *Int. J. Num. Meth. Eng.*, 2, 5–32, 1970.
7. O. C. ZIENKIEWICZ and I. P. KING, Discussion on 'The Analysis of a Four-Span Bridge using an Electrical Analogue Computer', *Proc. Inst. Civ. Eng.*, 37, 819–20, 1967.
8. R. G. ANDERSON, *A Finite Element Eigenvalue Solution System*, Ph.D. Thesis, University of Wales, Swansea, 1968.

APPENDIX 20A

Program listing for subroutines to form equation and solve by Gauss-Seidel Iteration.

Pr. 20–12

```
      SUBROUTINE FORMK
C
C                                 SUBROUTINE TO FORM K
C                                 COMPACT WITH POINTER MATRIX
C
      COMMON/CONTR/TITLE (12),NP,NE,NB,NDF,NCN,NLD,NMAT,NSZF,LI,NT4
      COMMON CORD(100,2),NOP(200,4),IMAT(200),ORT(25,2),NBC(25),NFIX(25)
     1,R1(200),SI(200,20),ISP(200,20)
     2,ESTIFM(12,12)
C
C                                 SET MAX NO. OF TERMS
C
      NMAX=20
      NOFF=20
C
C                                 ZERO ARRAYS
C
      DO 300 N=1,NSZF
      DO 280 M=1,NMAX
  280 SI(N,M)=0.
      DO 290 M=2,NOFF
  290 ISP(N,M)=0
  300 ISP(N,1)=N
C
C                                 SCAN ELEMENTS
C
      DO 400 N=1,NE
      CALL STIFT2(N)
C
C                                 RETURNS ESTIFM AS STIFFNESS MATRIX
C                                 STORE ESTIFM IN SI WITH A
C                                 TERM IN ISP AS A POINTER
C
C                                 FIRST THE ROWS
C
      I=0
      DO 350 JJ=1,NCN
      NROWB=(NOP(N,JJ)−1)*NDF
      DO 350 J=1,NDF
      NROWB=NROWB+1
      I=I+1
C
```

```
C                           THEN COLUMNS OF ESTIFM
C

      II = 0
      DO 330 KK = 1,NCN
      NCOLB = (NOP(N,KK) − 1)∗NDF
      DO 330 K = 1,NDF
      NCOLB = NCOLB + 1
      II = II + 1

C
C                           SEARCH ISP FOR COLUMN NO.
C

      DO 310 M = 1,NOFF
      IF(ISP(NROWB,M) − NCOLB) 305,320,305
  305 IF(ISP(NROWB,M)) 315,315,310
  310 CONTINUE
C
C                           FOUND A BLANK NOW STORE NCOLB
C
  315 ISP(NROWB,M) = NCOLB
C
C                           NOW STORE ESTIFM
C
  320 SI(NROWB,M) = ESTIFM(I,II) + SI(NROWB,M)
C
C                           END LOOP ON COLUMNS
  330 CONTINUE
C                           END LOOP ON ROWS
  350 CONTINUE
C                           END LOOP ON ELEMENTS
  400 CONTINUE
C
C                           INSERT BOUNDARY CONDITIONS
C

      DO 500 N = 1,NB
      NX = 10∗∗(NDF − 1)
      I = NBC(N)
      NROWB = (I − 1)∗NDF

C
C                           EXAMINE EACH DEGREE OF FREEDOM
      DO 490 M = 1,NDF
      NROWB = NROWB + 1
      ICON = NFIX(N)/NX
      IF(ICON) 450,450,420
```

```
C
C                                       STORE LARGE NO ON DIAGONAL
C
  420 SI(NROWB,1) = SI(NROWB,1)*10**20
      NFIX(N) = NFIX(N) − NX*ICON
  450 NX = NX/10
  490 CONTINUE
  500 CONTINUE
      RETURN
      END
```

Pr. 20–13

```
      SUBROUTINE SOLVE
C     SUBROUTINE FOR ITERATIVE SOLUTION OF EQUATIONS
      COMMON/CONTR/TITLE (12),NP,NE,NB,NDF,NCN,NLD,NMAT,NEQ ,LI,NT4
      COMMON CORD(100,2),NOP(200,4),IMAT(200),ORT(25,2),NBC(25),NFIX(25)
     1,R(200),A(200,20),ITEM(200,20), DIS(200)
      NT = 20
C
C                                       BUILT IN RELAXATION AND TOLERANCE
      TOLER = .1E−3
      RELAX = 1.8
C
C                                       NEGATIVE NEQ SKIPS SETTING UP
C                                       OF INITIAL DATA
C
      IF(NEQ.LT.0) GO TO 310
      DO 300 N = 1,NEQ
      DO 250 M = 1,NT
      IF(ITEM(N,M).NE.0) GO TO 250
C
C                                       ITEM(N,1) CONTAINS COUNT OF
C                                       NUMBER OF OFF DIAGONAL TERMS
C
      ITEM(N,1) = M − 1
      GO TO 260
  250 CONTINUE
  260 CONTINUE
  300 CONTINUE
  310 NEQ = IABS(NEQ)
C
C                                       SET MAX NO OF CYCLES
C
```

```
      NCYC=NEQ/2
      IF(NCYC.LT.25) NCYC=25
C
C                              UNKNOWNS ARE SET TO ZERO
C
      DO 320 N=1,NEQ
      IF(A(N,1).NE.0.) A(N,1)=1./A(N,1)
 320  DIS(N)=0.
C
C                              LOOP ON CYCLES
      DO 500 NC=1,NCYC
      SUM=0.
      SUMD=0.
C                              THEN ON EQUATIONS
C
      DO 450 N=1,NEQ
      FX=R(N)
      NUM=ITEM(N,1)
      DO 330 M=2,NUM
      L=ITEM(N,M)
 330  FX=FX-A(N,M)*DIS(L)
C
C                              FX IS TOTAL UNBALANCE OF RHS
C                              DX IS THE CHANGE
C
      DX=A(N,1)*FX-DIS(N)
      DIS(N)=DIS(N)+RLAX*DX
C
C                              SUM AND SUMD ARE CONVERGENCE
C                              PARAMETERS
C
      SUM=SUM+ABS(DX)
      SUMD=SUMD+ABS(DIS(N))
 450  CONTINUE
C
C                              SKIP OUT OF LOOP IF CONVERGED
C
      ND=NC
      IF(SUM.LT.SUMD*TOLER) GO TO 550
 500  CONTINUE
C
C                              MOVE FINAL RESULTS TO R
C
```

```
  550  DO 600 N=1,NEQ
  600  R(N)=DIS(N)
C
C                                      PRINT LAST VALUE OF SUM ETC
C
       WRITE(6,10) ND,SUM,SUMD
   10  FORMAT(20H0   LAST CYCLE NO.=,I10
      1, /      20H (SN−SN−1)/SN    =,E10.3
      2, /      20H              SN  =,E10.3)
       RETURN
       END
```

APPENDIX 20B

Program listing for subroutines to form equation and solve by the sparse matrix (front) method.

Pr. 20–14

```
       SUBROUTINE FORMK
C
C                                      SUBROUTINE TO FORM K
C                                      UPPER TRIANGULAR SECTION ONLY
C                                      COMPACT WITH POINTER MATRIX
C
       COMMON/CONTR/TITLE(12),NP,NE,NB,NDF,NCN,NLD,NMAT,NSZF,LI,NT4
       COMMON CORD(100,2),NOP(200,4),IMAT(200),ORT(25,2),NBC(25),NFIX(25)
      1,R1(200),SI(200,20),ISP(200,20)
      2,ESTIFM(12,12)
C
C                                      SET MAX NO. OF TERMS
C
       NMAX=20
       NOFF=20
C
C                                      ZERO ARRAYS
C
       DO 300 N=1,NSZF
       DO 280 M=1,NMAX
  280  SI(N,M)=0.
       DO 290 M=2,NOFF
  290  ISP(N,M)=0
  300  ISP(N,1)=N
C
C                                      SCAN ELEMENTS
```

```
      DO 400 N=1,NE
      CALL STIFT2(N)

C                                RETURNS ESTIFM AS STIFFNESS MATRIX
C                                STORE ESTIFM IN SI WITH A
C                                TERM IN ISP AS A POINTER
C
C                                FIRST THE ROWS
C

      I=0
      DO 350 JJ=1,NCN
      NROWB=(NOP(N,JJ)−1)*NDF
      DO 350 J=1,NDF
      NROWB=NROWB+1
      I=I+1

C
C                                THEN COLUMNS OF ESTIFM
C

      II=0
      DO 330 KK=1,NCN
      NCOLB=(NOP(N,KK)−1)*NDF
      DO 330 K=1,NDF
      NCOLB=NCOLB+1
      II=II+1

C
C                                SKIP IF TERM BELOW DIAGONAL
C

      IF(NCOLB−NROWB) 330,302,302
  302 CONTINUE

C
C                                SEARCH ISP FOR COLUMN NO.
C

      DO 310 M=1,NOFF
      IF(ISP(NROWB,M)−NCOLB) 305,320,305
  305 IF(ISP(NROWB,M)) 315,315,310
  310 CONTINUE

C
C                                FOUND A BLANK NOW STORE NCOLB
C

  315 ISP(NROWB,M)=NCOLB

C
C                                NOW STORE ESTIFM
C
```

```
C
  320 SI(NROWB,M) = ESTIFM(I,II) + SI(NROWB,M)
C
C                                        END LOOP ON COLUMNS
  330 CONTINUE
C                                        END LOOP ON ROWS
  350 CONTINUE
C                                        END LOOP ON ELEMENTS
  400 CONTINUE
C
C                                        INSERT BOUNDARY CONDITIONS
C
      DO 500 N = 1,NB
      NX = 10**(NDF-1)
      I = NBC(N)
      NROWB = (I-1)*NDF
C
C                                        EXAMINE EACH DEGREE OF FREEDOM
      DO 490 M = 1,NDF
      NROWB = NROWB + 1
      ICON = NFIX(N)/NX
      IF(ICON) 450,450,420
C
C                                        STORE LARGE NO ON DIAGONAL
C
  420 SI(NROWB,1) = SI(NROWB,1)*10.**20
      NFIX(N) = NFIX(N) - NX*ICON
  450 NX = NX/10
  490 CONTINUE
  500 CONTINUE
      RETURN
      END
```

Pr. 20–15

```
      SUBROUTINE SOLVE
C                                        SOLVES SPARSE MATRIX
C
      COMMON/CONTR/TITLE(12),NP,NE,NB,NDF,NCN,NLD,NMAT,NEQ ,LI,NT4
      COMMON CORD(100,2),NOP(200,4),IMAT(200),ORT(25,2),NBC(25),NFIX(25)
     1,R(200),A(200,20),ITEM(200,20),IMET(200)
      NT = 20
C
C                                        IF NEQ NEGATIVE SKIP
```

```
                    FORMATION OF FULL ITEM MATRIX

      IF(NEQ.LT.0) GO TO 360                                  SYM    5

                    OTHERWISE WORK THROUGH
                    EQUATIONS AND FILL ITEM AS NEEDED

      DO 220 M = 1,NT                                         SYM    6
220   IMET(M) = ITEM(1,M)                                     SYM    7
      DO 340 N = 2,NEQ                                        SYM    8
      DO 280 M = 1,NT                                         SYM    9
      IF(IMET(M) − N + 1) 225,280,225                         SYM   10
225   DO 240 L = 1,NT                                         SYM   11
      IF(ITEM(N,L))   230,260,230                             SYM   12
230   IF(ITEM(N,L) − IMET(M)) 240,280,240                     SYM   13
240   CONTINUE                                                SYM   14
      WRITE(6,100) N                                          SYM   15
100   FORMAT(43H ALLOWABLE SPACE EXCEEDED IN EQUATION TABLE,I4)  SYM   16
      STOP                                                    SYM   17
260   ITEM(N,L) = IMET(M)                                     SYM   18
280   CONTINUE                                                SYM   19
300   DO 320 M = 1,NT                                         SYM   20
320   IMET(M) = ITEM(N,M)                                     SYM   21
340   CONTINUE                                                SYM   22
360   NEQ = IABS(NEQ)                                         SYM   23
      NEQM = NEQ − 1                                          SYM   24

                    LOOP ON EQUATIONS

      DO 520 I = 1,NEQM                                       SYM   25

                    MODIFY RHS VECTOR

      R(I) = R(I)/A(I,1)                                      SYM   26

                    LOOP ON ROW TO BE ELIMINATED

      DO 460 M = 2,NT                                         SYM   27
      IN = ITEM(I,M)                                          SYM   28
      IF(IN) 365,480,365                                      SYM   29

                    SEEK APPROPRIATE ROWS
```

```
      365 DO 380 N = 1,NT                                        SYM   30
          IA = ITEM(IN,N)                                        SYM   31
          IF(IA) 370,400,370                                     SYM   32
      370 IMET(IA) = N                                           SYM   33
      380 CONTINUE                                               SYM   34
      400 CONTINUE                                               SYM   35
          TEMP = A(I,M)/A(I,1)                                   SYM   36
    C
    C                     LOOP ON COLUMN TO BE ELIMINATED
    C
          DO 420 N = 1,NT                                        SYM   37
          IA = ITEM(I,N)                                         SYM   38
          IF(IA) 405,440,405                                     SYM   39
      405 IF(IA − IN) 420,410,410                                SYM   40
      410 IM = IMET(IA)                                          SYM   41
    C
    C                     MODIFY TERM OF MATRIX
    C
          A(IN,IM) = A(IN,IM) − TEMP∗A(I,N)                      SYM   42
      420 CONTINUE                                               SYM   43
    C
    C                     MODIFY LOAD VECTOR
    C
      440 R(IN) = R(IN) − R(I)∗A(I,M)                            SYM   44
      460 CONTINUE                                               SYM   45
      480 CONTINUE                                               SYM   46
    C
    C                     RESET ROW FOR BACK-SUBSTITUTION
    C
          DO 500 M = 2,NT                                        SYM   47
          A(I,M) = A(I,M)/A(I,1)                                 SYM   48
      500 CONTINUE                                               SYM   49
      520 CONTINUE                                               SYM   50
          R(NEQ) = R(NEQ)/A(NEQ,1)                               SYM   51
    C
    C                     BACK-SUBSTITUTE
    C
          DO 560 IB = 1,NEQM                                     SYM   52
          I = NEQ − IB                                           SYM  ˜53
          DO 540 M = 2,NT                                        SYM   54
          J = ITEM(I,M)                                          SYM   55
          IF(J) 540,560,540                                      SYM   56
      540 R(I) = R(I) − A(I,M)∗R(J)                              SYM   57
```

560 CONTINUE   SYM   58
     RETURN   SYM   59
     END   SYM   60

APPENDIX 20C

A set of subroutines which can be used for solving a very large number of equations subject to a maximum semi-bandwidth limitation will be given here. These subroutines are, however, not compatible with the subroutine described previously.

As discussed in the last part of section 20.5.1, the assemblage and elimination processes go hand in hand, and the stiffness equations for a node are eliminated as soon as they are formed. The subroutine SOLV is used for the line-by-line elimination process (number of lines equal to the number of degrees of freedom per node) and the subroutine BSUB for the back-substitution process, in which reactions at boundary points are also computed. STORE and RDBK are two small subroutines for storing and reading back the modified equations respectively. These modified equations are not written on tape equation by equation, but are temporarily stored in a buffer area and then written as a block when the buffer area is full. The subroutine INIT sets the indices required in the above-mentioned subroutines and must be called once before starting on the solution of a problem.

(a) *Flow chart for INIT*

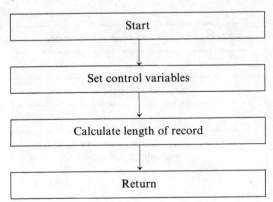

(*b*) *Flow chart for STORE*

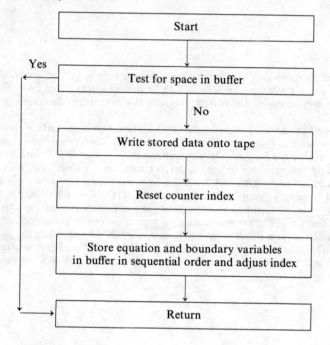

(*c*) *Flow chart for RDBK*

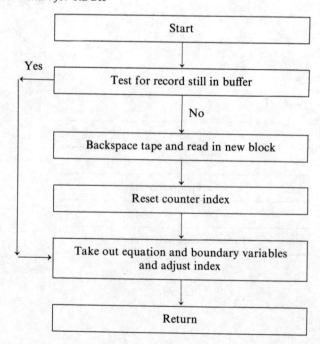

(d) *Flow chart for SOLV*

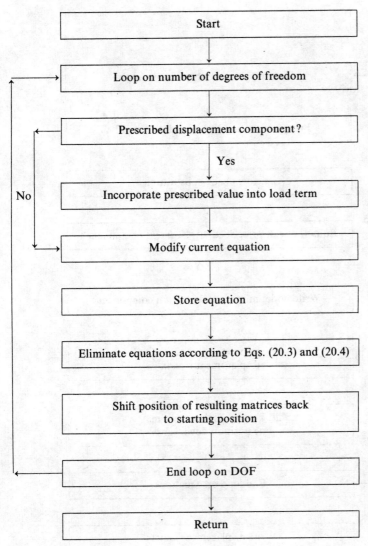

(e) *Flow chart for BSUB*

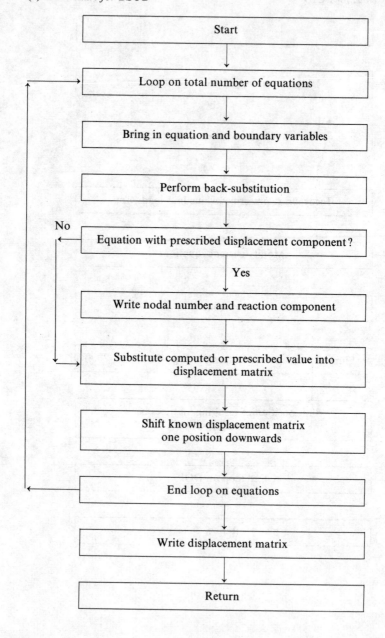

Variable definition for subroutines 20–16 to 20–20

VARIABLE	DEFINITION
NBAND	Maximum half band width
NDF	Number of degrees of freedom per node
NR	Variable for testing boundary point
BN	Variable for testing displacement component with prescribed value
BV	Prescribed value
NCOLN	Number of loading columns (vectors)
ST	Stiffness array
P	Load (displacement) array
X	Buffer area

Pr. 20–16

```
SUBROUTINE INIT (NBAND, NCOLN)
                              CONTROL COUNTERS
COMMON/BUFDA/NBD,NCOL,IS,NA,LRECL,NREC,L,X(8000)
                              DIMENSION OF X CAN BE CHANGED
                              NA HAS SAME DIMENSION AS X

NA=8000
IS=1
NBD=NBAND
NCOL=NCOLN
LRECL=NBD+NCOL+3
NREC=0
IF (LRECL-NA) 1,1,2
RETURN
WRITE (6,4) LRECL, NA
OFORMAT ('OLOGICAL RECORD LENGTH OF', 16, 'EXCEEDS BUFFER SET AT',
1   16)
STOP
END
```

Pr. 20–17

```
SUBROUTINE STORE (ST,P,NR,BN,BV)
DIMENSION ST(60,60),P(60,2)
COMMON/BUFDA/NBD,NCOL,IS,NA,LRECL,NREC,L,X(8000)
                              TEST IF ROOM IN CURRENT BUFFER
                              AUTOMATIC MESH GENERATOR
IF (IS+LRECL-NA) 5,5,50
                              ROOM IN BUFFER

DO 10 I=1, NBD
```

```
       X(IS) = ST(1,I)
10     IS = IS + 1
       DO 15 I = 1,NCOL
       X (IS) = P(1,I)
15     IS = IS + 1
       X(IS) = NR
       X(IS + 1) = BN
       X(IS + 2) = BV
       IS = IS + 3
       RETURN
C                                          NO ROOM LEFT IN BUFFER
C
50     L = IS - 1
       WRITE (2) (X(J), J = 1,L)
C                                          CHANNEL 2 PERIPHERAL STORAGE
C
       IS = 1
       NREC = NREC + 1
       GO TO 5
       END
```

Pr. 20–18

```
       SUBROUTINE RDBK (ST,P,NR,BN,BV)
       DIMENSION ST(60,60),P(60,2)
       COMMON/BUFDA/NBD,NCOL,IS,NA,LRECL,NREC,L,X(8000)
C                                          TEST IF NEXT RECORD IN BUFFER
C
10     IS = IS - LRECL
       IF (IS - 1) 40,12,12
C                                          RECORD IS IN BUFFER
C
 12    DO 11 I = 1, NBD
       ST (1,I) = X(IS)
11     IS = IS + 1
       DO 15 I = 1, NCOL
       P (1,I) = X(IS)
15     IS = IS + 1
       NR = X(IS)
       BN = X(IS + 1)
       BV = X(IS + 2)
       IS = IS + 3 - LRECL
       RETURN
C                                          LAST BLOCK WRITTEN MUST BE READ
```

```
        IF (NREC) 100,100,41
        NREC = NREC - 1
        BACKSPACE 2
        READ (2) (X(J), J = 1,L)
        BACKSPACE 2
        IS = L + 1
        GO TO 10
```

                                        ILLOGICAL ERROR

```
 00     WRITE (6,101)
 01     FORMAT ('O ATTEMPT TO READ BACK TOO MANY RECORDS.')
        STOP
        END
```

Pr. 20–19

```
        SUBROUTINE SOLV
        COMMON DIS(720,2),ST(60,60),Q(60,2),P(60,2),PST(2),BN(2),BV(2)
        COMMON NDF,NBAND,NSIZ,NDF1,NP,NELEM,NCOLN,NDATA
```
                          NCOLN = NUMBER OF LOADING COLUMNS
                          NR = 1—NODES WITH BOUNDARY CONDITIONS
                          BN———1 = FIXED, 0 = FREE
                          BV———SPECIFIED DISPLACEMENTS
                          NBAND = SEMI-BAND WIDTH
                          NDF = NUMBER OF DEGREES OF FREEDOM
                          NDF1 = NDF + 1, NSIZ = NBAND - NDF

```
        DO 111 JJ = 1,NDF
```
                        TEST FOR BOUNDARY CONDITIONS
```
        IF(NR.NE. 1) GO TO 58
        IF (ABS(BN(JJ)) .LT. .00001) GO TO 58
        ST11 = 0
        DO 5 J = 1,NCOLN
  5     PST(J) = BV(JJ)
        DO 8 J = 1,NCOLN
  8     P(1,J) = -BV(JJ) + P(1,J)/ST(1,1)
        DO 4 I = 2,NBAND:
  4     ST(1,I) = ST(1,I)/ST(1,1)
        ST(1,1) = -ST(1,1)
        GO TO 60
```
                        EQUATION WITH NO BOUNDARY CONDITION

```
 58     ST11 = 1./ST(1,1)
```

```
      DO 6 J=1,NCOLN
   6  PST(J)=P(1,J)*ST11
      ST(1,1)=ST11
  60  CALL STORE (ST,P,NR,BN(JJ),BV(JJ))
      DO 11 I=2,NBAND
      DO 16 J=1,NCOLN
  16  P(I,J)=P(I,J)−ST(1,I)*PST(J)
C                                MODIFIED LOAD MATRIX FORMED
C
      DO 11 J=2,NBAND
  11  ST(I,J)=ST(I,J)−ST(1,I)*ST(1,J)*ST11
C                                MODIFIED STIFFNESS MATRIX FORMED
C
      DO 14 I=2,NBAND
      DO 15 J=1,NCOLN
      P(I−1,J)=P(I,J)
  15  P(I,J)=0
      DO 14 J=2,NBAND
      ST(I−1,J−1)=ST(I,J)
      ST(I−1,J)=0
      ST(I,J−1)=0
  14  ST(I,J)=0
C                                SHIFT TO STARTING POSITION
C
 111  CONTINUE
      RETURN
      END

      Pr. 20–20
      SUBROUTINE BSUB
      COMMON DIS(720,2),ST(60,60),Q(60,2),P(60,2),PST(2),BN(2),BV(2)
      COMMON NDF,NBAND,NSIZ,NDF1,NP,NELEM,NCOLN,NDATA
C                                NP=NUMBER OF NODES
C
      NP2=NDF*NP
      DO 30 II=1,NP2
      M=NP2−II
      CALL RDBK (ST,P,NR,BNJJ,BVJJ)
C                                PERFORM BACK-SUBSTITUTION
C
      DO 11 J=1,NCOLN
      DO 11 I=2,NBAND
  11  P(1,J)=P(1,J)−ST(1,I)*P(I,J)
```

```
      DO 2 J=1,NCOLN
      P(1,J)=P(1,J)*ST(1,1)
      IF (NR .NE. 1) GO TO 88
      IF (BNJJ) 90,88,90
90    LK=M/NDF+1
```

WRITE NODAL NUMBER AND COMPUTED REACTION

```
      WRITE (6,10) LK ,P(1,J)
10    FORMAT(14,E16.8)
      DIS(M+1,J)=BVJJ
      P(1,J)=BVJJ
      GO TO 2
88    DIS(M+1,J)=P(1,J)
 2    CONTINUE
```

SHIFT KNOWN DISPLACEMENT MATRIX

```
      DO 4 I=2,NBAND
      L=NBAND-I+1
      DO 4 J=1,NCOLN
 4    P(L+1,J)=P(L,J)
30    CONTINUE
      WRITE (6,15)
15    FORMAT(16H X-DISPLACEMENT ,16H Y-DISPLACEMENT)
34    WRITE (6,7) ((DIS(I,J),I=1,NP2),J=1,NCOLN)
 7    FORMAT(2E16.8)
      RETURN
      END
```

Matrix Algebra

The mystique surrounding matrix algebra is perhaps due to the texts on the subject requiring the student to 'swallow too much' in one operation. It will be found that in order to follow the present text and carry out the necessary computation only a limited knowledge of a few basic definitions is required.

Definition of a matrix

The linear relationship between a set of variables x and b

$$a_{11}x_1 + a_{12}x_2 + a_{13}x_3 + a_{14}x_4 = b_1$$
$$a_{21}x_1 + a_{22}x_2 + a_{23}x_3 + a_{24}x_4 = b_2 \qquad \text{(A.1.1)}$$
$$a_{31}x_1 + a_{32}x_2 + a_{33}x_3 + a_{34}x_4 = b_3$$

can be written, in a shorthand way, as

$$[A]\{x\} = \{b\} \qquad \text{(A.1.1a)}$$

where

$$[A] = \begin{bmatrix} a_{11}, a_{12}, a_{13}, a_{14} \\ a_{21}, a_{22}, a_{23}, a_{24} \\ a_{31}, a_{32}, a_{33}, a_{34} \end{bmatrix} \qquad \text{(A.1.2)}$$

$$\{x\} = \begin{Bmatrix} x_1 \\ x_2 \\ x_3 \\ x_4 \end{Bmatrix} \quad \{b\} = \begin{Bmatrix} b_1 \\ b_2 \\ b_3 \end{Bmatrix}.$$

The above notation contains within it both the definition of a matrix and of the process of multiplication. Matrices are defined as 'arrays of numbers' of the type shown in (A.1.2). The particular form listing a single column of numbers is often referred to as a vector or column matrix. The multiplication of a matrix by a column vector is *defined* by the equivalence of the left sides of equations (A.1.1) and (A.1.1a).

If another relationship, using the same constants, but a different set of x and b, exists, and is written as

$$a_{11}x_1' + a_{12}x_2' + a_{13}x_3' + a_{14}x_4' = b_1'$$
$$a_{21}x_1' + a_{22}x_2' + a_{23}x_3' + a_{24}x_4' = b_2' \qquad \text{(A.1.3)}$$
$$a_{31}x_1' + a_{32}x_2' + a_{33}x_3' + a_{34}x_4' = b_3'$$

then we could write

$$[A][X] = [B] \qquad \text{(A.1.4)}$$

in which

$$[X] = \begin{bmatrix} x_1 & x_1' \\ x_2 & x_2' \\ x_3 & x_3' \\ x_4 & x_4' \end{bmatrix} \qquad [B] = \begin{bmatrix} b_1 & b_1' \\ b_2 & b_2' \\ b_3 & b_3' \end{bmatrix} \qquad \text{(A.1.5)}$$

implying both the statements (A.1.2) and (A.1.3) arranged simultaneously as

$$\begin{bmatrix} a_{11}x_1 + \cdots, & a_{11}x_1' + \cdots \\ a_{21}x_1 + \cdots, & a_{21}x_1' + \cdots \\ a_{31}x_1 + \cdots, & a_{31}x_1' + \cdots \end{bmatrix} = \begin{bmatrix} b_1 & b_1' \\ b_2 & b_2' \\ b_3 & b_3' \end{bmatrix}. \qquad \text{(A.1.4a)}$$

It is seen, incidentally, that matrices can be equal only if each of the individual terms is equal.

The multiplication of full matrices is defined above, and it is obvious that it has a meaning only if the number of columns in $[A]$ is equal to the number of rows in $[X]$ for relation of type (A.1.4). One property which distinguishes matrix multiplication is that, in general,

$$[A][X] \neq [X][A],$$

i.e., multiplication of matrices is not commutative as in ordinary algebra.

Matrix addition or subtraction

If relations of form from (A.1.1) and (A.1.2) are added then we have

$$a_{11}(x_1 + x_1') + a_{12}(x_2 + x_2') + a_{13}(x_3 + x_3') + a_{14}(x_4 + x_4') = b_1 + b_1'$$
$$a_{21}(x_1 + x_1') + a_{22}(x_2 + x_2') + a_{23}(x_3 + x_3') + a_{24}(x_4 + x_4') = b_2 + b_2' \quad \text{(A.1.6)}$$
$$a_{31}(x_1 + x_1') + a_{32}(x_2 + x_2') + a_{33}(x_3 + x_3') + a_{34}(x_4 + x_4') = b_3 + b_3'$$

which will also follow from

$$[A]\{x\} + [A]\{x'\} = [A]\{x + x'\} = \{b\} + \{b'\} = \{b + b'\}$$

if we define the addition of matrices by a simple addition of the individual terms of the array. Clearly this can be done only if the size of the matrices is identical, i.e., for example

$$
\begin{bmatrix} a_{11}, a_{12}, a_{13} \\ \\ a_{21}, a_{22}, a_{23} \end{bmatrix} + \begin{bmatrix} b_{11}, b_{12}, b_{13} \\ \\ b_{21}, b_{22}, b_{23} \end{bmatrix} = \begin{bmatrix} a_{11}+b_{11}, a_{12}+b_{12}, a_{13}+b_{13} \\ \\ a_{21}+b_{21}, a_{22}+b_{22}, a_{23}+b_{23} \end{bmatrix}
$$

or

$$[A]+[B] = [C] \tag{A.1.7}$$

implies that every term of C is equal to the sum of the appropriate terms of $[A]$ and $[B]$.

Subtraction obviously follows similar rules.

Transpose of matrix

This is simply a definition for re-ordering of the number of an array in the following manner

$$
\begin{bmatrix} a_{11} & a_{12} & a_{13} \\ a_{21} & a_{22} & a_{23} \\ a_{31} & a_{32} & a_{33} \end{bmatrix}^{\mathrm{T}} = \begin{bmatrix} a_{11} & a_{21} & a_{31} \\ a_{12} & a_{22} & a_{32} \\ a_{13} & a_{23} & a_{33} \end{bmatrix} \tag{A.1.8}
$$

and will be indicated by the symbol T as shown.

Its use is not immediately obvious but will be indicated later and can be treated here as a simple prescribed operation.

Inverse of a matrix

If in the relationship (A.1.1a) the matrix $[A]$ is 'square', i.e., it represents the coefficients of simultaneous equations of type (A.1.1) equal in number to the number of unknowns $\{x\}$, then in general it is possible to solve for the unknowns $\{x\}$ in terms of the known coefficients $\{b\}$. This solution can be written as

$$\{x\} = [A]^{-1}\{b\} \tag{A.1.9}$$

in which the matrix $[A]^{-1}$ is known as the 'inverse' of the square matrix $[A]$. Clearly $[A]^{-1}$ is also square and of the same size as $[A]$.

We could obtain (A.1.9) by multiplying both sides of (A.1.1a) by $[A]^{-1}$ and hence

$$[A]^{-1}[A] = [I] = [A][A]^{-1} \tag{A.1.10}$$

where $[I]$ is an identity matrix having zero on all 'off diagonal' positions and unity on each of the diagonal positions.

If the equations are singular and have no solution then clearly an inverse does not exist.

A sum of products

In problems of mechanics we often encounter a number of quantities such as forces which can be listed as a matrix 'vector'

$$\{F\} = \begin{Bmatrix} F_1 \\ F_2 \\ \vdots \\ F_n \end{Bmatrix}. \tag{A.1.11}$$

These, in turn, are often associated with the same number of displacements given by another vector, say,

$$\{\delta\} = \begin{Bmatrix} \delta_1 \\ \delta_2 \\ \vdots \\ \delta_n \end{Bmatrix}. \tag{A.1.12}$$

It is known that the work is represented as a sum of products of force and displacement

$$W = \sum F_n \delta_n.$$

Clearly the transpose becomes useful here as we can write, by the first rule of matrix multiplication

$$W = [F_1, F_2, \ldots F_n] \begin{Bmatrix} \delta_1 \\ \delta_2 \\ \vdots \\ \delta_n \end{Bmatrix} = \{F\}^{\mathrm{T}}\{\delta\} \equiv \{\delta\}^{\mathrm{T}}\{F\}. \tag{A.1.13}$$

Use of this fact is made frequently in this book.

Transpose of a product

An operation which sometimes occurs is that of taking the transpose of a matrix product. It can be left to the reader to prove from previous definitions that

$$([A][B])^{\mathrm{T}} = [B]^{\mathrm{T}}[A]^{\mathrm{T}}. \tag{A.1.14}$$

Symmetric matrices

In structural problems symmetric matrices are often encountered. If a term of a matrix $[A]$ is defined as a_{ij}, then for a symmetric matrix

$$a_{ij} = a_{ji}.$$

It can be shown that the inverse of a symmetric matrix is always symmetric.

Partitioning

It is easy to verify that a matrix product

$$[A][B]$$

in which, for example,

$$[A] = \begin{bmatrix} a_{11} & a_{12} & a_{13} & \vdots & a_{14} & a_{15} \\ a_{21} & a_{22} & a_{23} & \vdots & a_{24} & a_{25} \\ \hdashline a_{31} & a_{32} & a_{33} & \vdots & a_{34} & a_{35} \end{bmatrix}$$

$$[B] = \begin{bmatrix} b_{11} & b_{12} \\ b_{21} & b_{22} \\ b_{31} & b_{32} \\ \hdashline b_{41} & b_{42} \\ b_{51} & b_{52} \end{bmatrix}$$

could be obtained by dividing each matrix into submatrices, indicated by the dotted lines, and applying the rules of matrix multiplication first to each of such submatrix as if it were a scalar number and then carrying out further multiplication in the usual way. Thus, if we write

$$[A] = \begin{bmatrix} A_{11} & A_{12} \\ A_{21} & A_{22} \end{bmatrix} \qquad [B] = \begin{bmatrix} B_1 \\ B_2 \end{bmatrix}.$$

Then

$$[A].[B] = \begin{bmatrix} A_{11}B_1 + A_{12}B_2 \\ A_{21}B_1 + A_{22}B_2 \end{bmatrix}$$

can be verified as representing the complete product by further multiplication.

The essential feature of partitioning is that the size of subdivisions has to be such as to make the products of type $A_{11}B_1$ meaningful, i.e., the number of columns in A_{11} must be equal to the number of rows in B_1 etc. If the above definition holds, then all further operations can be conducted on partitioned matrices treating each partition as if it were a scalar.

It should be noted that any matrix can be multiplied by a scalar (number). Here, obviously, the requirements of equality of appropriate rows and columns no longer apply.

The Basic Equations of Chapter 2

2.1 $\quad \{f\} = [N]\{\delta\}^e = [N_i, N_j, N_m, \ldots] \begin{Bmatrix} \delta_i \\ \delta_j \\ \delta_m \\ \vdots \end{Bmatrix}$

2.2 $\quad \{\varepsilon\} = [B]\{\delta\}^e$

2.3 $\quad \{\sigma\} = [D](\{\varepsilon\} - \{\varepsilon_0\}) + \{\sigma_0\}$

2.9 $\quad \{F\}^e = \begin{Bmatrix} F_i \\ F_j \\ \vdots \end{Bmatrix} = [k]^e\{\delta\}^e + \{F\}^e_{\varepsilon_0} + \{F\}^e_{\sigma_0} + \{F\}^e_p$

$$\{F\}^e_{\varepsilon_0} = -\int [B]^T[D]\{\varepsilon_0\} \ \mathrm{d(vol)}$$

2.10
to
2.13
$$[k] = \int [B]^T[D][B] \ \mathrm{d(vol)} \qquad \{F\}^e_{\sigma_0} = +\int [B]^T\{\sigma_0\} \ \mathrm{d(vol)}$$

$$\{F\}^e_p = -\int [N]^T\{p\} \ \mathrm{d(vol)}$$

2.16 $\quad \{\sigma\} = [D][B]\{\delta\}^e - [D]\{\varepsilon_0\} + \sigma_0$

2.17 $\quad [S]^e = [D][B]$

Some Integration Formulae for a Triangle

(Fig. 4.1)

Let a triangle be defined in the x–y plane by three points (x_i, y_i), (x_j, y_j), (x_m, y_m) with the origin at the co-ordinates taken at the centroid, i.e.,

$$\frac{x_i+x_j+x_m}{3} = \frac{y_i+y_j+y_m}{3} = 0.$$

Then integrating over the triangle area

$$\int x \, \mathrm{d}x \, \mathrm{d}y = \int y \, \mathrm{d}x \, \mathrm{d}y = 0$$

$$\int \mathrm{d}x \, \mathrm{d}y = \frac{1}{2} \begin{vmatrix} 1 & x_i & y_i \\ 1 & x_j & y_j \\ 1 & x_m & y_m \end{vmatrix} = \Delta = \text{area of triangle}$$

$$\int x^2 \, \mathrm{d}x \, \mathrm{d}y = \frac{\Delta}{12} (x_i^2 + x_j^2 + x_m^2)$$

$$\int y^2 \, \mathrm{d}x \, \mathrm{d}y = \frac{\Delta}{12} (y_i^2 + y_j^2 + y_m^2)$$

$$\int xy \, \mathrm{d}x \, \mathrm{d}y = \frac{\Delta}{12} (x_i y_i + x_j y_j + x_m y_m)$$

APPENDIX 4

Some Integration Formulae for a Tetrahedron (Fig. 6.1)

Let a tetrahedron be defined in the co-ordinate system (x, y, z) by four points (x_i, y_i, z_i), (x_j, y_j, z_j), (x_m, y_m, z_m), (x_p, y_p, z_p) with the origin at the co-ordinates taken at the centroid, i.e.,

$$\frac{x_i+x_j+x_m+x_p}{4} = \frac{y_i+y_j+y_m+y_p}{4} = \frac{z_i+z_j+z_m+z_p}{4} = 0.$$

Then integrating over the tetrahedron volume

$$\int dx \, dy \, dz = \frac{1}{6} \begin{vmatrix} 1 & x_i & y_i & z_i \\ 1 & x_j & y_j & z_j \\ 1 & x_m & y_m & z_m \\ 1 & x_p & y_p & z_p \end{vmatrix} = V = \text{volume of tetrahedron.}$$

Provided the order of numbering is as indicated on Fig. 6.1 then also:

$$\int x \, dx \, dy \, dz = \int y \, dx \, dy \, dz = \int z \, dx \, dy \, dz = 0$$

$$\int x^2 \, dx \, dy \, dz = \frac{V}{20}(x_i^2 + x_j^2 + x_m^2 + x_p^2)$$

$$\int y^2 \, dx \, dy \, dz = \frac{V}{20}(y_i^2 + y_j^2 + y_m^2 + y_p^2)$$

$$\int z^2 \, dx \, dy \, dz = \frac{V}{20}(z_i^2 + z_j^2 + z_m^2 + z_p^2)$$

$$\int xy \, dx \, dy \, dz = \frac{V}{20}(x_i y_i + x_j y_j + x_m y_m + x_p y_p)$$

$$\int xz \, dx \, dy \, dz = \frac{V}{20}(x_i z_i + x_j z_j + x_m z_m + x_p z_p)$$

$$\int yz \, dx \, dy \, dz = \frac{V}{20}(y_i z_i + y_j z_j + y_m z_m + y_p z_p).$$

Some Vector Algebra

Some knowledge and understanding of basic vector algebra is needed in dealing with complexities of elements oriented in space such as occur in shells, etc. Some of the operations are here summarized.

Vectors (in the geometric sense) can be described by their components along the directions of the x, y, z axis.

Thus the vector V_{01} shown in Fig. A.5.1 can be written as

$$V_{01} = ix_1 + jy_1 + kz_1 \qquad (A.5.1)$$

in which i, j, k are unit vectors in directions of the axes x, y, z.

Alternatively the same vector could be written as

$$\{V_{01}\} = \begin{Bmatrix} x_1 \\ y_1 \\ z_1 \end{Bmatrix} \qquad (A.5.2)$$

(now a 'vector' in the matrix sense) in which the components are distinguished by positioning in the column.

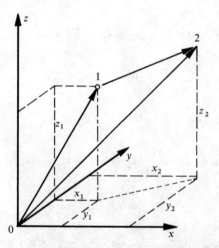

Fig. A.5.1   Vector addition

Addition and subtraction. Addition and subtraction is defined by addition and subtraction of components. Thus for example

$$V_{02} - V_{01} = V_{21} = i(x_2 - x_1) + j(y_2 - y_1) + k(z_2 - z_1). \quad \text{(A.5.3)}$$

The same result is achieved by the definitions of matrix algebra, thus

$$\{V_{02}\} - \{V_{01}\} = \{V_{21}\} = \begin{Bmatrix} x_2 - x_1 \\ y_2 - y_1 \\ z_2 - z_1 \end{Bmatrix}. \quad \text{(A.5.4)}$$

Length of vector. The length of the vector V_{21} is given, purely geometrically, as

$$l_{21} = \sqrt{(x_2 - x_1)^2 + (y_2 - y_1)^2 + (z_2 - z_1)^2} \quad \text{(A.5.5)}$$

or in terms of matrix algebra

$$l_{12} = \sqrt{\{V_{12}\}^{\mathrm{T}}\{V_{12}\}} \quad \text{(A.5.6)}$$

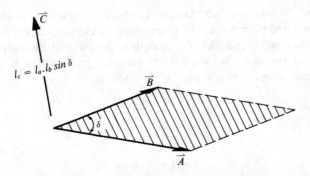

Fig. A.5.2 Vector multiplication (cross product)

Direction cosines. Direction cosines of a vector are simply, from the definition of the projected component lengths, given as

$$\cos \alpha_x = \lambda_{vx} = \frac{x_2 - x_1}{l_{12}}, \text{ etc.} \quad \text{(A.5.7)}$$

where α_x is the angle between the vector and x axis.

'Scalar' products. A scalar product of two vectors is *defined* as the product of the length of one vector by the scalar projection of the other vector on it. Or if γ is the angle between two vectors A and B and their length l_a and l_b respectively

$$A \cdot B = l_a l_b \cos \gamma = B \cdot A. \quad \text{(A.5.8)}$$

If

$$A = ia_x + ja_y + ka_z$$

and   (A.5.9)

$$B = ib_x + jb_y + kb_z$$

$$A \cdot B = a_x \cdot b_x + a_y b_y + a_z b_z \qquad\qquad (A.5.10)$$

if we note that, by above definition

$$i \cdot i = j \cdot j = k \cdot k = 1$$

$$i \cdot j = j \cdot k = k \cdot i = 0, \text{ etc.}$$

Using the matrix notation

$$\{A\} = \begin{Bmatrix} a_x \\ a_y \\ a_z \end{Bmatrix}, \qquad \{B\} = \begin{Bmatrix} b_x \\ b_y \\ b_z \end{Bmatrix} \qquad (A.5.11)$$

$$A \cdot B = \{A\}^{\mathrm{T}}\{B\} = \{B\}^{\mathrm{T}}\{A\}. \qquad (A.5.12)$$

'*Vector*' or *cross product*. Another product of the vector is *defined* as a vector oriented normally to the plane given by the two vectors and equal in magnitude to the product of the length of the two vectors, multiplied by the sine of the angle between them. Further, its direction follows the right-hand rule as shown in Fig. A.5.2 in which

$$A \times B = C. \qquad\qquad (A.5.13)$$

is shown.
    Thus

$$A \times B = -B \times A. \qquad\qquad (A.5.14)$$

It is worth noting that the magnitude (*or length*) of C is equal to the area of the parallelogram shown in Fig. A.5.2.

Using definition of Eq. (A.5.9) and noting that

$$i \times i = j \times j = k \times k = 0$$

$$i \times j = k, \qquad j \times k = i, \qquad k \times i = j \qquad (A.5.15)$$

we have

$$A \times B = \det \begin{vmatrix} i & j & k \\ a_x & a_y & a_z \\ b_x & b_y & b_z \end{vmatrix}$$

$$= (a_y b_z - a_z b_y)i + (a_z b_x - a_x b_z)j + (a_x b_y - a_y b_x)k. \qquad (A.5.16)$$

In matrix algebra this does not find a simple counterpart but we can use the above to define the vector C

$$\{C\} = A \times B = \left\{ \begin{array}{c} a_y b_z - a_z b_y \\ a_z b_x - a_x b_z \\ a_x b_y - a_y b_x \end{array} \right\} . \tag{A.5.17}$$

The vector product will be found particularly useful when the problem of erecting a normal direction to a surface (*vide* Chapter 11) is considered.

Elements of area and volume. If ξ and η are some curvilinear co-ordinates then vectors in two dimensional plane

$$\mathbf{d\xi} = \left\{ \begin{array}{c} \dfrac{\partial x}{\partial \xi} \\ \dfrac{\partial y}{\partial \xi} \end{array} \right\} d\xi; \qquad \mathbf{d\eta} = \left\{ \begin{array}{c} \dfrac{\partial x}{\partial \eta} \\ \dfrac{\partial y}{\partial \eta} \end{array} \right\} d\eta \tag{A.5.18}$$

defined from the relationship between the Cartesian and curvilinear co-ordinates, are vectors directed tangentially to the $\xi =$ const. and $\eta =$ const. contours respectively. As the *length* of the vector resulting from a cross product of $d\xi \times d\eta$ is equal to the area of the elementary parallelo-gram we can write

$$d(\text{Area}) = \det \left| \begin{array}{cc} \dfrac{\partial x}{\partial \xi} & \dfrac{\partial x}{\partial \eta} \\ \dfrac{\partial y}{\partial \xi} & \dfrac{\partial y}{\partial \eta} \end{array} \right| \tag{A.5.19}$$

by Eq. (A.5.17).

Similarly if we have three curvilinear co-ordinates ξ, η, ζ in the Car-tesian space the 'triple scalar' or box product defines a unit volume

$$d(\text{Vol}) = \mathbf{d\xi} \cdot (\mathbf{d\eta} \times \mathbf{d\zeta}) = \det \left| \begin{array}{ccc} \dfrac{\partial x}{\partial \xi} & \dfrac{\partial x}{\partial \eta} & \dfrac{\partial x}{\partial \zeta} \\ \dfrac{\partial y}{\partial \xi} & \dfrac{\partial y}{\partial \eta} & \dfrac{\partial y}{\partial \zeta} \\ \dfrac{\partial z}{\partial \xi} & \dfrac{\partial z}{\partial \eta} & \dfrac{\partial z}{\partial \zeta} \end{array} \right| \cdot d\xi \, d\eta \, d\zeta \tag{A.5.20}$$

This follows simply from the geometry. The bracketed product, by defi-nition, forms a vector whose length is equal to the parallelogram area with sides tangent to two of the co-ordinates. The second scalar multiplication by a length and cosine of the angle between that length and the normal to the parallelogram establishes an elementary volume.

Euler's Theorem of Variational Calculus

The transition from a variational statement to an equivalent governing differential equation is relatively simple and will be demonstrated here. The reverse process, however, is more involved and any generalized processes restrictive—for the very reason that frequently no variational principle can be established.

Let us take a problem in which

$$\chi = \int_V f(x, y, z, \phi, \phi_x, \phi_y, \phi_z) \, dV + \int_C (q\phi + \alpha\phi^2/2) \, dS \quad \text{(A.6.1)}$$

is to be minimized. In this f is an arbitrary function, $\phi_x = \partial\phi/\partial x$, etc., and C is a portion of the boundary surface on which prescribed values of ϕ are not imposed. On remainder $\phi = \phi_B$.

Considering an arbitrary small variation of the unknown function and its derivatives we have

$$\delta\chi = \int_V \left(\frac{\partial f}{\partial \phi} \delta\phi + \frac{\partial f}{\partial \phi_x} \delta\phi_x + \frac{\partial f}{\partial \phi_y} \delta\phi_y + \frac{\partial f}{\partial \phi_z} \delta\phi_z \right) dV$$

$$+ \int_C (q \, \delta\phi + \alpha\phi \, \delta\phi) \, dS. \quad \text{(A.6.2)}$$

As

$$\delta\phi_x = \delta\left(\frac{\partial\phi}{\partial x}\right) = \frac{\partial}{\partial x}(\delta\phi), \text{ etc.}$$

we can write Eq. (A.6.2) as

$$\delta\chi = \int_V \left(\frac{\partial f}{\partial \phi} \delta\phi + \frac{\partial f}{\partial \phi_x} \frac{\partial}{\partial x}(\delta\phi) + \cdots \right) dV$$

$$+ \int_C (q \, \delta\phi + \alpha\phi \, \delta\phi) \, dS = 0. \quad \text{(A.6.3)}$$

In the above we have equated $\delta\chi$ to zero, as at the minimum (or stationary point) the 'variation' becomes zero.

Now putting $dV = dx\,dy\,dz$ and integrating the second term of above equation by parts (as in Eq. (3.25) of Chapter 3) with respect to x we have

$$\int_V \frac{\partial f}{\partial \phi_x} \frac{\partial}{\partial x}(\delta\phi)\,dV = \int_S \frac{\partial f}{\partial \phi_x} \delta\phi l_x\,dS - \int_V \frac{\partial}{\partial x}\left(\frac{\partial f}{\partial \phi_x}\right)\delta\phi\,dV$$

in which l_x is the direction cosine of the normal to the outer surface with the x axis. Performing similar operations on the other similar terms of Eq. (A.6.3) and substituting we have finally

$$\delta\chi = \int_V \delta\phi \left\{\frac{\partial f}{\partial \phi} - \frac{\partial}{\partial x}\left(\frac{\partial f}{\partial \phi_x}\right) - \frac{\partial}{\partial y}\left(\frac{\partial f}{\partial \phi_y}\right) - \frac{\partial}{\partial z}\frac{\partial f}{\partial \phi_z}\right\}dV$$

$$+ \int_C \delta\phi \left\{q + \alpha\phi + l_x\frac{\partial f}{\partial \phi_x} + l_y\frac{\partial f}{\partial \phi_y} + l_z\frac{\partial f}{\partial \phi_z}\right\}dS. \qquad \text{(A.6.4)}$$

The second integral is only taken over the boundary C as on the remainder of surface S we have prescribed values of ϕ and therefore $\delta\phi = 0$.

For Eq. (A.6.4) to be true for any arbitrary variation $\delta\phi$ we must have

$$\frac{\partial f}{\partial \phi} - \frac{\partial}{\partial x}\left(\frac{\partial f}{\partial \phi_x}\right) - \frac{\partial}{\partial y}\left(\frac{\partial f}{\partial \phi_y}\right) - \frac{\partial}{\partial z}\left(\frac{\partial f}{\partial \phi_z}\right) = 0 \qquad \text{(A.6.5a)}$$

everywhere within the region V, and on the boundary C

$$l_x\frac{\partial f}{\partial \phi_x} + l_y\frac{\partial f}{\partial \phi_y} + l_z\frac{\partial f}{\partial \phi_z} + q + \alpha\phi = 0. \qquad \text{(A.6.5b)}$$

These two equations, if satisfied by ϕ, minimize χ. If the solution is unique then formulations (A.6.1) and (A.6.5) are equivalent. The above differential equations are known as the Euler equations of the problem.

If the functional depended also on higher derivatives of ϕ a similar procedure would result in appropriate Euler equations. Again, if χ were a functional of several independent functions ϕ, ψ, etc., and their derivatives, a similar variational process would result in a series of Euler equations defining several differential governing equations.

Author Index

Numbers in bold type refer to the list of references at end of each chapter.

Subject Index

MADE AND PRINTED BY OFFSET IN GREAT BRITAIN BY
WILLIAM CLOWES & SONS, LIMITED, LONDON, BECCLES AND COLCHESTER